SADLIER-OXFORD

R. James Milgram

Alfred S. Posamentier

Catherine D. LeTourneau

Edward William Quinn

Sadlier-Oxford
A Division of William H. Sadlier, Inc.
www.sadlier-oxford.com

Photo Credits

Cover: **Getty Images/Photographer's Choice/Michael Dunning:** train; **Rubik's Cube ® used by permission of Seven Towns Ltd. www.rubiks.com:** Rubik's Twist; **"Hilbert Cube 512" by Carlo H. Séquin, University of California, Berkeley:** Hilbert Cube; **Used under license from Shutterstock.com/Andresr:** skyscrapers.

Printed in the United States of America.

ISBN: 978-0-8215-8229-9

6 7 8 9 10 HESS 24 23 22 21 20

Contents

Chapter 

Linear Inequalities

Use with SOURCEBOOK pages 69–92.

Chapter 

Relations and Functions

Use with SOURCEBOOK pages 93–114.

Chapter 5

Linear Functions

Use with SOURCEBOOK pages 115–148.

Chapter 6

Systems of Linear Equations and Inequalities

Use with SOURCEBOOK pages 149–174.

Chapter 

Operations with Polynomials

Use with SOURCEBOOK pages 175–198.

Chapter 

Factoring Polynomials

Use with SOURCEBOOK pages 199–224.

Chapter 

Radical Expressions and Equations

Use with SOURCEBOOK pages 225–244.

Chapter 

Quadratic Functions and Equations

Use with SOURCEBOOK pages 245–278.

Chapter 11

Ratio, Proportion, and Trigonometry

Use with SOURCEBOOK pages 279–304.

Chapter 

Rational Expressions and Equations

Use with SOURCEBOOK pages 305–328.

Chapter 13

Exponential and Other Nonlinear Functions

Use with SOURCEBOOK pages 329–356.

Chapter 14

Data Analysis and Probability

Use with SOURCEBOOK pages 357–402.

Gridded-Response Form

Name ______________________________ Date ______________

1-1 Rational and Irrational Numbers

Name ______________________ Date ____________

Write all classifications of 2.1 that apply (*rational number*, *fraction*, *mixed number*, *integer*, *repeating decimal*, *terminating decimal*, *irrational number*).

2.1 can be written as the fraction $\frac{21}{10}$, so 2.1 is rational number.

2.1 is not a fraction, mixed number, integer, irrational number or repeating decimal.

2.1 is a terminating decimal.

So 2.1 is rational number and a terminating decimal.

Remember: Numbers that are not rational are *irrational*, such as decimals that do not terminate or repeat, square roots of nonperfect squares, and the number π.

Approximate the value of $\sqrt{86}$.

$81 \quad 86 \quad 100$ ← Locate 86 between two consecutive perfect squares.

$\sqrt{81} < \sqrt{86} < \sqrt{100}$ ← $81 = 9^2$ and $100 = 10^2$

$9 < \sqrt{86} < 10$ ← Find the square roots of the two consecutive perfect squares.

So $\sqrt{86}$ lies between 9 and 10, closer to 9 (since 86 is closer to 81 than to 100).

For each number, list all the terms that apply: *fraction*, *mixed number*, *integer*, *repeating decimal*, *terminating decimal*, *rational number*, and *irrational number*.

1. 36
   integer, terminating decimal, rational number

2. -8 ______

3. $-\frac{17}{3}$ ______

4. $\frac{2}{5}$ ______

5. $\sqrt{2}$ ______

6. $\sqrt{23}$ ______

7. $2.\overline{8}$ ______

8. $6.1\overline{234}$ ______

9. 2.010010001... ______

10. $-0.21384269\ldots$ ______

11. $-\sqrt{36}$ ______

12. $\sqrt{25}$ ______

13. $9\frac{7}{8}$ ______

14. $-9\frac{12}{13}$ ______

15. -115 ______

16. 0 ______

17. 9.25 ______

18. 13.0606 ______

If the number is rational, find its square root. If the radicand is a nonperfect square, give the two consecutive integers it lies between, and the closer integer.

19. $\sqrt{30}$

$\sqrt{25} < \sqrt{30} < \sqrt{36}$

$5 < \sqrt{30} < 6$

5 and 6; 5

20. $\sqrt{70}$

21. $\sqrt{81}$

22. $\sqrt{9}$

23. $\sqrt{13}$

24. $\sqrt{24}$

25. $\sqrt{100}$

26. $\sqrt{16}$

27. $\sqrt{145}$

28. $\sqrt{50}$

29. $\sqrt{79}$

30. $\sqrt{62}$

31. $\sqrt{105}$

32. $\sqrt{3}$

33. $\sqrt{10}$

34. $\sqrt{95}$

35. $-\sqrt{121}$

36. $-\sqrt{225}$

37. $-\sqrt{150}$

38. $-\sqrt{130}$

Solve. Show your work

39. A cabinet door in the shape of a square covers 5 square feet. Find the length of the side of the door to the nearest integer.

40. A farmer's square field covers 2000 square feet. Find the length of the side of the field to the nearest integer.

Problem Solving

41. The area of a square is 24.783 square feet. Find the width of the side of the square to the nearest integer. Explain your reasoning.

42. If the lengths of the sides of a square are between 3.7 feet and 5.2 feet and the area is a perfect square, then what are the possible areas of the square?

WRITE ABOUT IT

43. Explain how to find the next five perfect squares after 100. Then find them.

1-2 The Set of Real Numbers

Name ______________________ Date ____________

Determine if the set of positive multiples of 5 is *closed* under subtraction.

{5, 10, 15, 20, 25, . . .} ← Identify the elements of the set.
$10 - 5 = 5$ ← Test a case. Subtract two elements of the set.
$5 - 10 = -5$ ← Test another case.

-5 is not an element of the set.
No, the set of positive multiples of 5 is *not* closed under subtraction.

Use a number line to order the numbers $-2, -\frac{3}{2}, -\sqrt{9}, -|-1|$ from least to greatest.

The farther to the right a number is on the number line, the greater it is.

$-\sqrt{9}$ -2 $-\frac{3}{2}$ $-|-1|$

−4 −3 −2 −1 0

Read the order from least to greatest: $-\sqrt{9}, -2, -\frac{3}{2}, -|-1|$

Give an example to illustrate the type of number described.

1. a real number that is irrational

5.010010001...

2. a whole number that is not a natural number

3. a rational number with a terminating decimal

4. a real number with a nonperfect square radicand

Determine if each set of numbers is *closed* under the indicated operation. If it is *not closed*, give a counterexample.

5. {0, 1, 2}; subtraction

not closed
$1 - 2 = -1$
-1 is not an element of the set.

6. {Real Numbers}; addition

7. {10, 11, 12}; subtraction

8. {0, 1, 2}; multiplication

9. {4, 6, 8}; multiplication

10. {integers}; division

11. {odd integers}; addition

12. {natural numbers}; addition

13. {whole numbers}; division

Use with SOURCEBOOK Lesson 1-2, pages 4–5.

Find the value of each expression.

14. $-(-19.8)$ 19.8

15. $3.05 + (-3.05)$

16. $-|\sqrt{25}|$

17. $|-\sqrt{36}| - (-\sqrt{36})$

18. $-(-4.2) + |-7.5|$

19. $-|4\frac{1}{2} \bullet 2|$

20. $|\sqrt{25}| - |-\sqrt{25}|$

21. $|-6.2| - |-2.1|$

22. $|-2| - (-15)$

23. $|-\sqrt{64}| - (-\sqrt{81})$

24. $-(-12) - |-6|$

25. $|-1.2| - [-(-1)]$

Use the number line to compare and order each set of numbers from least to greatest.

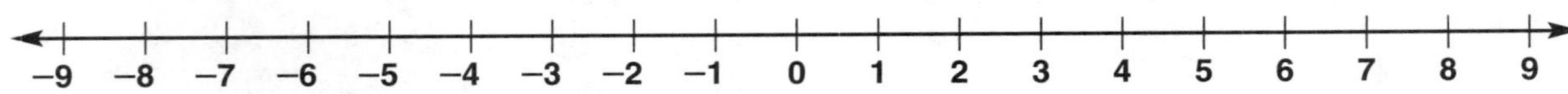

26. $|7 + 2|, -6, -5.4, -0.8, \sqrt{25}, \frac{9}{2}$

$|7 + 2| = 9, \sqrt{25} = 5, \frac{9}{2} = 4.5$

$-6, -5.4, -0.8, \frac{9}{2}, \sqrt{25}, |7 + 2|$

27. $-\frac{7}{4}, -|3|, -1.9, -2, -\sqrt{16}, -1.\overline{4}$

28. $-\frac{6}{3}, -3.21, 5, -\sqrt{49}, -1.\overline{23}, |-2|$

29. $-\sqrt{1}, 0, -\frac{5}{4}, -1.5, -1.\overline{09}, -|4|$

30. $-\sqrt{36}, -6.9, -\frac{25}{4}, 8.\overline{3}, -|10 - 2|, 9$

31. $-\frac{19}{7}, -2.9, -4, -2.\overline{85}, -\sqrt{4}, -|5 - 2|$

Problem Solving

32. Three negative numbers are labeled *a*, *b*, and *c*. List the numbers from least to greatest if $|a| > |c|$ and $b > c$. Explain your reasoning.

33. The set of numbers {0, 1} is closed for which operations: addition, subtraction, multiplication, division?

CRITICAL THINKING

34. A new operation is defined as $a \blacklozenge b = a + a - b$. Is the set of whole numbers closed under the operation $\blacklozenge$? If not, give a set that is closed under this operation.

1-3 Add and Subtract Real Numbers

Name ______________________ Date ____________

Add: $-29\frac{1}{3} + 17\frac{1}{2}$

$|-29\frac{1}{3}| - |17\frac{1}{2}|$ ← Subtract the lesser absolute value from the greater absolute value.

$29\frac{2}{6} - 17\frac{3}{6}$ ← Rename fractions using the LCD: 6.

$28\frac{8}{6} - 17\frac{3}{6}$ ← Regroup $29\frac{2}{6}$ as $28\frac{8}{6}$.

$11\frac{5}{6}$ ← Simplify.

$-11\frac{5}{6}$ ← The addend with the greater absolute value is negative. So the sum is negative.

Remember: When adding with *like signs*, use the sign of both addends for the sum.

Subtract: $-16.34 - (-19.58)$

$-16.34 + 19.58$ ← Add the opposite of the subtrahend.

$|19.58| + |-16.34|$ ← Apply the rules for adding with unlike signs.

$19.58 - 16.34$

3.24 ← Simplify using the sign of the addend with the greater absolute value.

Add or subtract using a number line.

1. $-4 + 1$

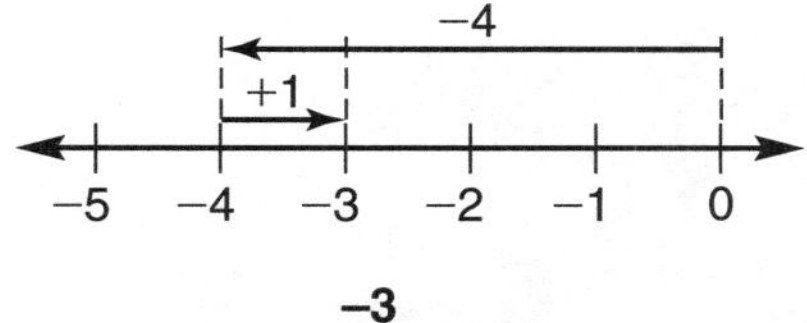

−3

2. $-6 + 2$

3. $8 + (-7)$

4. $-1.6 + (-3.2)$

5. $-2.35 + (-2.35)$

6. $3 + (-3) + 6$

7. $-5 - 2 + (-7)$

8. $6\frac{1}{4} - \left(-1\frac{1}{4}\right) + 2\frac{1}{2}$

9. $-7\frac{1}{3} - \left(-2\frac{1}{3}\right) - \left(-3\frac{1}{3}\right)$

Write each subtraction problem as an addition problem. Then find the sum.

10. $1.3 - 7.1$

$1.3 + (-7.1)$
$|-7.1| - |1.3| = 5.8$
$1.3 - 7.1 = -5.8$

11. $3.5 - 9.7$

12. $-3.21 - 6.4$

13. $-5.99 - 14.33$

14. $-4\frac{1}{2} - \left(-\frac{1}{2}\right)$

15. $-5\frac{2}{3} - \left(-\frac{7}{8}\right)$

16. $2\frac{2}{5} - \left(-3\frac{7}{10}\right)$

17. $6\frac{3}{4} - \left(-2\frac{1}{2}\right)$

Estimate by rounding. Then add or subtract using rules for signed numbers.

18. $6.4 + (-3.5)$

$6 + (-4) = 2$
$|6.4| - |-3.5| = 2.9$
$|6.4| > |-3.5|$
2.9

19. $7.1 + (-5.6)$

20. $5.3 - 8.6$

21. $11.2 - 13.1$

22. $-3\frac{1}{4} + \left(-2\frac{3}{8}\right)$

23. $-2\frac{1}{5} + \left(-3\frac{7}{10}\right)$

24. $\frac{1}{4} - \left(-2\frac{1}{4}\right)$

25. $\frac{1}{6} - \left(-7\frac{2}{3}\right)$

26. $-8.8 - 7.6$

27. $-9.3 - 4.2$

28. $-62 - (-141)$

29. $-93 - (-358)$

Problem Solving

30. The temperature at midnight was 52.8°F. It dropped 9.5°F overnight and then rose 15.2°F by noon. What was the change in temperatures between midnight and noon?

31. Two numbers have a sum of 2 and a difference of -16. What are the numbers?

CRITICAL THINKING

32. Lonnie says that the sign of the sum of two numbers is always the sign of the greater number. Explain why Lonnie is wrong and give an example.

1-4 Multiply and Divide Real Numbers

Name ________________________________ Date ____________

Multiply: $-2\frac{3}{4} \bullet 1\frac{1}{3}$

$\left|-2\frac{3}{4}\right| \bullet \left|1\frac{1}{3}\right| = \frac{11}{4} \bullet \frac{4}{3}$ ← Multiply the absolute values of the numbers and rename each factor.

$= \frac{11 \bullet \overset{1}{\cancel{4}}}{\underset{1}{\cancel{4}} \bullet 3} = \frac{11}{3}$ ← Divide by the GCF to simplify. Then multiply the numerators and denominators.

$= 3\frac{2}{3}$ ← Rename the product as a mixed number.

So $-2\frac{3}{4} \bullet 1\frac{1}{3} = -3\frac{2}{3}$ ← Factors have *unlike* signs. The product is negative.

Remember: When multiplying decimals, multiply as you would whole numbers and use the total number of decimal places in the factors for the number of decimal places in the product.

Find the quotient: $\frac{-0.144}{-1.2}$

$|-0.144| \div |-1.2|$ ← Divide the absolute values of the numbers.

$1.2.\overline{)0.1.44} \rightarrow 12\overset{0.12}{\overline{)1.44}}$ ← Multiply by 10 to make the divisor a whole number. Move each decimal point 1 place to the right.

So $-0.144 \div (-1.2) = 0.12$ ← Dividend and divisor have *like signs*, so the quotient is positive.

Remember: When dividing fractions $\frac{a}{b} \div \frac{c}{d} = \frac{a}{b} \bullet \frac{d}{c}$, $b, c, d \neq 0$.

Use a number line to model multiplication. Then find the product.

1. $2 \bullet (-2.5)$

−6 −5 −4 −3 −2 −1 0 1

$2 \bullet (-2.5) = -5$

2. $8 \bullet 1.1$

____

3. $4 \bullet (-3.5)$

____

4. $5 \bullet 3\frac{1}{3}$

____

5. $-6 \bullet \left(-2\frac{3}{4}\right)$

____

6. $-12 \bullet \left(-1\frac{1}{4}\right)$

____

Multiply or divide. Show your work. (*Hint:* watch for like signs)

7. $-8 \bullet (-12)$

$|-8| \bullet |-12| = 96$

96

8. $-2.7 \bullet (1.3)$

9. $-9.21 \bullet 0.4$

10. $-7.9 \bullet (-0.8)$

11. $1.56 \div (-0.3)$

12. $19.95 \div (-0.7)$

13. $-\frac{2}{5} \bullet \left(-\frac{1}{7}\right)$

14. $-\frac{3}{11} \bullet \left(-\frac{3}{8}\right)$

15. $-2\frac{1}{3} \bullet 3\frac{1}{4}$

16. $1\frac{1}{5} \bullet \left(-1\frac{1}{2}\right)$

17. $-\frac{2}{3} \div \left(-\frac{1}{4}\right)$

18. $-\frac{3}{5} \div \left(-\frac{7}{10}\right)$

19. $2\frac{1}{2} \div 1\frac{1}{3}$

20. $-4\frac{1}{4} \div 5\frac{1}{3}$

21. $-3\frac{3}{4} \div \left(-2\frac{1}{2}\right)$

22. $5\frac{1}{8} \div \left(-7\frac{3}{4}\right)$

23. $-3\frac{1}{5} \div -6.5$

24. $-2\frac{1}{6} \div 0.3$

25. $-4.2 \div \left(-1\frac{7}{8}\right)$

26. $5.25 \div \left(-3\frac{1}{4}\right)$

Problem Solving

27. During a trading day, Company A stock lost 0.05 times its morning price of \$34.80 per share. Company B stock gained 0.06 times its morning price of \$31.50 per share. Which stock price was greater at the end of the day? How much greater?

28. Jonas is trying to understand why the product of two negative numbers equals a positive number. Find the answer to each product below and give the rule for the pattern.

$(3) \bullet (-1) =$ ______; $(2) \bullet (-1) =$ ______;

$(1) \bullet (-1) =$ ______; $(0) \bullet (-1) =$ ______;

$(-1) \bullet (-1) =$ ______; $(-2) \bullet (-1) =$ ______

MENTAL MATH

Use mental math to simplify each expression.

29. $-30 \bullet (-28)$

30. $-55(-15)$

31. $-12 \bullet (40)$

32. $18 \bullet (-50)$

1-5 Integer Exponents

Name ______________________ Date ____________

Simplify: $5^{-2} + 5^0$

$5^{-2} + 5^0$ ← Identify the bases with negative and zero exponents.

$\frac{1}{5^2} + 1$ ← Use the rules for negative and zero exponents.

$\frac{1}{25} + 1 = 1\frac{1}{25}$ ← Simplify.

Remember: Any nonzero exponent raised to the zero power equals 1. If $a \neq 0$, $a^0 = 1$.

Remember: For any nonzero number a and any integer n, $a^{-n} = \frac{1}{a^n}$.

Simplify: $\frac{2^3 \bullet 2^5}{2^6}$

$\frac{2^{3+5}}{2^6}$ ← Add exponents to multiply powers with the same base.

$\frac{2^8}{2^6}$ ← Simplify.

2^{8-6} ← Subtract exponents to divide powers with the same base.

2^2 ← Write in exponential form.

4 ← Write in standard form and simplify.

Remember: For any real number a, $a \neq 0$, and integers m and n:

$a^m \bullet a^n = a^{m+n}$

$a^m \div a^n = a^{m-n}$

Write each expression as repeated multiplication and in exponential form. Then simplify in standard form.

1. 3^4

3 • 3 • 3 • 3
81

2. 5^0

3. $5 \bullet 5 \bullet 5$

4. 10^4

5. $-10 \bullet (-10) \bullet (-10)$

6. -4^4

7. $(-5)^2 \bullet (-5)^4$

8. $6^6 \div 6^2$

Find the value of each expression. Express answers in standard form.

9. 2^{-4}

$2^{-4} = \frac{1}{2^4} = \frac{1}{16}$

10. 6^0

11. 3^{-2}

12. 5^{-3}

13. 6^{-2}

14. $\left(\frac{2}{3}\right)^3$

15. $\left(\frac{1}{4}\right)^4$

16. $\left(\frac{-3}{-5}\right)^2$

17. $\left(\frac{2}{7}\right)^{-2}$

18. $\left(\frac{3}{2}\right)^{-3}$

19. $\left(-\frac{1}{5}\right)^3$

20. $\left(-\frac{2}{9}\right)^4$

Simplify. Express answers in standard form.

21. $6^2 + 4^0 - 2^3$
$36 + 1 - 8$
$37 - 8$
29

22. $5^2 - 7^0 + 3^3$

23. $8^3 - (0.3)^4$

24. $7^2 - (0.4)^3$

25. $2^7 - 8^2 - 1^{10}$

26. $9^3 - 6^2 + 1^{23}$

27. $4 \bullet 4^2 + 3^2$

28. $6 \bullet 6^2 + 2^3$

29. $3^2 \bullet 3^{-4} \bullet 3^6$

30. $5^3 \bullet 5^5 \bullet 5^{-6}$

31. $2^2 \bullet 3^2 \bullet 8$

32. $3^3 \bullet 5^2 \bullet 6^0$

33. $\frac{6 \bullet 3^4}{6^2 \bullet 3^2}$

34. $\frac{2^4 \bullet 4^2}{2^2 \bullet 4^4}$

35. $\frac{3^3}{3^{-2}}$

36. $\frac{5^2}{5^{-2}}$

37. $\frac{7^2 \bullet 7^5}{7^7 \bullet 7^{-2}}$

38. $\frac{6^5 \bullet 6^{-4}}{6^{-2} \bullet 6^3}$

39. $8^3 \bullet \frac{1}{8^{-1}}$

40. $4^5 \bullet \frac{1}{4^{-2}}$

41. $2^{-5} \div \frac{1}{4^{-3}}$

42. $5^{-1} \div \frac{1}{25^{-2}}$

43. $\frac{\left(\frac{2}{5}\right)^3 \bullet \left(\frac{2}{5}\right)^0 \bullet \left(\frac{2}{5}\right)^{-4}}{\left(\frac{2}{5}\right)^{-5} \bullet \left(\frac{2}{5}\right)^2 \bullet \left(\frac{2}{5}\right)^3}$

44. $\frac{\left(\frac{3}{4}\right)^0 \bullet \left(\frac{3}{4}\right) \bullet \left(\frac{3}{4}\right)^{-2}}{\left(\frac{3}{4}\right) \bullet \left(\frac{3}{4}\right)^{-5} \bullet \left(\frac{3}{4}\right)^4}$

Problem Solving

45. An ant is 6 feet from a wall. The first day, it walks half the distance to the wall. Each day, it walks half the remaining distance to the wall. How many feet does it walk each of the first five days? If it walked forever in this pattern, would it ever reach the wall?

46. Maria collected 3 cans on day 1, 6 cans on day 2, 12 cans on day 3, and 24 cans on day 4. Let d be the day. Write an expression for the number of cans she collects on day d. Then find the number of cans she collects on the 10th day.

TEST PREPARATION

47. Which expression below is equivalent to $4^3 \bullet 4 \bullet 4^5$?

A. $\frac{4^{10}}{4^2}$ **B.** $\frac{4^2}{4^{10}}$ **C.** $\frac{4}{4^{10}}$ **D.** $\frac{4^{10}}{4}$

1-6 The Order of Operations

Name ______________________ Date __________

Evaluate: $7 \bullet (3^3 - 5 \bullet 3) \div 4 + 3$

$7 \bullet (27 - 5 \bullet 3) \div 4 + 3$ ← Compute within parenthesis first; evaluate the exponent.

$7 \bullet (27 - 15) \div 4 + 3$ ← Within parentheses, multiply.

$7 \bullet (12) \div 4 + 3$ ← Within parentheses, subtract.

$84 \div 4 + 3$ ← Multiply from left to right.

$21 + 3$ ← Divide.

24 ← Add.

$7 \bullet (3^3 - 5 \bullet 3) \div 4 + 3 = 24$

Remember:
Order of Operations

1. Grouping Symbols: parentheses ( ), brackets [ ], braces { }, fraction bar —
2. Exponents.
3. Multiply or divide from left to right.
4. Add or subtract from left to right.

Evaluate each expression.

1. $24 - 16 + 6 \bullet 5 - 9^2$

$24 - 16 + 6 \bullet 5 - 81$
$24 - 16 + 30 - 81$
$8 + 30 - 81$
$38 - 81$
-43

2. $32 - 15 + 7 \bullet 2 - 8^2$

3. $|-27| \bullet 3 - (4 + 2)^2$

4. $|-19| \bullet 5 - (3 + 1)^2$

5. $5 \bullet (3 + 6) - \sqrt{25} \div 5 + |3^2|$

6. $7 \bullet (8 - 2) - \sqrt{16} \div 2 + |5^3|$

7. $11 + (-2^3) \div 4 + 4^2 \bullet (8 - 5)$

8. $17 - (-3^3) \div 3 + 2^3 \bullet (7 - 2)$

66

9. $9 \div 3^{-1} + |4 - 6| \bullet 9$

10. $15 \div 5^{-1} - |1 - 3| \bullet 4$

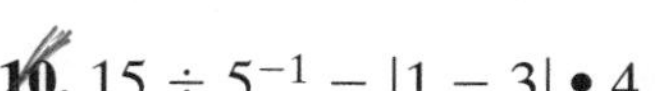

11. $24 \bullet 12^0 - 3(6 + 2)^2$

12. $30 \bullet 15^0 - 4(5 + 1)^2$

−114

13. $-4[-3(1.5 + 2^{-1}) + |4.5 - 5|]$

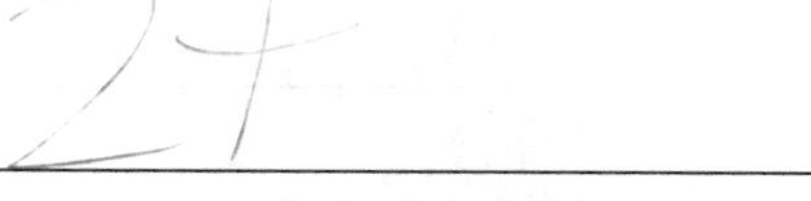

14. $-8[-2(3.5 + 2^{-1}) + |2.5 - 7|]$

8-20 even

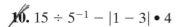

Evaluate each expression. Write the answer in simplest form.

15. $\frac{(1-2)^3 + 4^2 \div 8}{[3 \bullet (5-3)]^2 - 5^2}$

$\frac{(-1)^3 + 16 \div 8}{(3 \bullet (2))^2 - 25}$; $\frac{-1+2}{(6)^2 - 25}$

$\frac{1}{36-25}$; $\frac{1}{11}$

16. $\frac{(3-5)^2 + 6^2 \div 9}{[2 \bullet (4-6)]^2 - 3^2}$

17. $\frac{(\sqrt{81} - 4^3) \div |6-11|}{7-6-3}$

18. $\frac{(\sqrt{100} - 5^3) \div |-3-20|}{4-9-5}$

19. $\frac{[7 - 3 \bullet (2+8)^2] + |4 \bullet (3 - 15 \div 3)|}{9^2 \bullet (2 + 3^4)}$

20. $\frac{[24 - 2 \bullet (5+6)^2] + 7 \bullet (10 - 32 \div 16)}{7^2 \bullet (4 + 2^5)}$

Problem Solving

21. Insert grouping symbols to make the answer correct. Then evaluate the expression to justify your work.

$9 + 3 \bullet 4 - 6 + 12 \div 3 = -20$

22. Insert grouping symbols to make the answer correct. Then evaluate the expression to justify your work. (*Hint:* Use absolute value bars.)

$\frac{4 - 9 + 3^2 - 8}{7 + 11 - 13^2} = \frac{6}{11}$

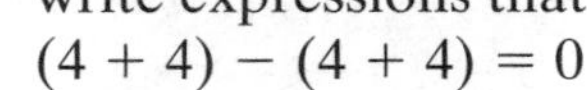

23. Use four 4s, any of the four operations, and grouping symbols to write expressions that are equal to 0 through 10. For example: $(4 + 4) - (4 + 4) = 0$

1-7 Scientific Notation

Name ______________________ Date __________

Write 0.00000364 in scientific notation:

$0.000003.64 \times \frac{1}{1{,}000{,}000}$ ← Move decimal point to the *right*.

3.64×10^{-6} ← Rename $\frac{1}{1{,}000{,}000}$ as a power of 10.

Divide: $\frac{1.44 \times 10^9}{3.2 \times 10^4}$

$\frac{1.44 \times 10^9}{3.2 \times 10^4}$ ← Group like factors.

0.45×10^5 ← Divide the decimal factors. Then divide the powers of 10 by subtracting their exponents.

$(4.5 \times 10^{-1}) \times 10^5$ ← Write 0.45 in scientific notation.

4.5×10^4 ← Multiply the powers of 10 by adding their exponents.

So $(1.44 \times 10^9) \div (3.2 \times 10^4) = 4.5 \times 10^4$

Remember: To add or subtract numbers in scientific notation, the numbers *must have the same power of 10.*

Write in scientific notation or standard form.

1. 7.81×10^8 **781,000,000**

2. 5.29×10^6

3. 1.049×10^8

4. 8.027×10^4

5. 68,600,000,000

6. 236,000,000

7. 40,840,000

8. 5059

9. 3.83×10^{-4}

10. 9.91×10^{-3}

11. 5.108×10^{-9}

12. 2.202×10^{-11}

13. 0.00000531

14. 0.0000000117

15. 0.08064

16. 0.0004037

Perform the indicated operations. Express answers in scientific notation.

17. $3.33 \times 10^5 + 7.4 \times 10^4$

$33.3 \times 10^4 + 7.4 \times 10^4$

$(33.3 + 7.4) \times 10^4$

$40.7 \times 10^4 = 4.07 \times 10^5$

18. $(6.3 \times 10^8) - (1.512 \times 10^8)$

19. $(5.81 \times 10^6) + (4.22 \times 10^7)$

20. $(8.3 \times 10^3)(2.8 \times 10^4)$

21. $(5.9 \times 10^2)(4.6 \times 10^5)$

22. $(4.2 \times 10^5)(7.5 \times 10^7)$

23. $(9.25 \times 10^5) \div (2.5 \times 10^2)$

24. $(7.84 \times 10^5) \div (5.6 \times 10^3)$

25. $(6.8 \times 10^{10}) \div (8 \times 10^8)$

Use with SOURCEBOOK Lesson 1-7, pages 14–15.

Perform the indicated operations. Express answers in scientific notation.

26. $2.1 \times 10^3 + 4.2 \times 10^3 - 1.9 \times 10^3$

$(2.1 + 4.2 - 1.9) \times 10^3$
4.4×10^3

27. $3.5 \times 10^4 + 5.6 \times 10^4 - 4.4 \times 10^4$

28. $19.8 \times 10^{-5} - 2.4 \times 10^{-5} - 5.7 \times 10^{-5}$

29. $18.6 \times 10^{-4} - 3.2 \times 10^{-4} - 2.8 \times 10^{-4}$

30. $(6 \times 10^3)(2.1 \times 10^7) \div (2 \times 10^5)$

31. $(8 \times 10^6)(1.7 \times 10^9) \div (4 \times 10^8)$

32. $(2 \times 10^4)(1.2 \times 10^9) \div (6 \times 10^2)$

33. $(2.4 \times 10^6)(3 \times 10^{12}) \div (12 \times 10^3)$

34. $(9 \times 10^{14}) \div (3 \times 10^6)(1.7 \times 10^3)$

35. $(8 \times 10^9) \div (2.5 \times 10^2)(1.1 \times 10^6)$

36. $4 \times 10^{12} + (1.8 \times 10^9)(2.6 \times 10^3)$

37. $5 \times 10^{14} + (2.4 \times 10^4)(1.4 \times 10^{10})$

Problem Solving

38. The average distance between Mars and the sun is about 227.9×10^6 km. Earth is about 78.4×10^6 km nearer the sun than Mars. The distance between Mars and the sun is about how many times as great as the distance between Earth and the sun? Round to two decimal places.

39. What are all the possible integer exponents that will make the equation true?
$(5.8 \times 10^?)(3.2 \times 10^?) = 1.856 \times 10^{12}$

WRITE ABOUT IT

40. Explain how scientific notation can make solving the problem below easier. Then solve.

$$\frac{2{,}580{,}000{,}000 \times 0.00000000045}{11{,}000{,}000{,}000{,}000}$$

1-8 Algebraic Expressions

Name ______________________________ Date __________

Billy has 15 more than twice as many checkers as Grace. If Grace has c checkers, write an expression for the number of checkers Billy has.

Let Grace's checkers be represented by c

Twice means *multiply by* 2. *More than* means *add*.

$2c$ $+ 15$

So the expression that represents Billy's checkers is $2c + 15$.

Evaluate $5w - 6vw$, when $v = -4$ and $w = 8$.

$5w - 6vw$ ← $6vw$ means $6 \bullet v \bullet w$.

$5(8) - 6(-4)(8)$ ← Substitute -4 for v and 8 for w.

$40 - (-192)$ ← Multiply.

$40 + 192$ ← Subtract by adding the opposite.

232 ← Add.

Remember: You can use a handheld to check your answer.

Write each word phrase as an algebraic expression.

1. 5 more than a

2. 3 more than five times d

3. 6 times the quotient of x and y

Write each algebraic expression as a word phrase.

4. $4x - 2$

the product of 4 and x, decreased by 2

5. $7w - 3$

6. $4(a + 11)$

7. $9(f - 13)$

8. $11 \div d + 45$

9. $32 \div g + 59$

Write an algebraic expression to represent each situation.

10. Carmen worked h hours. If she works 7 more hours, how many hours will she have worked?
Let h be the number of hours worked
***7 more* means add 7.**
$h + 7$

11. Tran worked w weeks. If he works 9 more weeks, how many weeks will he have worked?

12. Max gives an equal number of cards to 5 friends. If he gives c cards, how many does each friend get?

13. Olivia reads an equal number of pages for 8 days. If she reads p pages in all, how many pages does she read each day?

Use with SOURCEBOOK Lesson 1-8, pages 16–19.

Evaluate each algebraic expression for the given values of the variables. You can use your handheld to check.

14. $4a + 2(7 + a)$, when $a = 3$

$4(3) + 2(7 + 3)$
$12 + 2(10)$
$12 + 20$
32

15. $5b + 3(2 + b)$, when $b = 4$

16. $12 - 2v + 6v$, when $v = -1$

17. $-q^2 - 3qt + 1$, when $q = 2$ and $t = -2$

18. $-h^2 - 5hk + 6$, when $h = 3$ and $k = -3$

19. $\frac{c + d}{c - d}$, when $c = \frac{8}{11}$ and $d = \frac{10}{11}$

20. $\frac{(3x + y)^2}{x^2 + y}$ if $x = \frac{1}{4}$ and $y = -\frac{1}{4}$

21. $\frac{(2d + e)^2}{d^2 + 2e}$ if $d = \frac{1}{3}$ and $e = -\frac{1}{3}$

Solve. Show your work.

22. A length of rope is cut into 3 pieces. The second piece is 3 more than twice as long as the first piece, x. The third piece is 4 times as long as the second piece. Write an algebraic expression for the length of each piece.

23. Kyle increased a number by 6, multiplied the sum by 8, and then divided the product by -4. If his answer is -4, what was his starting number?

CHALLENGE

24. The quotient of the sum of two numbers and 9 is squared and then increased by 15. The sum is then tripled. Write an algebraic expression to represent the situation and evaluate it when $a = -5$ and $b = 14$.

1-9 Properties of Real Numbers

Name ______________________ Date __________

Simplify: $4x + 7(x - 9) - 11$

$4x + 7[x + (-9)] + (-11)$ ← Definition of Subtraction

$4x + (7)(x) + (7)(-9) + (-11)$ ← Use the Distributive Property.

$4x + 7x + (-63) + (-11)$ ← Multiply.

$(4x + 7x) + [(-63) + (-11)]$ ← Use the Associative Property to group like terms.

$(4 + 7)x + (-74)$ ← Use the Distributive Property to combine like terms.

$11x + (-74)$ ← Add the coefficients of like terms.

$11x - 74$ ← Definition of Subtraction

Commutative Property
$a + b = b + a$ $\quad a \bullet b = b \bullet a$

Associative Property
$(a + b) + c = a + (b + c)$
$(a \bullet b) \bullet c = a \bullet (b \bullet c)$

Distributive Property of Multiplication over Addition $a \bullet (b + c) = a \bullet b + a \bullet c$

Additive Identity Property $a + 0 = a$

Multiplicative Identity Property $a \bullet 1 = a$

Additive Inverse Property $a + (-a) = 0$

Multiplicative Inverse Property $a \bullet \frac{1}{a} = 1$

Substitute a number for *n* to make each statement true. Identify the property or definition that is illustrated.

1. $(-4 \bullet n) \bullet 13 = -4 \bullet (19 \bullet 13)$
   19; Associative Property

2. $22 + n = 22$
   ______

3. $n \bullet 1 = 9$
   ______

4. $n \bullet (5 + 7) = 8 \bullet 5 + 8 \bullet 7$
   ______

5. $2 + (n) = 0$
   ______

6. $3 \bullet \frac{1}{3} = n$
   ______

Write a justification for each step of the given simplification process.

7. $3x + 8y + 11x + 4y$
   a. $3x + 11x + 8y + 4y$ Commutative Prop.
   b. $(3 + 11)x + (8 + 4)y$ Distributive Prop.
   c. $14x + 12y$ Combine like terms.

8. $2x + 9y + 15x + 7y$
   a. $2x + 15x + 9y + 7y$ ______
   b. $(2 + 15)x + (9 + 7)y$ ______
   c. $17x + 16y$ ______

9. $4x - 8y + 9x - 7y$
   a. $4x + (-8y) + 9x + (-7y)$ ______
   b. $4x + 9x + (-8y) + (-7y)$ ______
   c. $(4 + 9)x + [-8 + (-7)]y$ ______
   d. $13x + (-15)y$ ______
   e. $13x - 15y$ ______

10. $2x + 3y + 5y - 6x$
   a. $2x + 3y + 5y + (-6x)$ ______
   b. $2x + 3y + (-6x) + 5y$ ______
   c. $2x + (-6x) + 3y + 5y$ ______
   d. $[2 + (-6)]x + (3 + 5)y$ ______
   e. $-4x + 8y$ ______

Use with SOURCEBOOK Lesson 1-9, pages 20–21.

Simplify each expression. Write a justification for each step.

11. $11t - 4(2t - 9)$

$11t + (-4)[2t + (-9)]$; Def. of Subtraction
$11t + (-4)(2t) + (-4)(-9)$; Distributive Prop.
$11t + (-8)t + 36$; Multiply.
$[11t + (-8)t] + 36$; Associative Prop.
$[11 + (-8)]t + 36$; Distributive Prop.
$3t + 36$; Add coefficients.

12. $20d - 6(3d - 2)$

13. $15a + 3(4 + 5a)$

14. $13b + 4(5 + 7b)$

15. $x - (1 - 3x)$

16. $2v - (3 - 4v)$

17. $4[3c + 9 - 4c] + 8$

18. $5[2d + 3 - 4d] + 2$

Problem Solving

19. Is there a Commutative Property for subtraction or division? Give an example for each. Then find an exception for each.

20. A new operation ♣ is defined as $a ♣ b = a + b + ab$. For example, $3 ♣ 2 = 3 + 2 + 3(2) = 5 + 6 = 11$. Is the operation ♣ commutative? Give an example.

WRITE ABOUT IT

21. Use examples to explain why the Associative Property does not work for subtraction and division. Give the exceptions.

1-10 Sets and Operations

Name ______________________________ Date ____________

Let $U = \{1, 2, 3, 4, \ldots, 16\}$
$A = \{1, 2, 3, 4, 5\}$
$B = \{4, 5, 6, 7, 8, 9, 10\}$
$C = \{10, 11, 12, 13, 14, 15, 16\}$

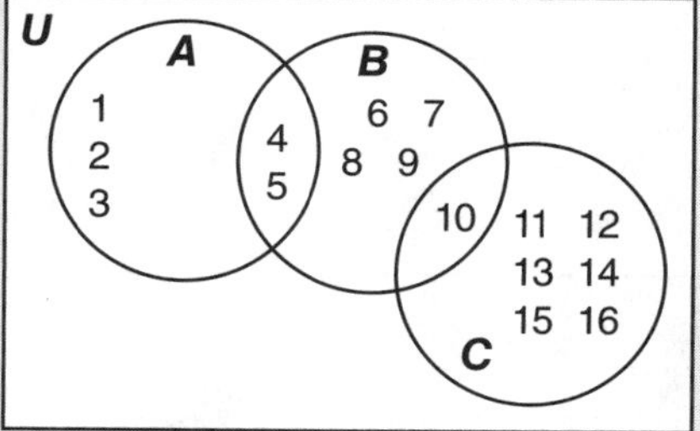

Refer to the Venn diagram, which shows how these sets are related, and specify each set by roster notation:

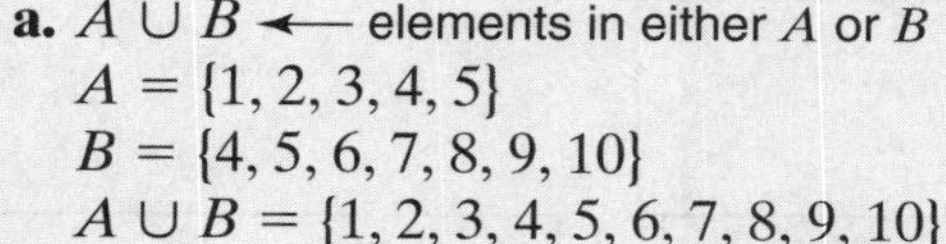

a. $A \cup B$ ⟵ elements in either A or B
$A = \{1, 2, 3, 4, 5\}$
$B = \{4, 5, 6, 7, 8, 9, 10\}$
$A \cup B = \{1, 2, 3, 4, 5, 6, 7, 8, 9, 10\}$

b. $A \cap B$ ⟵ elements in both A and B
$A = \{1, 2, 3, 4, 5\}$
$B = \{4, 5, 6, 7, 8, 9, 10\}$
$A \cap B = \{4, 5\}$

c. A' ⟵ every element not in A
$A = \{1, 2, 3, 4, 5\}$
$U = \{1, 2, 3, 4, \ldots, 16\}$
$A' = \{6, 7, 8, 9, 10, 11, 12, 13, 14, 15, 16\}$

d. $A \cap C$ ⟵ elements in both A and C
$A = \{1, 2, 3, 4, 5\}$
$C = \{10, 11, 12, 13, 14, 15, 16\}$
$A \cap C = \varnothing$ ⟵ A and C are disjoint sets.

List the elements of each set.

1. $\{a \mid a$ is a whole number and $a < 6\}$

Read as: "The set of all a such that a is a whole number and a is less than 6."
{0, 1, 2, 3, 4, 5}

2. $\{d \mid d$ is an integer and $d > -5\}$

____

3. $\{h \mid h$ is a whole number and $h < -2$

____

4. $\{y \mid y \in$ the set of integers and $y > -7\}$

____

List the elements of the complement of each set A, given its universe U.

5. $U = \{$whole numbers$\}$, $A = \{2, 3, 4\}$

$A' = \{0, 1, 5, 6, 7, \ldots\}$

6. $U = \{2, 4, 6, 8, 10\}$, $A = \{2, 4\}$

____

7. $U = \{2, 3, 8\}$, $A = \{2, 3, 8\}$

____

8. $U = \{$integers$\}$, $A = \{2\}$

____

9. $U = \{$whole numbers$\}$,
$A = \{$odd whole numbers$\}$

____

10. $U = \{$whole numbers$\}$,
$A = \{$whole numbers divisible by 2$\}$

____

Refer to the diagram, and specify each set by roster.

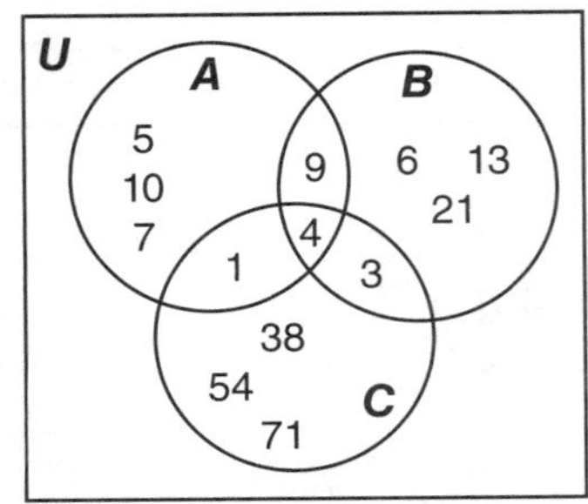

11. $A \cap B$

$A = \{1, 4, 5, 7, 9, 10\}$, $B = \{3, 4, 6, 9, 13, 21\}$

$A \cap B = \{4, 9\}$

12. $A \cup B$

13. $B \cup (A \cap C)$

14. $A \cap (B' \cap C)$

Choose the Venn diagram that models each situation.

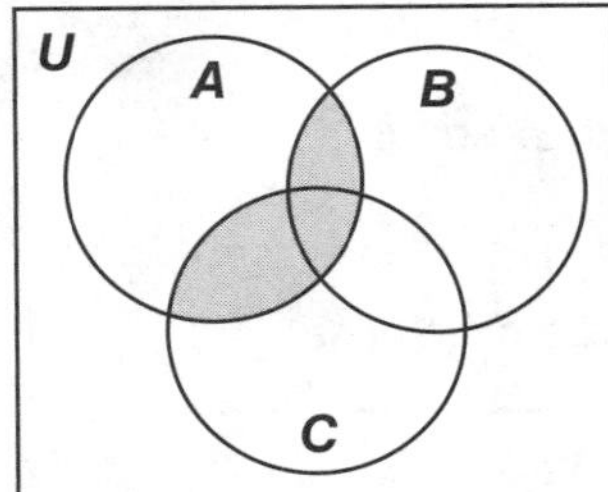

a.

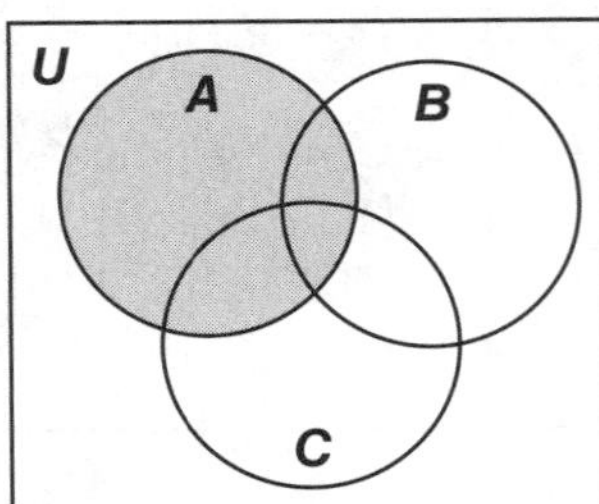

b.

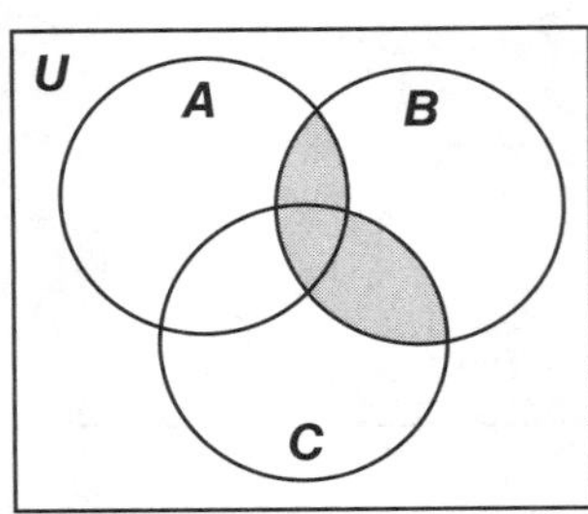

c.

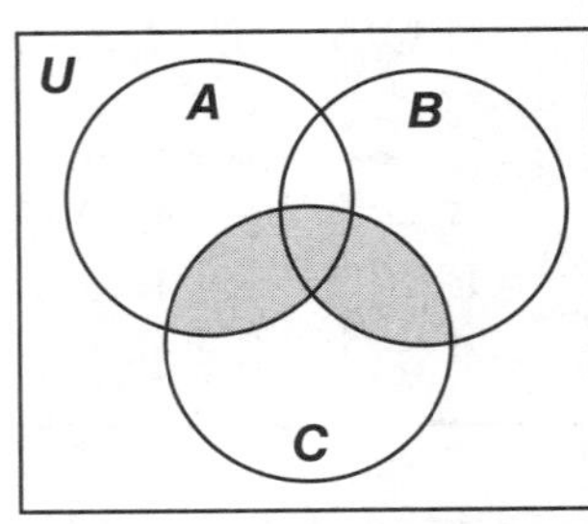

d.

15. $C \cap (A \cup B)$ d

16. $A \cap (C \cup B)$

17. $B \cap (A \cup C)$

18. $A \cap (B \cup A)$

Problem Solving

19. Of 25 students, all take either algebra or history or both. Of these students, 17 take algebra and 5 take both algebra and history. How many students take only algebra? Only history? Use a Venn diagram to help solve the problem.

20. A group of people were surveyed about the color of their cars. The data are as follows: 21, black; 21, white; 20, blue; 12, black and blue; 7, blue and white; 6, black and white; 4, all 3 colors. How many people were surveyed? Use a Venn diagram to help solve the problem.

CRITICAL THINKING

21. Use ∪, ∩, and ′ (prime) to describe the shaded portion in the Venn diagram at the right.

1-11 Operations with Matrices: Addition and Subtraction

Name ______________________________ Date ____________

Consider the matrices: $A = \begin{bmatrix} -1 & 2.5 & 4 \\ 3 & -5 & 2.8 \end{bmatrix}$ and $B = \begin{bmatrix} 6 & -3.8 & 9 \\ -2 & -4 & 1.9 \end{bmatrix}$

Find $A + B$.

$$A + B = \begin{bmatrix} -1 & 2.5 & 4 \\ 3 & -5 & 2.8 \end{bmatrix} + \begin{bmatrix} 6 & -3.8 & 9 \\ -2 & -4 & 1.9 \end{bmatrix}$$ ← Each matrix is 2 × 3, so you can add the matrices.

$$= \begin{bmatrix} -1 + 6 & 2.5 + (-3.8) & 4 + 9 \\ 3 + (-2) & -5 + (-4) & 2.8 + 1.9 \end{bmatrix}$$ ← Add corresponding elements.

$$= \begin{bmatrix} 5 & -1.3 & 13 \\ 1 & -9 & 4.7 \end{bmatrix}$$ ← Simplify.

Find $A - B$.

$$A - B = \begin{bmatrix} -1 & 2.5 & 4 \\ 3 & -5 & 2.8 \end{bmatrix} - \begin{bmatrix} 6 & -3.8 & 9 \\ -2 & -4 & 1.9 \end{bmatrix}$$ ← Each matrix is 2 × 3, so you can subtract the matrices.

$$= \begin{bmatrix} -1 - 6 & 2.5 - (-3.8) & 4 - 9 \\ 3 - (-2) & -5 - (-4) & 2.8 - 1.9 \end{bmatrix}$$ ← Subtract corresponding elements.

$$= \begin{bmatrix} -7 & 6.3 & -5 \\ 5 & -1 & 0.9 \end{bmatrix}$$ ← Simplify.

Write the dimensions of each matrix.

1. $\begin{bmatrix} 1 & -2 & 3 & 5 \\ -9 & 11 & -4 & 7 \end{bmatrix}$

2 rows, 4 columns
2 × 4

2. $\begin{bmatrix} 5 & 3 \\ 6 & 8 \\ 7 & 2 \end{bmatrix}$ ____________

3. $\begin{bmatrix} 1 & 8 \end{bmatrix}$ ____________

4. $\begin{bmatrix} 1 & 5 \\ 5 & 1 \end{bmatrix}$ ____________

5. $\begin{bmatrix} 2 & 3 & 5 \\ 1 & 0 & 7 \\ 4 & 0 & 0 \end{bmatrix}$ ____________

6. $\begin{bmatrix} 1 & 2 & 11 & 1 \\ 4 & 6 & 2 & 8 \\ 1 & 2 & 12 & 5 \end{bmatrix}$ ____________

7. $\begin{bmatrix} 5 & 0 & 3 & 2 & 9 \end{bmatrix}$ ____________

8. $\begin{bmatrix} 8 & 0 & 1 & 2 & 9 \\ 1 & 4 & 3 & 7 & 5 \end{bmatrix}$ ____________

9. $\begin{bmatrix} 3 \\ 8 \\ -9 \end{bmatrix}$ ____________

10. $\begin{bmatrix} -4 & 0 & -3 & 3 \end{bmatrix}$ ____________

11. $\begin{bmatrix} 6 & 15 & 11 \\ 13 & -8 & 4 \end{bmatrix}$ ____________

12. $\begin{bmatrix} 7 & -3 & 6 & 2 & 8 \\ 9 & 4 & -2 & 1 & 0 \\ 10 & -5 & -1 & 11 & 13 \end{bmatrix}$ ____________

Use with SOURCEBOOK Lesson 1-11, pages 26–27.

Add or subtract, as indicated.

13. $\begin{bmatrix} 1 & -1 \\ 8 & 10 \end{bmatrix} + \begin{bmatrix} 6 & -9 \\ 5 & 7 \end{bmatrix}$

$\begin{bmatrix} 1+6 & -1+(-9) \\ 8+5 & 10+7 \end{bmatrix} = \begin{bmatrix} 7 & -10 \\ 13 & 17 \end{bmatrix}$

14. $\begin{bmatrix} 3 & -2 \\ -7 & 6 \end{bmatrix} + \begin{bmatrix} 7 & -4 \\ 2 & 1 \end{bmatrix}$

15. $\begin{bmatrix} 8 & -2.3 & 6 \\ 6 & 5.9 & -5 \end{bmatrix} - \begin{bmatrix} -2 & 3 & 5.7 \\ 7 & 6.7 & -2 \end{bmatrix} + \begin{bmatrix} -4 & 8 & 5 \\ -2 & 1.5 & -4 \end{bmatrix}$

16. $\begin{bmatrix} 1 & 3.5 & -2.9 \\ 2 & 5 & 7 \end{bmatrix} - \begin{bmatrix} -7 & 1.1 & -8 \\ 3 & -6 & 7.5 \end{bmatrix} + \begin{bmatrix} 3 & 2 & 1 \\ -8 & 6 & 4 \end{bmatrix}$

Find matrix *X* that results in a true statement.

17. $\begin{bmatrix} 5 & -2 \\ 1 & 13 \end{bmatrix} + X = \begin{bmatrix} 11 & -2 \\ 19 & -5 \end{bmatrix}$

$X = \begin{bmatrix} 11 & -2 \\ 19 & -5 \end{bmatrix} - \begin{bmatrix} 5 & -2 \\ 1 & 13 \end{bmatrix} = \begin{bmatrix} 6 & 0 \\ 18 & -18 \end{bmatrix}$

18. $\begin{bmatrix} -8 & 6 \\ -2 & 31 \end{bmatrix} + X = \begin{bmatrix} 2 & -5 \\ 16 & -12 \end{bmatrix}$

19. $X - \begin{bmatrix} 3 & -2 & 1.6 \\ 3.4 & 9 & 15 \end{bmatrix} = \begin{bmatrix} -1 & 12 & 9.2 \\ 4.6 & -4 & 13 \end{bmatrix}$

20. $X - \begin{bmatrix} -8 & 19 & 5.7 \\ 8.2 & -3 & 24 \end{bmatrix} = \begin{bmatrix} -2 & 10 & 6.1 \\ 2.2 & -10 & 21 \end{bmatrix}$

Solve. Show your work.

21. At the beginning of May, a store had 80 red, 120 blue, and 90 black cell phones. During the month, the store sold 35 red, 74 blue, and 71 black cell phones. Write a matrix to indicate the inventory at the end of May.

22. In June, Vicki collected 28.2 pounds of cans, 78.7 pounds of bottles, and 110.1 pounds of newspapers. In July, she collected 59.4 pounds of cans, 113.6 pounds of bottles, and 168.9 pounds of newspapers. Write a matrix to indicate the total number of pounds of each she collected in June and July.

TEST PREPARATION

23. What are the dimensions of the matrix $\begin{bmatrix} -1 & 12 \end{bmatrix}$?

A. 1×2 **B.** 2×1 **C.** 12×-1 **D.** -1×12

1-12 Operations with Matrices: Multiplication

Name ______________________ Date __________

Consider the two matrices: $A = \begin{bmatrix} -1 & 9 & 5 \\ 2 & 7 & 3 \end{bmatrix}$ and $B = \begin{bmatrix} 6 \\ -1 \\ 4 \end{bmatrix}$.

Find $3A$.

$$3A = 3\begin{bmatrix} -1 & 9 & 5 \\ 2 & 7 & 3 \end{bmatrix} = \begin{bmatrix} 3(-1) & 3(9) & 3(5) \\ 3(2) & 3(7) & 3(3) \end{bmatrix} = \begin{bmatrix} -3 & 27 & 15 \\ 6 & 21 & 9 \end{bmatrix}$$

← For *Scalar Multiplication*; Multiply each element of the matrix by the same real number.

Find AB.

$$AB = \begin{bmatrix} -1 & 9 & 5 \\ 2 & 7 & 3 \end{bmatrix} \bullet \begin{bmatrix} 6 \\ -1 \\ 4 \end{bmatrix}$$

← Multiply; each row of the first matrix has the same number of elements as the column in the second matrix.

$$= \begin{bmatrix} -1(6) + 9(-1) + 5(4) \\ 2(6) + 7(-1) + 3(4) \end{bmatrix} = \begin{bmatrix} -6 + (-9) + 20 \\ 12 + (-7) + 12 \end{bmatrix} = \begin{bmatrix} 5 \\ 17 \end{bmatrix}$$

← Dimensions: A is **2** × 3, B is 3 × **1**, so AB is 2 × 1.

Multiply the matrix by the real number.

1. $4\begin{bmatrix} 8 & -3 & -9 \\ 2 & 0 & 3 \end{bmatrix}$

$\begin{bmatrix} 4(8) & 4(-3) & 4(-9) \\ 4(2) & 4(0) & 4(3) \end{bmatrix}$

$\begin{bmatrix} 32 & -12 & -36 \\ 8 & 0 & 12 \end{bmatrix}$

2. $5\begin{bmatrix} 11 & -2 & 6 \\ -1 & 2 & 9 \end{bmatrix}$ ______________

3. $6\begin{bmatrix} 3 & -1 \\ -4 & 6 \end{bmatrix} + \begin{bmatrix} -4 & 2 \\ 5 & -2 \end{bmatrix}$ ______________

4. $7\begin{bmatrix} -5 & 8 \\ -2 & 3 \end{bmatrix} + \begin{bmatrix} -1 & 6 \\ 4 & -5 \end{bmatrix}$ ______________

5. $3\begin{bmatrix} 1 & 2 & -3 \\ -4 & 5 & -4 \end{bmatrix} - 4\begin{bmatrix} 3 & -2 & 2 \\ -1 & 6 & 5 \end{bmatrix}$ ______________

6. $4\begin{bmatrix} 3 & -4 & -2 \\ -2 & 6 & -7 \end{bmatrix} - 2\begin{bmatrix} 2 & -1 & 1 \\ -6 & -5 & 2 \end{bmatrix}$ ______________

Find the dimensions of each product matrix AB, given the dimensions of matrices A and B.

7. $A_{2\times5} \bullet B_{5\times6} = AB_?$

$AB_{2\times6}$

8. $A_{3\times8} \bullet B_{8\times9} = AB_?$ ______________

9. $A_{1\times10} \bullet B_{10\times1} = AB_?$ ______________

10. $A_{4\times12} \bullet B_{12\times4} = AB_?$ ______________

11. $A_{3\times7} \bullet B_{7\times6} = AB_?$ ______________

12. $A_{2\times14} \bullet B_{14\times14} = AB_?$ ______________

Find the product matrix, if it exists. If it does not exist, tell why not.

13. $\begin{bmatrix} 3 & -1 \\ 4 & 2 \end{bmatrix} \bullet \begin{bmatrix} -2 \\ 5 \end{bmatrix}$

$\begin{bmatrix} 3(-2) + (-1)(5) \\ 4(-2) \quad + 2(5) \end{bmatrix} = \begin{bmatrix} -6 + (-5) \\ -8 \quad + 10 \end{bmatrix}$

$\begin{bmatrix} -11 \\ 2 \end{bmatrix}$

14. $\begin{bmatrix} -5 & -2 \\ 3 & 4 \end{bmatrix} \bullet \begin{bmatrix} 6 \\ 2 \end{bmatrix}$

15. $\begin{bmatrix} -1 & -2 \\ 2 & 3 \\ 1 & 6 \end{bmatrix} \bullet \begin{bmatrix} -2 & 3 \\ 1 & 4 \end{bmatrix}$

16. $\begin{bmatrix} 2 & -3 \\ -4 & 1 \\ -1 & 5 \end{bmatrix} \bullet \begin{bmatrix} 3 & 5 \\ -2 & 7 \end{bmatrix}$

17. $\begin{bmatrix} 1 & -8 \\ 20 & -9 \\ -21 & 11 \end{bmatrix} \bullet \begin{bmatrix} 3 \\ -2 \\ 19 \end{bmatrix}$

18. $\begin{bmatrix} 13 & -14 \\ 17 & -25 \end{bmatrix} \bullet \begin{bmatrix} 7 & 5 \\ -1 & 14 \\ 9 & 0 \end{bmatrix}$

Solve. Show your work.

19. Multiply matrices to find a store's cost of buying 20 pairs of pants for $5 each and selling 11 pairs of pants for $34 each.

20. Mechanical pencils cost $4.95, pens cost $2.99, and notebooks cost $3.49. Olivier bought 12 mechanical pencils, 8 pens, and 7 notebooks. Paulina bought 6 mechanical pencils, 12 pens, and 9 notebooks. Use matrices to find the total amount each person spent.

SPIRAL REVIEW

If the number is rational, find its square root. If the radicand is a nonperfect square, give the two consecutive integers it lies between, and the closer integer.

21. $\sqrt{625}$

22. $\sqrt{71}$

23. $\sqrt{36}$

24. $\sqrt{12}$

1-13 Technology: Evaluate Numerical and Algebraic Expressions

Name ________________ Date ________

You can use a handheld to evaluate the expression $\frac{-(7-3)^2}{7+2^2-3}$.

Step 1 Press [home], then choose [1] to select **Calculator.**

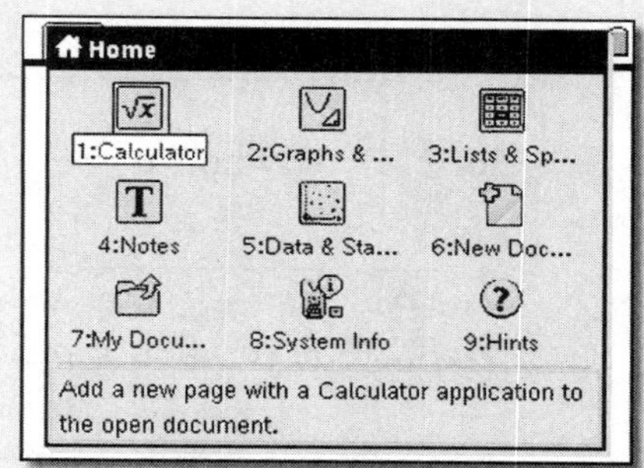

Step 2 Enter the expression $-(7-3)^2 \div (7+2^2-3)$. Press [enter].

Think
To end the exponent, press the right arrow on the circle.

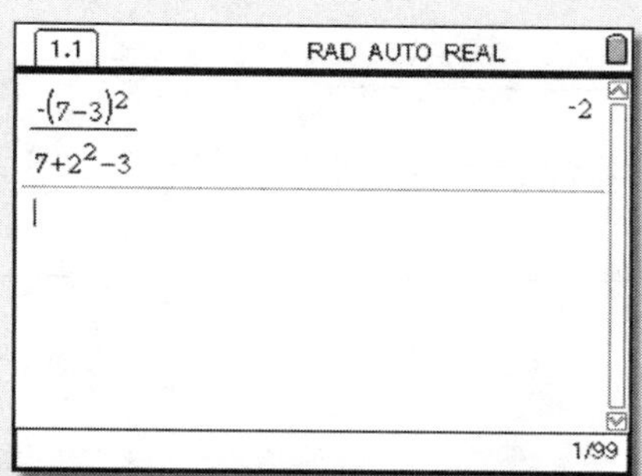

Use a handheld to evaluate the expression.

1. $52 - 13^2(8 - 11)$

559

2. $32 - 14^2(2 - 13)$

3. $7^3 + (4 + 8)^2$

4. $5^3 + (2 + 9)^2$

5. $11^2 - (7 - 12)^3$

6. $15^2 - (11 - 14)^3$

7. $7(5 + 8) - 2(13 - 21)$

8. $5(6 + 2) - 3(8 - 16)$

9. $3(2^3 + 5) - 4(5 - 3^2)$

10. $7(3^3 - 4) - 2(6^2 + 5)$

11. $24 \div 8 - 5(5^3 - 2)^2$

12. $48 \div 6 - 8(4^3 - 3)^2$

13. $\frac{31 + 17}{15 - 3}$

14. $\frac{68 - 8}{8 + 7}$

15. $\frac{6^2 + 3 - 9}{2^3 - 38}$

16. $\frac{4^2 + 7 - 3}{3^3 - 37}$

17. $\frac{(3 + 5)^2}{6 - 22}$

18. $\frac{(4 + 6)^2}{2 - 52}$

19. $\frac{4(2^3 + 3)}{12 - 4^2}$

20. $\frac{2(3^3 + 7)}{8 - 5^2}$

21. $\frac{5^3 - 110}{3^2 - 6}$

22. $\frac{6^3 - 116}{7^2 + 1}$

23. $\frac{8^3 - 24 + 7^2}{8 - 12 + 1^8}$

24. $\frac{5^3 - 44 + 9^2}{1^9 - 19 + 3^2}$

Use with SOURCEBOOK Lesson 1-13, pages 30–31.

Use a handheld to evaluate the algebraic expression for the given value. Then make a table for the expression starting at 0 using increments of 0.25.

25. $-27x$ when $x = 3.9$

−105.3

26. $-42x$ when $x = 5.6$

27. $-19x$ when $x = -7.1$

28. $-36x$ when $x = -8.4$

29. $11.5x$ when $x = -15$

30. $17.5x$ when $x = -6$

31. $8x - 3$ when $x = 15$

32. $5x - 11$ when $x = 12$

33. $-2x + 7$ when $x = -10.6$

34. $-3x + 4$ when $x = -8.2$

35. $15 - 4x$ when $x = -5$

36. $21 - 3x$ when $x = -7$

37. $29 - 2.7x$ when $x = 5$

38. $56 - 4.9x$ when $x = 4$

39. $8.2 + 3.4x$ when $x = 5$

40. $7.1 + 5.9x$ when $x = 6$

41. $3(x - 2.9)$ when $x = -4$

42. $2(x - 3.6)$ when $x = -2$

43. $4(3x - 5)$ when $x = -1.8$

44. $5(2x - 6)$ when $x = -2.4$

45. $1.7(4x - 1.8)$ when $x = 15$

46. $3.9(5x - 2.7)$ when $x = 12$

47. $11(2.3x + 5.1)$ when $x = -8$

48. $14(1.1x + 3.8)$ when $x = -6$

Solve. Show your work.

49. Marla and Ted's ages are both divisible by 7. Each age is the value of the expression below after inserting one set of parentheses. Use a handheld to find each age. In how many years will the older age be $1\frac{1}{2}$ times the younger age?

$32 \div 16 \times 24 - 2^3 + 12$

50. Taylor works for his father during the summer. He earns $12h + 13$ for each job, where h represents his number of hours on the job. Make a table on a handheld, with Table Step set at 0.5, to shows his hours on a job that paid $199.

TEST PREPARATION

51. Use a handheld to find which expression is equivalent to 12.

A. $\frac{(4^3 - 15) - 1}{(24 \div 12)^2}$ **B.** $\frac{(4^3 - 15) - 1}{(24 \div 12)^3}$ **C.** $\frac{(4^3 - 15) + 1}{(24 \div 12)^2}$ **D.** $\frac{(4^3 - 15) - 1}{(48 \div 12)^2}$

1-14 Technology: Operations with Matrices

Name ______________________________ Date ____________

You can use a handheld to multiply matrices.

$\begin{bmatrix} 2 & 4 \\ 3 & 5 \end{bmatrix} \bullet \begin{bmatrix} -1 & 6 \\ 2 & -3 \end{bmatrix}$

Remember: To multiply matrices, the number of columns in the first matrix must equal the number of rows in the second matrix.

Step 1 Press (home). Then choose (1) to select **Calculator.**

Step 2 Press (ctrl) (template key) to bring up the matrix dialog box.

Step 3 Choose the 2 by 2 matrix.

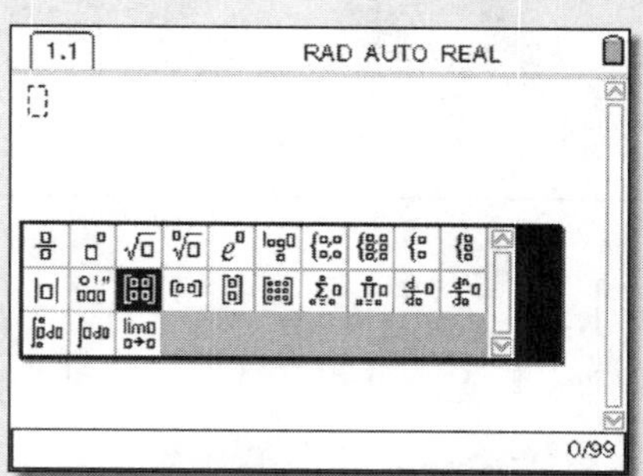

Step 4 Enter the values of the first matrix, tabbing after each value including the last value. Then press (template key). Repeat Steps 2–3 and enter the values of the second matrix. Then press (enter).

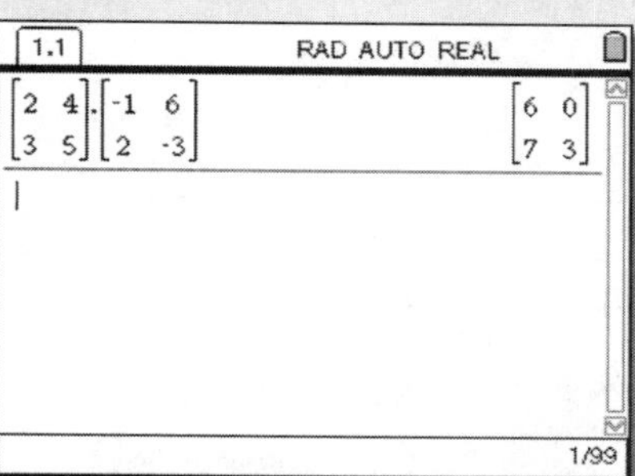

Use a handheld to perform the indicated operation.

1. $\begin{bmatrix} 1 & 5 & 3 & -1 \\ -2 & 3 & 8 & -4 \\ 3 & 7 & 4 & 5 \end{bmatrix} + \begin{bmatrix} 3 & 5 & 3 & 11 \\ 4 & -1 & 8 & -5 \\ 3 & -6 & -4 & 13 \end{bmatrix}$

$\begin{bmatrix} \mathbf{4} & \mathbf{10} & \mathbf{6} & \mathbf{10} \\ \mathbf{2} & \mathbf{2} & \mathbf{16} & \mathbf{-9} \\ \mathbf{6} & \mathbf{1} & \mathbf{0} & \mathbf{18} \end{bmatrix}$

2. $\begin{bmatrix} 9 & 2 \\ -7 & 11 \\ 14 & -8 \end{bmatrix} + \begin{bmatrix} 13 & -9 \\ 4 & 12 \\ -8 & -13 \end{bmatrix}$

____

3. $[-12 \quad 10 \quad 9 \quad -5] - [8 \quad -6 \quad -3 \quad 1]$

____

4. $\begin{bmatrix} 1 & -4 & -7 \\ 10 & -5 & 11 \end{bmatrix} - \begin{bmatrix} 5 & 8 & -2 \\ -7 & 8 & -13 \end{bmatrix}$

____

5. $\begin{bmatrix} -5 & 6 \\ 8 & 11 \end{bmatrix} \bullet \begin{bmatrix} 2 & 7 \\ -5 & -3 \end{bmatrix}$

____

6. $\begin{bmatrix} 3 & 5 \\ -4 & 13 \end{bmatrix} \bullet \begin{bmatrix} 7 & -8 \\ 11 & -6 \end{bmatrix}$

____

Use a handheld to perform the indicated operation.

7. $\begin{bmatrix} 14 & -3 \\ 2 & 8 \\ -3 & 0 \end{bmatrix} \bullet \begin{bmatrix} -6 & 2 & 15 \\ 3 & 12 & -7 \end{bmatrix}$

$\begin{bmatrix} -93 & -8 & 231 \\ 12 & 100 & -26 \\ 18 & -6 & -45 \end{bmatrix}$

8. $\begin{bmatrix} 9 & -3 \\ 10 & 22 \\ -8 & 11 \end{bmatrix} \bullet \begin{bmatrix} 4 & -5 & 13 \\ -15 & -8 & 2 \end{bmatrix}$

9. $\begin{bmatrix} 2 & 3 \\ -4 & 1 \\ -1 & 3 \\ 1 & 0 \\ -2 & 5 \end{bmatrix} \bullet \begin{bmatrix} 1 \\ -2 \end{bmatrix}$

10. $\begin{bmatrix} 1 & -2 & 3 & 0 \\ -4 & 0 & 1 & 3 \\ 2 & 7 & 1 & 7 \end{bmatrix} \bullet \begin{bmatrix} 3 & 2 \\ -1 & 0 \\ 2 & -4 \\ -3 & 2 \end{bmatrix}$

11. $\begin{bmatrix} 8 & -5 \\ 11 & 2 \end{bmatrix} + \begin{bmatrix} -4 & -2 \\ 6 & 7 \end{bmatrix} - \begin{bmatrix} 11 & 10 \\ -5 & -8 \end{bmatrix}$

12. $\begin{bmatrix} 13 & -1 \\ -6 & 0 \end{bmatrix} + \begin{bmatrix} -2 & -11 \\ 8 & 13 \end{bmatrix} - \begin{bmatrix} -3 & -6 \\ 15 & 13 \end{bmatrix}$

13. $\begin{bmatrix} 5 & -14 \\ -8 & 13 \end{bmatrix} - \begin{bmatrix} -23 & -4 \\ 17 & 9 \end{bmatrix} + \begin{bmatrix} 18 & 9 \\ -3 & -7 \end{bmatrix}$

14. $\begin{bmatrix} 21 & -10 \\ -11 & 9 \end{bmatrix} - \begin{bmatrix} -14 & -10 \\ 12 & 15 \end{bmatrix} + \begin{bmatrix} -2 & -13 \\ 8 & 16 \end{bmatrix}$

CRITICAL THINKING

Solve.

15. Find the value of each variable.

$\begin{bmatrix} b & 2 \\ -5 & a \end{bmatrix} + \begin{bmatrix} -4 & c \\ d & 6 \end{bmatrix} = \begin{bmatrix} 5 & -3 \\ 1 & 11 \end{bmatrix} \bullet \begin{bmatrix} 0 & -2 \\ -4 & 1 \end{bmatrix}$

16. Find the value of each variable.

$\begin{bmatrix} a & 1 \\ -2 & 3 \end{bmatrix} \bullet \begin{bmatrix} 3 & 0 \\ 2 & c \end{bmatrix} = \begin{bmatrix} 17 & b+1 \\ b & 3 \end{bmatrix}$

1-15 Problem-Solving Strategy: Make a Drawing

Read Plan Solve Check

Name ______________________________ Date ____________

Solve by making a drawing.

1. A battery operated car runs at a constant rate on a square-foot tiled floor. When set to travel along a straight row of tiles, the car took 28 seconds to travel from the beginning of the first tile to the end of the 7th tile. How long will it take the car to travel from the 8th tile line to the 20th?

____

2. Sally counts 18 cubes and triangular pyramids in her teacher's collection of manipulatives. These shapes have a total of 94 faces. Exactly how many of the manipulatives are cubes?

____

3. At exactly 12:00 P.M., two cars heading in opposite directions are aligned in parallel lanes of a highway. One car is moving 45 mph, the other 55 mph. At what time will the cars be 20 mi apart?

____

4. If six candidates for class president each shake hands with each other once, how many handshakes occur in all?

____

5. Seven students are playing a game in a circle. According to the rules, each player can trade tokens with other players, but not with players sitting adjacent to the player. How many trades are possible?

6. In the nation of Pangopu the national currency is the spid, a coin cut from silver blanks. Five spids can be cut from each silver blank, after which the scraps of three such blanks can be recast to form a fresh standard blank. How many spids can be made from a delivery of eleven standard silver blanks? (No spid can be cut from a partial blank.)

7. Tom and Mark live on the same block, but each drive to the tennis club separately, leaving at the same time. The club is 12 mi away. Mark drives straight to the club, averaging 60 mi/h. Tom, after driving 1.5 mi, realizes that he forgot his racket and returns home to get it. Is it possible for Tom to arrive at the club at the same time as Mark if he averages 65 mi/h throughout his trip?

8. You and seven other contestants are seated at equal intervals at a round table. You are asked to choose a contestant to leave the table. Then, counting clockwise, the third contestant from the removed contestant must also leave. This process continues until one contestant remains (the winner). In order for you to win, which contestant relative to you, should you select as the first to leave the table?

Enrichment:
Modular Arithmetic

Name ______________________ Date __________

Add: 10 + 8 + 6 + 4 + 2 (mod 12)

10 + 8 + 6 + 4 + 2 = 30 ← Find the sum.

30 ÷ 12 = 2 R 6 ← Divide the sum by 12 to find the remainder; this is the sum modulo m.

So, 10 + 8 + 6 + 4 + 2 = 6 (mod 12).

Remember: Addition Modulo *m*
Add as you would in regular addition. Then divide the result by m. The remainder is the sum modulo m.

Multiply: 10 • 5 • 3 (mod 8)

10 • 5 • 3 = 150 ← Find the product.

150 ÷ 8 = 18 R 6 ← Divide the product by 6 to find the remainder; this is the product modulo m.

So 10 • 5 • 3 = 6 (mod 8).

Remember: Multiplication Modulo *m*
Multiply as you would in regular multiplication. Then divide the result by m. The remainder is the product modulo m.

Find the sum in the indicated mod.

1. 2 + 3 (mod 4)
   2 + 3 = 5
   5 ÷ 4 = 1 R 1
   1 (mod 4)

2. 1 + 4 (mod 5) __________

3. 3 + 5 + 2 (mod 6) __________

4. 4 + 7 + 1 (mod 8) __________

5. 2 + 9 + 8 (mod 11) __________

6. 8 + 3 + 5 (mod 16) __________

7. 12 + 9 + 10 (mod 13) __________

8. 6 + 6 + 3 (mod 7) __________

9. 7 + 5 + 8 (mod 9) __________

10. 19 + 1 + 11 (mod 12) __________

11. 5 + 4 + 3 + 2 (mod 7) __________

12. 9 + 7 + 5 + 3 (mod 5) __________

13. 10 + 8 + 6 + 4 (mod 14) __________

14. 12 + 14 + 11 + 7 (mod 16) __________

15. 8 + 13 + 4 + 8 (mod 15) __________

16. 4 + 17 + 12 + 15 + 11 (mod 18) __________

17. 13 + 22 + 19 + 8 + 12 (mod 24) __________

18. 15 + 9 + 21 + 17 + 18 (mod 23) __________

Use with SOURCEBOOK Enrichment Lesson, pages 36–37.

Find the product in the indicated mod.

19. 3 • 4 (mod 5) **20.** 2 • 5 (mod 6) **21.** 4 • 6 (mod 7) **22.** 5 • 8 (mod 9)

23. 10 • 3 (mod 12) **24.** 10 • 3 • 12 (mod 13) **25.** 13 • 8 • 12 (mod 14) **26.** 7 • 7 • 4 (mod 11)

27. 11 • 15 • 2 (mod 16) **28.** 14 • 8 • 4 (mod 15) **29.** 5 • 4 • 3 • 3 (mod 7) **30.** 9 • 7 • 5 • 4 (mod 8)

31. 8 • 10 • 6 • 5 (mod 12) **32.** 5 • 2 • 11 • 13 (mod 14) **33.** 15 • 12 • 8 • 3 (mod 16)

34. 9 • 14 • 2 • 4 (mod 15) **35.** 16 • 5 • 6 • 7 (mod 22) **36.** 8 • 3 • 12 • 14 (mod 23)

Problem Solving

37. The workers on a loading dock can dock a truck, unload the cargo, and move the truck in 24 min. The loading dock is expecting eight trucks, which will arrive one after another.

a. If the first truck arrives at 6 P.M., after a 37-hr trip, at what time did the first truck begin the trip?

b. Find the time when all 8 trucks will be unloaded. Assume each truck arrives one after another.

WRITE ABOUT IT

38. Explain why $a \bullet b \bullet c \bullet x = 0 \pmod{x}$.

Test Prep: Multiple-Choice Questions

Strategy: Understand Distractors

Name ______________________ Date __________

The incorrect answer choices provided in multiple-choice questions may seem reasonable and can distract you from selecting the correct answer. These choices, called **distractors**, are often the results of common errors made when solving the problem.

To select the correct answer in a multiple-choice item, try using the following strategies:

- Underline important words.
- Restate the question.
- Apply appropriate rules, definitions, or properties.
- Analyze and eliminate answer choices.

Sample Test Item

Evaluate: $3 \bullet 2^2 - [-3 + (-7)]$
$= 3(4) - (-10)$
$= 12 + 10 = 22$

A. 2 ← −10 was added instead of subtracted. Eliminate this choice.

(B.) 22 ← This is the correct choice!

C. 26 ← The power was not evaluated first and −10 was added instead of subtracted. Eliminate this choice.

D. 46 ← The power was not evaluated first. Eliminate this choice.

Choose the correct answer. *TIP: Use any time you have left to check your answers.*

1. Simplify: $-\frac{-4^{-2}8^2}{4^2 8^{-8}}$

A. -2^{22} **C.** 2^{14}

B. -2^{14} **D.** 2^{22}

2. Evaluate: $2.6 + 4 \bullet \frac{2|-9|}{5} - 3^2$

F. −20.8 **H.** 8

G. −2.8 **J.** 26

3. Which number is irrational?

A. −8 **C.** $\frac{1}{4}$

B. 0 **D.** $\sqrt{10}$

4. What is the multiplicative inverse of −10?

F. $-\frac{1}{10}$ **H.** 1

G. $\frac{1}{10}$ **J.** 10

5. $A = \{4, 6, 7, 12, 20\}$; $B = \{-2, 6, 8, 12, 15\}$; and $C = \{0, 3, 8, 12, 19\}$
What is $A \cap B \cap C$?

A. $\{12\}$

B. $\{6, 8, 12\}$

C. $\{-2, 0, 3, 4, 6, 7, 8, 12, 15, 19, 20\}$

D. $\varnothing$

6. What is the value of $\frac{3x^{-6}}{x^{-2}}$ if $x = -3$?

F. $-\frac{1}{9}$ **H.** $\frac{1}{27}$

G. $-\frac{1}{27}$ **J.** $\frac{1}{9}$

7. Which Property of Equality is illustrated by $x + y = y + x$?

A. Associative **C.** Distributive

B. Commutative **D.** Identity

8. What is the product of 7.5×10^4 and 5×10^3?

F. 3.75×10^7 **H.** 3.75×10^{12}

G. 3.75×10^8 **J.** 3.75×10^{13}

Use with SOURCEBOOK Test Prep Lesson, page 38.

For More Practice Go To:
ONLINE www.progressinmathematics.com

Vocabulary Development

Name ______________________ Date __________

Chapter 1 Vocabulary

absolute value
additive inverse
base
Closure Property
combining like terms
complement of a set A
constant
corresponding elements
counterexample
cubed
disjoint sets
elements
empty set
evaluate
exponent
intersection of sets
irrational numbers
like terms
literal coefficent
matrix (matrices)
multiplicative identity
multiplicative inverses
negative exponent
negative square root
nonperfect square
null set
numerical coefficient
order of operations
perfect square
power
principal square root
radical sign
radicand
rational numbers
real numbers
reciprocal
repeating decimals
roster notation
scalar multiplication
scientific notation
set
set-builder notation
subset
Substitution Principle
squared
square root
term
terminating decimals
union of sets
universal set
universe
Venn diagram
zero exponent

From the vocabulary list above, choose the term(s) that best complete each sentence. Write the term(s) in the space(s) provided.

1. In the expression $\sqrt{4}$, the number 4 is a(n) ______________________ and $\sqrt{}$ is a ______________________.

2. For addition, the number 0 is called the ______________________.

3. For multiplication, $\frac{1}{8}$ is called the ______________________ of 8.

4. In the expression 8^9, the number 8 is the ______________________ and the number 9 is the ______________________.

5. Sets that do not intersect are called ______________________.

6. A set contained within a set is a(n) ______________________.

7. A set that contains no elements is called the ______________________ or the ______________________.

Choose two terms from the list that you did not use in Questions 1–7. For each term, write a definition in your own words and give an example.

8. ____

____

Use after SOURCEBOOK Lessons 1-1–1-12, pages 2–29.

Practice Chapter 1 Test

Name ______________________________ Date __________

If the number is rational, find its square root. If the radicand is a nonperfect square, give the two consecutive integers it lies between, and the closer integer.

1. $\sqrt{99}$ **2.** $\sqrt{49}$ **3.** $\sqrt{44}$ **4.** $\sqrt{225}$

Order each set of numbers from least to greatest.

5. $-\frac{2}{3}, -|5|, -0.9, -3.2, -\sqrt{9}, -1.\overline{7}$

6. $-5.9, -5, -\sqrt{36}, -\frac{11}{2}, |-5.\overline{14}|, |-7|$

Add, subtract, multiply, or divide using rules for signed numbers.

7. $8.9 + (-9.6)$ **8.** $-2\frac{3}{4} - \left(-3\frac{1}{8}\right)$ **9.** $-6.3(-13.25)$ **10.** $22\frac{1}{2} \div \left(-3\frac{1}{3}\right)$

Find the value of each expression. Express answers in standard form.

11. 4^{-2} **12.** 9^2 **13.** 13^0 **14.** $3^{-4} \bullet 3^3$

Evaluate.

15. $\dfrac{(5-10)^2 + 12^2 \div 16}{[3(6-7)]^2 - 4^2}$

16. $\dfrac{\sqrt{64} - 2^5 \div |8-12|}{12 - 8 + 4}$

Perform the indicated operations. Express answers in scientific notation.

17. $(2.6 \times 10^4)(7.3 \times 10^8)$

18. $(6.8. \times 10^9)(4.5 \times 10^6)$

19. $(2.278 \times 10^9) \div (3.4 \times 10^2) + 1.8 \times 10^6$

20. $(3.57 \times 10^7)(1.3 \times 10^3) - (2.5 \times 10^9)$

Evaluate each algebraic expression for $a = 3$ and $b = -5$.

21. $3ab - b + a^2$ **22.** $b^2 - (-a)$ **23.** $2(a - 4b) - a^2b^2$

Evaluate each algebraic expression for $a = 3$ and $b = -5$.

24. $ab + a^2 - 2b^2$

25. $\frac{4(a - b)^2}{(a + b)^3}$

26. $2a + b - 6a^2b$

Substitute a number for n to make each statement true. Identify the property or definition that is illustrated.

27. $(-34)(15) = (n)(-34)$

28. $-96 \bullet n = -96$

Refer to the diagram, and specify each set by roster.

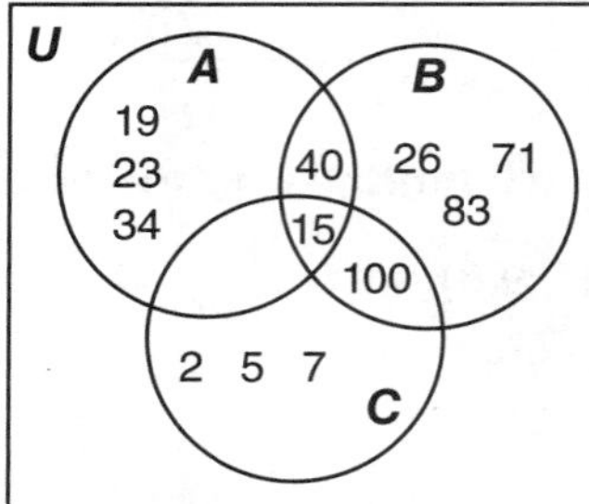

29. $A \cap B$

30. $A \cup B$

31. B'

32. $A \cup (B \cap C)$

Add, subtract, or multiply as indicated.

33. $\begin{bmatrix} 4 & -1 \\ -11 & 9 \end{bmatrix} + 2\begin{bmatrix} 3 & -2 \\ 10 & 9 \end{bmatrix}$

34. $\begin{bmatrix} 3 & -6 \\ -1 & 4 \end{bmatrix} \bullet \begin{bmatrix} 5 & -1 \\ 3 & 2 \end{bmatrix}$

35. $\begin{bmatrix} 2 & -2 & 1 \\ -4 & 3 & 0 \end{bmatrix} \bullet \begin{bmatrix} -4 & 2 \\ -2 & 1 \\ 3 & 4 \end{bmatrix}$

Problem Solving

36. The sum of two numbers is -9 and their difference is 31. What are the numbers?

37. A board is cut into 4 pieces. The first two pieces are of equal length. The third piece is 5 inches longer than the first piece and 6 inches shorter than the fourth piece. Write an algebraic expression for the length of the board before it is cut.

Tell About It

Explain how you solve the problem. Show all your work.

38. Bacteria in Wu's lab double every 3 hours. If Wu's experiment started with 20 cells, how many cells are there after 12 hours?

Cumulative Review: Chapter 1

Name ______________________________ Date ____________

Circle the best answer.

1. Which is a perfect square?

A. 20
B. 30
C. 50
D. 100

2. Which is the best estimate for $\sqrt{90}$?

F. 9.1 **G.** 9.5
H. 9.9 **J.** 30

3. Which number is irrational?

A. $\sqrt{9}$ **B.** $8.\overline{7}$
C. $\frac{22}{7}$ **D.** 2.151151115...

4. Simplify.

$4^3 \bullet 4^2 \bullet 4^{-6}$

F. -120 **G.** $\frac{1}{16}$
H. $\frac{1}{4}$ **J.** 4

5. Which is equivalent to the expression below?

$(1.8 \times 10^9) \div (1.2 \times 10^3)$

A. 0.6×10^3
B. 0.6×10^6
C. 1.5×10^6
D. 1.5×10^{12}

6. Simplify.

$11x - 7(9x - 2) + 8x - 10$

F. $-44x - 8$
G. $-44x + 4$
H. $21x - 19$
J. $21x - 12$

7. If $A = \{19, 22, 23, 34, 47\}$ and $B = \{19, 21, 23, 47, 91\}$ make up the universe, what is the complement of A?

A. $\{19, 21, 22, 23, 34, 47, 91\}$
B. $\{21, 91\}$
C. $\{22, 34\}$
D. $\{19, 23, 47\}$

8. Which set of numbers is closed under subtraction?

F. {0, 1, 2} **G.** {whole numbers}
H. {real numbers} **J.** {odd whole numbers}

9. Which is the opposite of 13?

A. -13 **B.** $-\frac{1}{13}$
C. $\frac{1}{13}$ **D** 13

10. Which is the dimension of the matrix?

$$\begin{bmatrix} 7 & 2 \\ 1 & 5 \\ 8 & 6 \end{bmatrix}$$

F. 2×3 **G.** 3×2
H. 2×4 **J.** 6×6

11. Divide.

$-\frac{2}{9} \div \left(-\frac{5}{6}\right)$

A. $-\frac{15}{4}$ **B.** $-\frac{4}{15}$
C. $\frac{4}{15}$ **D.** $\frac{5}{27}$

12. Simplify.

$|-8| \bullet 4 - (4 - 6)^2$

F. -68
G. -36
H. 26
J. 28

13. If A = {whole numbers} and B = {real numbers} then $A \cap B =$

A. {whole numbers}
B. {integers}
C. {real numbers}
D. $\varnothing$

14. If $A = \{3, 4, 6, 9\}$ and $A \cup B = \{2, 3, 4, 5, 6, 7, 8, 9\}$, which could be B?

F. {2, 3, 5, 7, 8, 9}
G. {3, 4, 5, 7, 8, 9}
H. {2, 3, 5, 7}
J. {2, 3, 4, 6, 8, 9}

15. If $A = \begin{bmatrix} 2 & -5 \\ 3 & 4 \\ 0 & 1 \end{bmatrix}$, which is $5A$?

A. $\begin{bmatrix} 7 & 0 \\ 8 & 9 \\ 5 & 6 \end{bmatrix}$ **B.** $\begin{bmatrix} 10 & -25 \\ 15 & 20 \\ 0 & 5 \end{bmatrix}$

C. $\begin{bmatrix} 10 & -25 \\ 3 & 4 \\ 0 & 1 \end{bmatrix}$ **D.** $\begin{bmatrix} 10 & -5 \\ 15 & 4 \\ 0 & 1 \end{bmatrix}$

16. If $A = \begin{bmatrix} -5 & 4 \\ 1 & 2 \end{bmatrix}$ and $B = \begin{bmatrix} 3 & 1 \\ 2 & -1 \end{bmatrix}$, which is AB?

F. $\begin{bmatrix} -15 & 4 \\ 2 & -2 \end{bmatrix}$ **G.** $\begin{bmatrix} -9 & -7 \\ -1 & 7 \end{bmatrix}$

H. $\begin{bmatrix} -23 & 1 \\ -1 & 3 \end{bmatrix}$ **J.** $\begin{bmatrix} -7 & -9 \\ 7 & -1 \end{bmatrix}$

17. If A is a 4×7 matrix and B is a 7×9 matrix, which is the dimension of AB?

A. 7×7
B. 4×9
C. 9×4
D. 28×63

18. Simplify.

$$\frac{|6 - 9|^3 - 5}{5(1 - 7)}$$

F. $-\frac{11}{15}$ **G.** $-\frac{2}{15}$

H. $\frac{11}{15}$ **J.** $\frac{16}{15}$

19. If $a = -2$ and $b = 4$, which is the value of $\frac{3a + b^2}{a^2 + 2b}$?

A. 0

B. $\frac{1}{2}$

C. $\frac{5}{6}$

D. $\frac{7}{8}$

20. Simplify.

$$(1.56 \times 10^4) + (3.56 \times 10^6)(1.2 \times 10^{-2})$$

F. 5.832×10^8
G. 5.832×10^4
H. 4.272×10^6
J. 4.272×10^{-4}

Tell About It

Explain how you solve the problem. Show all your work.

21. If $A' = \{4, 5, 6, 7\}$, $B' = \{1, 2, 6, 7, 8\}$, and $C' = \{1, 2, 3, 4\}$, and $A \cup B \cup C = \{1, 2, 3, 4, 5, 6, 7, 8, 9\}$, what is $A \cap B \cap C$?

2-1 Open Sentences and Solution Sets

Name ______________________ Date ____________

Using the replacement set $\{-1, 0, 1\}$, find the solution set for the open sentence $|2g + 3| = 4$.

Remember: *Open sentences* contain variables; they are neither true nor false. *Closed sentences* contain no variables; they are either true or false.

$|2g + 3| = 4$ Replacement set: $\{-1, 0, 1\}$	$|2(\mathbf{-1}) + 3| \stackrel{?}{=} 4$ $|\mathbf{-2} + 3| \stackrel{?}{=} 4$ $1 = 4$ **False**	$|2(\mathbf{0}) + 3| \stackrel{?}{=} 4$ $|\mathbf{0} + 3| \stackrel{?}{=} 4$ $3 = 4$ **False**	$|2(\mathbf{1}) + 3| \stackrel{?}{=} 4$ $|\mathbf{2} + 3| \stackrel{?}{=} 4$ $5 = 4$ **False**

Because each number in the set does not make the open sentence true, each number is not in the solution set. So the solution set is $\varnothing$.

Identify each as an *open sentence*, a *true sentence*, a *false sentence*, or an *expression*.

1. $11b$ ____________

2. $12 + d$ ____________

3. $t + 7.5 = 11.3$ ____________

4. $5y - 13 = -8$ ____________

5. $3(5) = 2^3 + 7$ ____________

6. $7(11) = 3^3 + 40$ ____________

7. $29 - 12 \div 4 = \sqrt{16}$ ____________

8. $4^2 - |-9| = 7^2 \div 7$ ____________

Using the replacement set {−2, 2}, find the solution set for each open sentence.

9. $3x + 1 = 7$

$3(-2) + 1 \stackrel{?}{=} 7$ $-6 + 1 \stackrel{?}{=} 7$ $-5 = 7$ **False**	$3(2) + 1 \stackrel{?}{=} 7$ $6 + 1 \stackrel{?}{=} 7$ $7 = 7$ **True**

{2}

10. $2w - 6 = 4$ ____________

11. $2b - 3 = -7$ ____________

12. $11 = 4b - 1$ ____________

13. $-9 = 13b - 8$ ____________

14. $9 = 2y + 5$ ____________

15. $3n - 4 = -6$ ____________

16. $-5 = 3p + 2$ ____________

Using the replacement set {−3, −2, 0, 1, 4}, find the solution set for each open sentence.

17. $5k + 1 = 21$

$5(-3) + 1 \stackrel{?}{=} 21$
$-14 = 21$ **False**
$5(0) + 1 \stackrel{?}{=} 21$
$1 = 21$ **False**
$5(4) + 1 \stackrel{?}{=} 21$
$21 = 21$ **True**

$5(-2) + 1 \stackrel{?}{=} 21$
$-9 = 21$ **False**
$5(1) + 1 \stackrel{?}{=} 21$
$6 = 21$ **False**

{4}

18. $7q - 2 = -16$

19. $-1 = 2m^2 - 3$

20. $3 = 11 - 2n^2$

21. $3j + 9.2 = 5.3j$

22. $5.8 - 2\ell = 3.8\ell$

Problem Solving

23. Lois runs 1 mile in 12 minutes. She runs no more than 6 miles each day. Write an algebraic expression to model how many minutes she runs each day. Tell what the variable represents, and write a domain set for that variable.

24. If the set of real numbers is the replacement set, what is the solution set for the open sentence $|5x + 11| = -8$? Explain.

MENTAL MATH

25. $29 + 38 + 51$

26. $25(11 \bullet 4)$

27. $24(23)$

28. $38(40)$

2-2 Solve Addition and Subtraction Equations

Name ____________________ Date ____________

Solve: $k - 12 = -19$

$k - 12 + 12 = -19 + 12$ ← Add 12 to isolate k.

$k = -7$

Check: $k - 12 = -19$

$-7 - 12 \stackrel{?}{=} -19$ ← Substitute −7 for k.

$-19 = -19$ **True**

Solution set: $\{-7\}$

Solve: $n + 17 = -5$

$n + 17 - 17 = -5 - 17$ ← Subtract 17 to isolate n.

$n = -22$

Check: $n + 17 = -5$

$-22 + 17 \stackrel{?}{=} -5$ ← Substitute −22 for n.

$-5 = -5$ **True**

Solution set: $\{-22\}$

Solve each equation. Write a justification for each step.
Then check the solutions. Write your solution.

1. $t - 11 = 4$

$t - 11 + 11 = 4 + 11$

$t = 15$

Check: $(15) - 11 \stackrel{?}{=} 4$

$4 = 4$ True

{15}

2. $b - 15 = 9$

3. $g + 24 = 7$

4. $y + 32 = 47$

5. $d + 1.8 = 3.7$

6. $t + 2.7 = 4.1$

7. $b - 4.6 = 5.2$

8. $p - 5.3 = 7.2$

9. $a - \frac{2}{3} = \frac{1}{6}$

10. $c - \frac{2}{5} = \frac{7}{10}$

11. $28 = b - 8$

12. $-12 = c - 2$

13. $-11 = d + 4$

14. $-2 = f + 13$

15. $-1.5 = h + 5.1$

16. $-6.2 = t + 4.8$

17. $5.1 = r - 7.2$

18. $9.1 = w - 1.6$

19. $-\frac{5}{7} = a - \frac{3}{7}$

20. $-\frac{3}{4} = d - \frac{1}{2}$

21. $-\frac{11}{3} = j + \frac{6}{7}$

22. $-\frac{9}{5} = k + \frac{5}{6}$

23. $-4\frac{1}{2} + 2.5 = z - 3\frac{1}{5}$

24. $-5\frac{7}{10} + 1.8 = q - 4\frac{3}{5}$

Use with SOURCEBOOK Lesson 2-2, pages 42–45.

Write and solve an equation for each problem.

25. Billy saved \$25 more than Jane. If Billy saved \$119, how much did Jane save?

26. A fir tree is 27 inches shorter than a pine tree. If the fir tree is 81 inches, how high is the pine tree?

27. Miggy uses 21 fewer bags of feed than Ernie. If Miggy uses 60 bags of feed, how many bags does Ernie use?

28. Fifteen less than a number is −54. What is the number?

29. Newton is 11 years younger than Ali. If Newton is 23 years old, how old is Ali?

30. Anna is 18 years older than Sheila. If Sheila is 5 years old, how old is Anna?

31. An airplane increases altitude by 2500 feet. If the plane's new altitude is 37,124 feet, what was the plane's altitude before the increase?

32. Fitz's average speed is 12 mi/h greater than Paul's average speed. If Fitz's average speed is 58 mi/h, what is Paul's average speed?

Problem Solving

33. A garden is increased by 180 ft^2 to have room for 60 ft^2 of tomatoes, 96 ft^2 of zucchini, 112 ft^2 of lettuce, 222 ft^2 of corn, and 40 ft^2 of peppers. What was the garden's original length if it was 11 ft longer than the width?

34. After a library gave 120 paperbacks, 80 magazines, and 52 hardbacks to a school, the school had 2985 paperbacks, magazines, and hard-covered books. How many did the school have before the gift?

TEST PREPARATION

35. Solve: $-\frac{3}{4} + y = -\frac{1}{6}$

A. $\left\{\frac{5}{12}\right\}$ **C.** $\left\{\frac{7}{12}\right\}$

B. $\left\{\frac{1}{2}\right\}$ **D.** $\left\{\frac{2}{3}\right\}$

36. Solve: $29.62 + x = 32$

F. {2.38} **H.** {29.94}

G. {3.62} **J.** {61.62}

2-3 Solve Multiplication and Division Equations

Name ______________________ Date __________

Solve: $\frac{d}{6} = -8$

$6 \bullet \frac{d}{6} = -8 \bullet 6$ ← Multiply each side by 6 to isolate *d*.

$d = -48$

Check: $\frac{d}{6} = -8$

$\frac{(-48)}{6} \stackrel{?}{=} -8$ ← Substitute −48 for *d*.

$-8 = -8$ **True**

Solution set: {−48}

Solve: $-\frac{5}{7}f = -45$

$\left[\left(-\frac{7}{5}\right) \bullet \left(-\frac{5}{7}\right)\right]f = -\frac{7}{5}(-45)$ ← Multiply each side by the reciprocal of $-\frac{5}{7}$.

$f = 63$

Check: $-\frac{5}{7}f = -45$

$-\frac{5}{\cancel{7}_1} \bullet (\cancel{63}^9) \stackrel{?}{=} -45$ ← Substitute 63 for *f*.

$-45 = -45$ **True**

Solution set: {63}

Solve each equation. Write a justification for each step. Then check each solution. Write your solution.

1. $3g = 24$

$\frac{3g}{3} = \frac{24}{3}$

$g = 8$

Check: $3(8) \stackrel{?}{=} 24$

$24 = 24$ True

{8}

2. $5h = 30$

3. $-111 = 37d$

4. $-256 = 32f$

5. $-2b = 3.8$

6. $-9n = 1.8$

7. $-2.16 = -7.2t$

8. $-7.15 = -1.1w$

9. $\frac{z}{3} = -2$

10. $\frac{p}{4} = -5$

11. $-3.2 = \frac{e}{1.1}$

12. $-4.2 = \frac{k}{3.1}$

13. $\frac{5a}{-6} = -10$

14. $\frac{7c}{-9} = -28$

15. $1\frac{1}{2} = -5d$

16. $9\frac{3}{4} = -3f$

Solve. Show your work.

17. Yoni's dog weighs twice as much as Uri's dog. If Yoni's dog weighs 62 pounds, what is the weight of Uri's dog?

____

18. A company ships 28 boxes with 45 games in each box. How many games does the company ship?

____

19. Olivia plants 435 trees in 15 rows. She plants the same number in each row. How many trees are in each row?

____

20. A maple tree is 3 times the height of an oak tree. If the maple is 27 feet high, how high is the oak?

____

21. The area of a rectangular plot of land is 562.48 km^2. If the width of the land is 15.8 km, what is its length? (*Hint:* $\text{Area}_{\text{rectangle}} = \ell w$)

____

22. A forest is rectangular in shape. Its length is 65.8 km. If the area of the forest is 3901.94 km^2, what is its width?

____

23. The area of a triangle is 5.4 cm^2. If its base is 3 cm, what is its height? (*Hint:* $\text{Area}_{\text{triangle}} = \frac{1}{2}bh$)

____

24. A triangular flag has a height of 8.5 in. Its area is 43.35 in.^{2} What is the length of its base?

____

25. Marsha used $\frac{3}{4}$ of the paper she bought to print flyers for a fundraiser. If she printed 1800 flyers, how many pieces of paper did she buy?

____

26. Yau and Sophia collected $\frac{2}{3}$ of all the cans that were collected for recycling. If they collected 3894 cans, how many cans were collected for recycling?

____

WRITE ABOUT IT

27. To solve the equation $\frac{2r}{5} = 30$, Nina multiplied by 5 and then divided by 2 to get $r = 75$. Explain why Nina's method works.

____

____

____

2-4 Solve Equations with Two Operations

Name ______________________ Date ____________

Solve: $4y + 9 = 21$

$4y + 9 - 9 = 21 - 9$ ← Undo the addition first.

$4y = 12$ ← Simplify.

$\frac{4y}{4} = \frac{12}{4}$ ← Undo the multiplication.

$y = 3$ ← Simplify.

Check: $4y + 9 = 21$

$4(\mathbf{3}) + 9 \stackrel{?}{=} 21$ ← Substitute 3 for y.

$\mathbf{12} + 9 \stackrel{?}{=} 21$

$21 = 21$ **True**

Solution set: {3}

Solve: $\frac{t}{3} - 4 = -11$

$\frac{t}{3} - 4 + 4 = -11 + 4$ ← Undo the subtraction first.

$\frac{t}{3} = -7$ ← Simplify.

$3\left(\frac{t}{3}\right) = 3(-7)$ ← Undo the division.

$t = -21$ ← Simplify.

Check: $\frac{t}{3} - 4 = -11$

$\frac{-21}{3} - 4 \stackrel{?}{=} -11$ ← Substitute -21 for t.

$\mathbf{-7} - 4 \stackrel{?}{=} -11$

$-11 = -11$ **True**

Solution set: $\{-21\}$

Solve each equation. Write a justification for each step. Then check each solution. Write your solution.

1. $7 = 2r - 3$

$7 + 3 = 2r - 3 + 3$

$10 = 2r$

$\frac{10}{2} = \frac{2r}{2}$

$5 = r$

Check: $7 = 2r - 3$

$7 \stackrel{?}{=} 2(5) - 3$

$7 = 7$ True

{5}

2. $3d - 9 = 12$ ____________

3. $-9 = 5w + 1$ ____________

4. $-23 = 7s + 5$ ____________

5. $\frac{m}{2} - 2 = 5$ ____________

6. $\frac{j}{3} - 6 = -8$ ____________

7. $3 = \frac{p}{-5} + 1$ ____________

8. $9 = \frac{q}{-3} + 5$ ____________

9. $1.2 - \frac{k}{4} = 8.4$ ____________

10. $7.6 - \frac{v}{8} = -2.3$ ____________

11. $7.3 = 10.2 - \frac{2w}{3}$ ____________

12. $3.2 = 22.45 - \frac{4x}{11}$ ____________

13. $-4.1 + \frac{5y}{11} = -\frac{2}{5}$ ____________

14. $-7.08 + \frac{8z}{15} = -\frac{3}{8}$ ____________

15. $-0.23 = \frac{2}{3} - \frac{4}{5}x$ ____________

For More Practice Go To:

ONLINE www.progressinmathematics.com Practice/Test Generator

Solve each equation. Write a justification for each step. Then check each solution. Write your solution.

16. $2a - 5a + 6 = 24$ ____________

17. $29 = 5z - 9z + 25$ ____________

18. $16 = 4n - 3 + 2n + 7$ ____________

19. $8m - 5 + 3m + 12 = 40$ ____________

20. $-27 = 11v - 24 - 2v + 15$ ____________

21. $-43 = 9h - 39 - 4h + 16$ ____________

Write and solve an equation for each problem.

22. The sum of three consecutive odd integers is 75. Find these integers.

____

23. The sum of three consecutive integers is −30. Find these integers.

____

24. Geometry The measure of angle *A* in triangle *ABC* is 3 times the measure of angle *B*, and the measure of angle *C* is half the measure of angle *B*. Find the measure of each angle.

____

25. Jacob worked 68 hours this week. He worked 4 hours less than 3 times the number of hours he worked last week. How many hours did Jacob work last week?

____

26. When a number is divided by −7 and the quotient is increased by 12, the result is 3. What is the number?

____

27. Nancy is 10 years less than 3 times her daughter's age. If Nancy is 41 years old, how old is her daughter?

____

28. Geometry An isosceles triangle has a perimeter of 35 feet. The third side is one-third the length of one of the congruent sides. What are the lengths of the sides of this isosceles triangle?

____

29. A rectangular field has a perimeter of 126 feet. If the length of the field is 12 feet less than twice the width, what is the area of the field? *Hint:* Perimeter (rectangle) $= \ell + w + \ell + w$, Area (rectangle) $= \ell w$

____

CHALLENGE

30. The expression $2n + 1$ will always yield odd numbers for all integers n. Using this expression, find the sum of ten consecutive odd integers. Then use your answer to find the ten odd integers whose sum is 620.

____

____

____

2-5 Solve Multistep Equations

Name ______________________________ Date ____________

Solve: $5c + 6 = 2c + 15$

$5c - 2c + 6 = 2c - 2c + 15$ ← Subtract $2c$

$3c + 6 = 15$

$3c + 6 - 6 = 15 - 6$ ← Undo the addition.

$3c = 9$

$\frac{3c}{3} = \frac{9}{3}$ ← Undo the multiplication.

$c = 3$

Check: $5c + 6 = 2c + 15$

$5(\mathbf{3}) + 6 \stackrel{?}{=} 2(\mathbf{3}) + 15$ ← Substitute 3 for c in the original equation.

$\mathbf{15} + 6 \stackrel{?}{=} 6 + \mathbf{15}$ ← Work each side separately.

$21 = 21$ **True**

Solution set: $\{3\}$

Solve: $5(6n - 2) = 8n + 1$

$5(6n) + 5(-2) = 8n + 1$ ← Use the Distributive Property.

$30n - 10 = 8n + 1$ ← Move the variable to one side.

$30n - 8n - 10 = 8n - 8n + 1$ ← Subtract $8n$ from both sides.

$22n - 10 = 1$

$22n - 10 + 10 = 1 + 10$ ← Undo the subtraction.

$22n = 11$

$\frac{22n}{22} = \frac{11}{22}$ ← Undo the division.

$n = \frac{1}{2}$

Check: $5(6n - 2) = 8n + 1$

$5[6(\frac{1}{2}) - 2] \stackrel{?}{=} 8(\frac{1}{2}) + 1$ ← Substitute $\frac{1}{2}$ for n in the original equation.

$5(3 - 2) \stackrel{?}{=} 4 + 1$ ← Work each side separately.

$5 = 5$ **True**

Solution set: $\{\frac{1}{2}\}$

Solve each equation. Then check your answer. Write your solution.

1. $3f - 2 = f + 8$

$2f = 10$

$\frac{2f}{2} = \frac{10}{2}$

$f = 5$

Check: $3f - 2 = f + 8$

$3(5) - 2 \stackrel{?}{=} (5) + 8$

$13 = 13$ True

$\{5\}$

2. $5a - 3 = 2a + 12$

____

3. $8b + 6 = 3b + 36$

____

4. $11d + 7 = 8d + 10$

____

5. $-10 + 9b = -2b + 12$

____

6. $-17 + 6m = -3m + 10$

____

7. $2(3x - 4) = 12 + 2x$

____

8. $3h - 12 = 2(5h + 1)$

____

9. $\frac{3}{4}(8a + 20) = 6a + 10$

____

10. $5.4n + 4.8 = 3(1.8n + 1.6)$

____

Write and solve an equation for each problem.

11. John is 10 years older than Chris. In two years, John will be twice as old as Chris. How old are they now?

12. A number tripled and then decreased by 5 equals 5 more than double the number. What is the number?

13. The sum of a number and two-thirds the number is the same as 4 less than twice the number. What is the number?

14. The product of 5 and 2 less than triple a number equals the product of 7 and 8 more than twice the number. What is the number?

15. Geometry If the side of a square is doubled and then increased by 7, the new perimeter is 8 more than 3 times the old perimeter. What is the side length of the original square? (*Hint:* $\text{Perimeter}_{\text{square}} = 4s$)

16. Geometry Audrey draws a triangle that has these sides: s, $\frac{1}{2}s$, and $\frac{2}{3}s$. When the length of s is doubled, the new perimeter is twice the old perimeter less 14. What are lengths of the triangle?

Problem Solving

17. Oscar and Amy rent a car for 5 days for $29.95 per day and $0.10 per mile. Oscar has $250 and Amy has half that amount to spend on the car. They will drive the same number of miles each day. What is the greatest number of miles they can drive each day?

18. Rectangle R's perimeter remains 180 feet when the length is halved and the width is doubled. What are the dimensions of rectangle R? (*Hint:* $\text{Perimeter}_{\text{rectangle}} = 2(\ell + w)$)

CHALLENGE

19. Joy shared part of a full bag of candy. Costas got $\frac{1}{2}$ of the candy. Lily got $\frac{1}{2}$ of what was left. Mali got $\frac{1}{3}$ of the remainder. Mali got 10 pieces. How many pieces were in the full bag?

2-6 Solve Absolute-Value Equations

Name ______________________ Date __________

Solve: $3|x+1| = 12$

$\frac{3|x+1|}{3} = \frac{12}{3}$ ← Divide by 3 to isolate the absolute-value expression.

$|x+1| = 4$

$x + 1 = 4$ or $x + 1 = -4$ ← Consider two cases.

$x + 1 - 1 = 4 - 1$ $\quad x + 1 - 1 = -4 - 1$ ← Solve each equation.

$x = 3$ $\quad x = -5$

Check: $3|x+1| = 12$

$3|\mathbf{3}+1| \stackrel{?}{=} 12$ and $3|\mathbf{-5}+1| \stackrel{?}{=} 12$

$3|\mathbf{4}| \stackrel{?}{=} 12$ $\quad 3|\mathbf{-4}| \stackrel{?}{=} 12$

$3(\mathbf{4}) \stackrel{?}{=} 12$ $\quad 3(4) \stackrel{?}{=} 12$

$12 = 12$ **True** $\quad 12 = 12$ **True**

Solution set: $\{-5, 3\}$

Find the solution for each equation. Then check your solutions.

1. $|b| = 2$

$b = 2$ or $b = -2$

Check: $|b| = 2$

$|2| \stackrel{?}{=} 2$ AND $|-2| \stackrel{?}{=} 2$

$2 = 2$ True $\quad 2 = 2$ True

$\{-2, 2\}$

2. $|d| = 11$ ______

3. $|r| = 9.1$ ______

4. $|v| = 15.4$ ______

5. $|p| = \frac{5}{8}$ ______

6. $|w| = \frac{4}{5}$ ______

7. $|f + 7| = 13$ ______

8. $|k + 9| = 22$ ______

9. $|m - 5| = 34$ ______

10. $|t - 14| = 47$ ______

11. $|7x| = 28$ ______

12. $|5y| = 95$ ______

13. $-|2u| = -16$ ______

14. $-|7w| = -98$ ______

15. $|v + 1.2| = 3.7$ ______

16. $|t + 7.3| = 4.8$ ______

17. $\left|g + \frac{1}{2}\right| = \frac{3}{4}$ ______

18. $\left|h + \frac{3}{8}\right| = \frac{1}{2}$ ______

19. $|11w| = -88$ ______

20. $-|2n| = 16$ ______

Use with SOURCEBOOK Lesson 2-6, pages 58–59.

Find the solution set for each equation. Then check your solutions.

21. $|k + 5| - 2 = 23$

$|k + 5| - 2 = 23$

$|k + 5| = 25$

$k + 5 = 25$ or $k + 5 = -25$

$k = 20$ $k = -30$

$\{-30, 20\}$

Check: $|-30 + 5| - 2 \stackrel{?}{=} 23$

True $\rightarrow$ $23 = 23$

$|20 + 5| - 2 \stackrel{?}{=} 23$

True $\rightarrow$ $23 = 23$

22. $|j + 7| - 4 = 15$

23. $|j - 4| + 8 = 8$

24. $|q - 2| + 11 = 11$

25. $3|n + 1| = 18$

26. $4|m + 3| = 40$

27. $-5|n + 1| = 25$

28. $2|a + 23| = -12$

29. $6|z - 2| + 4 = 40$

Write and solve an equation for each problem. Check your solutions.

30. Twelve more than the absolute value of a number decreased by 7 is 19. What are the possible values for the number?

31. Kyle wants to score within 4.5% of 94% on his next test. What are the maximum and minimum scores he is aiming for?

CRITICAL THINKING

32. Why does the equation $|x - 4| = -2$ have no solution? (*Hint:* Use the concept that the absolute value of two numbers is the distance between them.)

2-7 Formulas and Literal Equations

Name ______________________________ Date ______________

Solve for *h*: $p = \frac{h + 12r}{-3k}$

$(-3k)p = (-3k)\frac{h + 12r}{-3k}$ ← Multiply by $-3k$.

$-3kp = h + 12r$

$-3kp - 12r = h + 12r - 12r$ ← Subtract $12r$.

$-3kp - 12r = h$

Solve for *a*: $G = 9ah + 17b$

$G - 17b = 9ah + 17b - 17b$ ← Subtract $17b$.

$G - 17b = 9ah$

$\frac{G - 17b}{9h} = \frac{9ah}{9h}$ ← Divide by $9h$.

$\frac{G - 17b}{9h} = a$

Solve for each indicated variable.

1. Solve for x: $ax + b = c$

$$\begin{aligned} ax + b &= c \\ ax + b - b &= c - b \\ ax &= c - b \\ \frac{ax}{a} &= \frac{c - b}{a} \\ x &= \frac{c - b}{a} \end{aligned}$$

____

2. Solve for a: $ax + b = c$

____

3. Solve for d: $4(d + g) = b$

____

4. Solve for h: $3(h + k) = r$

____

5. Solve for g: $2(p - g) = 11$

____

6. Solve for t: $9(y - t) = 15$

____

7. Solve for d: $5d + 11a = 12p$

____

8. Solve for w: $9w + 13h = 24f$

____

9. Solve for u: $\frac{2x - 5u}{y} = 3n$

____

10. Solve for z: $\frac{11y - 10z}{x} = 6m$

____

11. Solve for a: $15a - 19b = 20b + 2a$

____

12. Solve for c: $23c - 12s = 46s - 6c$

____

13. Solve for a: $\frac{1}{2}a + \frac{2}{3}b = -a + \frac{5}{6}b - 2$

____

14. Solve for e: $\frac{2}{5}d + \frac{4}{9}e = -2d + \frac{7}{18}e - 1$

____

Solve for each indicated variable.

15. Solve for v: $h = -16t^2 + vt$
$h + 16t^2 = -16t^2 + 16t^2 + vt$
$h + 16t^2 = vt$
$\frac{h + 16t^2}{t} = \frac{vt}{t}$
$\frac{h + 16t^2}{t} = v$ or $v = \frac{h}{t} + 16t$

16. Solve for a: $z = -12x^2 + ax$

17. Solve for h: $S = 4\pi r^2 h$

18. Solve for r^2: $S = 4\pi r^2 h$

19. Solve for w: $P = 2\ell + 2w$

20. Solve for ℓ: $P = 2\ell + 2w$

21. Solve for a_1: $S = \frac{n}{2}(a_1 + a_n)$

22. Solve for a_n: $S = \frac{n}{2}(a_1 + a_n)$

23. Solve for w: $S = 2\ell w + 2\ell h + 2wh$

24. Solve for j: $10 - \frac{j}{3g} = \frac{j^2}{4g^2} + 10$

25. Solve for r: $20 + \frac{r^3}{7f} = \frac{r^5}{14f^2} + 20$

Solve. Show your work.

26. The formula for the volume of a sphere with radius r is $V = \frac{4}{3}\pi r^3$. What is the radius of a sphere with a volume of $\frac{9}{16}\pi$ ft^3?

27. Physics The formula $h = -16t^2 + 64t$ gives the height, h, at time t, of an object launched from the ground with a speed of 64 feet per second. Find the heights at $t = 0, 1, 2, 3,$ and 4 seconds. Explain what happens each second.

SPIRAL REVIEW

Multiply.

28. $\begin{bmatrix} 8 & -3 \\ -4 & 9 \end{bmatrix} \bullet \begin{bmatrix} -2 \\ -8 \end{bmatrix}$

Simplify.

29. $-4\frac{1}{5} - \left(-\frac{9}{10}\right)$

Solve.

30. $6x + 20 = 2x$

2-8 Technology: Solve Linear and Literal Equations

Name ______________________________ Date ______________

You can use a handheld to solve the equation $y = 5x - 4$ when $y = 11$.

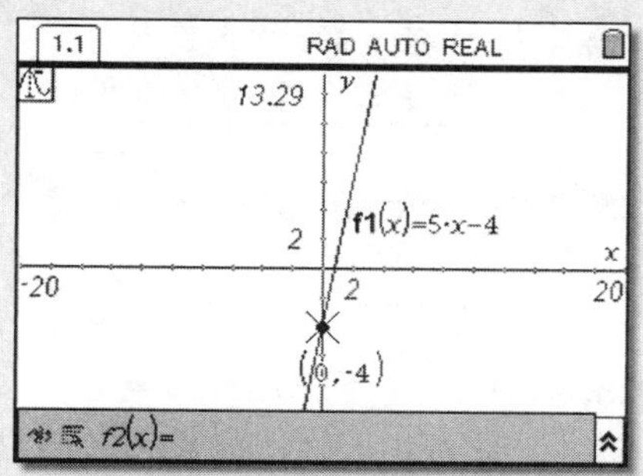

Step 1 Press (home). Then choose (2) to select **Graphs & Geometry**.

Step 2 Input $5x - 4$, then press (enter) to graph the line.

Step 3 Press (menu). Select **Trace**, then select **Graph Trace**.

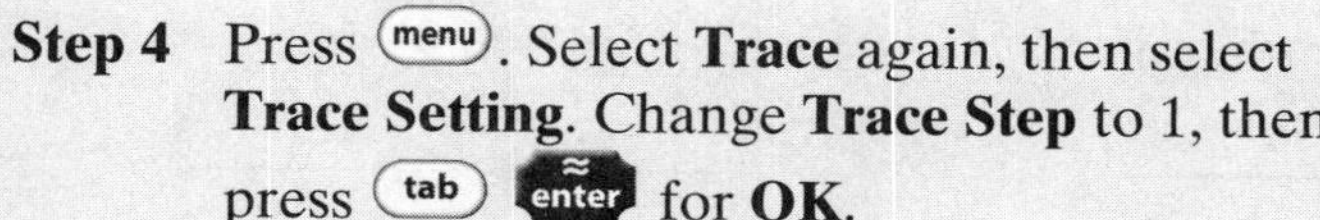

Step 4 Press (menu). Select **Trace** again, then select **Trace Setting**. Change **Trace Step** to 1, then press (tab) (enter) for **OK**.

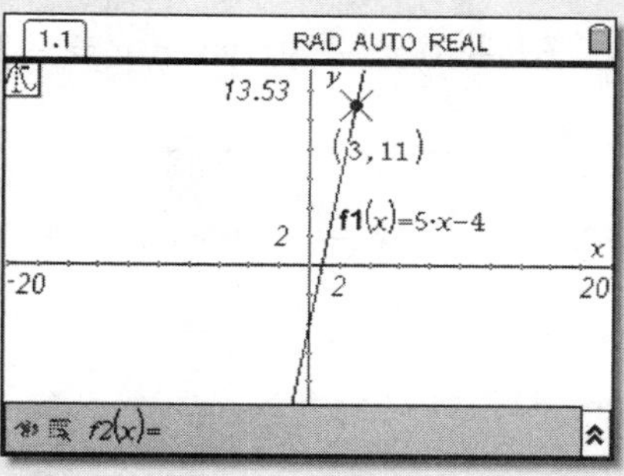

Step 5 Press ▷ to move the trace along the line until the y-coordinate of the graph equals 11. The x-value is the solution.

So $x = 3$ when $y = 11$.

Use a handheld to make a graph to solve the equation for the given value.

1. $y = 2x - 6$ when $y = 8$

$x = 7$

2. $y = 8x + 5$ when $y = 77$

____

3. $y = -5x + 3$ when $y = -97$

____

4. $y = -6x + 2$ when $y = -46$

____

5. $y = -2x - 5$ when $y = 3$

____

6. $y = -3x - 2$ when $y = 16$

____

7. $y = -2x + 1$ when $y = 19$

____

8. $y = -7x + 2$ when $y = 16$

____

9. $y = -0.5x + 1$ when $y = -4$

____

10. $y = -0.5x + 2$ when $y = -1$

____

11. $y = 2.5x + 3$ when $y = -7$

____

12. $y = 1.5x + 4$ when $y = -8$

____

13. $y = 3.2x - 1$ when $y = 16$

____

14. $y = 1.1x - 3$ when $y = 8$

____

15. $y = 3.1x - 1.5$ when $y = 14$

____

16. $y = 2.2x - 1.2$ when $y = -10$

____

17. $y = \frac{1}{2}x + 3$ when $y = -1$

____

18. $y = \frac{1}{4}x + 2$ when $y = -2$

____

19. $\frac{2}{3}x - 1 = y$ when $y = 3$

____

20. $\frac{3}{4}x - 2 = y$ when $y = 4$

____

21. $y = -\frac{1}{3}x + 1$ when $y = 4$

____

Use a handheld to make a graph to solve the equation for the given value.
(*Hint:* Solve for y first.)

22. $y + 2x = 3$ when $y = 5$

$x = -1$

23. $y + 3x = 6$ when $y = 12$

24. $4x + 5y = 42$ when $y = -6$

25. $2x + 3y = 14$ when $y = -2$

26. $3x - 3y = -21$ when $y = 5$

27. $5x - 2y = -19$ when $y = 7$

28. $3x + 5y = 52$ when $y = 8$

29. $7x + 4y = 84$ when $y = 7$

30. $4x + 3y = -53$ when $y = -7$

31. $6x + 2y = -30$ when $y = -3$

32. $7x - 3y = -6$ when $y = 9$

33. $5x - 2y = -9$ when $y = 7$

34. $-5x + 3y = -31$ when $y = -7$

35. $-4x + 7y = -34$ when $y = -2$

36. $6x - 2y = -18$ when $y = -3$

37. $8x - 3y = -28$ when $y = -4$

38. $9x - 5y = 2$ when $y = -4$

39. $4x - 9y = 46$ when $y = -2$

40. $3y - 7x = -41$ when $y = -2$

41. $2y - 9x = -33$ when $y = -3$

42. $1.2x - 1.5y = -3.6$ when $y = 4$

43. $2.5x - 3.2y = -13.5$ when $y = 5$

44. $-16.3 = 9.8x + 1.1y$ when $y = 3$

45. $-4.3 = 2.8x + 1.2y$ when $y = 10$

Problem Solving

46. Business Lauren gives riding lessons at dude ranches. She charges \$30 per hour plus \$25 for travel. She earned \$145 at Diamond H and \$100 at M^2D^2. How many more hours did she work at Diamond H than at M^2D^2?

47. Geometry A rectangular painting with perimeter 23.8 cm is 1.5 cm longer than its width. Find the width and length of the painting. (*Hint:* The formula for perimeter of a rectangle is $P = 2\ell + 2w$.)

CHALLENGE

48. Use a handheld to solve $5y - 2x = 9.3$ for x when $y = 2.8$.
Hint: Change the **Trace Step** value.

2-9 Problem-Solving Strategy: Solve a Simpler Problem

Read Plan Solve Check

Name ______________________ Date __________

Solve a simpler problem to answer each question.

1. If the sum of the interior angles for all quadrilaterals is the same, what is the sum of angles *A*, *B*, *C*, and *D* in the quadrilateral seen here?

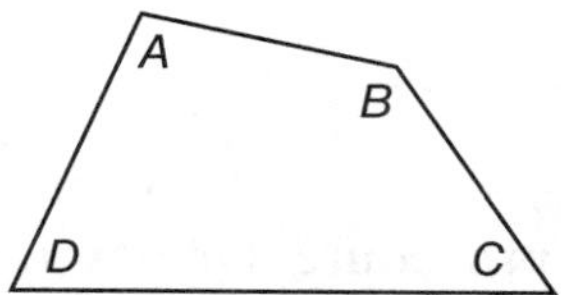

---

2. Regardless of how these two rectangles overlap, the difference between the area of the light grey region and the area of the dark grey region is always the same. What is that difference?

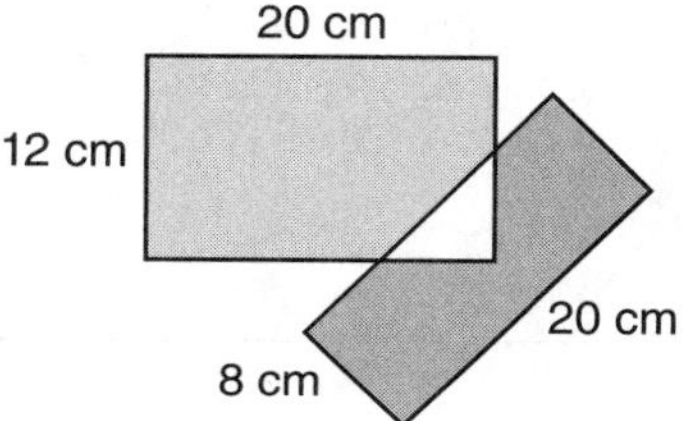

---

3. The sum (S) of the first n positive integers ($S = 1 + 2 + 3 + \ldots + N$) is $S = \frac{n(n + 1)}{2}$. Without using a calculator, determine the sum of the first 1000 multiples of 5: 5 + 10 + 15 + . . . + 5000.

---

4. In how many ways can nine people be selected from a group of ten people?

---

5. Find all values of x for which $(4x - 5)^{2x+5} = 1$.

Use with SOURCEBOOK Lesson 2-9, pages 64–65.

6. The divisors of 120 add up to 360. What is the sum of the *reciprocals* of the divisors of 120?

7. To enjoy a 20-oz pitcher of orange juice longer, Ignacio follows this procedure. On day 1, he drinks only 1 oz, and fills the pitcher with water. On day 2, he drinks only 2 oz of the mixture and again fills the pitcher with water. On day 3, he drinks only 3 oz of the mixture and again fills the pitcher with water. He continues this procedure until he empties the pitcher by drinking 20 oz of the mixture. How many ounces of water will Ignacio drink altogether?

8. How much shorter is the perimeter of the *c*-by-*d* rectangle than that of the *a*-by-*b* rectangle?

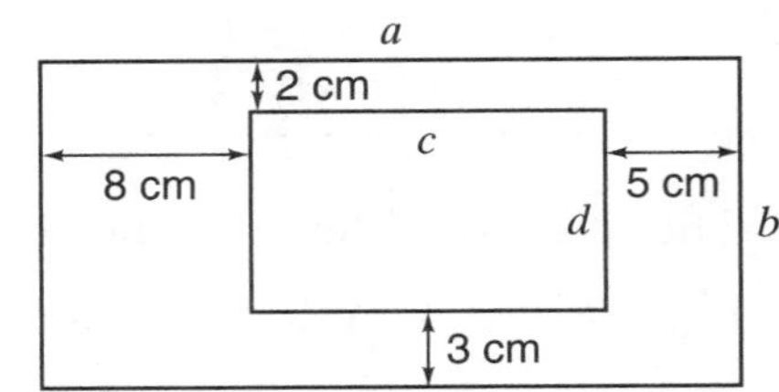

9. What is the product of $0.88\overline{8}$ and $2.33\overline{3}$?

10. Given these 12 numbers, what percent of their sum is their average?

522	223	435	1200
784	621	926	337
548	639	117	211

Enrichment:
Diophantine Equations

Name ______________________ Date __________

Determine if the following equation has integer solutions: $10x + 15y = 180$.
If possible identify one integer solution.

Remember: Equations of the form $ax + by = c$, are *Diophantine*, if and only if the GCF of a and b is a factor of c.

1 Find the GCF of 10 and 15.
$10 = 2 \bullet 5$
$15 = 3 \bullet 5$
GCF = 5

2 Determine if 5 is a factor of 180.
$180 \div 5 = 36$

So the equation has integer solutions.

3 Identify one integer solution.
$10x + 15y = 180$
$15y = 180 - 10x$ ← Subtract $10x$ from both sides.
$y = 12 - \frac{2}{3}x$ ← Divide both sides by 15; Simplify.

Think
When x is a multiple of 3, y is an integer.

Let $x = 3$, then $y = 12 - \frac{2}{3}(3) = 12 - 2 = 10$

The ordered pair (3, 10), is an integer solution to the equation, $10x + 15y = 180$.

Tell whether each equation has integer solutions. If it does, find one solution—that is, one (x, y) pair that satisfies the equation.

1. $24x + 15y = 130$

GCF of 24 and 15: 3.
3 is not a factor of 130.
No integer solutions possible.

2. $9x + 24y = 145$

____

3. $4x - 6y = 72$

____

4. $5x - 10y = 75$

____

5. $33x - 14y = -420$

____

6. $117x - 45y = -135$

____

7. $-18x + 26y = 248$

____

8. $-16x + 45y = 115$

____

9. $-42x + 70y = -28$

____

Solve for positive integer values of x and y.

10. $4x + 6y = 72$

$6y = 72 - 4x$

$y = 12 - \frac{2}{3}x$

(3, 10), (6, 8), (9, 6), (12, 4), (15, 2)

11. $9x + 12y = 144$

12. $14x + 35y = 140$

13. $60x + 45y = 540$

14. $24x + 16y = 88$

15. $48x + 36y = 276$

16. $42x + 84y = 210$

17. $26x + 91y = 650$

18. $98x + 70y = 1428$

Problem Solving

19. Including tax, Mr. Adebayor bought shirts for $27 each and pants for $36 each. He spent a total of $369. What are all the possible combinations of shirts and pants that Mr. Adebayor could have bought?

20. Including tax, a box of bandages costs $6 and a box of antiseptic wipes costs $15. Miss Gallas buys at least one of each and spends a total of $180. Listed as ordered pairs, what are all the possible combinations of each box that Miss Gallas could buy?

MENTAL MATH

Evaluate.

21. 10% of 37.4

22. 20% of 37.4

23. 5% of 37.4

24. 15% of 37.4

Test Prep: Short-Answer Questions

Strategy: Show All Your Work

Name ______________________________ Date ______________

To solve problems that require writing and solving an equation, be sure to show all the steps and **explain your thinking.**

To solve the problem, try using these strategies:

- Reread the test item.
- Use the Test-Prep strategy.
- Apply appropriate rules, definitions, or properties.
- Analyze your answers.

Sample Test Item
The circumference of a circle is 39.25 centimeters. What is the radius of the circle? Use 3.14 for π. ***Show all your work.***

Write a verbal model to explain your thinking:
circumference = 2 • π • radius

Write and solve an algebraic equation:
Let r = the radius.

$39.25 = 2(3.14)r$
$39.25 = 6.28r$
$6.25 = r$

Answer: The radius is 6.25 cm.

Solve. Show all your work.
TIP: Even if you are not sure of your answer, do not erase your work; you might get partial credit.

1. A triangular banner has an area of 2.25 ft^2. The height of the triangle is 3 ft. What is the length of the base of the triangle?

Answer: ______________________________

2. A 54-in. piece of rope is cut into 3 pieces. The second piece is twice the length of the first. The third piece is 3 times the length of the second. What is the length of the shortest piece of rope?

Answer: ______________________________

3. Marissa earns \$200 per week, plus 10% commission on her total sales. One week, she earned \$380. What were her total sales?

Answer: ______________________________

4. Barry buys a jacket that is on sale for 30% off the retail price. If the sale price of the jacket is \$42, what was the retail price?

Answer: ______________________________

5. A movie theater charges \$9 for an adult ticket and \$5.50 for a child ticket. Mr. and Mrs. Wu and a group of children go to the movies. They spend \$51 on tickets. How many children did they take?

Answer: ______________________________

6. Brenna earns \$6 per hour babysitting, plus a \$5 tip for each individual job. One week she babysits for 19 hours and earns \$139. How many babysitting jobs did she have that week?

Answer: ______________________________

Use with SOURCEBOOK Test Prep Lesson, page 68.

Vocabulary Development

Name ______________________________ Date ____________

Chapter 2 Vocabulary

absolute-value equation	domain set	open sentences
addition equation	equivalent equations	replacement set
algebraic equations	formula	solution
closed sentences	literal equation	solution set
division equation	multiplication equation	subtraction equation

From the vocabulary list above, choose the term(s) that best complete each sentence. Write the term(s) in the space(s) provided.

1. An equation that contains only the operation of addition is called a(n) ______________________.

2. The ______________________ for an equation contains all the values for the variable that make the equation a true sentence.

3. A(n) ______________________ is an equation that states a rule for a relationship among particular quantities.

4. A(n) ______________________ is an equation with two or more variables.

5. A(n) ______________________ or a(n) ______________________ is the set of elements that can be substituted for a variable.

6. To solve a(n) ______________________, you must consider two cases for solution.

7. ______________________ contain the symbol = and show that two algebraic expressions are equal.

Tell whether each statement is true or false. If false, rewrite the statement to make it true.

8. Open sentences contain variables and are always true.

____

9. Closed sentences contain variables and are either true or false.

____

10. Equivalent equations are equations that have the same solution.

____

Use after SOURCEBOOK Lessons 2-1–2-7, pages 40–61.

Practice Chapter 2 Test

Name ______________________________ Date ____________

Identify each as an *open sentence*, a *true sentence*, a *false sentence*, or an *expression*.

1. $12 + 6(3) = 30$ ____________

2. $d - 94 = 231$ ____________

3. $5(9) = 4^3 - 15$ ____________

4. $2.3 + 5f$ ____________

Using the replacement set {−3, 3}, find the solution set for each open sentence.

5. $3a - 5 = 4$ ____________

6. $2 = 5c + 17$ ____________

7. $-2 = 4n - 1$ ____________

Solve each equation. Write a justification for each step.

8. $f - 23 = 15$ ____________

9. $k + 19 = -12$ ____________

10. $55 = 5a$ ____________

11. $\frac{t}{3} = -4$ ____________

Solve each equation. Then check your solution.

12. $t - 5.8 = 6.9$ ____________

13. $b + 7.3 = 8.4$ b=1.1

14. $-9 = f + 14$ f=-23

15. $7.2 = h + 5.4$ h=1.8

16. $-\frac{7}{12} = a - \frac{5}{12}$ $-\frac{1}{6}$=a

17. $\frac{3}{8} = d - \frac{7}{8}$

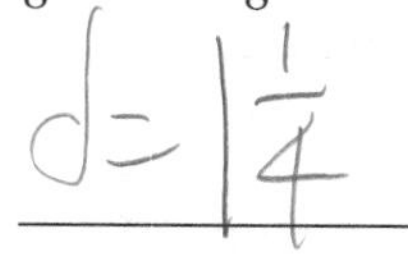

18. $-4b = 36$ b=9

19. $-5.6s = 22.4$ ____________

20. $\frac{y}{5.2} = -2.5$ ____________

21. $-9 = \frac{w}{8.7}$ ____________

22. $3q = \frac{5}{6}$ ____________

23. $\frac{6}{7} = \frac{9f}{14}$ ____________

Solve each equation. Then check your solutions.

24. $-6 + \frac{a}{2} = -9$

25. $13 + \frac{4g}{5} = 1$

26. $\frac{d}{5} + \frac{7}{10} = \frac{1}{2}$

27. $-1.7j - 4.8 = 2$

28. $6n - 7 + 3n + 11 = -23$

29. $-12 + 8m = -2m + 48$

30. $5(2x - 3) = 21 + 4x$

31. $\frac{5}{7}(14d + 63) = 10d + 19$

32. $4(3z + 12) - 11 = 12z + 37$

Find the solution set for each equation. Then check your results on a separate sheet of paper.

33. $|r| = 15$

34. $|t + 11| = 13$

35. $|g - 2.3| = 11.5$

36. $3|m - 4| = 9$

Solve for each indicated variable.

37. Solve for a: $az + bd = cx$

38. Solve for h: $7(h + f) = \ell$

39. Solve for r: $2r + 9t = 8r + 3t$

Problem Solving

40. Julio has a rectangular garden plot. He plans on planting vegetables in a triangular partition whose base and height are equal in measure. If the figure has an area of 24.5 ft^2, what are its dimensions?

41. The sum of three consecutive odd integers is -51. What are the integers?

Tell About It

Explain how you solve the problem. Show all your work.

42. If the length and width of a rectangle are doubled, how do the perimeters of the original and new rectangles compare?

Cumulative Review: Chapters 1–2

Name ______________________________ Date ______________

Circle the best answer.

1. Which is an integer?

A. $\sqrt{5}$ **B.** $\frac{3}{4}$

C. 5.8 **D.** $-\sqrt{9}$

2. Which set of numbers is closed under division, except by 0?

F. set of integers

G. set of natural numbers

H. set of rational numbers

J. set of whole numbers

3. Simplify: $-12 - (-8)$

A. -20 **B.** -4

C. 4 **D.** 20

4. Which is the multiplicative inverse of 23?

F. 23 **G.** $\frac{1}{23}$

H. $-\frac{1}{23}$ **J.** -23

5. Evaluate for $a = 2, b = -1$.

$-a^3 + ab - b^2 + a^2b$

A. -1 **B.** -5

C. -11 **D.** -15

6. Simplify: $\begin{bmatrix} 8 & 2 \\ 2 & 3 \end{bmatrix} + \begin{bmatrix} 4 & -2 \\ 1 & -3 \end{bmatrix}$

F. $\begin{bmatrix} 32 & -4 \\ 2 & -9 \end{bmatrix}$ **G.** $\begin{bmatrix} 4 & 4 \\ 1 & 6 \end{bmatrix}$

H. $\begin{bmatrix} 12 & 0 \\ 3 & 0 \end{bmatrix}$ **J.** $\begin{bmatrix} 12 & 6 \\ 3 & -1 \end{bmatrix}$

7. Multiply: $(4.5 \times 10^6)(2.7 \times 10^4)$

A. 1.215×10^{24} **B.** 12.15×10^{24}

C. 1.215×10^{11} **D.** 1.215×10^{10}

8. Which illustrates the Commutative Property of Addition?

F. $4(8) = 8(4)$

G. $12 + 15 = 15 + 12$

H. $2 + (3 + 4) = (2 + 3) + 4$

J. $5(7 + 8) = 5(7) + 5(8)$

9. Simplify: $9[4a - 11 + 2a] + 50$

A. $15a + 39$ **B.** $18a + 39$

C. $54a - 49$ **D.** $54a + 39$

10. Simplify: 4^{-3}

F. -64 **G.** -12

H. $\frac{1}{12}$ **J.** $\frac{1}{64}$

11. If A = set of even integers and B = set of odd integers, which set equals $A \cap B$?

A. set of integers

B. set of whole numbers

C. set of real numbers

D. $\varnothing$

12. Simplify: $4\begin{bmatrix} -4 & 2 \\ 3 & -1 \end{bmatrix}$

F. $\begin{bmatrix} -16 & 8 \\ 12 & -4 \end{bmatrix}$ **G.** $\begin{bmatrix} 0 & 6 \\ 7 & 3 \end{bmatrix}$

H. $\begin{bmatrix} -16 & 8 \\ 3 & -1 \end{bmatrix}$ **J.** $\begin{bmatrix} -16 & 2 \\ 3 & -4 \end{bmatrix}$

13. Using the replacement set {2, 6, 20, 32}, which is the solution set for $4x + 8 = 16$?

A. {2} **B.** {6}
C. {20} **D.** {32}

14. Solve: $|f - 3| = 10$

F. {7, 13} **G.** {−13, 13}
H. {−7, 7} **J.** {−7, 13}

15. Solve.

$7x + 11 = 2x - 9$

A. $x = 4$ **B.** $x = \frac{2}{9}$
C. $x = -2$ **D.** $x = -4$

16. Solve.

$4(3b + 2) = 2b + 18$

F. $b = 1$ **G.** $b = \frac{8}{5}$
H. $b = \frac{13}{7}$ **J.** $b = 2$

17. Solve: $d - 17 = -19$

A. $d = 36$ **B.** $d = 2$
C. $d = -2$ **D.** $d = -36$

18. Solve for a: $3a + 2b = 5a$

F. $a = 2b$ **G.** $a = b$
H. $a = -b$ **J.** $a = -2b$

19. Solve: $12h + 13 - 4h = 6h + 21$

A. $h = 1$ **B.** $h = \frac{17}{7}$
C. $h = 4$ **D.** $h = 6$

20. Solve for y.

$8y - 2x - 4y = 3c$

F. $y = \frac{3c + 2x}{4}$ **G.** $y = \frac{5cx}{4}$
H. $y = \frac{3cx}{2}$ **J.** $y = \frac{3c - 2x}{4}$

21. What is the solution set for $-|3w| = 24$?

A. {−8, 8} **B.** {−8}
C. {8} **D.** ∅

22. What is the solution set for $5(3q + 1) - 4 = 15q + 1$?

F. {1} **G.** {0}
H. $\{q \mid q$ is any real number$\}$ **J.** ∅

Tell About It

Explain how you solve each problem. Show all your work.

23. The sum of two integers is 68. If one is 17 more than twice the other integer, what are the integers?

24. The two base angles of an isosceles triangle have equal measure. If the third angle is 5 more than 3 times a base angle, what is the measure of each angle of the triangle? (*Hint:* The sum of the measures of angles of a triangle is 180°.)

3-1 Write and Graph Inequalities

Name ______________________ Date __________

Sometimes to represent a verbal situation as an algebraic sentence, you must translate the words into an inequality.

The number of pages Tanya has read *is* <u>*at least*</u> 16.

↓

If p = the number of pages, then $p \geq 16$.

An inequality can also be expressed in set-builder notation, interval notation, or be graphed on a number line.

Remember:
less than $<$
greater than $>$
less than *or* equal to $\leq$
at most $\leq$
greater than *or* equal to $\geq$
at least $\geq$
not equal to $\neq$

Set-builder Notation
$\{x \mid x \geq -10\}$

Read as: The set of all real numbers x, such that x-values are greater than or equal to -10.

Interval Notation
$[-10, \infty)$

The interval has no greatest number. -10 is the least number included.

Graph

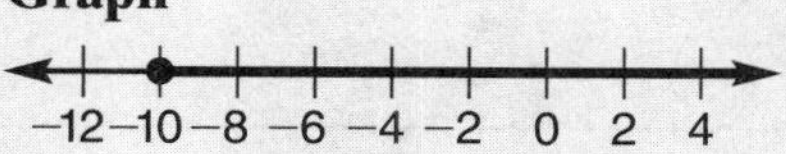

The dot shows that -10 is part of the solution set.

Define a variable, and write an inequality for each word sentence.

1. Sunil's daily exercise time is at most 52 minutes. $t \leq 52$
2. The height of the tree is no more than 38 inches. ____________
3. Carla's test score is more than 83%. ____________
4. The number of fish in the aquarium is less than 43. ____________
5. The number of flies caught in the flytrap is no less than 5. ____________
6. The temperature on the mountain's trail was at least -10 degrees. ____________
7. The amount of miles Nancy ran is not equal to 4.8. ____________

Express each inequality in both set-builder and interval notation.

8. $t < -21$ $\{t \mid t < -21\}$; $(-\infty, -21)$
9. $d < 15$ ____________
10. $h > 29$ ____________
11. $r > -73$ ____________
12. $-267 \geq g$ ____________
13. $527 \geq k$ ____________
14. $92 \leq w$ ____________
15. $73 \leq y$ ____________
16. $p > 125.4$ ____________
17. $n > -304.7$ ____________
18. $54.7 \geq m$ ____________
19. $-298.1 \geq q$ ____________
20. $-16.3 \leq v$ ____________
21. $91.4 \leq z$ ____________
22. $y < 3254$ ____________
23. $7102 > g$ ____________

For More Practice Go To:

ONLINE www.progressinmathematics.com  Practice/Test Generator

Graph each solution set on a number line. Then describe a verbal situation the inequality could represent.

24. $c < 6$

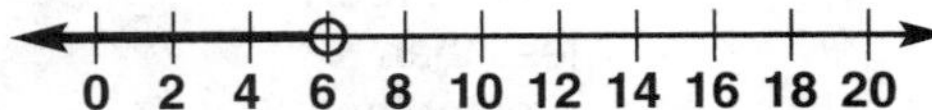

The number of red cars, c, in the parking lot is less than 6.

25. $b > -8$

−10 −8 −6 −4 −2 0 2

26. $f \geq 24$

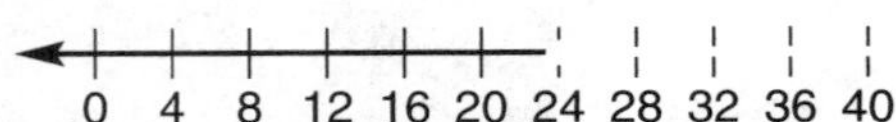

27. $g \geq -52$

−55 −54 −53 −52 −51 −50

28. $\{r \mid r \leq 16\}$

0 2 4 6 8 10 12 14 16 18 20

29. $\{a \mid a < -125\}$

−175 −150 −125 −100 −75

30. $[1125, \infty)$

1124 1125 1126 1127 1128

31. $(-\infty, -28)$

−33 −32 −31 −30 −29 −28 −27

Problem Solving

32. Measurement A city's record high temperature is 112° F and record low temperature is −15° F. What is the range of the city's temperatures, expressed in interval notation?

33. Probability The probability of an event is at most 1 and at least 0. What is the range of possible probabilities, expressed in interval notation?

CRITICAL THINKING

34. Grace collected at least 340 cans to recycle. Juanita collected fewer than 340 cans to recycle. Who collected more cans? Explain.

3-2 Solve Inequalities Using Addition or Subtraction

Name ______________________________ Date ____________

Solve: $d - 34 \geq 15$ ← subtraction inequality

$d - 34 \mathbf{+ 34} \geq 15 \mathbf{+ 34}$ ← Use the Addition Property of Inequality.

$d \geq 49$

Graph: $d \geq 49$

45 46 47 48 49 50 51 52 53 54 55

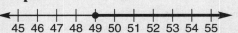

The graph shows the solution set for $\{d \mid d \geq 49\}$ or $[49, \infty)$.

Check:

Try $d = 49 \longrightarrow 49 - 34 \overset{?}{\geq} 15$

$15 \geq 15$ **True**

Solve: $12 - 4 \geq 3g - 2g + 20$ ← addition inequality

$8 \geq \mathbf{g} + 20$ ← Combine like terms.

$8 \mathbf{- 20} \geq g + 20 \mathbf{- 20}$ ← Use the Subtraction Property of Inequality.

$-12 \geq g$

Graph: $-12 \geq g$

−15 −14 −13 −12 −11 −10 −9 −8 −7 −6

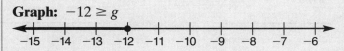

The graph shows the solution set for $\{g \mid g \leq -12\}$ or $(-\infty, -12]$.

Check:

Try $g = -12 \longrightarrow 12 - 4 \overset{?}{\geq} 3(\mathbf{-12}) - 2(\mathbf{-12}) + 20$

$8 \overset{?}{\geq} \mathbf{-12} + 20$

$8 \geq 8$ **True**

Solve each inequality. Check to justify your solutions.

1. $t - 6 > 7$
   $t - 6 + 6 > 7 + 6$
   $t > 13$
   Check: Let $t = 14$
   $14 - 6 \overset{?}{>} 7$
   $8 > 7$ True

2. $h - 9 > 11$

3. $p - 5.3 \leq 4.0$

4. $\ell - 6.7 \leq 2.9$

5. $12 < s + 7$

6. $20 < m + 14$

7. $-29 > j - 19$

8. $-33 > p - 2$

9. $-85 \geq q - 24$

10. $-51 \geq k - 63$

11. $4n - 3n + 3 \geq -23$

12. $9y + 39 - 8y \geq -22$

Solve each inequality. Write the solution set in both set-builder and interval notation. On a separate sheet of paper, graph and check the solution set.

13. $f + 2 < 12 - 15$
$f + 2 < -3$
$f + 2 - 2 < -3 - 2$
$f < -5; \{f \mid f < -5\}; (-\infty, -5)$

14. $q + 5 < 14 - 26$

15. $h - 5 > -7 + 21$

16. $r - 2 > -7 + 17$

17. $5h - 4h - 2 \geq 5$

18. $6d - 5d - 7 \geq 15$

19. $5 \leq 3 + 4r - 3r + 7$

20. $7 \leq 5 + 7g - 6g + 11$

21. $25 - 11 < 5t - 4t - 9$

22. $31 - 24 < 7t - 6t - 3$

23. $11d + 15 - 10d > 9 - 25$

24. $17b + 42 - 16b > 28 - 33$

25. $-5x + 12 + 6x \leq 13 - (-7)$

26. $9v - 18 + (-8v) < 64 + (-48)$

27. $94 + (-72) > 10z - 22 - 9z$

Solve. Show your work.

28. Victoria made 8 more baskets than Yolanda at a game. If Victoria made at most 12 baskets, how many baskets could Yolanda have made?

29. After Mr. Cheng spent \$145 on groceries and \$29 on office supplies, he had at least \$78 in his wallet. What is the least amount he could have started with, if he paid cash?

CHALLENGE

30. Solve the inequality $x - k < 24$ for x. Then determine the set of values of k that would make the solution set contain only negative numbers.

3-3 Solve Inequalities Using Multiplication or Division

Name ______________________ Date ____________

Solve: $-3d \le 24$ ← multiplication inequality

$\frac{-3d}{-3} \ge \frac{24}{-3}$ ← Divide by a negative number; reverse the inequality symbol.

$d \ge -8$

Graph: $d \ge -8$

−11 −10 −9 −8 −7 −6

The graph shows the solution set for $\{d \mid d \ge -8\}$ or $[-8, \infty)$.

Check:

Try $d = -8 \longrightarrow -3(\mathbf{-8}) \overset{?}{\le} 24$

$24 \le 24$ **True**

Solve: $\frac{v}{7} + v < 16$ ← Identify like terms.

$\frac{8}{7}v < 16$ ← Simplify: combine like terms.

$\left(\frac{7}{8}\right) \bullet \left(\frac{8}{7}v\right) < 16 \bullet \left(\frac{7}{8}\right)$ ← Use the Multiplication Property of Inequality.

$v < 14$

Graph: $v < 14$

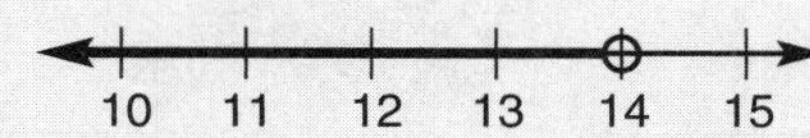

The graph shows the solution set for $\{v \mid v < 14\}$ or $(-\infty, 14)$.

Check:

Try $v = 13 \longrightarrow \frac{\mathbf{13}}{7} + (\mathbf{13}) \overset{?}{<} 16$

$7\left[\frac{13}{7} + 13\right] \overset{?}{<} \mathbf{7}(16)$

$104 < 112$ **True**

Solve each inequality.

1. $-2c > 24$

$\frac{-2c}{-2} < \frac{24}{-2}$

$c < -12$

2. $-4a > 20$

3. $2n \le 10$

4. $5t \le 35$

5. $\frac{v}{9} < 6$

6. $\frac{h}{3} < 5$

7. $\frac{k}{-5} > 2$

8. $\frac{y}{-8} > -4$

9. $21 \ge -7s$

10. $30 \ge -15f$

11. $-9 < \frac{k}{11}$

12. $-7 < \frac{u}{12}$

13. $\frac{u}{-6.1} < -9.4$

14. $-\frac{5}{6}p > 2$

15. $\frac{16}{-17}q > \frac{8}{34}$

Solve each inequality. Write the solution set in both set-builder and interval notation. On a separate sheet of paper, graph and check the solution set.

16. $-7x + 3x \geq 3$

$-4x \geq 3$

$\frac{-4x}{-4} \leq \frac{3}{-4}$

$x \leq -\frac{3}{4}$; $\{x \mid x \leq -\frac{3}{4}\}$; $(-\infty, -\frac{3}{4}]$

17. $-9b + 3b \geq 5$ ________

18. $v + \frac{v}{9} < 15$ ________

19. $d + \frac{d}{6} < -2$ ________

20. $0.75 \geq -5n + 2n$ ________

21. $-2.4 \geq -12m + 4m$ ________

22. $-3 \leq \frac{i}{-2}$ ________

23. $8 \leq \frac{c}{-6}$ ________

24. $-\frac{6}{10} < \frac{h}{10}$ ________

25. $-\frac{9}{2} < \frac{a}{2}$ ________

26. $-\frac{3}{4} \geq -\frac{5}{4} - e$ ________

27. $\frac{7}{2} \geq -\frac{\ell}{2} - \frac{\ell}{2}$ ________

Problem Solving

28. If one school bus can hold 64 students, what is the least number of buses needed to transport 700 students on a field trip? ________

29. Carlos can spend at most $147 on mechanical pencils for the office. If each pencil costs $2.50, what is the greatest number of mechanical pencils he can buy? ________

TEST PREPARATION

30. Which is the solution set of $-12 \geq \frac{c}{3}$?

A. $(-\infty, -36]$ **B.** $(-36, \infty)$ **C.** $[-36, \infty)$ **D.** $(-\infty, -36)$

3-4 Solve Multistep Inequalities

Name ______________________ Date ____________

Solve: $4.22 + 1.2g \geq 5.1 + 3.4g$

$\mathbf{100}(4.22 + 1.2g) \geq \mathbf{100}(5.1 + 3.4g)$ ← Multiply both sides by 100

$\mathbf{422 + 120g \geq 510 + 340g}$

$422 + 120g - \mathbf{120g} \geq 510 + 340g - \mathbf{120g}$ ← Use the Subtraction Property of Inequality.

$422 \geq 510 + \mathbf{220g}$

$422 - \mathbf{510} \geq 510 - \mathbf{510} + 220g$ ← Use the Subtraction Property of Inequality.

$\mathbf{-88} \geq 220g$

$\frac{-88}{\mathbf{220}} \geq \frac{220g}{\mathbf{220}}$ ← Use the Division Property of Inequality.

$-0.4 \geq g$

Graph: $\{g | g \leq -0.4\}$ or $(-\infty, -0.4]$

−1 0

Check: Try $g = -1$.

$4.22 + 1.2(-1) \overset{?}{\geq} 5.1 + 3.4(-1)$

$4.22 - \mathbf{1.2} \overset{?}{\geq} 5.1 - \mathbf{3.4}$

$3.02 \geq 1.7$ **True**

Remember: When graphing a solution set that does not include a boundary point, place a *circle* at the point. Otherwise, place a *dot* at the point.

Solve each inequality. Write the solution in set-builder and interval notation. On a separate sheet of paper, graph and check the solution set.

1. $\frac{1}{2} + \frac{2}{3}b \geq \frac{5}{6}$

LCD of 2, 3, and 6 = 6

$6\left(\frac{1}{2} + \frac{2}{3}b\right) \geq 6\left(\frac{5}{6}\right)$

$3 + 4b \geq 5$

$3 - 3 + 4b \geq 5 - 3$

$4b \geq 2$

$\frac{4b}{4} \geq \frac{2}{4}$

$b \geq \frac{1}{2}$; $\{b \mid b \geq \frac{1}{2}\}$; $[\frac{1}{2}, \infty)$

2. $\frac{2}{3} + \frac{3}{4}c \geq \frac{7}{12}$

____

3. $\frac{7}{5} - \frac{3}{10}f \leq \frac{3}{5}$

____

4. $\frac{9}{8} - \frac{3}{2}m \leq \frac{1}{4}$

____

5. $\frac{3}{4} > \frac{2}{3}n - \frac{11}{12}$

____

6. $\frac{7}{2} > \frac{8}{3}j - \frac{7}{6}$

____

7. $3 - 1.5y < 5.4 - 2.7y$

____

8. $2 - 2.9h < 8.3 - 3.8h$

____

9. $5.26 - 2.4c \geq 20.59 + 4.9c$

____

Use with SOURCEBOOK Lesson 3-4, pages 76–79.

Solve each inequality. Write the solution in set-builder and interval notation. Check to justify your work.

10. $-6 \geq 11 - 4a + 3$
$-6 \geq 14 - 4a$
$-20 \geq -4a$
$5 \leq a$ or $a \geq 5$
$\{a \mid a \geq 5\}$; $[5, \infty)$
Check: $-6 \overset{?}{>} 11 - 4(6) + 3$
$-6 > -10$ True

11. $-5 \geq 7 - 8t + 12$

12. $4 > -2 + 3r + 8$

13. $10b > -8 + 5b + 3$

14. $15 - 2n - 20 < -11n$

15. $9 - 3s + 15 \leq -6s$

16. $3(y - 4) \geq 18$

17. $7(x + 5) \geq -7$

18. $6(w - 2) + 3w < 6$

19. $4(g - 7) + 8g < 8$

20. $9(q - 2) - 11q \leq 7$

21. $5(h + 3) - 9h \leq -3$

Problem Solving

22. Juan scored 15 points more on this test than on his previous test. If the average of the two tests is at least 92 and both scores are integers, what are the least scores he could have had on the two tests?

23. A store sells khakis for \$19.99 and boots for \$51.99. It is having a 35%-off sale. Jeanie needs a new pair of boots, plans to spend \$20 at lunch, and only has \$150 with her. How many pairs of khakis could Jeanie buy? Suppose sales tax is 6%.

MENTAL MATH

24. 15(23)

25. 28(40)

3-5 Solve Compound Inequalities

Name ______________________ Date __________

Solve: $3g > 6$ OR $2g \le -6$

$\frac{3g}{3} > \frac{6}{3}$ OR $\frac{2g}{2} \le \frac{-6}{2}$ ← Use the Division Property of Inequality.

$g > 2$ OR $g \le -3$ ← The solution set is $\{g \mid g \le -3 \text{ OR } g > 2\}$ or $(-\infty, -3] \cup (2, \infty)$

Check: Try $g = 3$ and -4

$3(\mathbf{3}) \overset{?}{>} 6$ OR $2(\mathbf{-4}) \overset{?}{\le} -6$

$9 > 6$ **True** OR $-8 \le -6$ **True**

Graph:

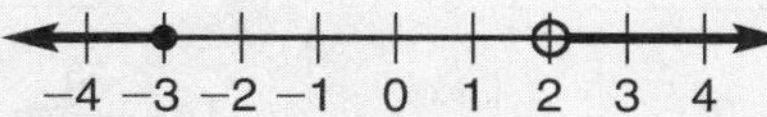

The graph identifies the solutions of the compound inequality.

Graph each compound inequality. Write the solution set in set-builder notation and interval notation.

1. $-2 < d \le 5$

$-2 < d$ AND $d \le 5$

−3 −2 −1 0 1 2 3 4 5

−3 −2 −1 0 1 2 3 4 5

$\{d \mid -2 < d \le 5\}, (-2, 5]$

2. $-3 < a \le 3$

____

3. $f < 1$ OR $f > 3$

____

4. $d < -2$ OR $d > 4$

____

5. $-5 \le x \le 2$

____

6. $0 \le x \le 6$

____

Write the inequality for each graph. Write the solution set in set-builder and interval notation.

7. −2 −1 0 1 2 3

$x > -\frac{1}{2}$ AND $x < 2$

So $-\frac{1}{2} < x < 2$

$\{x \mid -\frac{1}{2} < x < 2\}; \left(-\frac{1}{2}, 2\right)$

8. −1 0 1 2

____

9.

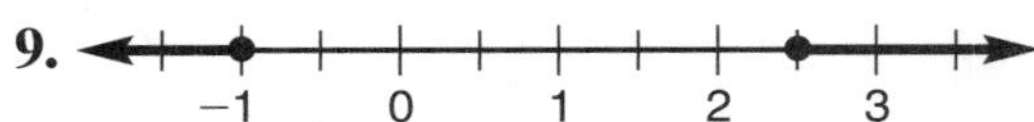

____

10.

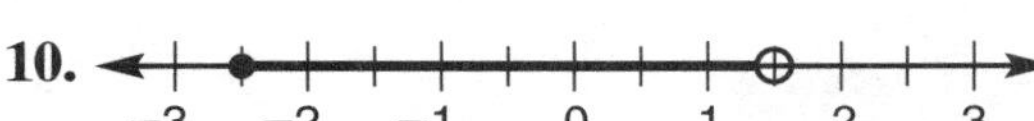

____

Use with SOURCEBOOK Lesson 3-5, pages 80–83.

Solve and check the compound inequality. Graph the solution set.

11. $2y + 8 < 6$ AND $-2y - 5 < 3$

$2y + 8 < 6$ AND $-2y - 5 < 3$

$\underline{-8\ -8}$ $\quad$ $\underline{+5\ +5}$

$2y < -2$ AND $-2y < 8$

$\frac{2y}{2} < \frac{-2}{2}$ $\quad$ $\frac{-2y}{-2} > \frac{8}{-2}$

$y < -1$ AND $y > -4$

$-4 < y < -1$

−5 −4 −3 −2 −1 0 1

12. $3z + 7 < 22$ AND $-3z - 9 < -3$

13. $-7h - 1 \geq 20$ AND $-5h + 4 < 29$

14. $-\frac{8}{6}m \leq \frac{5}{3}$ OR $\frac{1}{2}m \leq -\frac{7}{6}$

15. $-\frac{2}{5}n \geq -\frac{4}{15}$ OR $\frac{3}{5}n \geq \frac{9}{20}$

16. $4.89 > 1.1j + 5$ OR $3.4 \geq 4 - 1.2j$

Problem Solving

17. Juanita is shopping online for a used MP3 Player. She can spend at least \$50, but no more than \$210. Shipping and handling will cost \$10.20. If sales tax is 7%, what is Juanita's price range for MP3 Players?

18. Dylan's mother tells Dylan he must spend less time playing electronic games. On the weekends he spends $9\frac{1}{2}$ hours playing electronic games. If he plays between 13 and 19 hours each week, how many hours does he play games on weekdays?

CHALLENGE

19. Describe the graph of the compound inequality $x < 1$ AND $x > 2$ and the solution.

3-6 Solve Absolute-Value Inequalities

Name ______________________________ Date ______________

Solve: $2|c-6|-1 \geq 11$ ← Isolate the absolute-value expression.

$2|c-6|-1+1 \geq 11+1$ ← Use the Addition Property of Inequality.

$\frac{2|c-6|}{2} \geq \frac{12}{2}$ ← Use the Division Property of Inequality.

$|c-6| \geq 6$ ← Rewrite this statement as a disjunction.

$c-6 \leq -6$ OR $c-6 \geq 6$

$\underline{+6 \quad +6} \qquad \underline{+6 \quad +6}$ ← Use the Addition Property of Inequality.

$c \leq 0$ OR $c \geq 12$

Graph:
$\{c|c \leq 0$ OR $c \geq 12\}$ OR $(-\infty, 0] \cup [12, \infty)$

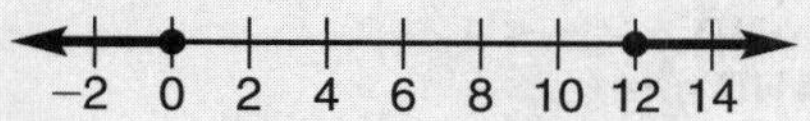

Check: $c = -1$ and 20

$2|(-1)-6|-1 \overset{?}{\geq} 11$ OR $2|20-6|-1 \geq 11$

$2|-7|-1 \overset{?}{\geq} 11 \qquad 2|14|-1 \overset{?}{\geq} 11$

$2(7)-1 \overset{?}{\geq} 11 \qquad 28-1 \overset{?}{\geq} 11$

$13 \geq 11 \qquad 27 \geq 11$

True **True**

Remember: If an absolute-value inequality involves the "less than" symbol, rewrite the inequality as a conjunction.

Solve the inequality. Write the answer in set-builder and interval notation. Check your work.

1. $|a|+9<12$

$|a|+9-9<12-9$

$|a|<3$

$a>-3$ AND $a<3$

$\{a|-3<a<3\}$; $(-3, 3)$

Check: $a=0$

$|0|+9 \overset{?}{\leq} 12$

$9 \leq 12$ True

2. $|d|+6<7$

____

3. $|w|-2>3$

____

4. $|f|-7>11$

____

5. $6|x| \leq 18$

____

6. $5|t| \leq 30$

____

7. $8|y|-6 \geq 42$

____

8. $3|z|+18>27$

____

9. $-4|b|+4>-16$

____

Solve the inequality. On a separate sheet of paper, graph and check the solution set.

10. $|q - 5| + 13 \leq 14$

$|q - 5| + 13 \leq 14$
$|q - 5| \leq 1$
$q - 5 \geq -1$ AND $q - 5 \leq 1$
$q \geq 4$ AND $q \leq 6$
$4 \leq q \leq 6$

11. $|m - 4| + 6 \leq 9$

12. $-\frac{2}{3}|a| \leq -5$

13. $-\frac{3}{4}|b| \leq -3$

14. $|2x + 3| - 4\frac{4}{5} > 6\frac{1}{5}$

15. $|2x - 4| - 3\frac{1}{6} > 4\frac{5}{6}$

16. $|5a + 3| - 9 < 7$

17. $|4g - 9| - 3 < 7$

18. $-4 + |2h - 1| \leq 7$

19. $-4 + |3k - 2| \leq 9$

20. $1.7 + |\ell - 3| \geq 2.8$

21. $3.5 + |m - 2| \geq 5.7$

22. What integers are the solutions to $|x - 4| < 8$ AND $|-3x| > 12$?

23. What integers are the solutions to $|x + 1| < 4$ OR $|-x - 1| < 3$?

SPIRAL REVIEW

Write *rational* or *irrational* for each number.

24. $\frac{2}{3}$ ______

25. $\sqrt{5}$ ______

26. $\sqrt{100}$ ______

27. π ______

Find the value of each expression.

28. $3^2 + 7^{-2} - 11^0$ ______

29. $19 - 21 - (-2)[8(-3) + 4]$

30. $\dfrac{2\frac{1}{3}}{1\frac{1}{5}}$ ______

Solve.

31. $3x + 19 = 21$

32. $5c - 17 = 2c + 14$

33. $3(2b - 4) = 7 - (b + 8)$

3-7 Technology: Solve Linear Inequalities

Name ______________________________ Date ______________

You can use the **Solve** function on a handheld to solve the inequality $3x + 9 > 7x - 11$.

Step 1 Press (home). Then choose (1) to select **Calculator**.

Step 2 Press menu. Select **Algebra**, then **Solve**.

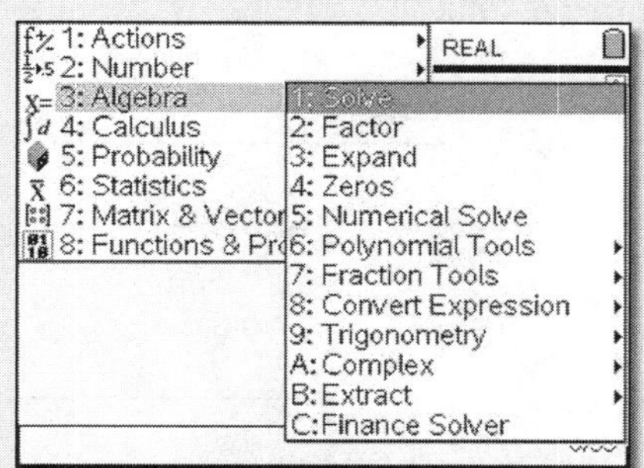

Step 3 Input $3x + 9 > 7x - 11, x$. Then press (enter).

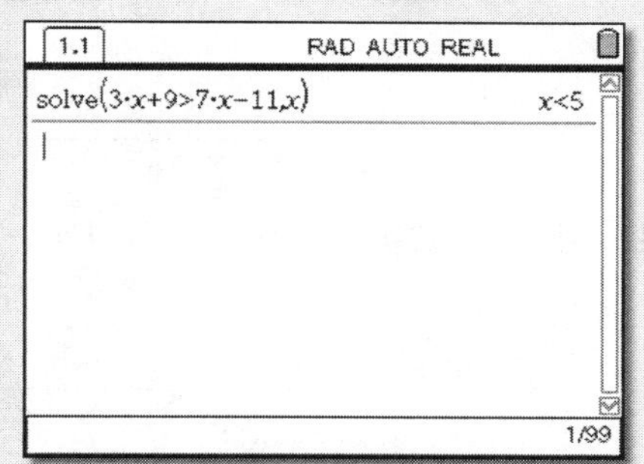

Remember: ",x" means solve the inequality for x.

So the solution is $\{x \mid x < 5\}$ or $(-\infty, 5)$.

To verify that the solution determined satisfies the inequality, graph the solution set and choose test points.

$x = 4$: $3(4) + 9 \overset{?}{>} 7(4) - 11$

$21 \overset{?}{>} 17$ True

$x = 5$: $3(5) + 9 \overset{?}{>} 7(5) - 11$

$24 \overset{?}{>} 24$ False

$x = 6$: $3(6) + 9 \overset{?}{>} 7(6) - 11$

$27 \overset{?}{>} 31$ False

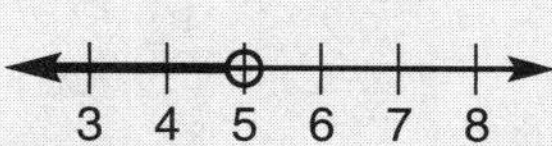

Use a handheld to find the solution of the inequality. Represent your answer in set builder and interval notation.

1. $9x > 7x - 12$

$\{x \mid x > -6\}$; $(-6, \infty)$

2. $8x > 2x - 24$

____

3. $11x - 9 \le 3x - 49$

____

4. $12x - 2 \le 2x - 62$

____

5. $3x + 1 \ge 7x + 17$

____

6. $2x + 3 \ge 9x + 24$

____

7. $11x - 8 < 5x + 34$

____

8. $13x - 9 < 2x + 90$

____

9. $3x - 8 > 56 - 5x$

____

10. $4x - 11 > 43 - 2x$

____

11. $3x - 15 \ge 75 - 6x$

____

12. $7x - 8 \ge 100 - 5x$

____

Use a handheld to find the solution of the inequality. Represent your answer in set builder and interval notation.

13. $14x - 13 \leq 8.3 + 8x$

$\{x \mid x \leq 16\}; (-\infty, 16]$

14. $17x - 11 \leq 79 + 15x$

15. $3x + 10 \geq 5x + 22$

16. $1.8x - 3.5 \geq 5.86$

17. $3.9x - 4.7 \geq 21.82$

18. $4.8x + 2.9 < 2.3x + 19.9$

19. $5.3x + 1.6 < 3.7x + 16.64$

20. $1.3x - 4.5 < 4.4x + 7.59$

21. $5.7x - 2.8 < 7.9x + 8.42$

22. $\frac{2}{3}x + \frac{1}{5} \leq \frac{3}{4}$

23. $\frac{5}{8}x + \frac{1}{3} \leq \frac{1}{6}$

24. $\frac{2}{5}x + \frac{1}{2} \geq \frac{5}{4}x + \frac{4}{5}$

25. $\frac{5}{3}x + \frac{1}{4} \geq \frac{7}{2}x + \frac{3}{8}$

26. $\frac{9}{2}x + \frac{7}{10} > 2.4x - |-3.08|$

27. $\frac{11}{2}x + \frac{9}{10} > 3.2x - |-4.16|$

Problem Solving

28. Clayton gave Mia clues to help her guess the number he chose. Clue #1: Eight less than 7 times the number is at least 22. Clue #2: Thirteen more than 5 times the number is at most 52. Clue #3: The number is an integer. Write the inequalities, solve them on a handheld, and give the possible solutions.

29. A farmer removes the fence around a 122,500-square-foot square field and uses it to enclose a rectangular field that is 2 feet longer than twice its width. What are the possible integer widths of the rectangular field?

CHALLENGE

30. Solve $|3x - 5| < 2$ using a handheld.

3-8 Problem-Solving Strategy:
Reason Logically

Read Plan Solve Check

Name ______________________________ Date ______________

Reason logically to solve each problem.

1. A container holds 12 red balls and 4 blue balls. You may *double* the number of balls in the container at any time (by adding more red and blue balls), but you may never *remove* any balls). In this manner, can you reduce the percent of red balls to 20%? Explain.

____

2. Is there a two-digit number with the property that, when the tens and ones digits are reversed, the resulting number is three times the value of the original?

____

3. You can perfectly cover an ordinary 8-by-8 checkerboard with 32 of these tiles, ▭▭. In the given checkerboard, six squares are missing. Can you cover this board using the same tiles? Explain.

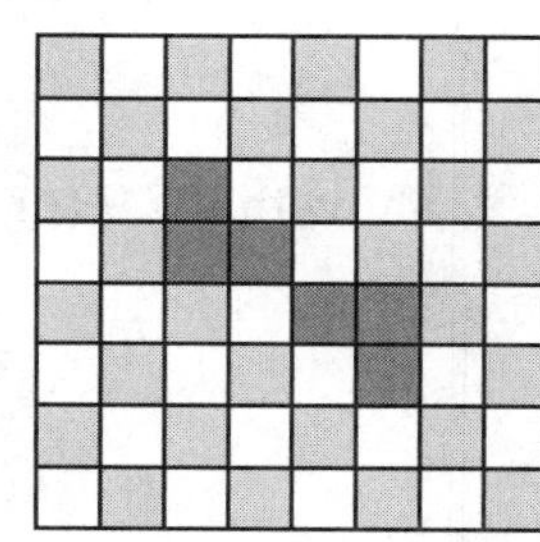

____

4. Can you cover the checkerboard shown above with tiles shaped like this ? Explain.

____

5. Two digits are missing from this number: 3,481_,62_,728. Could this number be a square number? Explain.

____

6. For what missing digit N would the following number be evenly divisible by 9? Explain.

$$23{,}018{,}142{,}N12{,}531{,}212$$

7. Is there a three-digit number x with the property that, if any one of its digits is removed to form a two-digit number y, then x is twice y. Explain.

8. Find all possible numbers that follow this rule: When removing the first digit of a three-digit number x, the two-digit number y is one-fifth x. Explain.

9. Show that $7.\overline{9}$ (or, $7.999\ldots$) is equal to 8.

10. When a particular integer is divided by 12, the remainder is 7. Find the sum of the remainders when this number is divided by 3, 4, and 6.

11. Good'n'Sweet sells 79,000 jars of marmalade over the course of 5 days. Each day 2000 more jars were sold than on the previous day. How many jars were sold on day 4?

Enrichment:
The Triangle Inequality Theorem

Name ______________________________ Date ______________

Suppose the side lengths of a triangle are x, $2x$, and $2x + 12$. What are the possible values of x?

Substitute the side lengths of the triangle into the triangle inequalities. Then solve for x. Let $a = x$, $b = 2x$ and $c = 2x + 12$.

$a + b > c$	$a + c > b$	$b + c > a$
$x + 2x > 2x + 12$	$x + 2x + 12 > 2x$	$2x + 2x + 12 > x$
$3x > 2x + 12$	$3x + 12 > 2x$	$4x + 12 > x$
$x > 12$	$x > -12$	$3x > -12$
		$x > -4$

Because x is a length, x cannot be negative or zero. So the least value x could represent is 1. Substituting values into the solutions, however, shows that no values where $x \le 12$ are true. So the possible values of x can be represented by $\{x \mid x > 12\}$.

Tell whether it is possible for a triangle to have the given side lengths.

1. 4 in., 8 in., 13 in.

Is $4 + 8 > 13$? No; $12 < 13$
Is $4 + 13 > 8$? Yes; $17 > 8$
Is $8 + 13 > 4$? Yes; $21 > 4$
not possible

2. 6 cm, 8 cm, 15 cm ______________

3. 5 m, 6 m, 7 m ______________

4. 7 ft, 9 ft, 11 ft ______________

5. 12 km, 6 km, 8 km ______________

6. 20 in., 25 in., 12 in. ______________

The lengths of two sides of a triangle are given. Give the range of possible lengths for the third side.

7. 6 in. and 7 in.

$6 + 7 > x$	$6 + x > 7$	$7 + x > 6$
$13 > x$	$x > 1$	$x > -1$

$\{x \mid 1 \text{ in.} < x < 13 \text{ in.}\}$

8. 10 m and 8 m ______________

9. 15 ft and 20 ft ______________

10. 60.5 mm and 17.5 mm ______________

11. 13.4 mi and 52.6 mi ______________

12. 62 cm and 25.5 cm ______________

Find the possible values of x for the given expressions of the lengths of the sides of each triangle.

13. $x + 2$, $3x - 4$, and x

$$x + 2 + 3x - 4 > x$$
$$4x - 2 > x$$
$$-2 > -3x$$
$$\frac{2}{3} < x$$
$$x + 2 + x > 3x - 4$$
$$2x + 2 > 3x - 4$$
$$6 > x$$
$$3x - 4 + x > x + 2$$
$$4x - 4 > x + 2$$
$$3x > 6$$
$$x > 2$$
$$\{x \mid 2 < x < 6\}$$

14. $x + 3$, $3x - 5$, and $x + 1$

15. x, $x + 4$, and $x - 2$

16. x, $x + 1$, and $2x - 1$

17. $7x - 4$, $3x + 1$, and $2x + 2$

18. $6x - 15$, $x + 65$, and $4x - 30$

Problem Solving

19. Agatha and Christine are making a triangular garden that has sides of length x, $4x - 10$, and $2x + 3$. What is one possible set of lengths that can be used to make the garden?

20. Simone was designing a triangular peace garden. She knew two lengths of the triangle would be 35 m and 80 m. Give the range of possible lengths for the third side.

CHALLENGE

21. A triangle has sides of length $3x - 7$, $x + 4$, and $2x$. If the lengths of the sides of the triangle must be integers, what is the least possible perimeter of the triangle?

Test Prep: Multiple-Choice Questions

Strategy: Apply Mathematical Reasoning

Name ______________________________ Date ______________

When solving problems, it is helpful to **justify your steps** to make sure your process is reasonable and that you do not miss any steps.

To select the correct answer in a multiple-choice item, try using the following strategies.

- Underline important words.
- Restate the question.
- Use the Test-Prep strategy.
- Apply appropriate rules, definitions, properties, or strategies.
- Analyze and eliminate answer choices.

Sample Test Item

Solve: $\frac{x}{3} + 2 \leq -4$

$\frac{x}{3} \leq -6$ ← Subtract 2 from each side.

$x \leq -18$ ← Multiply each side by 3.

(A.) $x \leq -18$ ← This is the correct choice.

B. $x \geq -18$ ← The inequality symbol was reversed. Eliminate this choice.

C. $x \leq -6$ ← The left side was multiplied by 3. Eliminate this choice.

D. $x \geq -6$ ← The left side was multiplied by 3, and the inequality symbol was reversed. Eliminate this choice.

Choose the correct answer. *TIP: Cross out incorrect answers as you eliminate them.*

1. Which value is in the solution set of $5 - 2x > 7$?

A. -5 **C.** 1

B. 0 **D.** 5

2. What is the quotient of 1.02×10^3 and 2×10^{-4}?

F. 5.1×10^{-12} **H.** 5.1×10^6

G. 5.1×10^{-1} **J.** 5.1×10^7

3. Simplify: $\frac{9x^{-15}}{6x^{-3}} \bullet \frac{4x^2}{3x}$

A. $\frac{2}{x^{11}}$ **C.** $6x^6$

B. $\frac{2}{x^4}$ **D.** $6x^{10}$

4. Solve: $12 - \frac{3}{4}x = 24$

F. $x = -16$ **H.** $x = 9$

G. $x = -9$ **J.** $x = 16$

5. Evaluate: $(8 - 3)^2 - 2|3 - 5|^3$

A. -487 **C.** 41

B. 9 **D.** 537

6. Solve: $|5x - 12| > 18$

F. $-1.2 < x < 6$ **H.** $x < -6$ or $x > 1.2$

G. $-6 < x < 1.2$ **J.** $x < -1.2$ or $x > 6$

7. Solve: $5 - |x + 1| \geq 2$

A. $-4 \leq x \leq 2$ **C.** $x \leq -4$ or $x \geq 2$

B. $-2 \leq x \leq 4$ **D.** $x \leq -2$ or $x \geq 4$

8. Evaluate: $5\sqrt{x^2 - y} + (2y^2 - x)$, for $x = 1$ and $y = -3$.

F. -7 **H.** 27

G. -2 **J.** 45

Use with SOURCEBOOK Test Prep Lesson, page 92.

For More Practice Go To:
ONLINE www.progressinmathematics.com

Vocabulary Development

Name ______________________ Date __________

Chapter 3 Vocabulary

absolute-value inequality
addition inequality
Addition Property of Inequality
boundary point
comparison symbols
compound inequality
conjunction
disjunction
division inequality
Division Property of Inequality
inequality
interval notation
multiplication inequality
Multiplication Property of Inequality
multistep inequality
subtraction inequality
Subtraction Property of Inequality

From the vocabulary list above, choose the term(s) that best complete each sentence. Write the term(s) in the space(s) provided.

1. A(n) ______________ joined by the word AND is a(n) ______________.

2. ( ) means *not included* or *open* in ______________.

3. An inequality that contains more than one operation is a(n) ______________.

4. An ______________ can be written as a compound inequality.

5. A statement that compares two expressions or quantities that are not equal is a(n) ______________.

6. Use the Subtraction Property of Inequality to solve a(n) ______________.

7. To solve a division inequality, use the ______________.

8. A(n) ______________ joined by the word OR is a(n) ______________.

Choose three terms from the list that you didn't use in Questions 1–8. For each term, write a definition in your own words and give an example.

9. ____

Use after SOURCEBOOK Lessons 3-1–3-6, pages 70–85.

Practice Chapter 3 Test

Name ______________________________ Date ____________

Write an inequality that represents each word sentence.

1. Arthur set the timer for at least 45 minutes. ________

2. The weight of the box is greater than 54 pounds. ________

3. The number of cars that passed through the intersection is at most 1300. ________

4. The number of windows in the office building is no less than 100. ________

Express each inequality in both set-builder and interval notation.

5. $w < 89$ ____________ **6.** $k \geq 259$ ____________ **7.** $m < 0$ ____________

Graph each solution set on a number line. Then describe a situation the inequality could represent.

8. $q > 5$ **9.** $a \leq -4$ **10.** $f \geq 1$

____________ ____________ ____________

Solve each inequality. Write the solution set in both set-builder and interval notation. On a separate sheet of paper, graph and check the solution set.

11. $d + 3 < 9 - 12$ **12.** $5 \leq 8 + 5r - 4r + 1$ **13.** $11c - 7.4 - 10c < -5.6$

____________ ____________ ____________

14. $-a - \frac{6}{5} < -3$ **15.** $-4 \leq \frac{r}{-3}$ **16.** $-\frac{3}{2} \geq -\frac{t}{3} - \frac{t}{3}$

____________ ____________ ____________

17. $\frac{3}{5} - \frac{3}{2}n \leq \frac{7}{10}$ **18.** $8 - 2.7d < 5.9 - 3.4d$ **19.** $-5 < 4z - (6z + 7)$

____________ ____________ ____________

Use after SOURCEBOOK Lessons 3-1–3-6, pages 70–85.

Graph each compound inequality. Write the solution set in both set-builder and interval notation.

20. $-2 \leq n \leq 4$

21. $h < -2$ OR $h \geq 1$

22. $v \leq -3$ OR $v > 2$

Solve and check each compound inequality. On a separate sheet of paper, graph the solution set.

23. $1 < x - 4 < 7$

24. $-10 \leq 3b - 1 < 14$

25. $-2x - 3 \geq 1$ OR $2x + 8 > 14$

Solve each inequality. On a separate sheet of paper, graph and check the solution set.

26. $-\frac{3}{4}|c| \geq -3$

27. $|3w + 2| - 1 < 5$

28. $1.4 + |x - 1| \geq 3.7$

Solve. Check your work.

29. Cheng can spend \$35 to make a project. He has already spent \$28. He still needs pipe cleaners that cost \$1.25 per box. What is the greatest number of boxes of pipe cleaners he can buy?

30. Jonas charges \$75 plus \$65 per hour for tractor work. How many hours does he work to earn at least \$335?

Tell About It

Explain how you solve the problem. Show all your work.

31. Solve the inequality $-x + 2 > a$ for x. Then find the least value of a that makes the solution set all negative numbers.

Cumulative Review: Chapters 1–3

Name ______________________________ Date ____________

Circle the best answer.

1. Which is the best estimate of $\sqrt{42}$?

A. 6.1
B. 6.5
C. 6.9
D. 7.1

2. What is the opposite of $\frac{3}{4}$?

F. $\frac{4}{3}$ **G.** $\frac{3}{4}$
H. $-\frac{3}{4}$ **J.** $-\frac{4}{3}$

3. Simplify.

$-8 \bullet 3 + |-8| - 9$

A. -25 **B.** -26
C. -39 **D.** -41

4. Simplify.

$5^2 \bullet 5^3 \bullet 5^{-3}$

F. 125 **G.** 25
H. 5 **J.** -2250

5. Which is equivalent to the expression below?

$(3.1 \times 10^4)\ (8.3 \times 10^5)$

A. 25.73×10^4
B. 25.73×10^{10}
C. 257.3×10^9
D. 2.573×10^{10}

6. Simplify.

$12x - 5(2x + 11) + 13x + 14$

F. $-16x$
G. $15x - 41$
H. $15x + 25$
J. $22x + 25$

7. If $A = \{1, 2, 3, 4, 5, 6\}$ and $B = \{4, 5, 6, 7, 8, 9\}$ then $A \cap B =$

A. $\{1, 2, 3, 4, 5, 6, 7, 8, 9\}$
B. $\{1, 2, 3, 7, 8, 9\}$
C. $\{4, 5, 6\}$
D. $\{1, 2, 3\}$

8. What is the dimension of the matrix?

$$\begin{bmatrix} 1 & 2 & 3 \\ 2 & 3 & 1 \end{bmatrix}$$

F. 2×3 **G.** 3×2
H. 6×1 **J.** 1×6

9. Solve.

$3.9 + 2n = 1.8$

A. $n = -1.05$ **B.** $n = -1$
C. $n = 2.85$ **D.** $n = 11.4$

10. Solve.

$-55 = 5(3b - 2)$

F. $b = -\frac{53}{15}$ **G.** $b = -\frac{53}{8}$
H. $b = -3$ **J.** $b = -2$

11. Solve for x.

$ax + b = c$

A. $x = c - b + a$ **B.** $x = \frac{c - b}{a}$
C. $x = \frac{c + b}{a}$ **D.** $x = \frac{c + b}{-a}$

12. Solve.

$9(2c + 1) = 6 - (13 - 2c)$

F. $c = 1$ **G.** $c = \frac{4}{5}$
H. $c = -\frac{4}{5}$ **J.** $c = -1$

13. Solve.

$|f + 7| = 9$

A. $f = 2, 16$
B. $f = -2, 16$
C. $f = -16, 2$
D. $f = -16, -2$

14. Solve.

$|2d + 1| = 15$

F. $d = -7$ or $d = 8$
G. $d = 7$ or $d = 8$
H. $d = -8$ or $d = 7$
J. $d = -8$ or $d = -7$

15. Which inequality represents "The number of chairs in the auditorium is at least 267."

A. $c > 267$
B. $c < 267$
C. $c \leq 267$
D. $c \geq 267$

16. Which describes $\{x | x < 2.9\}$?

F. $(2.9, \infty)$
G. $(-\infty, 2.9]$
H. $[2.9, \infty)$
J. $(-\infty, 2.9)$

17. Solve.

$-2d + 5 < 9 - 12$

A. $d > 4$
B. $d < 4$
C. $d > -4$
D. $d < -4$

18. Solve.

$-7 < 2x + 7 < 13$

F. $0 < x < 3$
G. $0 > x > 10$
H. $-7 < x < 3$
J. $-7 > x > 10$

19. Which inequality is graphed below?

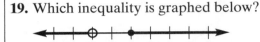

A. $d \leq 2$ OR $d \geq 4$
B. $d < 2$ OR $d \geq 4$
C. $d < 2$ OR $d > 4$
D. $2 < d \leq 4$

20. Which inequality is graphed below?

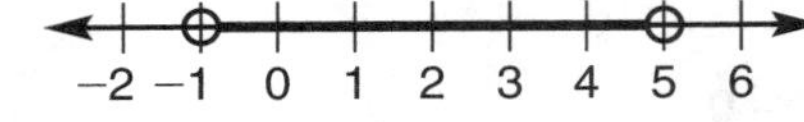

F. $-1 < x < 5$ **G.** $-1 < x \leq 5$
H. $-1 \leq x \leq 5$ **J.** $x < -1$ or $x > 5$

21. Solve for a:

$|2a - 3| + 2 > 11$

A. $-3 < a < 6$ **B.** $-6 < a < 11$
C. $a < -3$ *or* $a > 6$ **D.** $a < -6$ *or* $a > 6$

22. Solve for v:

$-2|3v - 1| \geq -16$

F. $-\frac{7}{3} \leq v \leq 3$ **G.** $-\frac{13}{3} < v < 5$

H. $v < -\frac{7}{3}$ OR $v > 3$ **J.** $v < -\frac{13}{3}$ OR $v > 5$

Tell About It

Explain how you solve each problem. Show all your work.

23. Victor chose a number, doubled it, added 12, then divided by 4, and finally subtracted 1. If the answer is 4, what number did he choose?

24. Wu collected 23 fewer than 5 times the number of bottles that Sabrina collected. If Wu collected 147 bottles, how many bottles did Sabrina collect?

4-1 Introduction to Relations

Name ________________________ Date ____________

Write the domain and range of relation M.

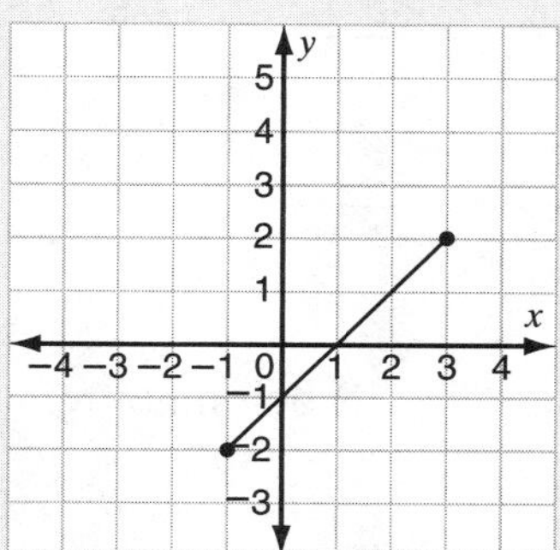

There are infinitely many ordered pairs in this relation.

Domain: $\{x \mid -1 \le x \le 3\}$
Range: $\{y \mid -2 \le y \le 2\}$

You can also represent a relation using a rule. Relation M can be represented by $y = x - 1$.

Find g, if $\left(g, \frac{2}{3}\right)$ belongs to M.

$y = x - 1$

$\frac{2}{3} = g - 1$ ← Substitute g for x and $\frac{2}{3}$ for y.

$\frac{2}{3} + 1 = g - 1 + 1$ ← Add 1 to both sides.

$1\frac{2}{3} = g$

For relation M, an input value of $1\frac{2}{3}$ results in an output value of $\frac{2}{3}$.

Write the domain and range of each relation.

1.

x	y
−3	−1
−2	2
0	5
1	9
4	10

Domain: {−3, −2, 0, 1, 4}
Range: {−1, 2, 5, 9, 10}

2.

x	y
−2	−1
0	0
2	1
4	3
6	5

____

3.

x	y
−1.5	−6
0.5	−4
2.5	−2
3.5	13
4.5	22

____

4.

x	y
−3.2	−1
−2.6	0
−2.4	3
3.4	11
5.2	34

____

5.

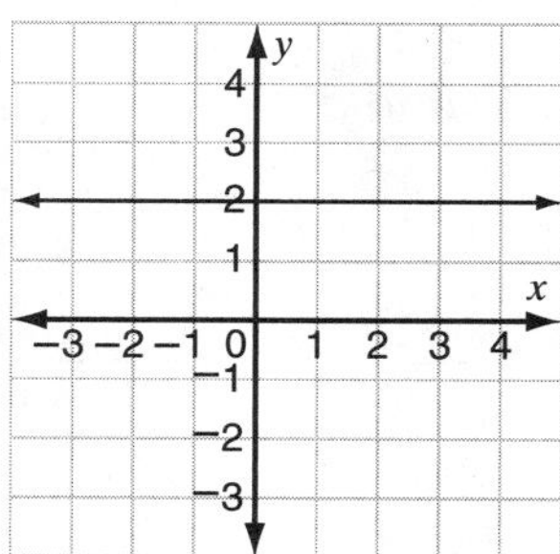

____

6.

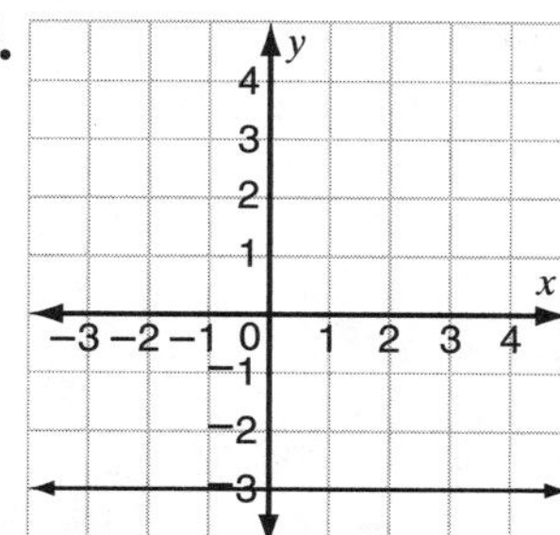

____

7.

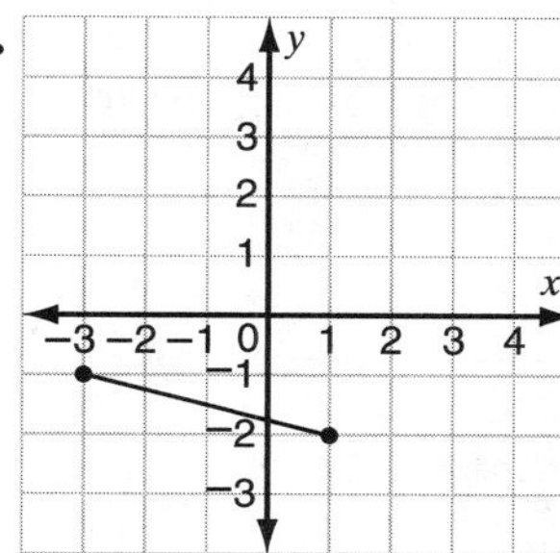

____

8. the graph of a line segment with endpoints $(-2, 3)$ and $(3, -2)$

____

9. the graph of a line segment with endpoints $(-4, 1)$ and $(3, 4)$

____

10. the graph of a line that includes points $(-2, -2)$ and $(3, 3)$

____

Use with SOURCEBOOK Lesson 4-1, pages 94–95.

Write the domain and range of each relation.

11.

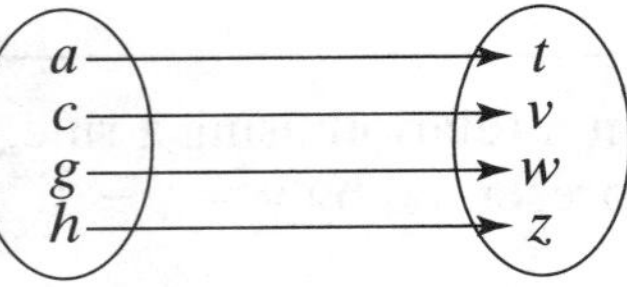

12.

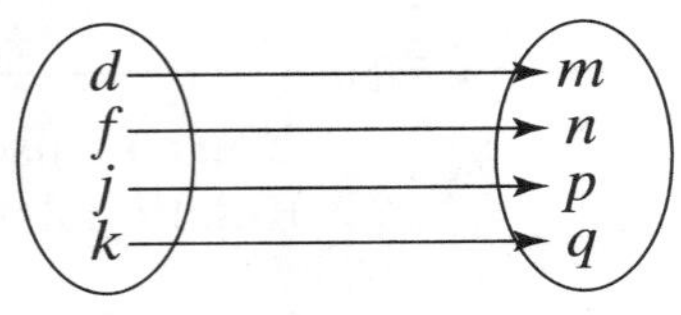

13.

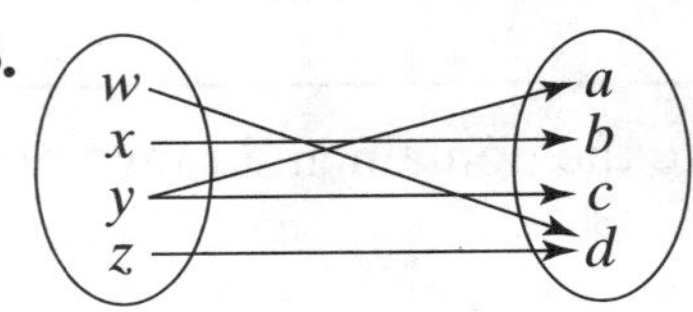

Relation R is represented by the rule $y = -2x^2$. Solve.

14. Does the ordered pair $(-2, 3)$ belong to R?

$y = -2x^2$

$3 \stackrel{?}{=} -2(-2)^2$

$3 \stackrel{?}{=} -2(4) = -8$ **False,** $3 \neq -8$

No, $(-2, 3)$ is not in R.

15. Does the ordered pair $(1, -2)$ belong to R?

16. Does the ordered pair $(-2, -2)$ belong to R?

17. Does the ordered pair $(-1, -2)$ belong to R?

18. If $(3, b)$ belongs to R, find b.

19. If $(a, -50)$ belongs to R, find a.

20. If $(3c, f)$ belongs to R, find f.

21. If $(5\ell, -k)$ belongs to R, find k.

22. If $(2z, -j)$ belongs to R, find z.

$\sqrt{\frac{j}{8}}$

23. If $\left(\frac{1}{2}d, -e\right)$ belongs to R, find d.

CHALLENGE

24. What are the domain and range of this relation?

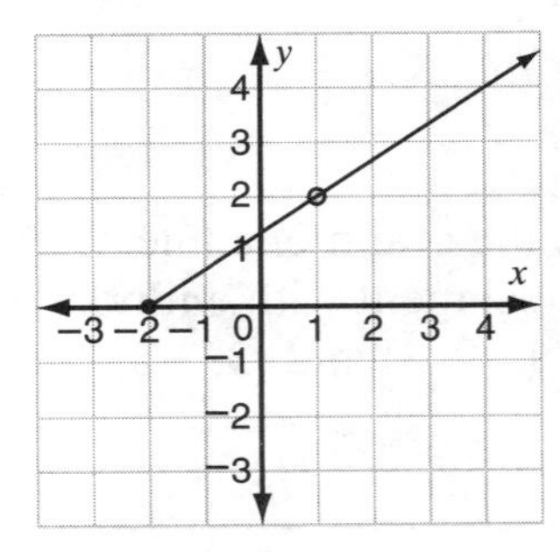

4-2 Introduction to Functions

Name ______________________________ Date ____________

The mapping diagram represents a set of ordered pairs.

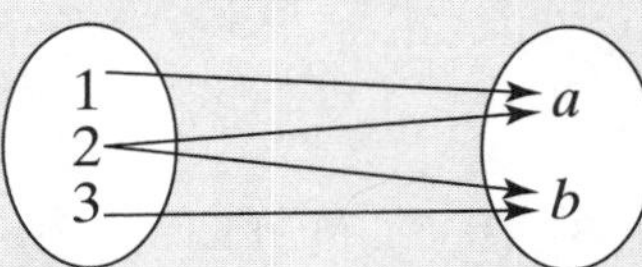

Determine if this relation is also a function.

Think

A function is a relation that pairs each domain value to exactly one range value.

This relation is not a function; domain value 2 corresponds to two range values: *a* and *b*.

If you know an input value for a function, you can find the corresponding output value.

If $f(x) = 9x - 5$, find $f(-3)$.

$f(-3) = 9(-3) - 5$ ← Substitute -3 for x.

$= -27 - 5$ ← Simplify.

$= -32$

The ordered pair $(-3, -32)$ satisfies $f(x) = 9x - 5$.

Write the domain and range of each relation and tell whether the relation is a function.

1.

x	y
−4	−16
−2	−4
0	0
2	−4
4	−16

Domain: {−4, −2, 0, 2, 4}
Range: {−16, −4, 0, −4, −16}
function; every input value has exactly one output value.

2.

x	y
−2	−6
−1	−3
0	0
1	−3
2	−6

____

3.

x	y
−2	−5
−1	−3
0	0
1	1
1	2

____

4.

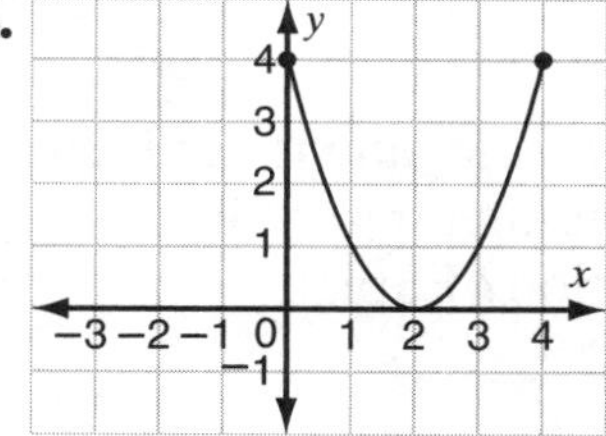

____

5.

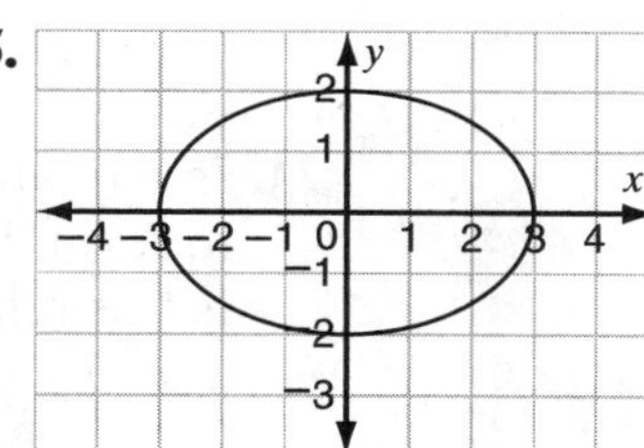

____

6.

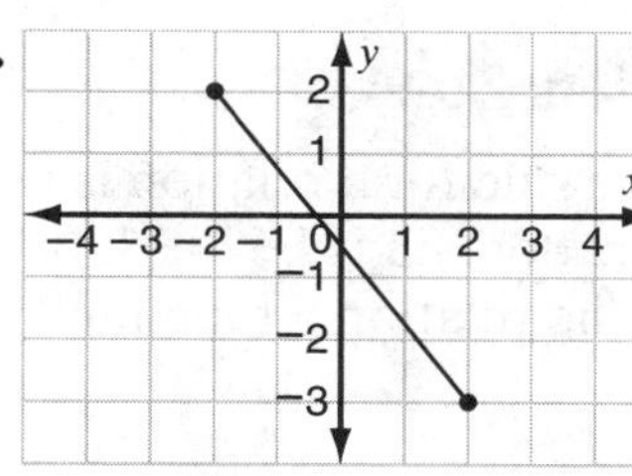

____

7.

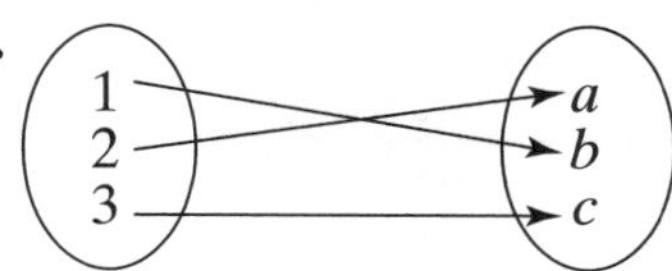

____

8.

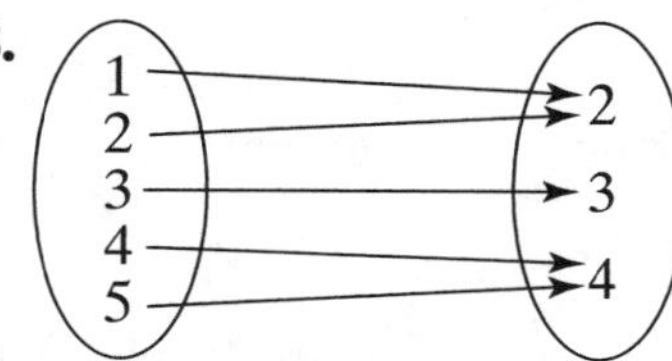

____

9.

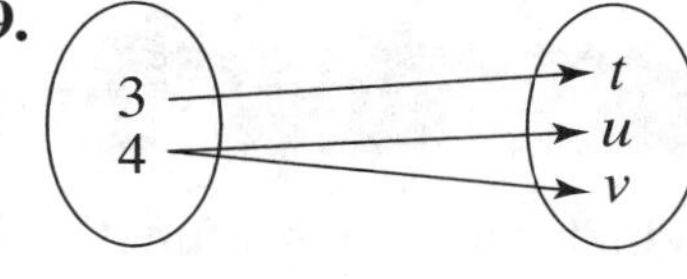

____

Use with SOURCEBOOK Lesson 4-2, pages 96–99.

Circle the best answer.

10. Given the relation $P = \{(-3, 4), (-2, 5), (2, 2), (x, 5)\}$, which replacement for x makes this relation a function?

a. -3 **b.** -2
c. 2 **d.** 3

11. Given the relation $G = \{(-1, 3), (x, 4), (3, 7), (4, 8)\}$, which replacement for x makes this relation a function?

a. -1 **b.** 0
c. 3 **d.** 4

12. The relation $K = \{(-2, 4), (-1, -2), (-1, 5), (0, 1), (1, 3)\}$ is *not* a function. Omitting which ordered pair will make the resulting set a function?

a. $(-2, 4)$ **b.** $(-1, -2)$
c. $(0, 1)$ **d.** $(1, 3)$

13. The relation $W = \{(-1, 3), (0, 2), (1, 1), (2, 2), (2, 3)\}$ is *not* a function. Omitting which ordered pair will make the resulting set a function?

a. $(-1, 3)$ **b.** $(0, 2)$
c. $(1, 1)$ **d.** $(2, 3)$

Evaluate each expression, given $f(x) = 5x - 2$, $g(x) = x^2 + 3x - 2$, and $h(x) = \sqrt{x - 1}$.

14. $f(3) + g(2)$

$f(3) = 5(3) - 2 = 13$
$g(2) = (2)^2 + 3(2) - 2 = 8$
$f(3) + g(2) = 13 + 8 = 21$

21

15. $f(-2) + h(1)$

16. $4[f(7) - h(26)]$

17. $5[f(9) - h(37)]$

18. $\dfrac{g(-4) - f(-3)}{h(50)}$

19. $\dfrac{g(-3) - f(-4)}{h(65)}$

Problem Solving

20. The rule for a relation is $y = (x + 1)^2$. The domain is $\{-2, -1, 0, 1, 2, 3\}$. Is the relation a function?

21. In a relation, each domain value is doubled to form the corresponding range value. Is this relation a function? Explain.

TEST PREPARATION

22. Which relation is a function?

A. $\{(-2, 3), (-1, 4), (0, 5), (0, 6), (1, 7)\}$

B. $\{(-1, 5), (0, 5), (1, 5), (2, 5), (3, 5)\}$

C. $\{(-5, -5), (-5, -4), (-5, 1), (-5, 2), (-5, 3)\}$

D. $\{(-2, 1), (-2, 0), (1, 0), (1, 1), (1, -3)\}$

4-3 Write Function Rules

Name ______________________ Date ____________

Write a function rule for the total cost of \$200 plus \$15 per hour.

Let h represent number of hours. ← independent variable
Let c represent total cost. ← dependent variable (varies with hours)
You know: total cost = basic fee + hourly charges
$c = 200 + 15h$ ← function rule relating h and c

Because c depends on h, c is a function of h.
$c(h) = 200 + 15h$ ← function rule in function notation

Identify the independent and dependent variables in each situation. Then use function notation to express each relationship.

1. The larger a drain, the faster water empties from a tank.

ℓ: the size of the drain (independent variable)
w: the water that empties (dependent variable)
$w(\ell)$

2. The bigger a fan blade, the more wind generated.

____

3. The faster Kyle types, the less time it takes to type a report.

____

4. The faster Mr. Harris drives, the less time it takes to get home.

____

Write a function for each situation. Use function notation.

5. the area of a square, A, when you know the length of the side, s

s is the independent variable and A is the dependent variable.
$A = s^2$
$A(s) = s^2$

6. the perimeter of a square, P, when you know the length of the side, s

____

7. the total cost, c, for h hours at an hourly rate of \$12.50 per hour

____

8. the total cost, c, for h hours at an hourly rate of \$25.75 per hour

____

9. the distance traveled, d, at a speed of s miles per hour for 5 hours

____

10. the distance traveled, d, for h hours at a speed of 55 miles per hour

____

Write a rule that expresses the relationship for each pair of input and output values in each table.

11.

x	y
−0.25	−0.375
0	0
1.2	1.8
5.75	8.625

Pattern: $-0.25(1.5) = -0.375$
$0(1.5) = 0$
$1.2(1.5) = 1.8$
$5.75(1.5) = 8.625$
$y = 1.5x$

12.

a	b
−0.23	0.253
−0.20	0.22
0	0
2.1	−2.31

____

13.

f	g
−1.15	−0.5
−0.322	−0.14
0	0
6.21	2.7

____

14.

p	q
−109.3	4.372
0	0
0.525	−0.021
4.450	−0.178

____

15.

ℓ	m
−1.5	−2
−0.5	0
0	1
1.5	4

____

16.

q	r
−5.5	24
−1.2	6.8
0	2
2.4	−7.6

____

17.

x	y
−5	24
−2	3
0	−1
7	48

____

18.

g	h
−3	−26
0	1
4	65
6	217

____

19.

m	n
−5	6.25
0	0
3	2.25
11	30.25

____

Solve.

20. Harriet pays $35.99 per month and $0.75 per text message for her cell phone. What rule, in function notation, models Harriet's total monthly cost, c, if she writes t text messages?

____

21. Denise pays $350 for seed and $3.50 per acre for fuel to plant a field. What rule, in function notation, models Denise's total cost, c, to plant a acres?

____

CRITICAL THINKING

22. Write a rule that expresses the relationship for each pair of x- and y-values in the table.

x	−3	−2	−1	0	1	2
y	26	7	0	−1	0	7

____

4-4 Arithmetic Sequences

Name ______________________ Date __________

Determine if each sequence is arithmetic. If it is, find a_{20}, the 20th term of the sequence.

5, 10, 20, 40,...

Test for common difference, d.

$10 - 5 = 5$

$20 - 10 = 10$ ← $10 \neq 5$, so there is no common difference.

The sequence is *not* arithmetic.

10, 7, 4, 1, −2,...

Test for the common difference, d.

$7 - 10 = -3$

$4 - 7 = -3$ ← so the common difference, $d = -3$.

$a_n = a_1 + (n - 1)d$ ← Write the rule to find the nth term.

$a_{20} = 10 + (20 - 1)(-3)$ ← Substitute 20 for n, 10 for a_1, and −3 for d.

$a_{20} = 10 + (19)(-3)$ ← Simplify.

$a_{20} = 10 + (-57) = -47$

Determine whether each sequence could be arithmetic. If arithmetic, use a pattern to write the next four terms.

1. 2, 11, 20, 29, ...

$11 - 2 = 9$; $20 - 11 = 9$
$29 - 20 = 9$; $29 + 9 = 38$
$38 + 9 = 47$; $47 + 9 = 56$
$56 + 9 = 65$
arithmetic; 38, 47, 56, 65

2. 1, 3, 9, 27, ...

____

3. $x + 2, 2x + 4, 3x + 6, 4x + 8, \ldots$

____

4. $y + 5, 3y + 9, 5y + 13, 7y + 17, \ldots$

____

5. 0.112, 1.12, 11.2, 112, ...

____

6. $\frac{3}{4}, \frac{3}{2}, \frac{9}{4}, 3, \ldots$

____

Find the indicated term of each arithmetic sequence.

7. a_{10} of 11, 5, −1, −7, ...

$d = 5 - 11 = -6$
$a_n = a_1 + (n - 1)d$
$a_{10} = 11 + (10 - 1)(-6)$
$a_{10} = 11 + 9(-6) = 11 - 54$
$a_{10} = -43$

8. a_{10} of 15, 7, −1, −9, ...

____

9. a_{50} of 0.2, 0.4, 0.6, 0.8, ...

____

10. a_{50} of 0.1, 0.4, 0.7, 1.0, ...

____

11. a_9 of $\frac{1}{3}, \frac{2}{3}, 1, \frac{4}{3}, \ldots$

____

12. a_{10} of $\frac{1}{8}, \frac{1}{2}, \frac{7}{8}, \frac{5}{4}, \ldots$

____

Use with SOURCEBOOK Lesson 4-4, pages 102–105.

Write a function rule for the nth term of each arithmetic sequence.

13. 1, 4, 7, 10, ...

$d = 4 - 1 = 3$
$a_n = 1 + (n - 1)3$
$a_n = 1 + 3n - 3$
$a_n = 3n - 2$

14. −1, 1, 3, 5, ...

15. 6, 11, 16, 21, ...

16. −7, −15, −23, −31, ...

17. −2.3, 1.7, 5.7, 9.7, ...

18. −7.6, −9.6, −11.6, −13.6, ...

19. $\frac{9}{2}, \frac{17}{2}, \frac{25}{2}, \frac{33}{2}, \ldots$

20. $\frac{10}{3}, \frac{19}{3}, \frac{28}{3}, \frac{37}{3}, \ldots$

21. $\frac{1}{2}, 0.3, \frac{1}{10}, -0.1, \ldots$

Solve.

22. Yuri is training for a marathon. He ran 2.5 km the first week and increased his distance by 1.5 km each week. How many weeks will it take him to run 13 km?

23. A tractor trailer travels 315 miles the first day of a trip. Each day thereafter it travels another 105 miles. What is the first day on which it will have traveled more than 1000 miles?

Problem Solving

24. Yolanda puts some money aside for an MP3 player and saves an additional $5.50 each month thereafter. If she saves $64.50 after one year, how much did she originally put aside?

25. Bhavin buys a tree sapling with a height of 5 cm. After 6 months it has grown to be 47 cm tall. If it continues growing at this average rate, how tall will the tree be 14 months after Bhavin bought it?

MENTAL MATH

26. 52(48)

27. 2(19)(15)

28. $3\frac{2}{3} + \left(6\frac{1}{2} + 8\frac{1}{3}\right)$

4-5 Geometric Sequences

Name ______________________ Date __________

Determine if each sequence is geometric. If it is, find the next term and the 10th term of the sequence.

6, 6, 12, 36, …

$6 \div 6 = 1$
$12 \div 6 = 2$ ← $2 \neq 1$; no common ratio.

The sequence is *not* geometric.

Remember: In a geometric sequence, each term after the first is found by *multiplying* the previous term by a constant (called the common ratio, r, with $r \neq 0$ or 1).

If a_1 is the first term, the nth term of a geometric sequence is: $a_n = a_1 \bullet r^{n-1}$

40, 20, 10, 5, …

$\frac{a_2}{a_1} = \frac{20}{40} = \frac{1}{2}; \frac{a_3}{a_2} = \frac{10}{20} = \frac{1}{2}; \frac{a_4}{a_3} = \frac{5}{10} = \frac{1}{2}$

So the sequence appears to be geometric.

Next term: $5 \bullet \frac{1}{2} = \frac{5}{2}$.

nth term: $a_n = a_1 r^{(n-1)}$

$a_{10} = 40\left(\frac{1}{2}\right)^{10-1}$ ← Substitute 10 for n, 40 for a_1, and $\frac{1}{2}$ for r.

$a_{10} = 40\left(\frac{1}{512}\right) = \frac{5}{64}$

Determine whether each sequence could be geometric, arithmetic, or neither. If geometric, use a pattern to write the next four terms.

1. 380, 38, 3.8, 0.38, …

$\frac{38}{380} = \frac{1}{10}, \frac{3.8}{38} = \frac{1}{10}, \frac{0.38}{3.8} = \frac{1}{10}$

$0.38 \bullet \frac{1}{10} = 0.038, 0.038 \bullet \frac{1}{10} = 0.0038$

$0.0038 \bullet \frac{1}{10} = 0.00038, 0.00038 \bullet \frac{1}{10} = 0.000038$

geometric; 0.038, 0.0038, 0.00038, 0.000038

2. 0.13, 1.3, 13, 130, …

____

3. 5, 6, 8, 11, …

____

4. $\frac{1}{2}, \frac{1}{6}, -\frac{1}{6}, -\frac{1}{2}, \ldots$

____

Find the indicated term of each geometric sequence.

5. a_7 of $\frac{1}{16}, \frac{1}{4}, 1, 4, \ldots$

$\frac{\frac{1}{4}}{\frac{1}{16}} = 4; a_n = a_1 \bullet r^{n-1}$

$a_7 = \frac{1}{16}(4)^{7-1} = \frac{1}{16}(4)^6 = \frac{4096}{16}$

256

6. a_8 of $\frac{1}{81}, \frac{1}{27}, \frac{1}{9}, \frac{1}{3}, \ldots$

____

7. a_9 of 800, 400, 200, 100, …

____

8. a_9 of 1600, 400, 100, 25, …

____

9. a_{10} of 1, −2, 4, −8, …

____

10. a_{10} of −2, 8, −32, 128, …

____

Find the indicated term of each geometric sequence.

11. a_7 of 9, 45, 225, 1125, …

12. a_7 of 96, 144, 216, 324, …

13. a_6 of 82, −123, 184.5, 276.75, …

14. a_6 of 18, 5.4, 1.62, 0.486, …

15. a_6 of 24, 9.6, 3.84, 1.536, …

16. a_{20} of $b, b^5, b^9, b^{13}, \ldots$

Write a recursive formula for the *n*th term of each geometric sequence.

17. 16, −12.8, 10.24, −8.192, …

$a_n = ra_{n-1}$
$r = -12.8 \div 16 = -0.8$
$a_n = -0.8 \cdot a_{n-1}$

18. $2, \frac{10}{3}, \frac{50}{9}, \frac{250}{27}, \ldots$

19. $z^{12}, z^8, z^4, 1, \ldots$

Solve.

20. The population of a town decreased by two thirds each year for 3 years. If it started with a population of 540,000, what is the population after 3 years?

21. Biology A cell doubles every half-hour. If a lab sample started with 2 cells, how many cells are in the sample 10 hours later?

Problem Solving

22. A ball is dropped from a height of 36 ft. After 2 bounces it reaches a height of 4 ft. What height will the ball reach after another bounce?

23. Sono marks the middle of a board. He makes another mark half-way between the first mark and the end of the board. He makes more marks using the same pattern 6 more times. If the distance between the end of the board and the nearest mark is $\frac{1}{2}$ in., how many feet long is the board?

SPIRAL REVIEW

24. Solve. $3x + 19 = 10$

25. Solve. $|x + 8| = -12$

26. Solve. $11b + 13 \geq -4b + 28$

4-6 Problem-Solving Strategy:
Review of Strategies

Read Plan Solve Check

Name ______________________________ Date ______________

Solve using a strategy that you have used before.

1. In a 64-team single elimination basketball tournament, how many games must be scheduled to decide the winner?

____

2. A highway sensor recorded 16 vehicles—only 4-wheeled cars and 2-wheeled motorcycles—and accounted for exactly 60 tires. How many of these vehicles were motorcycles?

____

3. At 8 A.M., a town clock chimes 8 times for 8 seconds. If it chimes at the same rate, how long does it take to chime 12 times at 12 P.M.?

____

4. Can the digits of the number 8,137,542 be rearranged so that the resulting 7-digit number is a prime number?

____

5. Multiply: 0.0603060306030603 … • 0.66666666 …

____

6. A pipe is cut into 2 equal parts. One of these is shipped to Cleveland. Three-fourths of the remaining half is cut into 9 equal parts. What fraction of the original pipe does each one of these nine parts comprise?

7. An item costs \$18.78. A coupon allows the customer to take 40% off the cost. Sales tax is $7\frac{3}{4}$%. Does it matter to the customer whether tax or the coupon is applied first? Explain.

8. What is the area of the shaded region inside the 12-by-16 rectangle?

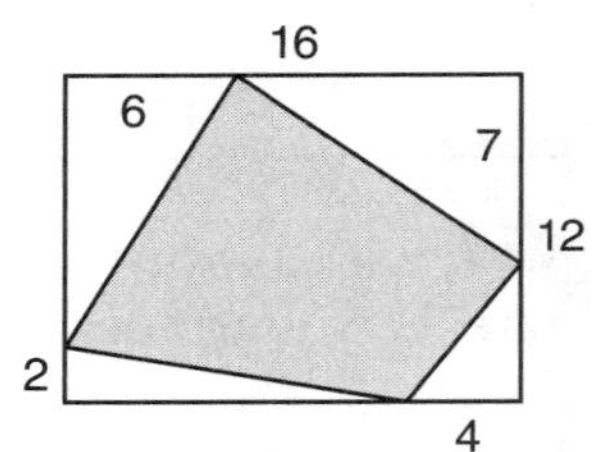

9. Can you find digits A, B, C, and D so that the number appearing as AB,CD4 is a sum of two positive integer powers of 6? Explain.

10. Is it possible to cover the checkerboard with tiles of this shape: ☐☐? Explain.

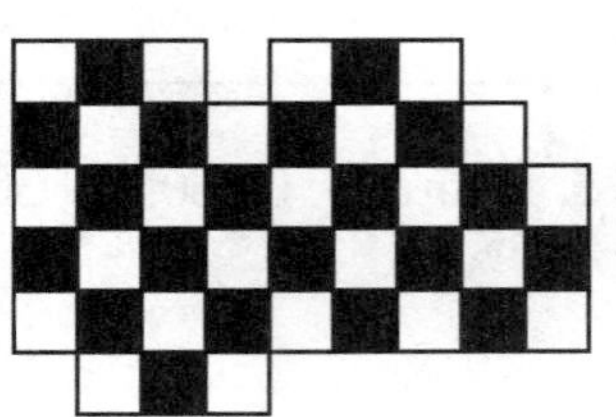

Enrichment:
Step Functions

Name ______________________ Date __________

Use your handheld to compare the graph of each function to $f(x) = \lfloor x \rfloor$. How does each constant affect the graph?

> **Remember:** For any number x, $\lfloor x \rfloor$ is the greatest integer less than or equal to x.

$f(x) = \lfloor x \rfloor + 4$

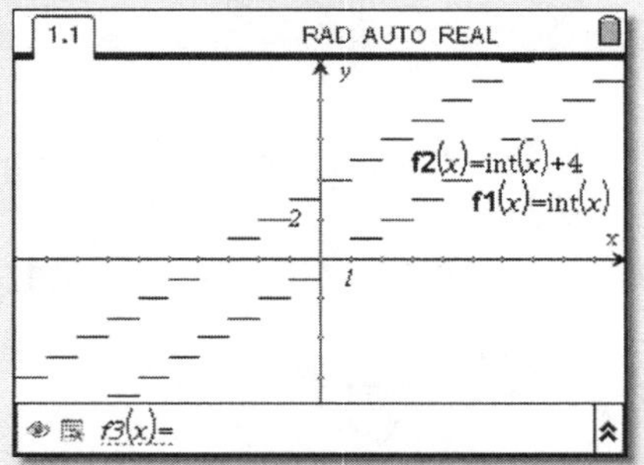

The graph shifted *up* 4 units.

$f(x) = \lfloor x \rfloor - 4$

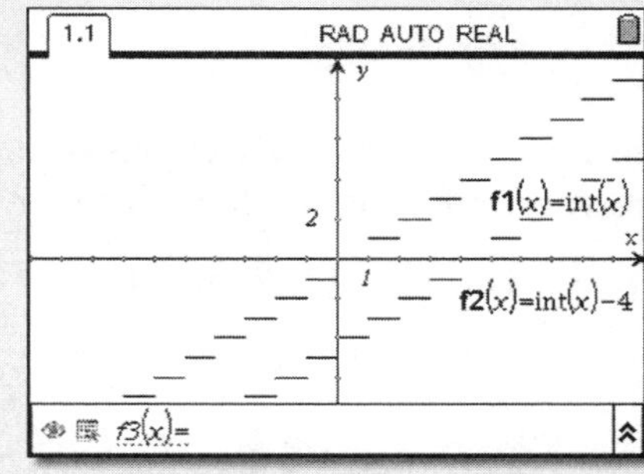

The graph shifted *down* 4 units.

For $f(x) = \lfloor x \rfloor + k$: When k is greater than 0, the graph of $f(x) = \lfloor x \rfloor$ is shifted *up* k units.
When k is less than 0, the graph of $f(x) = \lfloor x \rfloor$ is shifted *down* k units.

Complete each table to show the value of the indicated function. Use your handheld to compare the graph of each function to $f(x) = \lfloor x \rfloor$. How does each constant affect the graph?

1.

x	$\lfloor x + 5 \rfloor$	$f(x)$
$1\frac{1}{2}$	$\lfloor 6\frac{1}{2} \rfloor$	6
$\frac{1}{2}$	$\lfloor 5\frac{1}{2} \rfloor$	5
0	$\lfloor 5 \rfloor$	5
$-\frac{1}{2}$	$\lfloor 4\frac{1}{2} \rfloor$	4
$-1\frac{1}{2}$	$\lfloor 3\frac{1}{2} \rfloor$	3

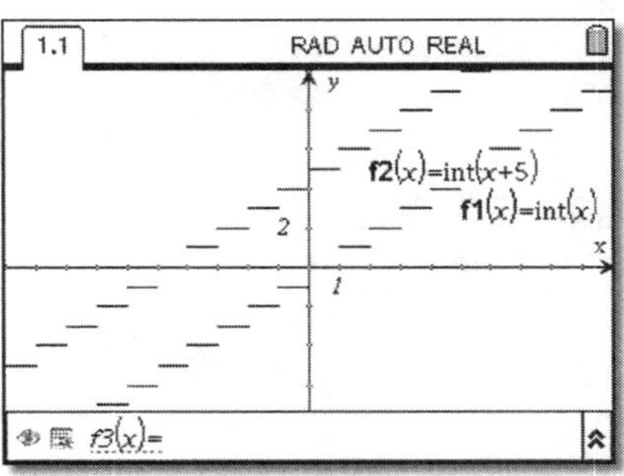

The graph shifted left 5 units;
For $f(x) = \lfloor x + k \rfloor$, the graph $f(x) = \lfloor x \rfloor$ is shifted left k units.

2.

x	$\lfloor x - 3 \rfloor$	$f(x)$
$1\frac{1}{2}$		
$\frac{1}{2}$		
0		
$-\frac{1}{2}$		
$-1\frac{1}{2}$		

1.1 RAD AUTO REAL
f1(x)=int(x)
f2(x)=int(x−3)
f3(x)=

____

3.

x	$\lfloor -x \rfloor$	$f(x)$
$1\frac{1}{2}$		
$\frac{1}{2}$		
0		
$-\frac{1}{2}$		
$-1\frac{1}{2}$		

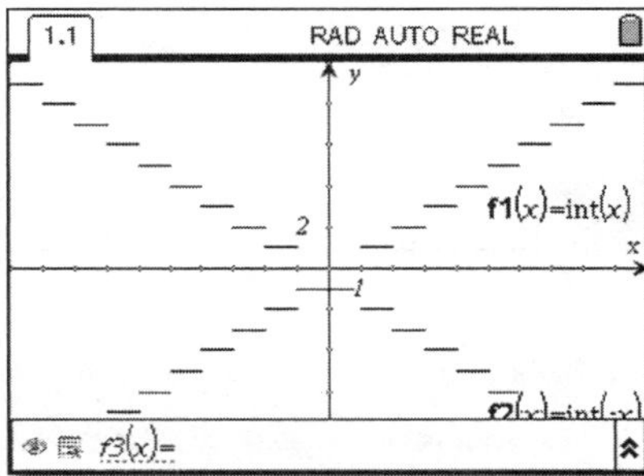

____

Use your handheld to compare the graph of each function to $f(x) = \lfloor x \rfloor$. How does each constant affect the graph?

4. $f(x) = -\lfloor x \rfloor$ **5.** $f(x) = \lfloor 2 - x \rfloor$ **6.** $f(x) = \lfloor -2 - x \rfloor$

______ ______ ______

Find the value of each expression. (*Hint:* For any number x, the value of $\lceil x \rceil$ is the least integer greater than or equal to x.)

7. $\lceil 13.8 \rceil$ **8.** $\lceil 11.3 \rceil$ **9.** $\lceil -12.9 \rceil$ **10.** $\lceil -14.7 \rceil$ **11.** $\lceil 0.75 \rceil$

14 ______ ______ ______ ______

Solve each problem. Then classify the function.

12. The graph shows the relationship between the number of minutes a plumber works and the amount the plumber charges. How much does the plumber charge if he works 15 min? 65 min? 180 min? 500 min?

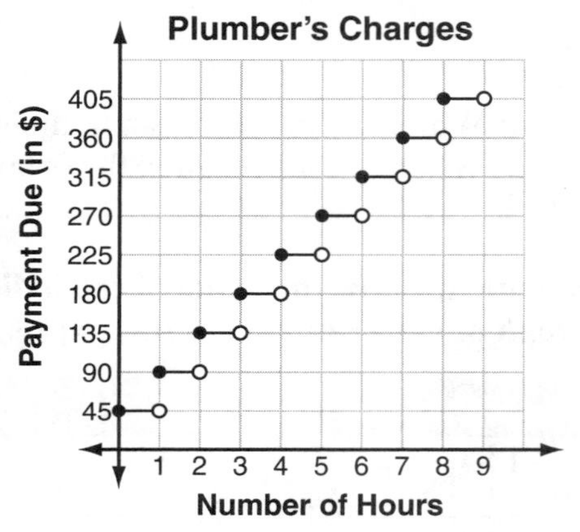

______

13. The graph shows the relationship between the weight of a parcel and the cost of shipping as charged by ABC Post. What is the shipping cost of a parcel weighing 13 oz? 1 lb? 3 lb 7 oz? 5.25 lb?

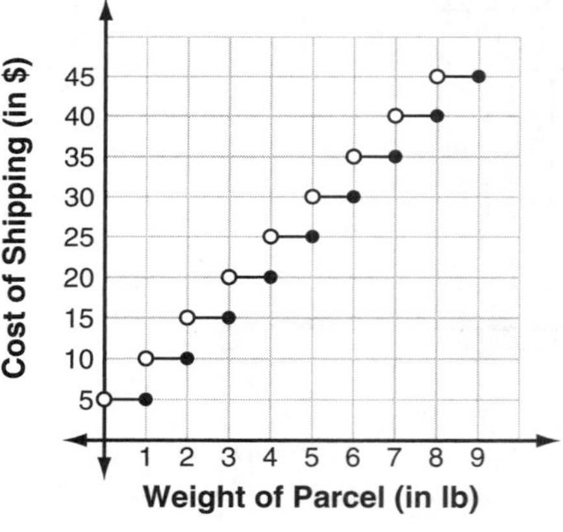

______

WRITE ABOUT IT

14. Explain the difference in the type of function indicated by $f(x) = \lfloor x + 2 \rfloor$ and $f(x) = \lceil x + 2 \rceil$.

______

______

Test Prep: Gridded-Response Questions

Strategy: Apply Mathematical Reasoning

Name ______________________________ Date ______________

Look for relationships in the given text, diagrams, or tables in a question.

To solve a gridded-response question, try using the following strategies.

- Underline important words.
- Restate the question.
- Apply appropriate rules, definitions, properties, or strategies.
- Analyze your answers.

Record your answers on the gridded-response answer sheet. Explain how you used strategies. Show all your work. *TIP: Use all the time you are given.*

1. What is the next term in the sequence?

$-3, 6, -18, 72, -360\ldots$

Answer: ______________________

2. What is the eighth term in the sequence?

48, 24, 12, 6…

Answer: ______________________

3. How many dots will make up the fifth figure?

Answer: ______________________

4. Use the function table below. What is $f(4.8)$?

x	0	0.1	0.2	0.3
$f(x)$	0.5	0.8	1.1	1.4

Answer: ______________________

5. Today, Michelle puts 1 cent in a jug. Tomorrow, she adds 2 cents. On the next day, she adds 3 cents. If she continues this pattern for 10 more days, how many cents will she have?

Answer: ______________________

6. What is the next term in the sequence?

$\frac{1}{5}, \frac{3}{5}, 1\frac{4}{5}, 5\frac{2}{5}\ldots$

Answer: ______________________

7. Using the table, how many cups of flour are needed for 28 servings?

servings	4	6	8	10
cups	$\frac{2}{3}$	1	$1\frac{1}{3}$	$1\frac{2}{3}$

Answer: ______________________

8. What is the perimeter of the sixth figure in the sequence, if $p = 42$ for the first figure?

Answer: ______________________

Use with SOURCEBOOK Test Prep Lesson, page 104.

Vocabulary Development

Name ______________________ Date __________

Chapter 4 Vocabulary

arithmetic sequence	function notation	output value
common difference	function rule	range of a relation
common ratio	geometric sequence	recursive formula
dependent variable	independent variable	relation
domain of a relation	input value	sequence
function	ordered pair	*n*th term of the sequence

From the vocabulary list above, choose the term(s) that best complete each sentence. Write the term(s) in the space(s) provided.

1. A(n) ______________________ is a special type of relation that pairs each domain value with exactly one range value.

2. An ordered set of elements that follows a pattern is called a(n) ______________________.

3. The x-value of a relation is the ______________________.

4. The ______________________ is denoted by a_n.

5. A relationship that is represented by a set of ordered pairs is called a(n) ______________________.

6. A rule for calculating a new term of a sequence from the term preceding it is called a(n) ______________________.

7. The y-value of a relation is the ______________________.

8. A(n) ______________________ describes a function.

9. A sequence with a common difference is a(n) ______________________.

Tell whether each statement is *true* or *false*. If it is false, change it to make it true.

10. Each new term of a geometric sequence is found by adding the common difference to the preceding term.

____

11. In the expression $y = 3x - 9$, x is the independent variable.

____

Use after SOURCEBOOK Lessons 4-1–4-5, pages 94–109.

Practice Chapter 4 Test

Name ______________________________ Date ______________

Write the domain and range of each relation and tell whether the relation is a function.

1.

x	y
−3	−8
−1	−2
0	1
2	7
4	13

2. 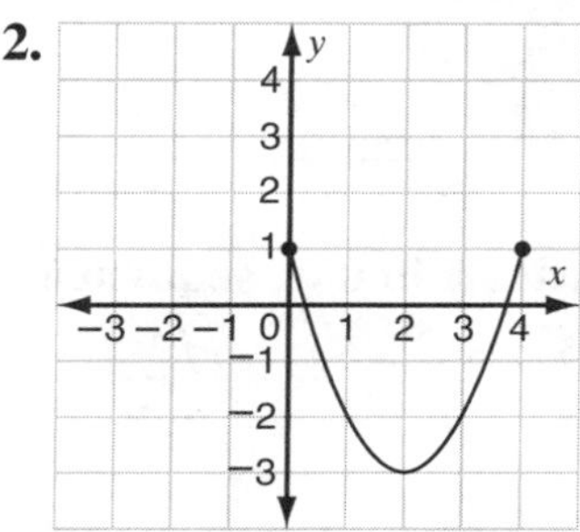

3. 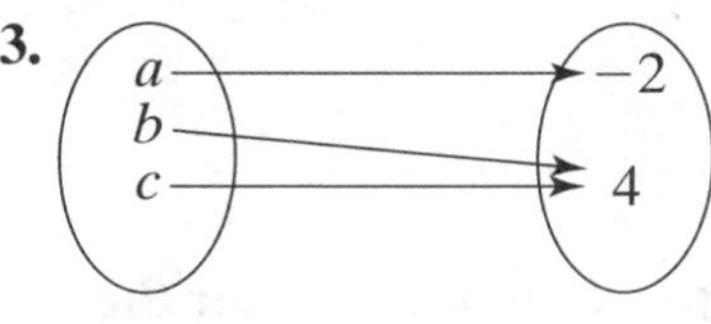

4. Does the ordered pair (2, 3) belong to the relation $y = x^3$?

5. Does the ordered pair (3, −36) belong to the relation $y = -4x^2$?

6. Given the relation $K = \{(-7, 9), (x, 8), (-6, 4), (-5, 2)\}$, which replacement for x makes this relation a function?

a. −7 **c.** −5
b. −6 **d.** −4

Write a function rule for each situation. Use function notation.

7. the area of a right isosceles triangle, A, when both base and height are s

8. the total cost, c, for h hours at an hourly rate of $32.50 per hour

Write a rule that expresses the relationship for each pair of input and output values in each table.

9.

x	y
−3	6
−1	2
0	0
2	−4
4	−8

10.

x	y
−3	−21
−1	−7
0	0
2	14
4	28

11.

x	y
−3	−11
−1	−5
0	−2
2	4
4	10

12.

x	y
−3	−15
−1	−7
0	−3
2	5
4	13

Determine whether each sequence could be geometric, arithmetic, or neither. If geometric or arithmetic, write the next four terms.

13. 100, 50, 0, −50, …

14. 19, 18, 20, 19, …

15. 8, 4, 2, 1, …

Find the indicated term of each arithmetic sequence.

16. a_{10} of 20, 9, −2, −13, . . .

17. a_{100} of 2, 2.5, 3, 3.5, . . .

18. a_{10} of $\frac{2}{3}, \frac{4}{3}, 2, \frac{8}{3}, \ldots$

Write a function rule for the *n*th term of each arithmetic sequence.

19. 15, 18, 21, 24, . . .

20. −12, −17, −22, −27, . . .

21. 14.6, 16.9, 19.2, 21.5, . . .

Find the indicated term of each geometric sequence.

22. a_7 of $\frac{2}{27}, -\frac{2}{9}, \frac{2}{3}, -2, \ldots$

23. a_6 of 50, 70, 98, 137.2, . . .

24. a_9 of $\frac{5}{2}, \frac{5}{6}, \frac{5}{18}, \frac{5}{54}, \ldots$

Write a recursive formula for the *n*th term of each geometric sequence.

25. −48, 24, −12, 6, . . .

26. 80, 48, 28.8, 17.28, . . .

27. 5, 10, 20, 40, . . .

Problem Solving

28. Gloria opens a savings account in January with $275. Each month she increases her deposit by $10. How much money will she deposit the following December?

29. Philip bought a house for $420,000. It decreased 10% in value each year. What was Philip's house worth 3 years after he bought it?

Tell About It

Explain how you solve the problem. Show all your work.

30. Write the domain and range.
Is the relation a function?

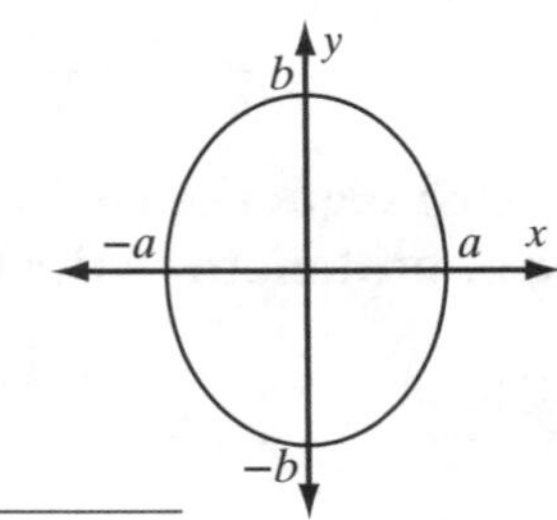

Cumulative Review: Chapters 1–4

Name ______________________________ Date ____________

Circle the best answer.

1. Which is an integer?

A. $\sqrt{147}$ **B.** 11.2

C. $-\frac{50}{5}$ **D.** $-\frac{35}{3}$

2. Which is the multiplicative inverse of $-\frac{2}{7}$?

F. $-\frac{7}{2}$ **G.** $-\frac{2}{7}$

H. $\frac{2}{7}$ **J.** $\frac{7}{2}$

3. Simplify.

$|-12| \bullet 4 - (6 - 4)^3$

A. −56
B. 40
C. 42
D. 52

4. Which algebraic expression represents "5 times the sum of *a* and *b*"?

F. $a + 5b$
G. $5(a - b)$
H. $5a + b$
J. $5(a + b)$

5. Which set is the same as the set below?

$\{d \mid d$ is a whole number and $d < 5\}$

A. $\{\ldots, -2, -1, 0, 1, 2, 3, 4\}$
B. $\{1, 2, 3, 4\}$
C. $\{0, 1, 2, 3, 4, 5\}$
D. $\{0, 1, 2, 3, 4\}$

6. Simplify.

$16f - 4(3f - 2) - 8f + 9$

F. $20f + 7$
G. $20f + 17$
H. $-4f + 17$
J. $-4f + 7$

7. Which is an open sentence?

A. $9x + 13 = 24$
B. $63n + 11$
C. $29 = 13 + 4^2$
D. $18 - 17 = -1$

8. Solve.

$19.6 = w - 2.8$

F. $w = 23.4$
G. $w = 22.4$
H. $w = 16.8$
J. $w = 17.2$

9. Solve.

$-26 = -2(4r - 7)$

A. $n = -5$
B. $n = -2$
C. $n = 2$
D. $r = 5$

10. Solve for *y*.

$9y + 5x = 11y - 8x$

F. $y = \frac{13}{2}x$ **G.** $y = \frac{13}{20}x$

H. $y = -\frac{13}{20}x$ **J.** $y = -\frac{13}{2}x$

11. Solve.

$|p + 9| = 12$

A. $\{p \mid p = 3\}$
B. $\{p \mid p = -3\}$
C. $\{p \mid p = -3, 3\}$
D. $\{p \mid p = -21, 3\}$

12. Solve.

$15(-4g + 8) + 6 = -1 - (9 - 8g)$

F. $g = 4$
G. $g = 2$
H. $g = -2$
J. $g = -4$

13. Which describes $\{y \mid y \geq -2\}$?

A. $(-2, \infty)$
B. $[-2, \infty)$
C. $(-\infty, -2)$
D. $(-\infty, -2]$

18. Which is the domain of the relation graphed below?

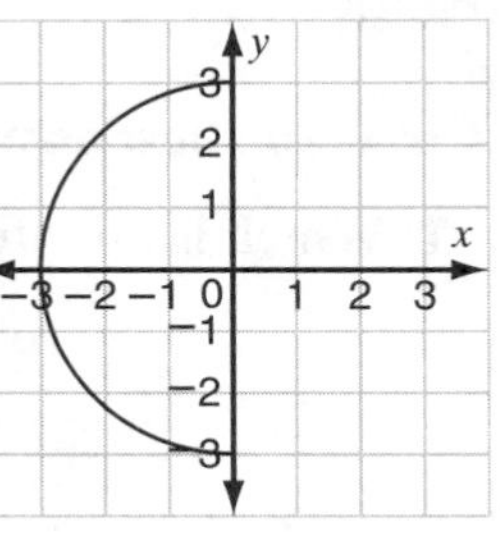

F. $\{x \mid -3 \leq x \leq 0\}$
G. $\{y \mid -3 \leq y \leq 0\}$
H. $\{x \mid -3 \leq x \leq 3\}$
J. $\{y \mid -3 \leq y \leq 3\}$

14. Solve.

$-4x + 7 > -5$

F. $x < 3$
G. $x > 3$
H. $x < -3$
J. $x > -3$

19. Which is an arithmetic sequence?

A. $\frac{2}{5}, \frac{3}{8}, \frac{4}{11}, \frac{5}{14}, \frac{6}{17}, \ldots$
B. $-15, -12, -13, -10, -11, \ldots$
C. $19, 38, 76, 152, 304, \ldots$
D. $24, 18, 12, 6, 0, \ldots$

15. Solve.

$-8 < 3x + 1 < 16$

A. $-3 > x > -5$
B. $-3 < x < 5$
C. $3 < x < 5$
D. $5 < x < 3$

20. Which is the recursive formula for the nth term of the sequence?

$12, 10, \frac{25}{3}, \frac{125}{18}, \frac{625}{108}, \ldots$

F. $a_n = 12 \bullet a_{n-1}$ **G.** $a_n = 10 \bullet a_{n-1}$
H. $a_n = \frac{5}{6} \bullet a_{n-1}$ **J.** $a_n = \frac{6}{5} \bullet a_{n-1}$

16. Solve for a:

$|3a - 6| + 6 \geq 9$

F. $-3 \leq a \leq 3$ **G.** $a \leq 1$ OR $a \geq 3$
H. $a \leq -1$ OR $a \geq 3$ **J.** $-1 \leq a \leq 3$

21. Which is a function rule for the nth term of the sequence?

$2, -3, -8, -13, -18, \ldots$

A. $a_n = -5n - 7$ **B.** $a_n = 5n - 3$
C. $a_n = 2n - 5$ **D.** $a_n = -5n + 7$

17. Which inequality is graphed below?

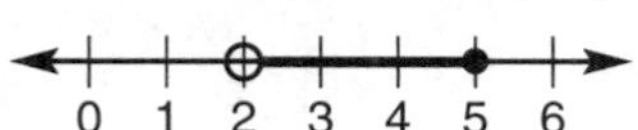

A. $2 \leq x \leq 5$ **B.** $2 \leq x < 5$
C. $2 < x \leq 5$ **D.** $2 < x < 5$

22. Which is the 8th term of the sequence?

$312, 31.2, 3.12, 0.312, \ldots$

F. 0.0312 **G.** 0.00312
H. 0.000312 **J.** 0.0000312

Tell About It

Explain how you solve each problem. Show all your work.

23. If $f(x) = -x^2 + 7x + 2$ and $g(x) = \sqrt{x + 3}$, how would you find $4f(2) - 6g(6)$?

24. If May invests $5,000 at 8% compounded annually, how much money will she have at the end of 8 years? Round to the nearest cent.

5-1 Identify Linear Functions and Their Graphs

Name ______________________________ Date ______________

Determine if $f(x) = x^3 - 1$ represents a linear function.

Make a function table. Look at the rate of change.

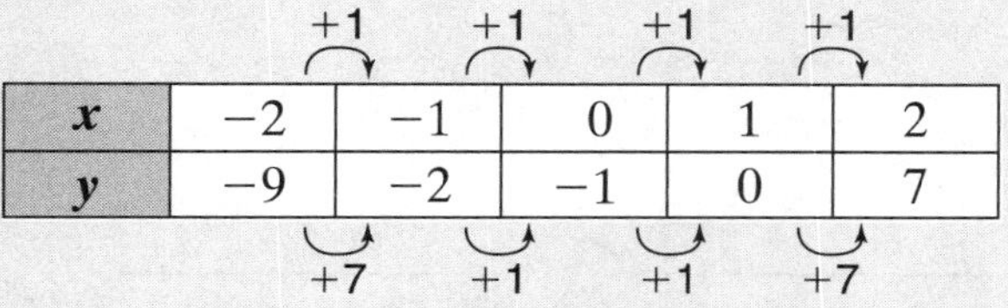

x	−2	−1	0	1	2
y	−9	−2	−1	0	7

The constant change of +1 in x does not correspond to a constant change in y.

Because the $\dfrac{\text{change in } y}{\text{change in } x}$ is not constant,

$f(x) = x^3 - 1$ is not a linear function.

Remember: You can also use a graph to determine if a function is linear. If the graph of a function is a nonvertical line, it is a linear function.

Find the slope of the line.

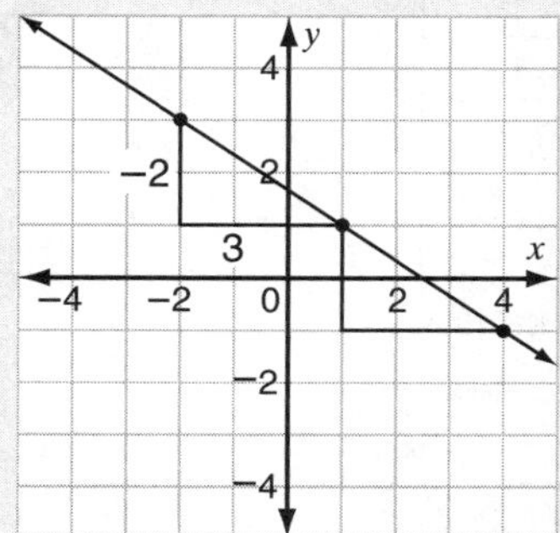

$$\text{Slope } (m) = \frac{\text{vertical change}}{\text{horizontal change}} = \frac{y_2 - y_1}{x_2 - x_1}$$

$$= \frac{1 - 3}{1 - (-2)}$$ ← Substitute (−2, 3) and (1, 1) into the formula, and simplify.

$$= \frac{-2}{3} = -\frac{2}{3}$$

The slope is $-\frac{2}{3}$; because the slope is negative, the line slants down from left to right.

Tell whether the relation represents a linear function. Explain *why* or *why not*. Find the slope of the line if it represents a linear function.

1.

x	y
−2	−6
−1	1
0	0
1	1
2	16

change in x constant: +1
change in y varies
16 − 1 = 15; 1 − 0 = 0
0 − 1 = −1; 1 − (−6) = 7
not a linear function

2.

x	y
−2	−32
−1	−1
0	0
1	−1
2	−32

____

3.

x	y
−2	−3
−1	−1
0	1
1	3
2	5

____

4.

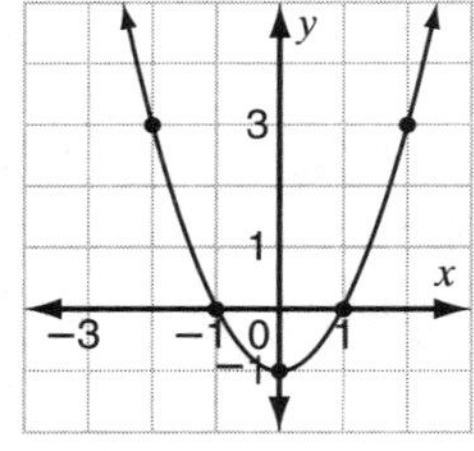

____

5.

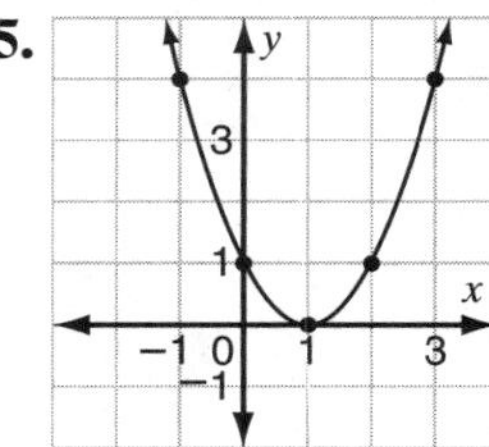

____

6.

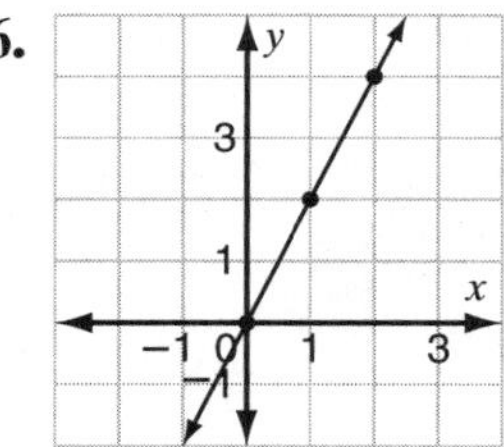

____

7.

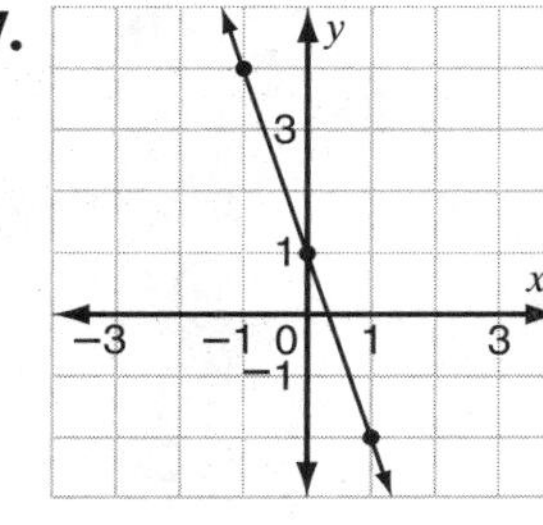

____

Use with SOURCEBOOK Lesson 5-1, pages 116–119.

Tell whether the relation represents a linear function. Explain *why* or *why not*. Find the slope of the line if it represents a linear function.

8. $y = -4x + 8$

x	y
−2	16
−1	12
0	8
1	4
2	0

linear function
constant rate: $\frac{-4}{1}$
slope (m) = −4

9. $y = -3x - 6$

10. $y = -2x^2 + 5$

11. $y = 3x^2 - 2$

12. $y = x - 2.5$

13. $y = -x - 3.9$

14. $y = \frac{2}{3}x - 1$

15. $y = \frac{1}{4}x + 1$

16. $y = -\frac{2}{5}x - 1$

17. $y = -\frac{1}{6}x + 1$

18. $y = 8$

19. $x = -4$

20. $y = -0.25x + 2$

21. $y = 0.125x - 2$

22. $y = -4x^3$

23. $y = \frac{x}{3} + 1$

Find the slope of the line for each graph.

24.

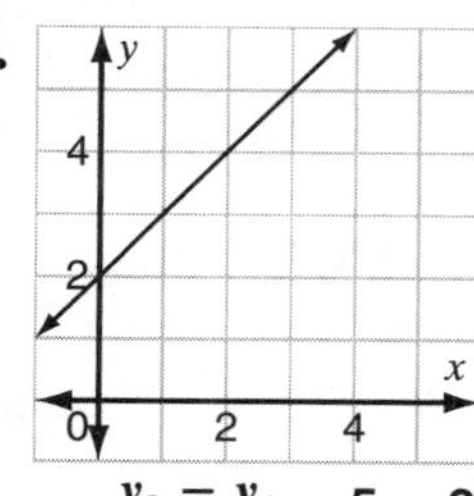

$$m = \frac{y_2 - y_1}{x_2 - x_1} = \frac{5 - 2}{3 - 0} = \frac{3}{3} = 1$$

The slope is 1.

25.

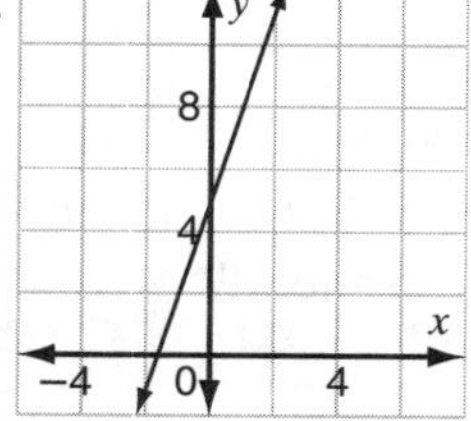

26.

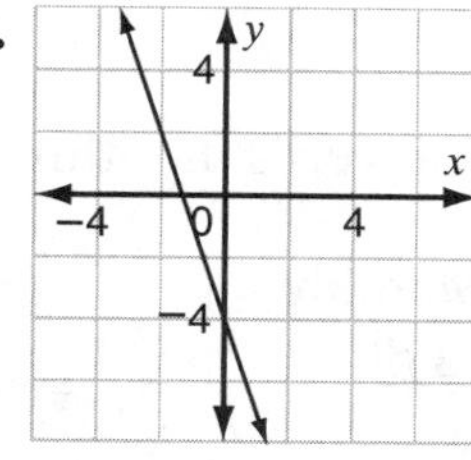

27.

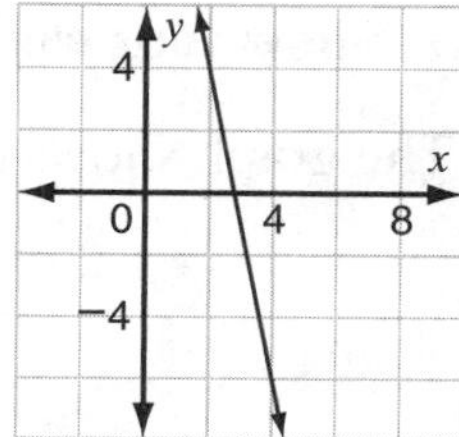

28.

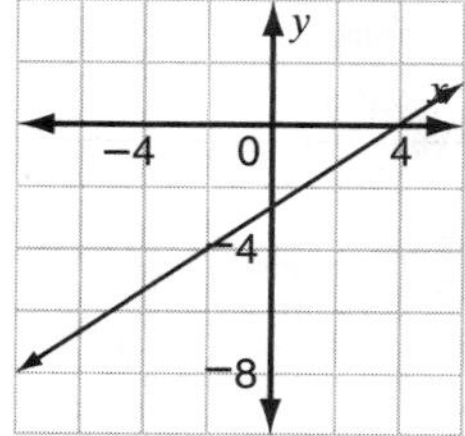

29.

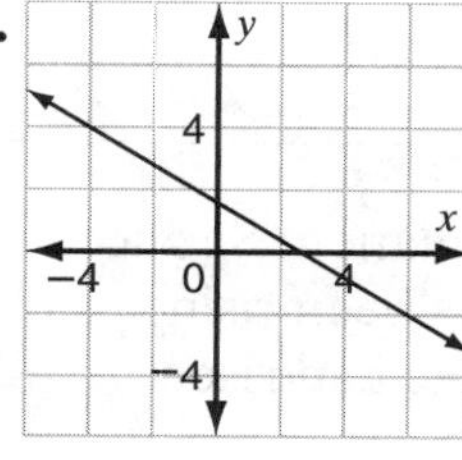

30.

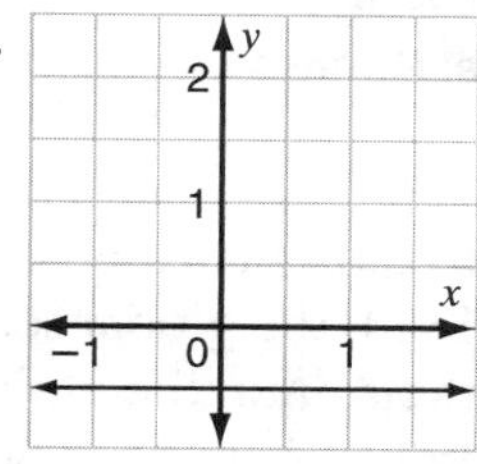

31.

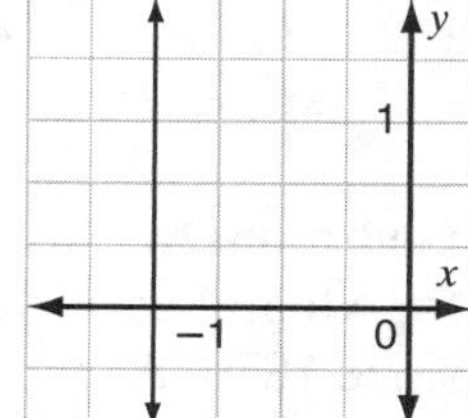

Find the slope of the line that contains the given points. Describe the line.

32. (3, 8) and (9, 6)

$$m = \frac{y_2 - y_1}{x_2 - x_1} = \frac{6 - 8}{9 - 3} = \frac{-2}{6} = -\frac{1}{3}$$

slope = $-\frac{1}{3}$; The line slants down from left to right.

33. (2, 7) and (11, 4)

34. (−8, −9) and (−6, −7)

35. (−11, −7) and (−8, −10)

36. (6.3, 8) and (6.3, 12)

37. $\left(-2, \frac{2}{5}\right)$ and $\left(4, \frac{2}{5}\right)$

38. (3.4, −2.5) and (5.4, −7.5)

39. (1.8, −3.9) and (5.8, −6.9)

40. $\left(2\frac{1}{5}, 3\frac{2}{3}\right)$ and (4, 6)

41. $\left(\frac{7}{3}, \frac{4}{3}\right)$ and $\left(-\frac{1}{3}, \frac{2}{3}\right)$

42. (2.7, 6.3) and (1, 8)

43. (−4.1, 7.1) and (9, −6)

Solve. Show your work.

44. The graph shows the cost of Keri's monthly calling plan on her cell phone.

a. What is the slope of this line? What does it mean?

b. This month, Keri used 28 additional minutes. How much was this month's bill?

45. Environment According to data provided by the Permanent Service for Mean Sea Level (PSMSL), the global sea level has been rising since 1870. According to their data, the global sea level had risen about 1 cm by 1920 and about 12 cm by 1980.

a. Using the rate for 1920 to 1980, at about what rate is the sea level rising?

b. At this rate, by how much will the global sea level have risen from 1870 to 2101?

Problem Solving

46. One side of a roof has a slope of $\frac{1}{4}$. The horizontal length of the roof is 48 ft. What is the height of the roof if the highest point is above the center of the horizontal length?

47. A hill rises 80 ft vertically over a 15-ft horizontal distance. A nearby hill rises at the same rate but is 300 ft tall. If the hills' highest points are above the center of the horizontal length of each hill, what is the horizontal length of the nearby hill?

CHALLENGE

48. A line with a slope of $\frac{7}{8}$ passes through the point $(-15, -13)$.
A different line with a slope of -1 passes through the point $(4, -2)$.
At what point do the two lines cross?

5-2 Direct Variation

Name ______________________ Date __________

Explain whether each equation represents a direct variation. If so, name the constant of variation.

$5y + 2x = 0$ ← Solve the equation for y.

$5y + 2x - 2x = 0 - 2x$ ← Subtract $2x$ from both sides.

$5y = -2x$

$\frac{5y}{5} = -\frac{2x}{5}$ ← Divide both sides by 5.

$y = -\frac{2}{5}x$

The equation is a direct variation, with a constant of variation of $-\frac{2}{5}$.

$3y - 7x = 11$ ← Solve the equation for y.

$3y - 7x + 7x = 11 + 7x$ ← Add $7x$ to both sides.

$3y = 7x + 11$

$\frac{3y}{3} = \frac{7x + 11}{3}$ ← Divide both sides by 3.

$y = \frac{7}{3}x + \frac{11}{3}$ ← not in the form $y = kx$

The equation is not a direct variation because it cannot be written in the form $y = kx$.

Explain whether each relation represents a direct variation. If so, make a graph and state the constant of variation.

1.

x	y
3	12
−5	−20
7	28

$k = \frac{y}{x} = \frac{12}{3} = \frac{-20}{-5} = \frac{28}{7} = 4$

yes; $k = 4$

2.

x	y
−3	−18
2	12
8	48

____

3.

x	y
−8	−23
5	14
9	26

____

4.

x	y
−11	−14
6	3
12	9

____

5.

x	y
−2	−8.8
3	13.2
10	44

____

6.

x	y
−5	−16
2	6.4
7	22.4

____

Explain whether each relation represents a direct variation. If so, state the constant of variation.

7. $y + 8x = 0$

$y = -8x$

Yes, the equation can be written in the form $y = kx$, where $k = -8$.

8. $y + 11x = 0$

____

9. $2y + 3x = 2.5$

____

10. $4y - 2x = 1.8$

____

11. $-3.8x = \frac{1}{2}y$

____

12. $-11.4x = -\frac{3}{4}y$

____

Solve. Show your work.

13. The value of y varies directly with x, and $y = 5$ when $x = 7$. Find x when $y = 2$.

$k = \frac{y}{x} = \frac{5}{7} = \frac{2}{x}$; $14 = 5x$; $x = 2.8$

14. The value of y varies directly with x, and $y = 4.1$ when $x = 3.4$. Find y when $x = 5.1$.

15. The value of y varies directly with x, and $y = -\frac{3}{8}$ when $x = \frac{1}{2}$. Find x when $y = 4$.

16. The value of y varies directly with x, and $y = \frac{2}{3}$ when $x = 5\frac{1}{4}$. Find y when $x = \frac{5}{8}$.

17. Geometry The area of a rectangle varies directly with its width. If the area is 30 square feet when its width is 8 feet, find the area when the width is 12 feet.

18. The distance traveled varies directly with the travel time. If 280 miles is traveled in 4 hours, find the travel time when the distance is 665 miles.

19. Currency The value of the U.S. dollar varies directly with the value of the Euro. If 14 U.S. dollars is worth about 9.11 Euros, about how many dollars are worth 100 Euros?

20. Physics *Hooke's Law* for an elastic string states that the distance a spring stretches varies directly as the force is applied. If a force of 250 Newtons (N) stretches a spring 8 cm, how much force (in N) is required to stretch the same spring 7.2 cm?

21. The cost of a pie dish varies directly as the square of its radius. If a pie dish has a diameter of 12 in. and costs $7.99, how much will a pie dish with a diameter of 9 in. cost?

TEST PREPARATION

22. What is the constant of variation in the equation $-7y + 2\frac{1}{3} = 5x + \left|-2\frac{1}{3}\right|$?

A. $-\frac{7}{5}$ **B.** $-\frac{5}{7}$ **C.** $\frac{5}{7}$ **D.** $\frac{7}{5}$

23. The value of y varies directly with x, and $y = -\frac{1}{2}$ when $x = \frac{3}{10}$. What is y if $x = 7$?

F. $\frac{35}{3}$ **G.** $\frac{3}{35}$ **H.** $-\frac{3}{35}$ **J.** $-\frac{35}{3}$

5-3 Equations in Slope-Intercept Form

Name ______________________ Date __________

Given the equation $y = \frac{3}{4}x - 2$, identify the slope and y-intercept.

Then graph the line.

$y = \frac{3}{4}x - 2$

Think
The slope-intercept form of a linear equation is $y = mx + b$, where m is the slope and b is the y-intercept.

So the slope $(m) = \frac{3}{4}$, and the y-intercept $(b) = -2$.

Remember: The ordered pair for the y-intercept of a line is always $(0, b)$.

Plot the y-intercept, $(0, -2)$.

$m = \frac{3}{4} = \frac{\text{vertical change}}{\text{horizontal change}}$

Count 3 units up and 4 units to the right from $(0, -2)$ to plot another point.

Draw the line through both points.

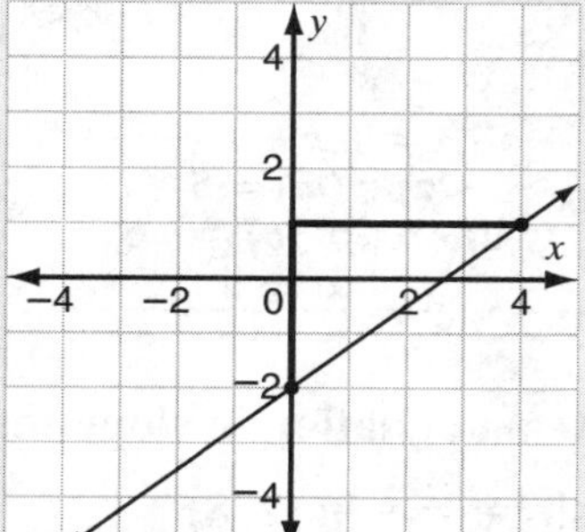

Write an equation in slope-intercept form for the line with the given slope and y-intercept.

1. slope: 4; y-intercept: -9

$y = mx + b$
$m = 4; b = -9$
$y = 4x - 9$

2. slope: 2; y-intercept: -5

____

3. slope: $-\frac{7}{2}$; y-intercept: $\frac{3}{5}$

____

4. slope: $-\frac{11}{9}$; y-intercept: $\frac{17}{5}$

____

5. slope: 2.5; y-intercept: -7.9

____

6. slope: 5.3; y-intercept: -4.1

____

Identify the slope and y-intercept of the line whose equation is given. Graph the equation on a separate sheet of paper.

7. $y = x + 8$

slope $(m) = 1$
y-intercept $(b) = 8$

8. $y = -x + 12$

____

9. $5y + 2x = -15$

____

10. $5x + 2y = 12$

____

11. $2x = -10$

____

12. $5y = -25$

____

13. $2x + 8y = 0$

____

14. $5x - y = 0$

____

15. $1.4x + 0.7y - 2 = 0.1$

____

Use with SOURCEBOOK Lesson 5-3, pages 122–125.

Write the slope-intercept form of the equation of the line shown.

16.

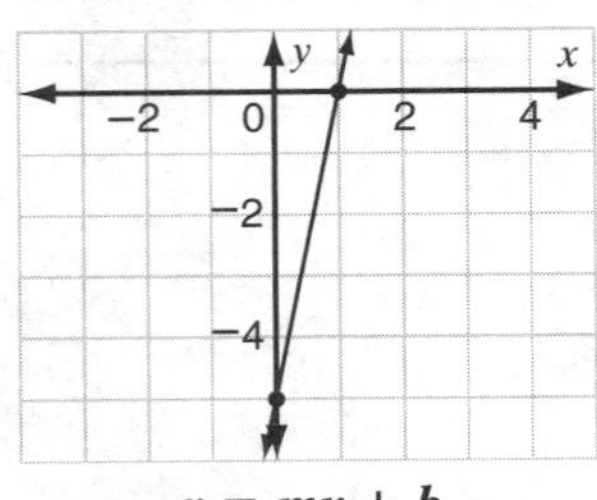

$y = mx + b$
slope (m) = 5
y-intercept (b) = −5
$y = 5x - 5$

17.

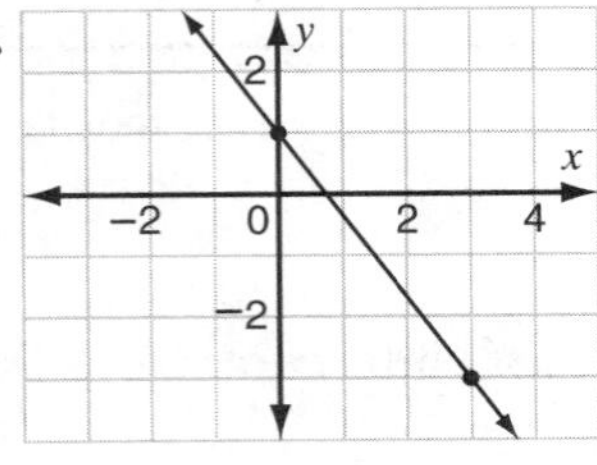

____

18.

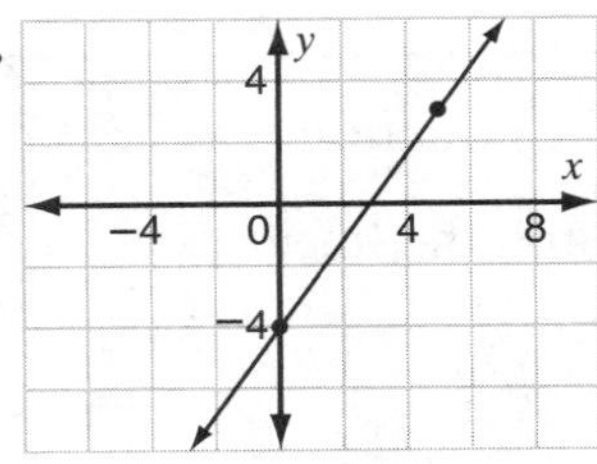

____

Write an equation in slope-intercept form with the given slope and containing the given point.

19. slope = −9; (2, 8)

$y = mx + b$; $8 = (-9)(2) + b$
$8 = -18 + b$; $26 = b$
$y = -9x + 26$

20. slope = $\frac{2}{9}$; (5, −2)

____

21. slope = 3.5; (−2.8, 2.9)

____

Solve. Show your work.

22. Wu earns $22 per hour plus a set-up fee of $45 to paint houses. Write an equation in slope-intercept form that represents how much Wu earns for painting houses.

____

23. Janice can install 8 fence posts per hour. Write an equation in slope-intercept form that represents how many fence posts Janice can install.

____

Problem Solving

24. Traveling Ava is driving at a constant rate. After $3\frac{3}{4}$ h of travel, she is 291.25 miles from home. After $5\frac{1}{2}$ h of travel, she is 422.5 miles from home. How many miles from home was she when she *began* driving?

____

25. Celine makes $10.75 per hour at her part-time job. If she wants to buy a pair of jeans for $22.75, a blouse for $35.95, and boots for $51.95, but owes her parents $33.25, how many complete hours must she first work?

____

WRITE ABOUT IT

26. Explain how to find the equation of a line with slope $-\frac{7}{2}$ that passes through the point (−5, 1).

____

____

____

5-4 Equations in Point-Slope Form

Name ______________________ Date __________

Write the point-slope form of the line with slope $\frac{6}{5}$ that contains point $(-4, -2)$. Then graph the line.

$y - y_1 = m(x - x_1)$ ← Use the point-slope form, where m is the slope and the point (x_1, y_1) lies on the line.

$y - (-2) = \frac{6}{5}[x - (-4)]$ ← Substitute -2 for y_1, $\frac{6}{5}$ for m, and -4 for x_1.

$y + 2 = \frac{6}{5}(x + 4)$ ← Simplify.

Plot the point $(-4, -2)$.

Use the slope to locate point $(-4 + 5, -2 + 6)$, or $(1, 4)$, on the line.

Connect the points.

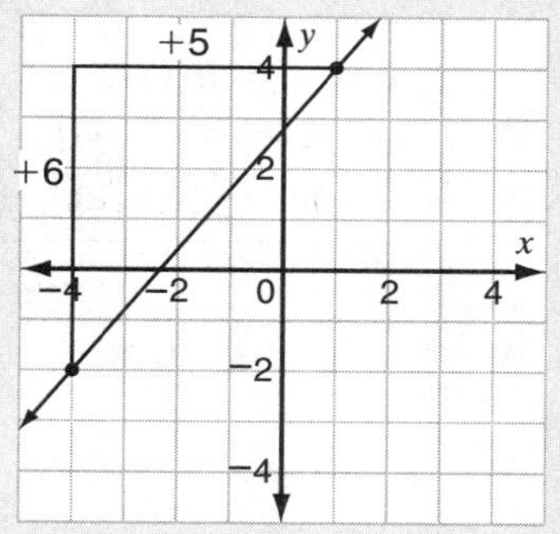

Write an equation of a line in point-slope form with the given slope that passes through the given point. Then graph the line on a separate sheet of paper.

1. slope: $-\frac{2}{3}$; point: $(8, 12)$

$\mathbf{y - y_1 = m(x - x_1)}$

$\mathbf{y_1 = 12,\ m = -\frac{2}{3},\ x_1 = 8}$

$\mathbf{y - 12 = -\frac{2}{3}(x - 8)}$

2. slope: $-\frac{5}{2}$; point: $(2, 15)$ ______________

3. slope: -8; point: $\left(\frac{2}{3}, -\frac{4}{5}\right)$ ______________

4. slope: -13; point: $\left(-\frac{7}{2}, \frac{6}{11}\right)$ ______________

5. slope: 1.4; point: $(-2.5, 3.5)$ ______________

6. slope: 0.7; point: $(4.5, -6.5)$ ______________

7. slope: 0.5; point: $(-1.25, 2.75)$ ______________

8. slope: -0.75; point: $(-1.5, -3)$ ______________

9. slope: 0.125; point: $(-4, -8)$ ______________

Graph each equation.

10. $y - 2 = x - 1$

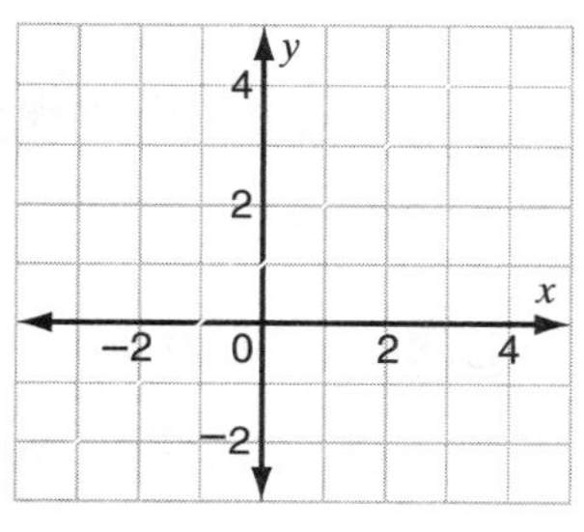

11. $y + 3 = 2(x - 1)$

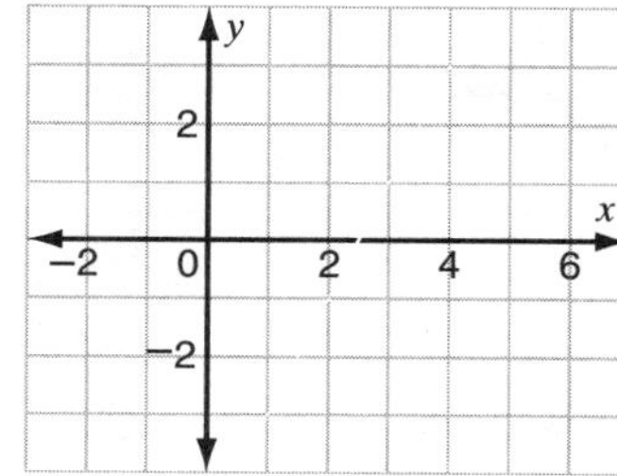

12. $y + 3 = \frac{2}{3}(x - 3)$

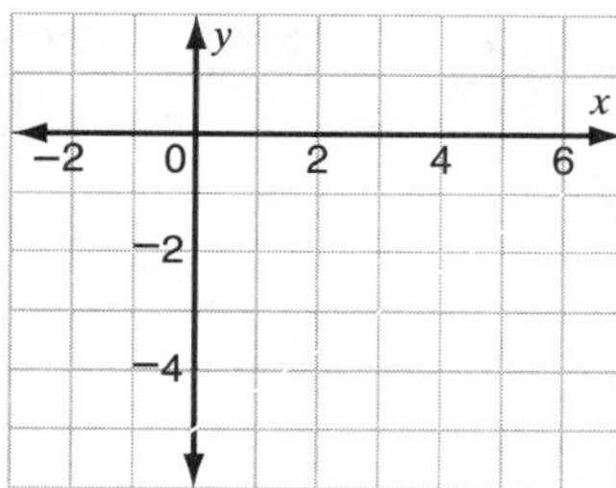

Write an equation in point-slope form of a line that passes through the given points.

13. (2, 8) and (−4, 6)

$m = \frac{6-8}{-4-2} = \frac{-2}{-6} = \frac{1}{3}$

$y - y_1 = m(x - x_1)$

Let $(2, 8) = (x_1, y_1)$

$y - 8 = \frac{1}{3}(x - 2)$

14. (5, 11) and (−6, 3)

15. (−3, 7) and (4, 14)

16. (4, −6) and (5, −4)

17. (6, 2) and (8, −5)

18. (−12, −9) and (13, −10)

19. (5.2, 1.9) and (−3.8, −5.1)

20. $\left(3\frac{1}{2}, 2\frac{2}{3}\right)$ and $\left(6\frac{1}{2}, -1\frac{1}{3}\right)$

21. $\left(4\frac{1}{5}, 6\frac{3}{4}\right)$ and $\left(-2\frac{4}{5}, 8\frac{3}{4}\right)$

Problem Solving

22. Health Insurance Shari's health insurance plan requires that she pay a monthly fee and also pay for each visit (her co-pay). In April, May, and June, Shari went to the doctor's office several times. She recorded the number of times and the amount she paid for health insurance in the table at the right.

Month	Visits	Cost
April	4	$135.75
May	2	$94.75
June	3	$115.25

a. What is her co-pay?

b. If Shari goes to the doctor 7 times in July, how much will she pay for health insurance?

MENTAL MATH

Multiply.

23. −95 • 32

24. $2 \bullet 7\frac{1}{8}$

25. 19.9 • 4.5

5-5 Change the Form of a Linear Equation

Name ____________________ Date __________

Rewrite the linear equation in the indicated form. Then find the value of y if $(2, y)$ lies on the line.

$7x + 3y = 21$; slope-intercept form

$7x - 7x + 3y = 21 - 7x$ ← Subtract $7x$ from both sides.

$3y = 21 - 7x$

$\frac{3y}{3} = \frac{21 - 7x}{3}$ ← Divide both sides by 3.

$y = 7 - \frac{7}{3}x$

or

$y = -\frac{7}{3}x + 7$

$7x + 3y = 21$

$7(2) + 3y = 21$ ← Substitute 2 for x.

$14 + 3y = 21$ ← Simplify.

$14 - 14 + 3y = 21 - 14$ ← Subtract 14 from both sides.

$3y = 7$

$\frac{3y}{3} = \frac{7}{3}$ ← Divide both sides by 3.

$y = \frac{7}{3}$

The point $\left(2, \frac{7}{3}\right)$ lies on the line $7x + 3y = 21$.

Find the x- and y-intercepts of each equation. Then draw its graph on a separate sheet of paper.

1. $8x - 5y = 40$

$8(0) - 5y = 40$, $y = -8$ | $8x - 5(0) = 40$, $x = 5$

x-intercept: 5; y-intercept: -8

2. $-2x + 5y = -3.8$

____

3. $-1 = 2x + 3y$

____

Tell whether the graph is a horizontal or vertical line.

4. $2x = 12$

$x = 6$
$x + 0y = 6$, so no y-intercept
x-intercept is 6.
vertical line

5. $6x = -18$

____

6. $1.2y = 6$

____

Write each equation in the indicated form.

7. $8x + 2y = 15$
slope-intercept form

$8x - 8x + 2y = -8x + 15$
$2y = -8x + 15$
$\frac{2y}{2} = \frac{-8x + 15}{2}$
$y = -4x + 7.5$

8. $9x + 3y = 7$
slope-intercept form

____

9. $y + 2 = -\frac{3}{4}(x - 3)$
standard form

____

10. $y + 3 = -\frac{4}{5}(x - 4)$
standard form

____

11. $y - 5.6 = -2(x - 4.7)$
standard form

____

12. $y - 7.9 = -3(x - 1.7)$
standard form

____

Use with SOURCEBOOK Lesson 5-5, pages 128–131.

Tell if the given point is on the given line.

13. $(3.5, 4.7); 5x + 2y = 27$

$5(3.5) + 2(4.7) \stackrel{?}{=} 27$

$17.5 + 9.4 \stackrel{?}{=} 27$

$26.9 = 27$ **False; No**

14. $(4.1, 5.2); 3x + 5y = 38$

15. $(1.5, -4.5); y = -2x - 1.5$

16. $(6.4, -1.3); y = -3x + 17.9$

17. $\left(-\frac{2}{3}, \frac{1}{4}\right); y - 2 = -\frac{2}{3}(x + 1)$

18. $\left(-\frac{1}{2}, \frac{3}{8}\right); y - 1 = -\frac{1}{4}(x + 2)$

Find the value of *x* or *y* so that the given point lies on the given line.

19. $(-2.4, y); y = 3x + 1$

$y = 3(-2.4) + 1$

$y = -7.2 + 1$

$y = -6.2$

20. $(-9.2, y); y = 2x + 3$

21. $\left(x, \frac{2}{3}\right); 2x + 4y = 2$

22. $\left(x, \frac{7}{8}\right); 3x + 5y = 4$

23. $\left(x, \frac{5}{3}\right); y - 2 = -\frac{3}{4}(x - 1)$

24. $\left(x, \frac{5}{6}\right); y - 3 = -\frac{2}{3}(x - 2)$

Solve.

25. U.S. Energy Consumption The amount of renewable energy consumed increased from 5.893 quadrillion BTUs in 2002 to 6.844 quadrillion BTUs in 2006. Based on this data, what do you predict will be the amount of renewable energy consumed in 2011. Round each decimal to the nearest thousandth.

26. Oil Prices In May 2007, the price of crude oil was at \$61 per barrel. A year later, it was at \$126 per barrel. If the price of crude oil had continued to climb at this rate, would 1 barrel have cost more than \$200 in December 2008?

CRITICAL THINKING

27. If the y-intercept of a line is $-\frac{17}{3}$ and the slope is $\frac{5}{3}$, what is the x-intercept?

5-6 Parallel and Perpendicular Lines

Name ______________________________ Date ______________

The equation of $\overleftrightarrow{AB}$ is $3x + 2y = 8$.
The equation of $\overleftrightarrow{CD}$ is $y = -\frac{3}{2}x + 7$.
Determine if $\overleftrightarrow{AB} \parallel \overleftrightarrow{CD}$.

Write $\overleftrightarrow{AB}$ in slope-intercept form.

$3x + 2y = 8$

$3x - 3x + 2y = 8 - 3x$ ← Subtract $3x$ from both sides.

$2y = 8 - 3x$

$\frac{2y}{2} = \frac{8 - 3x}{2}$ ← Divide both sides by 2.

$y = 4 - \frac{3}{2}x$ or $y = -\frac{3}{2}x + 4$

slope of $\overleftrightarrow{AB}$: $-\frac{3}{2}$

slope of $\overleftrightarrow{CD}$: $-\frac{3}{2}$

Both slopes are equal, so the lines are parallel.

Line 1 passes through $(-2, 1)$ and $(4, -3)$.
Line 2 passes through $(-3, -2)$ and $(5, 6)$.

Determine if line 1 $\perp$ line 2.

Think
If two lines are perpendicular, the product of their slopes is -1. Calculate the slopes.

Find the slope of line 1.

$m = \frac{y_2 - y_1}{x_2 - x_1} = \frac{-3 - 1}{4 - (-2)} = \frac{-4}{6} = -\frac{2}{3}$

Find the slope of line 2.

$m = \frac{y_2 - y_1}{x_2 - x_1} = \frac{-2 - 6}{-3 - 5} = \frac{-8}{-8} = 1$

Calculate the product of the slopes.

$-\frac{2}{3} \bullet 1 = -\frac{2}{3}$ ← The product of the slopes is not -1.

So lines 1 and 2 are *not* perpendicular.

Tell whether each pair of lines is *parallel*, *perpendicular*, or *neither*.

1. $y = \frac{7}{3}x - 11$ and $3x + 7y = 14$

$3x + 7y = 14$
$7y = -3x + 14$
$y = -\frac{3}{7}x + 2$
Slope: $-\frac{3}{7}$
$-\frac{3}{7} \bullet \frac{7}{3} = -1$
perpendicular lines

2. $6x - 5y = 24$ and $y = -\frac{5}{6}x - 2$

not perpendicular lines

3. Line 1 passes through $(2, 4)$ and $(7, -8)$.
Line 2 passes through $(-4, -11)$ and $(1, -23)$.

not perpendicular

4. Line 1 passes through $(-7, 12)$ and $(-3, 21)$.
Line 2 passes through $(6, -2)$ and $(10, 7)$.

not perpendicular

Find the equation of the line specified.

5. perpendicular to $2x + y = -4$ and passing through $(3, 5)$

$y = -2x - 4$; $m = -2$
Perpendicular slope is $\frac{1}{2}$.
$y - 5 = \frac{1}{2}(x - 3)$
$y = \frac{1}{2}x + \frac{7}{2}$

6. perpendicular to $3x + y = -7$ and passing through $(1, 8)$

$y = \frac{1}{3}x + \frac{8}{3}$

7. parallel to $-3y = 8x + 7$ and passing through $(-1, -2)$

Use with SOURCEBOOK Lesson 5-6, pages 132–135.

Find the equation of the line specified.

8. parallel to $3x + 2y = 8$ with a y-intercept of -6

9. parallel to $9x + 5y = 2$ with a y-intercept of -2

10. perpendicular to $3y = 24$ and passing through $(-7, 11)$

11. perpendicular to $-2y = 16$ and passing through $(4, -9)$

12. perpendicular to $-5y = 2x + 1$ with y-intercept $-\frac{19}{5}$

For exercises 13–15, use $A(-2, -2)$, $B(-1, 3)$, $C(4, 4)$, and $D(3, -1)$.

13. Is $\overleftrightarrow{AB} \perp \overleftrightarrow{BC}$?

slope of $\overleftrightarrow{AB} = \frac{3 - (-2)}{-1 - (-2)} = \frac{5}{1}$

slope of $\overleftrightarrow{BC} = \frac{4 - 3}{4 - (-1)} = \frac{1}{5}$

$\left(\frac{5}{1}\right)\left(\frac{1}{5}\right) \neq -1$

not perpendicular

14. Is $\overleftrightarrow{AB} \perp \overleftrightarrow{AD}$?

15. Is $\overleftrightarrow{AB} \parallel \overleftrightarrow{CD}$?

Problem Solving

Use a separate sheet of paper for each problem.

16. Given $A(-6, 3)$, $B(4, -3)$, $C(-4, -4)$, $D(-1, 1)$, and $F(7, 3)$, find E, such that $\overleftrightarrow{AB} \perp \overleftrightarrow{CD}$, $\overleftrightarrow{CD} \parallel \overleftrightarrow{EF}$, and E's x-coordinate is an integer between 0 and 3.

17. Given $A(-3, -1)$, $B(2, 5)$, $C(8, 6)$, and $D(3, 0)$, show that the opposite sides of quadrilateral $ABCD$ are parallel, and determine if the diagonals are perpendicular.

SPIRAL REVIEW

18. Determine whether each sequence could be geometric, arithmetic, or neither. Use a pattern to write the next three terms.

460, 46, 4.6, 0.46, . . .

19. Write a recursive formula for the nth term of the geometric sequence below.

$-1, 3, -9, 27, \ldots$

5-7 Graph a Linear Inequality in the Coordinate Plane

Name ______________________ Date __________

Graphing Linear Inequalities				
Inequality	$y \leq mx + b$	$y < mx + b$	$y \geq mx + b$	$y > mx + b$
Boundary Line	solid	dashed	solid	dashed
Shading	below	below	above	above

Graph the solution to the linear inequality.

$-5x - 2y > -6$ ← Solve for y.

$-2y > 5x - 6$ ← Use the Addition Property of Inequality.

$y < -\frac{5}{2}x + 3$ ← Use the Division Property of Inequality.

Remember: Reverse the inequality symbol when dividing by a negative number.

Graph $y = -\frac{5}{2}x + 3$. ← Use a dashed line for <.

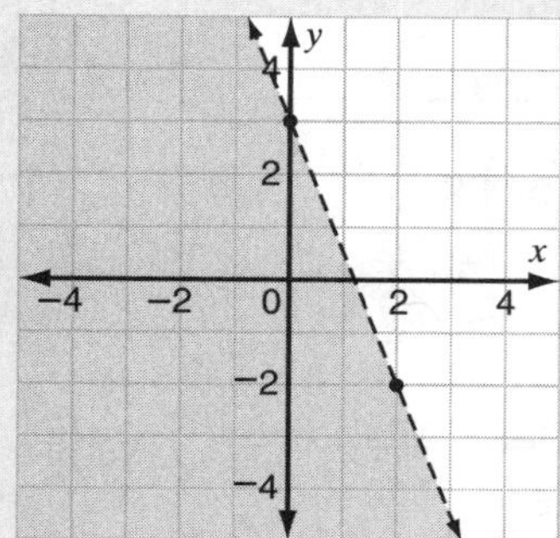

Shade the half-plane *below* the line. ← Shade below for <.

Check: Does (0, 0) satisfy $y < -\frac{5}{2}x + 3$?

$\mathbf{0} \overset{?}{<} -\frac{5}{2}(\mathbf{0}) + 3$

$0 < 3$ **True**

Tell whether the ordered pair is a solution to the inequality.

1. $y < 2x + 5$; $(-2, 3)$

3 < 2(−2) + 5
3 < −4 + 5
3 < 1 false
no

2. $y < -2x + 5$; $(1, 5)$

______

3. $3x + 4y \geq -3$; $(-2, 1)$

______

4. $2x + 5y \geq -4$; $(-3, 3)$

______

5. $5y > -2$; $\left(-4\frac{3}{4}, 7\frac{7}{8}\right)$

______

6. $2y > -8$; $\left(-2\frac{7}{8}, -1\frac{3}{4}\right)$

______

7. $3x - 2y < -12$; $(-2.5, 1.4)$

______

8. $4x - y < -17$; $(-3.6, 2.5)$

______

9. $3x - 4y \geq 1$; $\left(\frac{3}{2}, \frac{1}{2}\right)$

______

Use with SOURCEBOOK Lesson 5-7, pages 136–137.

Graph each linear inequality on a separate sheet of paper. Then describe the solution set. (*Hint:* When the boundary line is vertical, shade to the left for $\leq$ and $<$; shade to the right for $\geq$ and $>$.)

10. $x + y < 1$

$x - x + y < -x + 1$

$y < -x + 1$

The graph has a dashed boundary line, $y = -x + 1$, and is shaded below.

11. $x + y < 2$

12. $3x > 7$

13. $-2y \geq 11$

14. $2x - y < 3$

15. $-9x + 3y < 0$

16. $8x + 2y > 4.8$

17. $6x + 3y > 12.3$

18. $\frac{4}{5}x + 4y \geq 9$

Solve. Show your work.

19. A manufacturer takes 3 hours to make a chair and 2 hours to make a stool. If it spends a maximum of 800 hours making chairs and stools and makes 70 stools, what is the maximum number of chairs it can make?

20. Which inequalities have $(2.4, -0.5)$ as a solution?

$y > -6x + 9$ $\quad$ $3x \leq 15$

$2x - y \geq 8$ $\quad$ $3.9x + 1.1y < 8.81$

CRITICAL THINKING

21. Explain why no solution to the inequality $y \geq 2x + 2$ can be an ordered pair of the form $(+, -)$.

5-8 Absolute-Value Functions

Name ______________________________ Date ______________

Graph the function. Identify the vertex, axis of symmetry, x- and y-intercepts, domain, and range. Tell whether the graph opens up or down.

$y = |x + 1| - 2$

Choose positive, negative, and zero values for x.

x	$y = \|x + 1\| - 2$
−3	0
−2	−1
−1	−2
0	−1
1	0

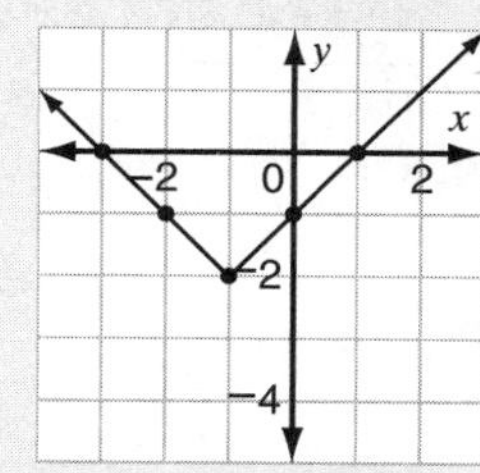

The vertex is $(-1, -2)$.
The axis of symmetry is $x = -1$.
The x-intercepts are $-3, 1$.
The y-intercept is -1.
The domain is all real numbers.
The range is $y \geq -2$.
The graph opens up.

Identify the vertex of each of the following absolute-value functions.
(*Hint:* The vertex occurs where the absolute-value expression equals zero.)

1. $y = |x + 7|$

$|x + 7| = 0$
$x = -7;\ y = 0$
$(-7, 0)$

2. $y = |x + 9|$ ________

3. $y = |x - 4|$ ________

4. $y = |x - 10|$ ________

5. $y = |x| + 6$ ________

6. $y = |x| + 11$ ________

7. $y = |x| - 22$ ________

8. $y = |x| - 15$ ________

9. $y = |x + 3| - 6$ ________

10. $y = |x + 8| - 16$ ________

11. $y = |x - 4| - 12$ ________

12. $y = |x - 25| - 31$ ________

13. $y = |x + 11| + 19$ ________

14. $y = |x + 13| + 14$ ________

15. $y = |x - 39| + 42$ ________

16. $y = |x - 26| + 51$ ________

17. $y = -|x - 6| + 2$ ________

18. $y = -|x - 7| + 8$ ________

19. $y = -|x + 6.5|$ ________

20. $y = -|x + 7.3|$ ________

21. $y = \left|x + \frac{2}{3}\right| - \frac{5}{4}$ ________

22. $y = \left|x + \frac{5}{8}\right| - \frac{7}{12}$ ________

23. $y = -\left|x - \frac{1}{9}\right| - 1.2$ ________

24. $y = -\left|x - \frac{1}{8}\right| - 2.7$ ________

Graph each absolute-value function on a separate sheet of paper. Identify the vertex, axis of symmetry, x- and y-intercepts, domain, and range. Tell whether the graph opens up or down.

25. $y = |x + 6|$

vertex: $(-6, 0)$
axis of symmetry: $x = -6$
x-intercept: -6; y-intercept: 6
domain: all real numbers
range: $y \geq 0$; opens up

26. $y = |x + 8|$ ______

27. $y = |x| + 9$ ______

28. $y = |x| + 12$ ______

29. $y = -|x| + 7$ ______

30. $y = -|x| + 5$ ______

31. $y = -|x + 2|$ ______

32. $y = -|x + 4|$ ______

33. $y = |x - 1.8| + 2.9$ ______

34. $y = |x - 2.5| + 1.8$ ______

35. $y = -\left|x + \frac{2}{3}\right| - \frac{1}{6}$ ______

36. $y = -\left|x + \frac{1}{4}\right| - \frac{1}{2}$ ______

Graph and compare each function.

37. How is the graph of $y = |x + 12|$ related to the graph of $y = |x|$?

______

38. How is the graph of $y = |x| - 8$ related to the graph of $y = |x|$?

______

TEST PREPARATION

39. Which equation has a vertex of $(-8, 11)$?

A. $y = -|x + 8| - 11$ **C.** $y = |x - 8| + 11$

B. $y = |x + 8| - 11$ **D.** $y = -|x + 8| + 11$

40. Which vertex belongs to the equation $y = -|2x + 3| + 4$?

F. $\left(-\frac{2}{3}, 4\right)$ **H.** $\left(-\frac{3}{2}, 4\right)$

G. $\left(-4, \frac{3}{2}\right)$ **J.** $\left(-4, \frac{2}{3}\right)$

5-9 Technology: Graph Linear Functions and Inequalities

Name ______________________________ Date ____________

You can use a handheld to graph the equation $y = 3x - 4$.

Step 1 Press (home). Choose (2) to select **Graphs & Geometry**.

Step 2 Input $3x - 4$. Press (enter) to graph the line.

Think
The number between f and (x) shows how many graphs of functions are in the handheld's memory.

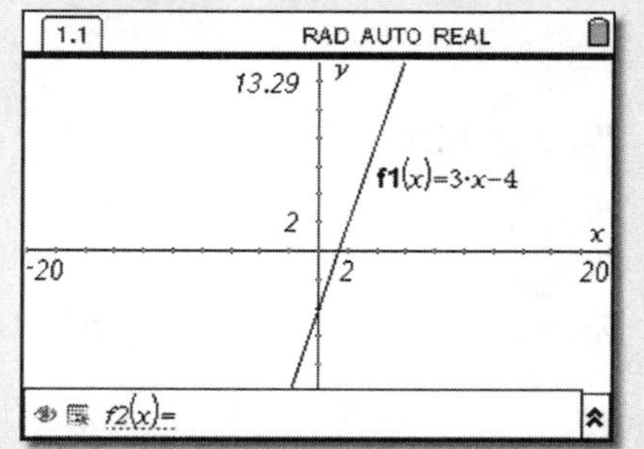

You can use a handheld to graph the inequality $y \leq 2x + 1$.

Step 1 Press (ctrl) (esc) to clear the handheld.

Then press (home). Choose (2) to select **Graphs & Geometry**.

Step 2 Use (clear) to delete the equal sign. Input $y \leq 2x + 1$.

Press (enter) to graph the inequality.

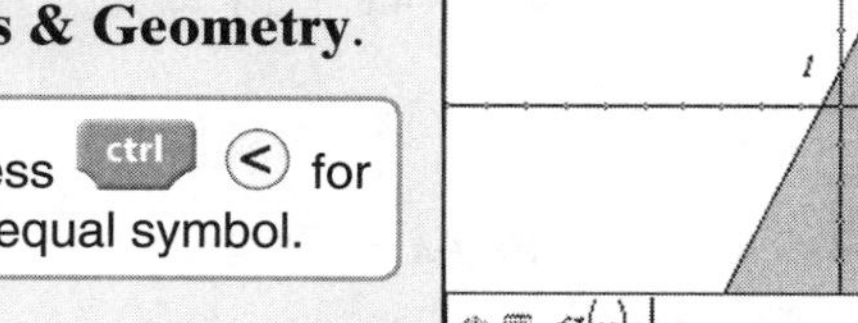

Remember: Press (ctrl) (<) for the less than or equal symbol.

Think
$f(x)$ changes to y because an inequality is not a function.

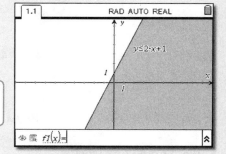

Use a handheld to graph each linear function. (*Hint:* Solve for y first.)

1. $y = 2x - 9$ **2.** $y = 4x - 3$ **3.** $y = -2x - 5$ **4.** $y = -3x - 2$

5. $y = -0.2x + 1.3$ **6.** $y = -0.8x + 2.1$ **7.** $y = 3.5x - 4.2$ **8.** $y = 2.6x - 1.7$

9. $y = \frac{2}{3}x + 7$ **10.** $y = \frac{3}{5}x + 4$ **11.** $y = -\frac{2}{7}x - 8$ **12.** $y = -\frac{3}{8}x - 2$

13. $x + y = 5$ **14.** $x + y = 2$ **15.** $x - y = 4$ **16.** $x - y = 3$

17. $3x - y = 8$ **18.** $4x - y = 5$ **19.** $2x + 3y = 10$ **20.** $3x + 4y = 7$

21. $5x - 2y = 11$ **22.** $7x - 4y = 6$ **23.** $2x + 3y = -9$ **24.** $3x + 2y = -5$

Use with SOURCEBOOK Lesson 5-9, pages 140–141.

Use a handheld to graph each inequality. (*Hint:* Solve for *y* first.)

25. $y > 3x - 5$

26. $y > 2x - 7$

27. $y \leq -3x + 2$

28. $y \leq -2x + 5$

29. $y \geq 1.2x + 3.4$

30. $y \geq 3.9x + 1.8$

31. $y < -0.2x + 5.1$

32. $y < -0.1x + 4.5$

33. $y > -\frac{3}{2}x + \frac{1}{3}$

34. $y > -\frac{4}{3}x + \frac{1}{5}$

35. $2x + y < 7$

36. $3x + y < 1$

37. $x - y \geq -4$

38. $x - y \geq -7$

39. $2x + y \leq -6$

40. $3x + y \leq -9$

41. $-3x + 5y \leq 2$

42. $-4x + 2y \leq 3$

43. $5x + 3y < -8$

44. $7x + 2y < -11$

45. $3x - 5y > 12$

46. $4x - 7y > 10$

47. $8x - 2y < -13$

48. $9x - 5y < -17$

Solve. Show your work.

49. Plant A sells gravel for \$18.50 per cubic yard plus \$55 for delivery within 50 miles. Plant B sells gravel for \$16.75 per cubic yard plus \$0.45 per mile for delivery. A customer who can spend no more than \$500 lives 23 miles from Plant A and 48 miles from Plant B. Find the greatest whole number of cubic yards that this customer could buy from each plant. Which deal is better?

50. Graph the equation $y = \frac{2}{5}x + 7$. Graph three equations so the four graphs together form a rectangle. What are the equations?

CHALLENGE

51. Write an inequality with solutions only in the first, second, and third quadrant but not the origin. Is it possible to write an inequality whose solutions are only in two quadrants? Explain.

5-10 Technology: Families of Lines

Name ____________________ Date ____________

You can use a handheld to graph the equations $y = 2x + 1$, $y = 3x + 1$, $y = -2x + 1$, and $y = -0.2x + 1$. How does the value of m affect the graph of $y = mx + b$?

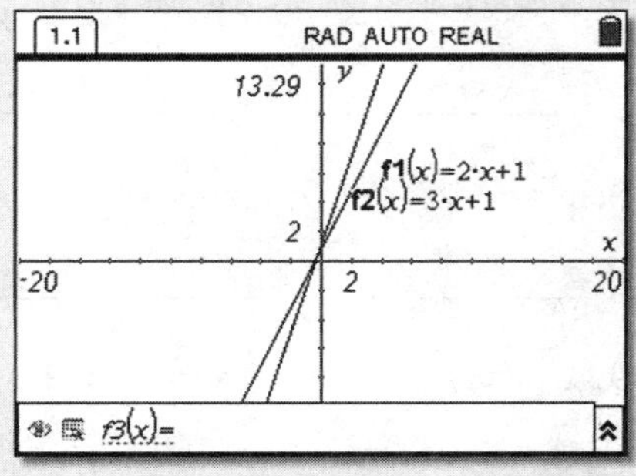

Step 1 Press (home). Then choose (2) to select **Graphs & Geometry**.

Step 2 Input $2x + 1$, then press enter to graph the line.

Step 3 Input $3x + 1$, then press enter to graph the line.

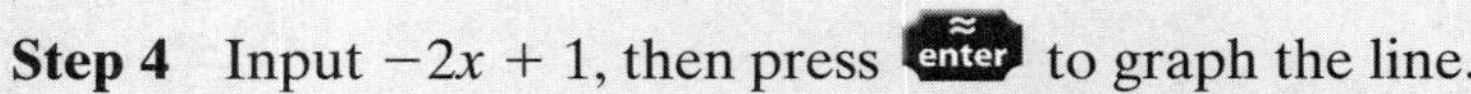

Step 4 Input $-2x + 1$, then press enter to graph the line.

Step 5 Input $-0.2x + 1$, then press enter to graph the line.

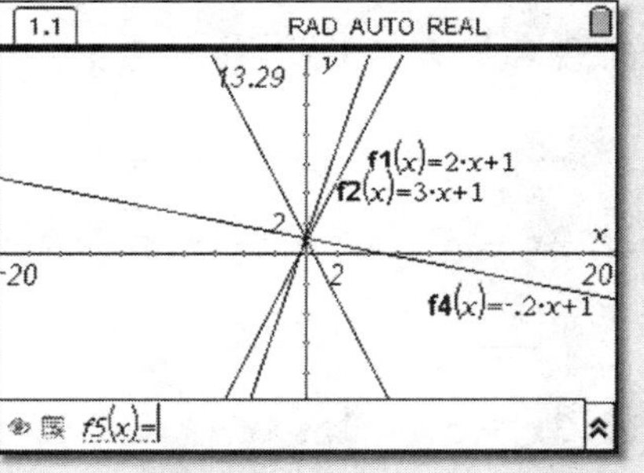

The value of m changes the slope of the graph. If m is positive, then the graph slants up. If m is negative, then the graph slants down. The greater the absolute value of m, the steeper the line.

Predict how the graphs of the functions will compare. Then use a handheld to verify your prediction.

1. $y = 5x$, $y = 5x + 3$, $y = 5x - 2$, $y = 5x + 2.8$, and $y = 5x - 1.9$

parallel, different y-intercepts

2. $y = 10x$, $y = 10x + 5$, $y = 10x - 7$, $y = 10x + 3.1$, and $y = 10x - 0.8$

____

3. $y = -x + 6$, $y = 3x + 6$, $y = -0.8x + 6$, $y = -3x + 6$, and $y = 2.3x + 6$

____

4. $y = -2x - 9$, $y = 2x - 9$, $y = -0.6x - 9$, $y = -4x - 9$, and $y = 1.8x - 9$

____

5. $y = -5x + 1$, $y = 3x - 1$, $y = -2x + 7$, $y = -3x - 8$, and $y = 0.4x + 12$

____

6. $y = -7x - 3$, $y = 4x + 2$, $y = -5x + 3$, $y = -8x + 11$, and $y = 0.9x + 15$

____

Predict how the graphs of the functions will compare. Then use a handheld to verify your prediction.

7. $y = 4x + 3.2$, $y = 1.2x + 3.2$, $y = -5.3x + 3.2$, $y = 0.9x + 3.2$, and $y = -0.1x + 3.2$

8. $y = -9x - 1.5$, $y = 3.4x - 1.5$, $y = -0.3x - 1.5$, $y = 2x - 1.5$, and $y = -0.7x - 1.5$

9. $x + y = -12$, $x + y = 8$, $x + y = -1$, $x + y = 4$, and $x + y = -6.8$

10. $x - y = -6$, $x - y = 2$, $x - y = -4$, $x - y = 11$, and $x - y = -9.5$

11. $2x - 3y = -6$, $3x + 2y = 4$, $4x - y = -2$, $x - 5y = -10$, and $7x - y = -2$

12. $3x + 5y = 15$, $3x + 3y = 9$, $7x - y = -3$, $3x + 7y = 21$, and $8x - y = -3$

13. $4x + 2y = 3$, $4x + 2y = 7$, $4x + 2y = -1$, $4x + 2y = 11$, and $8x + 4y = 28$

14. $3x + 5y = 1$, $3x + 5y = -2$, $3x + 5y = -10$, $6x + 10y = 29$, and $3x + 5y = -15$

Solve.

15. A graph with slope 2 and y-intercept -5 is shifted 3 units up and the slope is halved. This graph is then shifted 7 units down and the slope is doubled. What is the equation of each graph? How do the final and original graphs compare? Graph each equation on a handheld to check your answers.

16. May graphed $2x + y = -2$, $2x + y = -5$, $2x + y = 3$, $8x + 4y = -7$, and $2x + y = -10$. Mick graphed $x - 2y = 4$, $x - 2y = 10$, $x - 2y = -6$, $2x - 4y = 7$, and $x - 2y = 20$. How are May's and Mick's graphs similar? How are they different?

CRITICAL THINKING

17. In $y = mx + b$, where x is positive, how are the values of x and y affected as m increases? Make a table of values on a handheld to check your answer.

5-11 Problem-Solving Strategy:
Consider Extreme Cases

Read › Plan › Solve › Check

Name ______________________________ Date ______________

Consider extreme cases to solve.

1. A vertex of the square on the right is hinged at the center point *P* of the square on the left. Regardless of how the square is positioned about this hinge, the area of the shaded region of intersection is the same. What is that area?

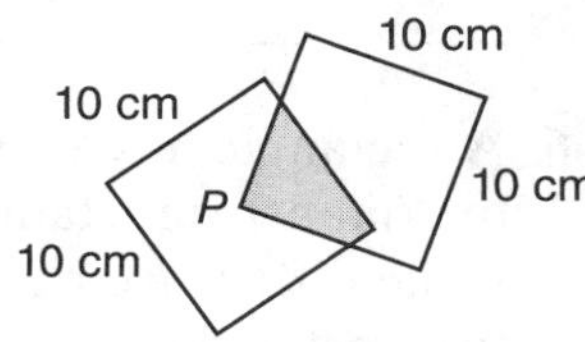

2. After three 100-point exams, Margarita's average in Science class is 82%. With two exams remaining, can Margarita get the 93% final average required to earn an A?

3. Mr. Vinck writes a different number on 100 note cards. He divides the cards into two piles: one has 79 cards, and the other 21. The cards are then placed into two separate rows with their numbers showing. A student removes an equal number of the cards from both rows. How many more cards remain with their numbers showing in the larger row than the smaller row?

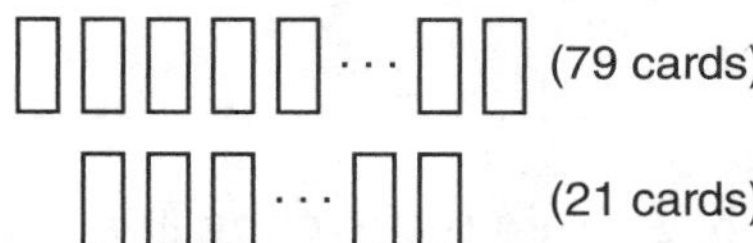

4. A jar holds exactly 16 blue balls, 14 red balls, and 12 yellow balls (each identical except for color). If balls are pulled randomly, what is the minimum number of balls that must be pulled in order to guarantee that at least one ball of every color is pulled?

5. What is the greatest number by which 76 can be multiplied to get a product with fewer than four digits?

---

6. A rectangle has a length of 10 in. and a width of 5 in. Another rectangle overlaps this rectangle. It has a length of 7 in. and a width of 3 in. What is the difference between the two nonoverlapping regions of the two rectangles?

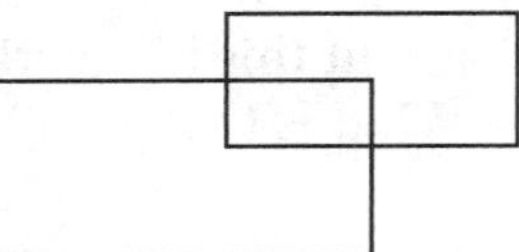

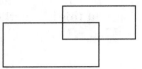

7. One postal route has 60 houses on it. One day, the letter carrier has 301 letters to deliver. After all the letters have been distributed, one house received more letters than any other house. What is least number of letters the house could have received?

---

8. A train is traveling at a constant speed of 75 mph. A passenger notices a second train traveling on a parallel track about 1 mile behind. The second train passes the first 5 minutes later. How fast was the second train traveling assuming its speed was constant?

---

9. Find the missing digits in the following seven-digit number so that the number itself is equal to the product of three consecutive numbers. What are three numbers?

1,5_ _, _80

Enrichment:
Slope in Coordinate Geometry

Name ______________________ Date ____________

Prove that quadrilateral $EFGH$ at right is a parallelogram.

$m_{\overline{EF}} = \frac{-1-1}{4-7} = \frac{-2}{-3} = \frac{2}{3}$ $m_{\overline{GH}} = \frac{-4-(-6)}{5-2} = \frac{2}{3}$

$m_{\overline{EH}} = \frac{-1-(-6)}{4-2} = \frac{5}{2}$ $m_{\overline{FG}} = \frac{1-(-4)}{7-5} = \frac{5}{2}$

Line segments EF and GH have the same slope; they are parallel.
Line segments EH and FG have the same slope; they are parallel.

Because this quadrilateral has two pairs of parallel sides, the quadrilateral is a parallelogram.

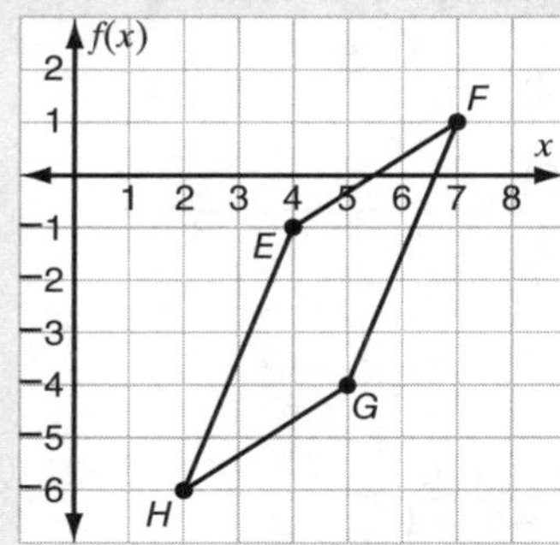

Determine whether the quadrilateral is a parallelogram. Show your work.

1.

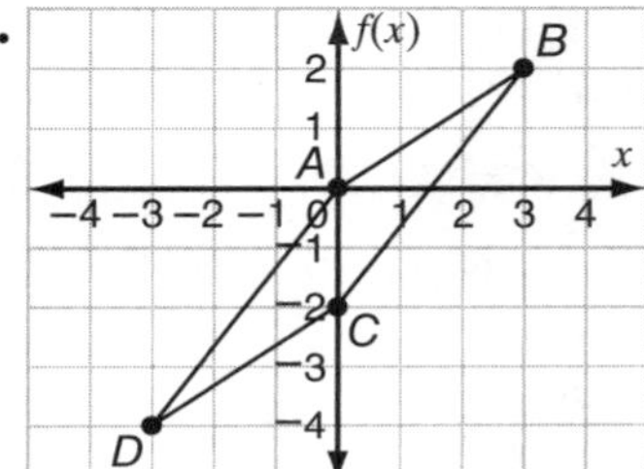

$$m_{\overline{AB}} = \frac{2-0}{3-0} = \frac{2}{3};\ m_{\overline{DC}} = \frac{-2-(-4)}{0-(-3)} = \frac{2}{3}$$

$$m_{\overline{AD}} = \frac{-4-0}{-3-0} = \frac{4}{3};\ m_{\overline{CB}} = \frac{-2-2}{0-3} = \frac{4}{3}$$

$$m_{\overline{AB}} = m_{\overline{DC}};\ m_{\overline{AD}} = m_{\overline{CB}}$$

parallelogram

2.

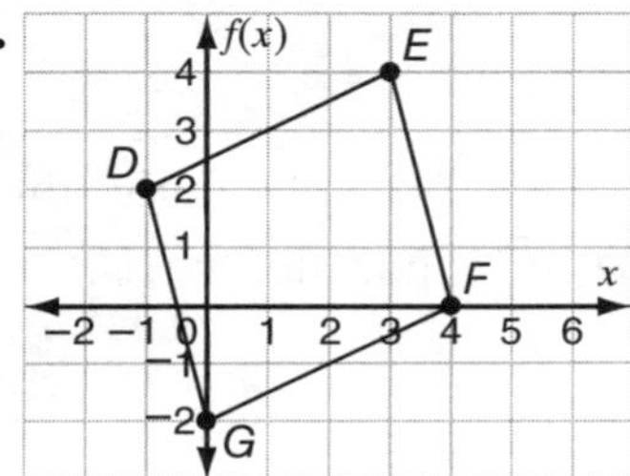

____

3.

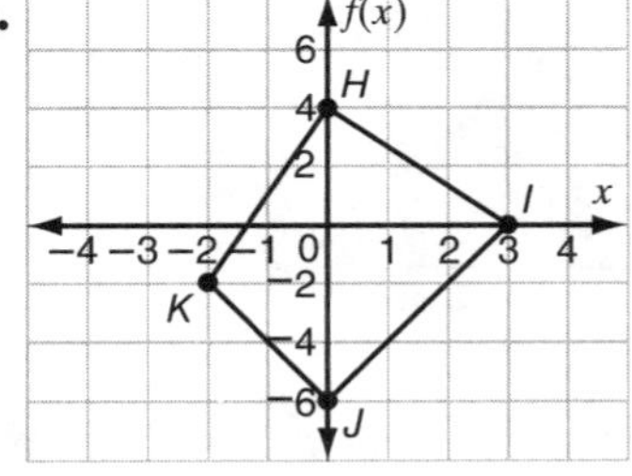

____

4.

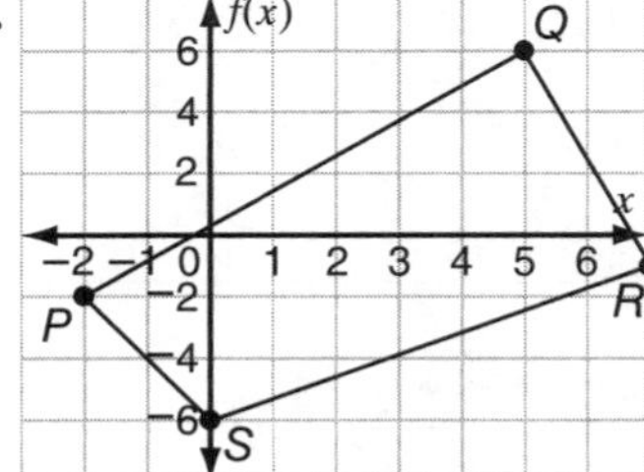

____

Determine whether each triangle is a right triangle. Show your work.
(*Hint:* Determine if two sides of the triangle are perpendicular.)

5.

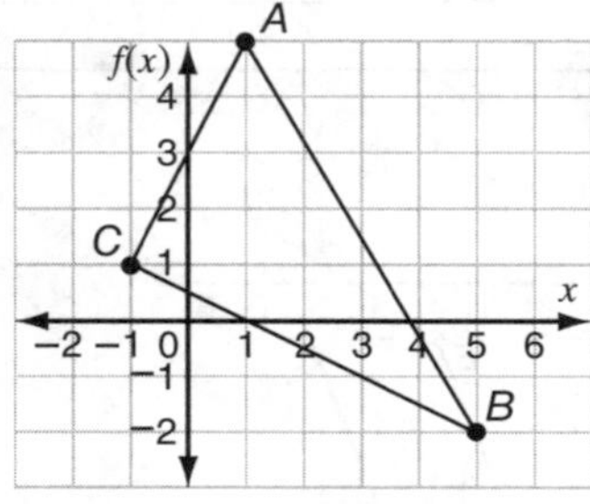

$m_{\overline{CA}} = \frac{1-5}{-1-1} = \frac{-4}{-2} = 2$

$m_{\overline{BC}} = \frac{-2-1}{5-(-1)} = \frac{-3}{6} = -\frac{1}{2}$

$2 \bullet \left(-\frac{1}{2}\right) = -1$; right triangle

6.

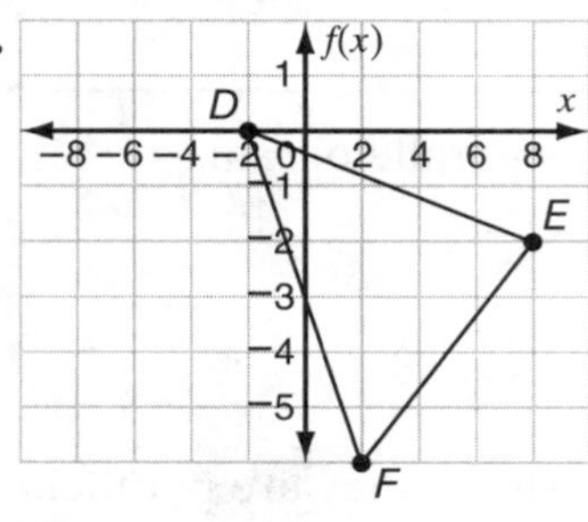

7.

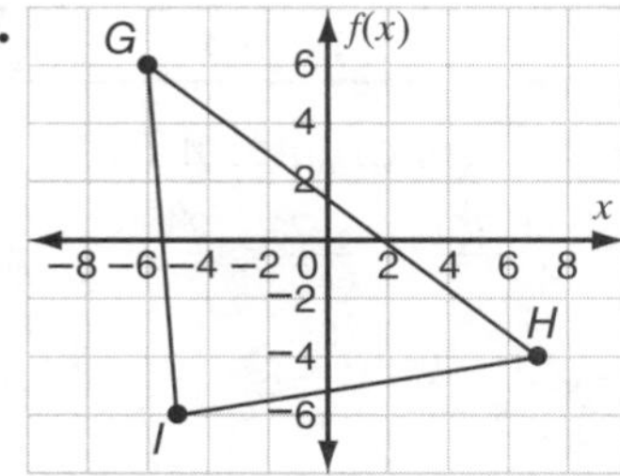

Solve. Show your work.

8. M_1 is the midpoint of $\overline{ST}$. M_2 is the midpoint of $\overline{TU}$. Prove that $\overline{M_1M_2}$ is parallel to $\overline{SU}$.

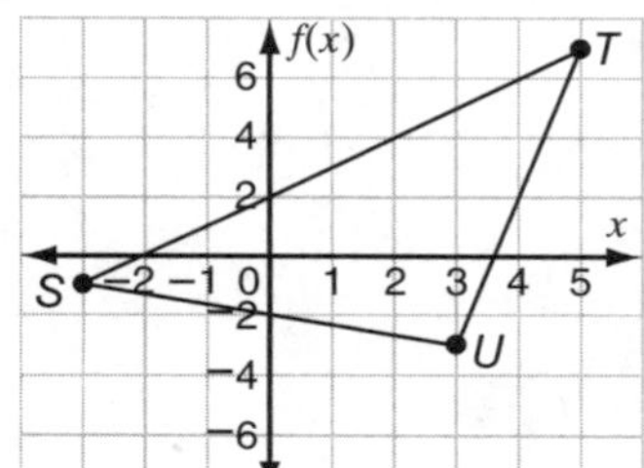

9. M_1 is the midpoint of $\overline{WX}$. M_2 is the midpoint of $\overline{VY}$. Prove that $\overline{M_1M_2}$ is parallel to $\overline{VW}$.

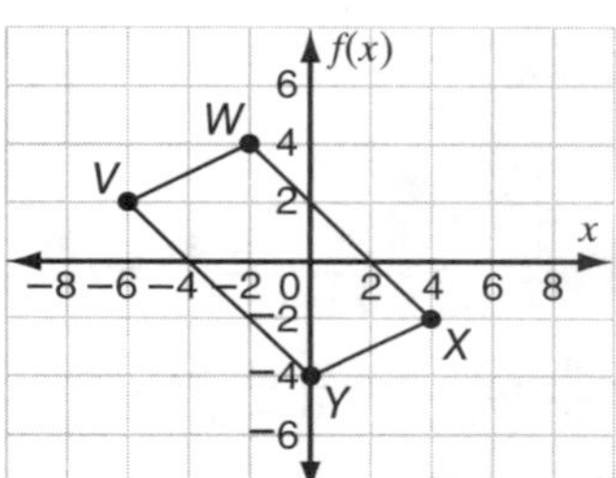

TEST PREPARATION

10. Which represents the slope of a line that runs through the points $(-3, 5)$ and $(6, -4)$?

A. $\frac{1}{9}$ **C.** -1

B. $-\frac{1}{9}$ **D.** 1

11. Which is the equation of a line that is perpendicular to a line having a slope of $-\frac{1}{2}$?

F. $-\frac{y}{2} + 3 = x - 4$ **H.** $2y + 3 = x - 4$

G. $-2y + 3 = x - 4$ **J.** $\frac{y}{2} + 3 = x - 4$

Test Prep: Multiple-Choice Questions

Strategy: Understand Distractors

Name ______________________ Date __________

When choosing the answer to a multiple-choice question, make sure that you **answer the question asked**. Distractors may be solutions to other questions that can be answered using the given information.

To select the correct answer in a multiple-choice item, try using the following strategies.

- Underline important words.
- Restate the question.
- Use the Test-Prep strategy.
- Apply appropriate rules, definitions, properties, or strategies.
- Analyze and eliminate answer choices.

Choose the correct answer. *TIP: Mark your answer sheet carefully.*

1. The graph of which equation is parallel to the graph of $y = \frac{1}{6}x - 1$?

A. $y = -6x - 1$ **C.** $y = 6x - 1$

B. $y = -\frac{1}{6}x + 1$ **D.** $y = \frac{1}{6}x + 1$

2. Beth is 5 years older than Holly. Randy is 8 years older than twice Holly's age. If Randy is 16 years old, how old is Beth?

F. 4 **H.** 11

G. 9 **J.** 13

3. The graph of which equation is perpendicular to the line shown?

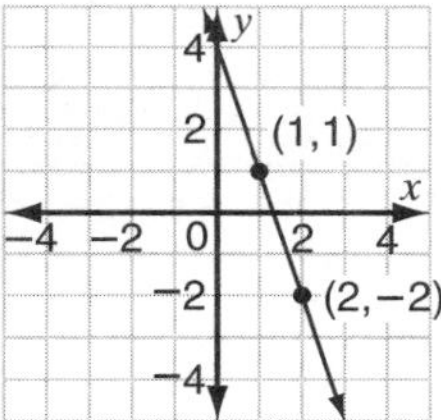

A. $y = -3x$

B. $y = -\frac{1}{3}x$

C. $y = 3x$

D. $y = \frac{1}{3}x$

4. Last week, Max had $5000 in sales. This week, his sales were at least $\frac{1}{10}$ greater. Which number line represents the additional amount of sales he had this week?

F. 200 300 400 500 600 700

G. 4000 4500 5000 5500 6000 6500

H. 200 300 400 500 600 700

J. 4000 4500 5000 5500 6000 6500

5. Which list is in order from greatest to least?

A. $\sqrt{2}, |-0.9|, -\left|-\frac{3}{10}\right|, -\frac{1}{3}, -0.8$

B. $\sqrt{2}, -\left|-\frac{3}{10}\right|, -\frac{1}{3}, -0.8, |-0.9|$

C. $|-0.9|, -0.8, -\frac{1}{3}, -\left|-\frac{3}{10}\right|, \sqrt{2}$

D. $-0.8, -\frac{1}{3}, -\left|-\frac{3}{10}\right|, |-0.9|, \sqrt{2}$

6. A company is ordering ink cartridges. Black cartridges cost $15 each and color cartridges cost $20 each. The total cost of the order is $190. Which equation, written in standard form, represents the situation?

F. $15x - 20y = 190$ **H.** $y = -0.75x + 9.5$

G. $15x + 20y = 190$ **J.** $y = 0.75x + 9.5$

SOURCEBOOK Test Prep Lesson, page 148.

For More Practice Go To:
ONLINE www.progressinmathematics.com

Vocabulary Development

Name ______________________________ Date ____________

Chapter 5 Vocabulary

absolute-value function	family of graphs	point-slope form
axis of symmetry	half-planes	slope-intercept form
boundary	linear equation in standard form	slope (m)
constant of variation	linear function	vertex
direct variation	linear inequality in two variables	x-intercept
		y-intercept

From the vocabulary list above, choose the term(s) that best complete each sentence. Write the term(s) in the space(s) provided.

1. A function rule that contains an absolute-value expression is called a(n) ______________________.

2. A constant rate of change represents a(n) ______________________.

3. $\frac{\text{rise}}{\text{run}}$ is a way to describe a(n) ______________________.

4. A linear function that can be written in the form $y = kx$ is a(n) ______________________, where k is a nonzero constant called the ______________________.

5. The y-coordinate of the point where the graph crosses the y-axis is the ______________________.

6. $Ax + By = C$ is the ______________________.

7. The x-coordinate of the point where the graph crosses the x-axis is the ______________________.

8. The number sentence $2x + 8y < 1$ is a(n) ______________________.

9. A linear equation in the form $y - y_1 = m(x - x_1)$ is in the ______________________.

Choose three terms from the list that you did not use in questions 1–9. For each term, write a definition in your own words and give an example.

10. ____

Use after SOURCEBOOK Lesson 5-1–5-8 pages 116–139.

Practice Chapter 5 Test

Name ______________________________ Date ____________

Tell whether each relation represents a linear function. Find the slope of all linear functions.

1.

x	y
−2	3
−1	4
0	5
1	6
2	7

2.

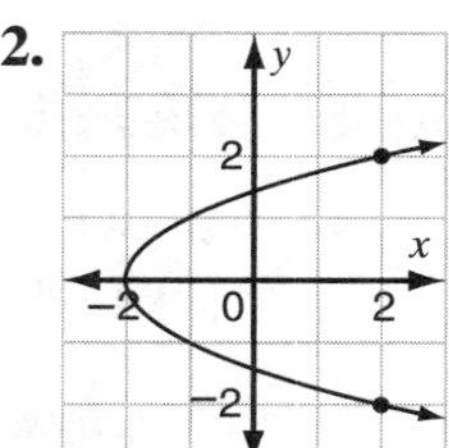

3. $y = \frac{7}{8}x + 9$

________ ________ ________

Find the slope of the line that connects the given points. Describe the line.

4. (3, 9) and (12, 1) **5.** (−2, 7) and (4, 10)

________ ________

Explain whether each of the following represents a direct variation. If so, state the constant of variation.

6. $y + 15x = 0$ **7.** $4x + 7y = -4$ **8.** $4y + 2x = 0$

________ ________ ________

Write an equation in slope-intercept form for the line with the given slope and *y*-intercept.

9. slope: 7; *y*-intercept: −19 **10.** slope: $-\frac{4}{5}$; *y*-intercept: $\frac{2}{3}$ **11.** slope: 9.3; *y*-intercept: −11.25

________ ________ ________

Identify the slope and *y*-intercept of the line whose equation is given. Graph the line on a separate sheet of paper.

12. $y = -7x + 3$ **13.** $y = 5x - 2$ **14.** $7x + 5y = -20$ **15.** $2x - 6y = -30$

________ ________ ________ ________

Write an equation in point-slope form of a line that passes through the given points.

16. (1, 7) and (−2, 10) **17.** (2, −5) and (5, −1) **18.** (−9, −5) and (−7, −6)

________ ________ ________

Use after SOURCEBOOK Lessons 5-1–5-8, pages 116–139.

Write each equation in the form given.

19. $2x + 6y = 1$; slope-intercept form

20. $y - 2 = \frac{1}{4}(x + 8)$; standard form

Write an equation in slope-intercept form for the line that is described.

21. perpendicular to $2x + y = -5$ and passing through $(1, 1)$

22. parallel to $4x + 3y = 5$ with a y-intercept of -2

Graph each linear inequality on a separate sheet of paper. Describe the solution set.

23. $x + y < -3$

24. $5x \leq 15$

25. $-2y \leq 16$

26. $6x - y < 2$

Graph each absolute-value function on grid paper. Identify the vertex, axis of symmetry, *x*- and *y*-intercepts, domain, and range. Tell whether the graph opens up or down.

27. $y = |x + 9|$

28. $y = -|x| - 4$

29. $y = |x - 3| + 6$

Solve. Show your work.

30. The cost of a spice varies directly with its weight. If 5.2 ounces of spice cost $2.90, find the cost of 7.8 ounces of the spice.

31. What is the equation of a line that is parallel to the line that passes through the points $(3, 7)$ and $(3, -10)$ and that contains the point $(9, 7)$?

Tell About It

Explain how you solve the problem. Show all your work.

32. How can you determine which of the points below are solutions to the inequality $5y < 3x - 8$? $(9, -4)$, $(-1, 6)$, $(-1, -20)$, and $(2, 15)$

Cumulative Review: Chapters 1–5

Name ______________________________ Date ____________

Circle the best answer.

1. Which number is irrational?

A. $\sqrt{16}$ **B.** $-\sqrt{25}$

C. $\sqrt{0.81}$ **D.** $\sqrt{6}$

2. Simplify.

$-5.9 - (-9.4)$

F. -15.3 **G.** -3.5

H. 3.5 **J.** 15.3

3. Simplify.

$|-24| \bullet 4^2 - |(3 - 5)^3|$

A. 9208
B. 392
C. 376
D. 184

4. What are the dimensions of the matrix below?

$$\begin{bmatrix} 3 & -5 & 8 & 5 & 5 \\ -2 & 9 & -2 & 3 & 1 \end{bmatrix}$$

F. 2×5 **G.** 5×2

H. 10×1 **J.** 10

5. $5\begin{bmatrix} -2 & 1 \\ -9 & 4 \end{bmatrix} =$

A. $\begin{bmatrix} -10 & 5 \\ -9 & 4 \end{bmatrix}$ **B.** $\begin{bmatrix} -2 & 1 \\ -45 & 20 \end{bmatrix}$

C. $\begin{bmatrix} 3 & 6 \\ -4 & 9 \end{bmatrix}$ **D.** $\begin{bmatrix} -10 & 5 \\ -45 & 20 \end{bmatrix}$

6. Solve.

$\frac{c}{-2} = -6$

F. $c = -12$ **G.** $c = -4$

H. $c = -3$ **J.** $c = 12$

7. Solve.

$19d + 2.3 = 7d - 1.3$

A. $d = -3$ **B.** $d = -0.3$

C. $d = 0.3$ **D.** $d = 3$

8. Solve.

$5(3x + 2) = 4x - 7$

F. $x = -\frac{17}{11}$ **G.** $x = -\frac{9}{11}$

H. $x = \frac{3}{11}$ **J.** $x = \frac{5}{19}$

9. Solve for a.

$3a + 7b = 2a - 9b$

A. $a = 16b$
B. $a = 2b$
C. $a = -2b$
D. $a = -16b$

10. Write $x < 23$ in interval notation.

F. $(-\infty, 23]$

G. $[-\infty, 23]$

H. $(-\infty, 23)$

J. $[-\infty, 23)$

11. Which inequality is graphed below?

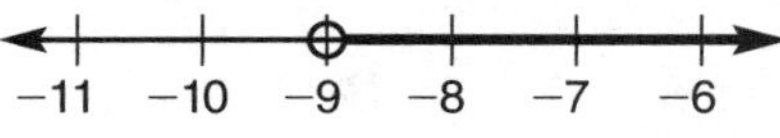

A. $x \geq -9$
B. $x > -9$
C. $x \leq -9$
D. $x < -9$

12. Solve.

$-2d - 18 \geq -12$

F. $d \leq -3$
G. $d \geq -3$
H. $d \geq 3$
J. $d \leq 3$

13. Solve for a.

$|2a - 4| + 3 \leq 13$

A. $-7 \leq a \leq 7$ **B.** $-3 \leq a \leq 3$
C. $-3 \leq a \leq 7$ **D.** $-7 \leq a \leq -3$

14. What is the domain of the relation?

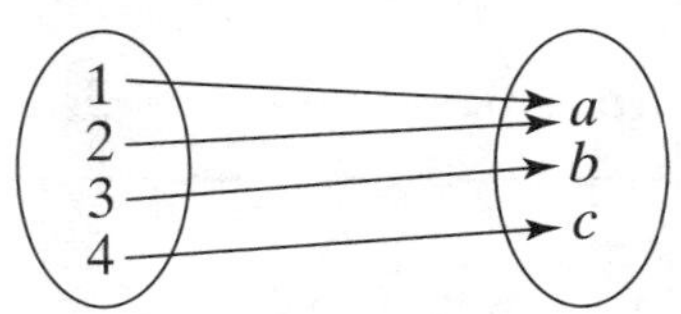

F. $\{a, b, c\}$
G. $\{1a, 2a, 3b, 4c\}$
H. $\{1, 2, 3, 4\}$
J. {all real numbers}

15. Which is a geometric sequence?

A. $\frac{3}{4}, 1, \frac{5}{4}, \frac{3}{2}, \frac{7}{4}, \ldots$
B. $-10, 20, -60, 240, -1200, \ldots$
C. $1, 3, 9, 27, 81, \ldots$
D. $240, 230, 220, 210, 200, \ldots$

16. What is the 10th term of the sequence?

$10, 20, 30, 40, \ldots$

F. 100 **G.** 110
H. 120 **J.** 130

17. Which is a linear function?

A. $y = x^3 + 9$ **B.** $2y = x^2 - 3$
C. $-4y = x^2 + 1$ **D.** $9y = 6x + 2$

18. Which function is a direct variation?

F. $y = 23x$ **G.** $y = 2x^2$
H. $y = -8x - 1$ **J.** $x = 3$

19. Write a rule that expresses a relationship between the values in the table.

x	y
−5	−7
−2	−1
0	3
3	9
6	15

A. $y = 2x + 3$ **B.** $y = 2x + 1$
C. $y = 2x - 3$ **D.** $y = 3x - 1$

20. What are the x- and y-intercepts of the equation $4x - 2y = 28$?

F. x-intercept: -14; y-intercept: 7
G. x-intercept: 14; y-intercept: -7
H. x-intercept: 7; y-intercept: -14
J. x-intercept: -7; y-intercept: 14

21. Which equation has a slope of 4 and a y-intercept of -2?

A. $y = -2x + 4$ **B.** $4x + 2y = -2$
C. $y = 4x - 2$ **D.** $-2y = 4x$

22. What is the vertex of the equation $y = |x - 2| + 4$?

F. $(2, -4)$ **G.** $(2, 4)$
H. $(-2, -4)$ **J.** $(-2, 4)$

Tell About It

Explain how you solve each problem. Show all your work.

23. Carlos started a business with 8 customers. Each month, his business increased by 4 customers. He would like 52 customers a month. How many months will it take him to reach his goal?

24. The formula for the surface area of a sphere is $SA = 4\pi r^2$. How can you find the surface area of a hemisphere (half of a sphere), including the base of the hemisphere?

6-1 Solve Systems of Linear Equations Graphically

Name ______________________ Date ____________

Solve the system by graphing: $\begin{cases} y = 3x - 1 \\ 2x - y = -1 \end{cases}$

Graph each line.

$y = 3x - 1$ ← The slope is 3, and the y-intercept is -1.

$2x - y = -1$ ← Solve for y to put the equation in slope-intercept form.
$y = 2x + 1$ ← The slope is 2, and the y-intercept is 1.

Locate the point of intersection.

(2, 5) ← This is the point where the two lines appear to intersect.

Check the solution in each of the original equations.

$y = 3x - 1$	$2x - y = -1$
$\mathbf{5} \stackrel{?}{=} 3(\mathbf{2}) - 1$	$2(\mathbf{2}) - \mathbf{5} \stackrel{?}{=} -1$
$\mathbf{5} \stackrel{?}{=} \mathbf{6} - 1$	$\mathbf{4} - \mathbf{5} \stackrel{?}{=} -1$
$5 = 5$ **True**	$-1 = -1$ **True**

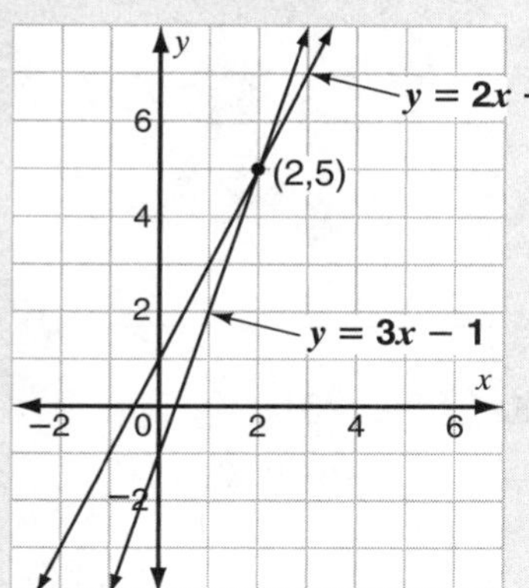

Remember: A *consistent* system has at least one solution. An *independent* system describes two different lines that share a solution.

Graph each system of equations and check the solution on a separate sheet of paper. Find the number of solutions and describe the system.

1. $\begin{cases} 4x - 2y = 4 \\ 3x + 2y = 10 \end{cases}$

$4x - 2y = 4$ is $y = 2x - 2$.
$3x + 2y = 10$ is $y = -\frac{3}{2}x + 5$.
intersecting lines
1 solution: (2, 2); consistent and independent system

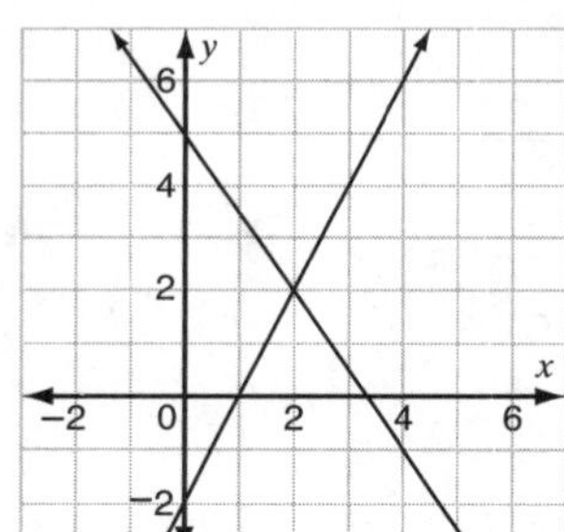

2. $\begin{cases} 10x + 5y = -20 \\ 6x - 3y = 12 \end{cases}$

____

3. $\begin{cases} 4x + 5y = -20 \\ 8x + 10y = 40 \end{cases}$

____

4. $\begin{cases} 7x + 3y = -21 \\ 14x + 6y = 36 \end{cases}$

____

5. $\begin{cases} x - 2y = 11 \\ 2x + y = 2 \end{cases}$

____

6. $\begin{cases} 2x - y = -7 \\ 3x + 4y = 6 \end{cases}$

____

7. $\begin{cases} y = -\frac{2}{3}x + 7 \\ 2x + 3y = 21 \end{cases}$

____

8. $\begin{cases} y = \frac{3}{5}x + 2 \\ 3x - 5y = -10 \end{cases}$

____

Graph each system of equations and check the solution on a separate sheet of paper. Find the number of solutions and describe the system.

9. $\begin{cases} 4x + 2y = 18 \\ x + 2y = 3 \end{cases}$

10. $\begin{cases} 6x + y = -14 \\ 4x + 5y = 8 \end{cases}$

11. $\begin{cases} 2x - 4y = -34 \\ -2x + 7y = 52 \end{cases}$

12. $\begin{cases} 3x - 5y = 31 \\ -3x + 8y = -37 \end{cases}$

13. $\begin{cases} 3y = -4x + 5 \\ 8x + 6y = 10 \end{cases}$

14. $\begin{cases} 5y = -2x + 3 \\ 6x + 15y = 9 \end{cases}$

15. $\begin{cases} 3x = 5y + 16 \\ x - 16 = 7y \end{cases}$

16. $\begin{cases} 5x = 4y - 19 \\ x + 17 = 14y \end{cases}$

17. $\begin{cases} 9y = 2y - 14 \\ y + 8 = 4 \end{cases}$

18. $\begin{cases} 8x = 4x + 24 \\ x + 9 = 2 \end{cases}$

19. $\begin{cases} 4x = 3y - 1 \\ x - 8 = -6 \end{cases}$

20. $\begin{cases} 5x = 2y + 10 \\ x - 6 = -2 \end{cases}$

21. $\begin{cases} 3x + 7y = 5y + 3x - 8 \\ 2x - 6y = -2 - 6y \end{cases}$

22. $\begin{cases} 5x + 2y = 2y + 3x - 6 \\ 4y - 3x = -4 - 3x \end{cases}$

23. $\begin{cases} \frac{1}{2}y = \frac{2}{3}y - \frac{1}{4} \\ 8x - 18 = 6y \end{cases}$

24. $\begin{cases} \frac{1}{4}y = \frac{1}{5}x - \frac{1}{3} \\ 15y = 12x - 30 \end{cases}$

25. $\begin{cases} 1.2y = 3.6x + 6 \\ 4.6x + 13.8 = 2.3y \end{cases}$

26. $\begin{cases} 1.8y = 5.4x - 3.6 \\ 17.5x - 21 = 3.5y \end{cases}$

Write the system of equations that is shown by each graph. Describe each system as consistent or inconsistent and as dependent or independent.

27.
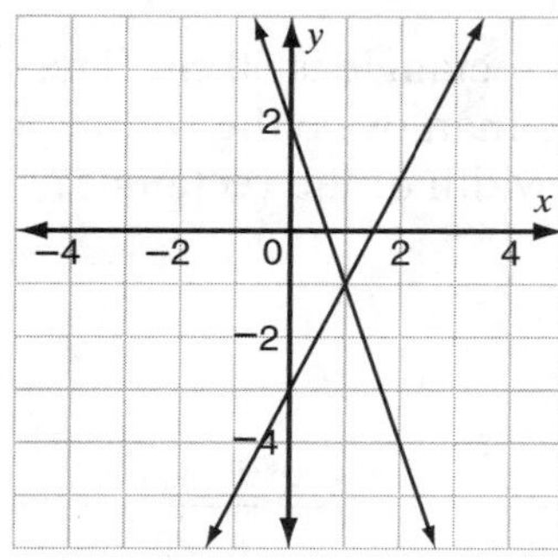

$\begin{cases} y = -3x + 2 \\ y = 2x - 3 \end{cases}$

consistent and independent

28.
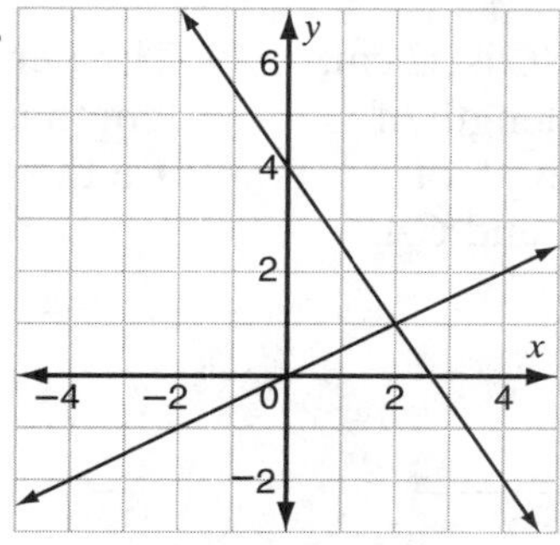

29.
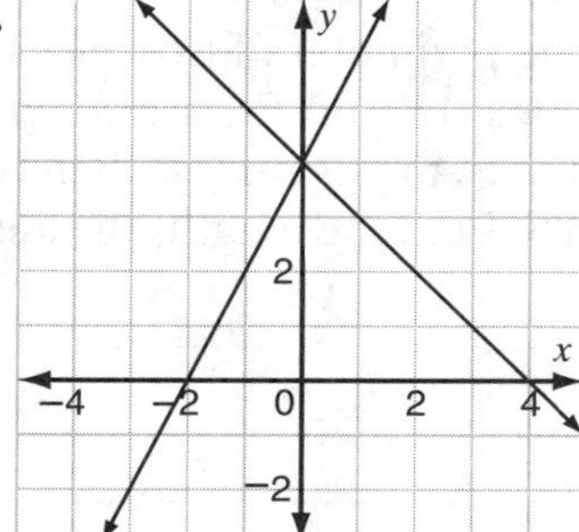

30.
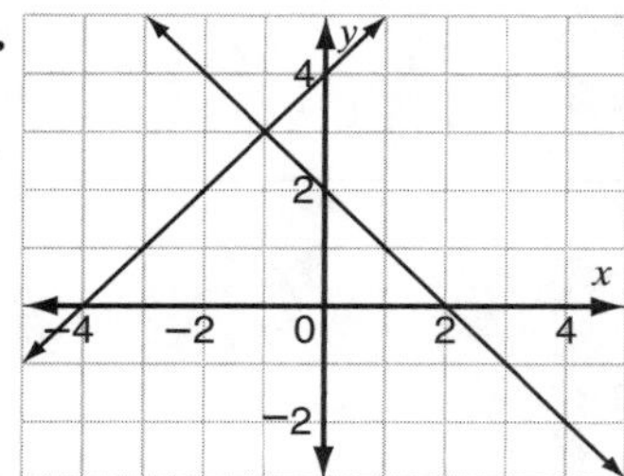

31.
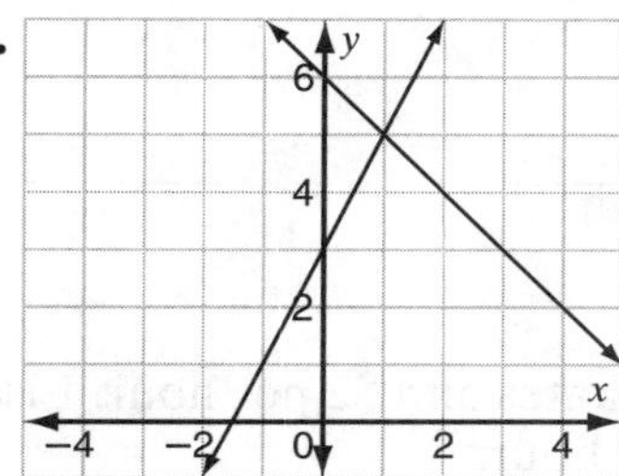

32.
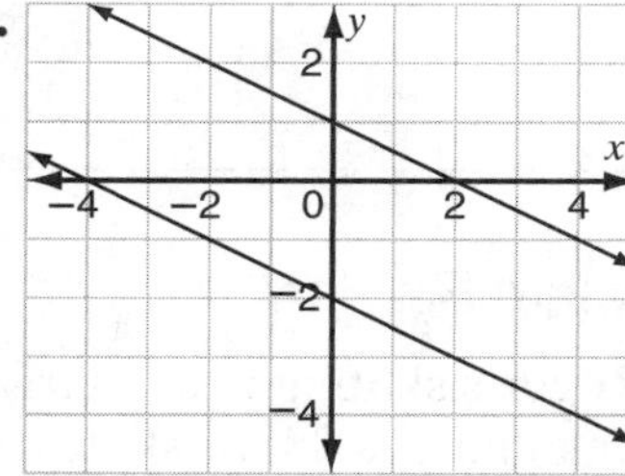

33.
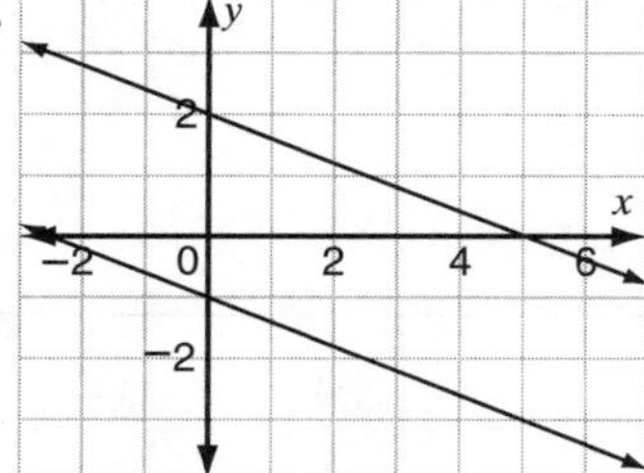

34.
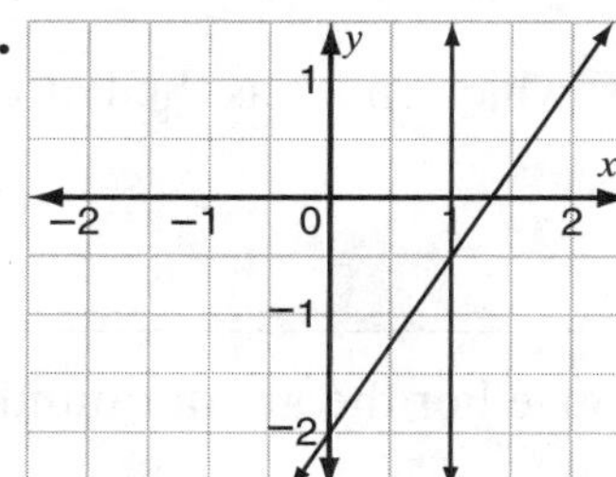

35.
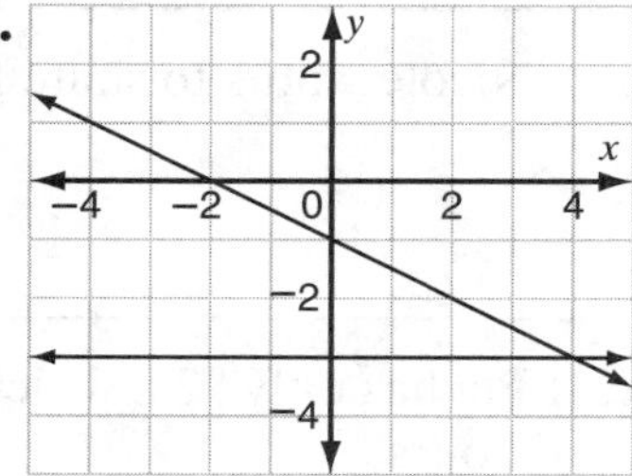

Solve. Show your work.
Use a separate sheet of paper to graph all systems of equations.

36. The sum of two numbers is 55. Their difference is 7. Find the numbers.

37. The sum of two numbers is 6. One number is 18 more than the other number. Find the numbers.

Solve. Use a separate sheet of paper to graph all systems of equations.

38. The perimeter of isosceles triangle ABC is 52 cm. Sides AB and BC are congruent. The length of side CA is 12 cm less than twice the length of AB. Find the lengths of sides AB, BC, and CA.

____

39. The perimeter of a rectangle is 30 cm. The length is 3 cm more than twice the width. What are the length and width of the rectangle?

____

40. Chiara has a can that contains 100 nickels and dimes. The number of dimes is 10 more than twice the number of nickels. How many nickels and how many dimes does Chiara have?

____

41. Carlos has 20 coins in his pocket. He has only quarters and dimes. The number of quarters is 1 less than half the number of dimes. How many dimes and quarters does Carlos have?

____

Problem Solving

42. Roger's skating rink charges \$4 for skates and \$2 per hour. Lisa's skating rink charges \$8 for skates and \$1 per hour.

a. When is the total cost the same for both skating rinks? What is that total cost?

____

b. If Nicole wants to skate for 2 hours, which rink has the better deal?

____

c. If Pia has only \$20, which rink will give her the greater number of hours?

____

CRITICAL THINKING

43. For what values of a and b does the system of equations have no solution?

$$\begin{cases} y = \frac{3}{4}x + 2 \\ ax + y = b \end{cases}$$

____

____

____

6-2 Solve Systems of Linear Equations by Substitution

Name ______________________ Date __________

Solve: $\begin{cases} 2x + y = 13 \\ 3x - 2y = 2 \end{cases}$

Solve the first equation for y.

$2x + y = 13$ ← first equation

$-2x + 2x + y = -2x + 13$ ← Use the Subtraction Property of Equality.

$y = -2x + 13$

Substitute: $3x - 2y = 2$ ← second equation

$3x - 2(-2x + 13) = 2$ ← Substitute $-2x + 13$ for y.

$3x + 4x - 26 = 2$ ← Then use the Distributive Property.

$7x - 26 = 2$ ← Combine like terms.

$7x - 26 + 26 = 2 + 26$ ← Use the Addition Property of Equality.

$7x = 28$

$\frac{7x}{7} = \frac{28}{7}$ ← Use the Division Property of Equality.

$x = 4$

$2(4) + y = 13$ ← Substitute 4 for x into the equation $2x + y = 13$. Solve for y.

$8 + y = 13$

$-8 + 8 + y = -8 + 13$ ← Use the Subtraction Property of Equality.

$y = 5$

Check: Substitute 4 for x and 5 for y in both of the original equations.

First equation:

$2x + y = 13$

$2(\mathbf{4}) + \mathbf{5} \stackrel{?}{=} 13$

$\mathbf{8} + \mathbf{5} \stackrel{?}{=} 13$

$13 = 13$ **True**

Second equation:

$3x - 2y = 2$

$3(\mathbf{4}) - 2(\mathbf{5}) \stackrel{?}{=} 2$

$\mathbf{12} - \mathbf{10} \stackrel{?}{=} 2$

$2 = 2$ **True**

So the solution of the system of equations is (4, 5).

Solve each system of equations. Check your answer on a separate sheet of paper.

1. $\begin{cases} y = x + 3 \\ 3x + 2y = 11 \end{cases}$

$3x + 2y = 11$

$3x + 2(x + 3) = 11$

$3x + 2x + 6 = 11$

$5x + 6 = 11$

$5x = 5$

$x = 1$

$y = (1) + 3 = 4$

(1, 4)

2. $\begin{cases} y = x - 3 \\ 3x + 2y = 14 \end{cases}$

____

3. $\begin{cases} x - 3y = -10 \\ 5x + 3y = 4 \end{cases}$

____

4. $\begin{cases} x + 4y = 6 \\ 6x + 2y = -8 \end{cases}$

____

5. $\begin{cases} 4x - 5y = 8 \\ 0.5x + 1.5y = -7.5 \end{cases}$

____

6. $\begin{cases} 6x - 2y = -28 \\ 0.7x + 2.8y = -6.3 \end{cases}$

____

Solve each system of equations. Check your answer on a separate sheet of paper.

7. $\begin{cases} 16x - 2y = 8 \\ 8x + 3y = 12 \end{cases}$

8. $\begin{cases} 9x - 3y = 3 \\ 12x + 5y = 13 \end{cases}$

9. $\begin{cases} 2x - 5y = 0 \\ 3x + 2y = 57 \end{cases}$

$y = -4 + 8x$; $8x + 3(-4 + 8x) = 12$

$8x - 12 + 24x = 12$; $32x = 24$; $x = \frac{3}{4}$

$16\left(\frac{3}{4}\right) - 2y = 8$; $12 - 2y = 8$

$-2y = -4$; $y = 2$

$\left(\frac{3}{4}, 2\right)$

10. $\begin{cases} 7x - 4y = 0 \\ 2x + 3y = 58 \end{cases}$

11. $\begin{cases} \frac{1}{2}x - \frac{3}{5}y = \frac{13}{20} \\ \frac{2}{3}x + \frac{3}{4}y = -\frac{1}{6} \end{cases}$

12. $\begin{cases} \frac{4}{5}x - \frac{1}{4}y = \frac{7}{10} \\ -\frac{1}{3}x + \frac{5}{16}y = -\frac{3}{8} \end{cases}$

Solve. Show your work.

13. Age Julio's father is 4 times as old as Julio. In 10 years, he will be 2 less than Julio's age times 3. How old are Julio and his father?

14. Money Mary collected $2.75 in nickels and dimes. Ten less than twice the number of nickels represents the number of dimes she has. How many of each kind of coin did Mary collect?

CHALLENGE

15. Solve: $\begin{cases} y = ax \\ 2ax + 3y = 4a \end{cases}$

6-3 Solve Systems of Linear Equations by Elimination

Name ____________________ Date __________

Solve: $\begin{cases} 5a + 3b = 113 \\ 7a - 3b = 7 \end{cases}$

1 Add the equations.

$$\begin{array}{r} 5a + 3b = 113 \\ +\ 7a - 3b = 7 \\ \hline 12a = 120 \end{array}$$

← $3b$ and $-3b$ are opposites.

← Use the Addition Property of Equality.

$$\frac{12a}{12} = \frac{120}{12}$$ ← Use the Division Property of Equality.

$$a = 10$$

2 Substitute 10 for a in one of the original equations. Solve for b.

$$5(10) + 3b = 113$$ ← Solve for b by substituting 10 for a.

$$50 - 50 + 3b = 113 - 50$$ ← Use the Subtraction Property of Equality.

$$\frac{3b}{3} = \frac{63}{3}$$ ← Use the Division Property of Equality.

$$b = 21$$

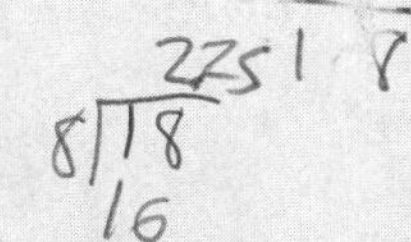

Check: Substitute 10 for a and 21 for b in both of the original equations to check.

$$5a + 3b = 113 \qquad\qquad 7a - 3b = 7$$

$$5(\mathbf{10}) + 3(\mathbf{21}) \stackrel{?}{=} 113 \qquad\qquad 7(\mathbf{10}) - 3(\mathbf{21}) \stackrel{?}{=} 7$$

$$\mathbf{50 + 63 = 113} \qquad\qquad \mathbf{70 - 63 = 7}$$

$$113 = 113 \text{ **True**} \qquad\qquad 7 = 7 \text{ **True**}$$

So the solution of the system of equations is (10, 21).

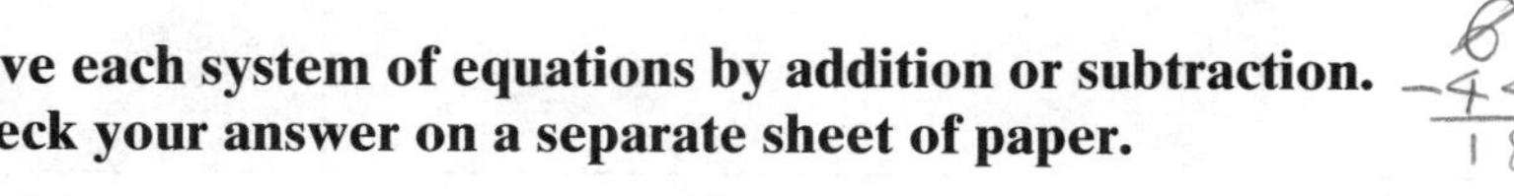

Solve each system of equations by addition or subtraction. Check your answer on a separate sheet of paper.

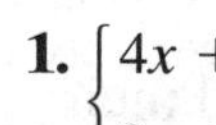

1. $\begin{cases} 4x + y = 56 \\ 2x + y = 34 \end{cases}$

$$\begin{array}{r} \mathbf{4x + y = 56} \\ \mathbf{-\ (2x + y = 34)} \\ \hline \mathbf{2x = 22} \\ \mathbf{x = 11} \\ \mathbf{4(11) + y = 56} \\ \mathbf{44 + y = 56} \\ \mathbf{y = 12} \end{array}$$

(11, 12)

2. $\begin{cases} 5x + y = 62 \\ 3x + y = 44 \end{cases}$

3. $\begin{cases} -4x + 5y = 36 \\ 4x + 6y = 52 \end{cases}$

4. $\begin{cases} 3x + 2y = 45 \\ -3x + 6y = 3 \end{cases}$

5. $\begin{cases} 2x - 0.7 = 5y \\ 0.3 + 5y = 3x \end{cases}$

6. $\begin{cases} -2y = 6x + 3.8 \\ 5x + 2.8 = 2y \end{cases}$

7. $\begin{cases} a + b = \frac{9}{10} \\ 5a + b = \frac{5}{2} \end{cases}$

8. $\begin{cases} 6c + d = \frac{4}{3} \\ c + d = \frac{1}{2} \end{cases}$

Solve each system of equations by addition or subtraction. Check your answer on a separate sheet of paper.

9. $\begin{cases} 4p - 8q = -2 \\ 8p + 3 = -8q \end{cases}$

10. $\begin{cases} 12v - 6w = 6 \\ 24v + 3 = -6w \end{cases}$

11. $\begin{cases} -2t = u \\ 2u = 2t + 14.4 \end{cases}$

12. $\begin{cases} -3m = n \\ 2n = 3m - 13.5 \end{cases}$

Solve. Show your work.

13. Wie spent \$7.75 for x apples at \$1.25 per pound and y oranges at \$2 per pound. Jason spent \$8.25 for x apples at \$1.25 per pound and y oranges at \$2.25 per pound. How many pounds of fruit did each person buy?

14. Exercise Holly spends 30.5 min on an exercise bike and 45.5 min on an elliptical trainer, and she burns 504.25 cal. Kate spends 23 min on the exercise bike and 45.5 min on the elliptical trainer, and she burns 472 cal. How many cal per min are burned on each machine?

15. The sum of two numbers is $\frac{31}{35}$, and their difference is $\frac{11}{35}$. What are the numbers?

16. The sum of two numbers is -12.43 and their difference is 117.77. What are the numbers?

TEST PREPARATION

17. If $-2y = x$ and $3x + 2y = -4$, then what is xy?

A. 6 **B.** -2 **C.** -4 **D.** -12

18. If $-\frac{1}{2}x + 5 = y$ and $\frac{1}{2}x - \frac{1}{3}y = 1$, then what is $x \div y$?

F. 0.75 **G.** 1 **H.** $\frac{4}{3}$ **J.** 12

6-4 Solve Equivalent Systems of Linear Equations with the Same Solution

Name ______________________________ Date ____________

Solve: $\begin{cases} 4x + 5y = -7 \\ 6x - 7y = 33 \end{cases}$

1 Add the equations.

$$\begin{array}{rl} 7(4x + 5y = -7) & \\ +\ 5(6x - 7y = 33) & \\ \hline 28x + 35y = -49 & \\ +\ 30x - 35y = 165 & \\ \hline 58x \qquad = 116 & \end{array}$$

← Use the Multiplication Property of Equality.

$$\frac{58x}{58} = \frac{116}{58}$$

← Use the Division Property of Equality.

$$x = 2$$

2 Substitute 2 for x in one of the original equations. Solve for y.

$4(2) + 5y = -7$ ← Solve for y by substituting 2 for x.

$$8 + 5y = -7$$
$$8 - 8 + 5y = -7 - 8$$
$$5y = -15$$

$5y \div 5 = -15 \div 5$ ← Use the Division Property of Equality.

$$y = -3$$

Check: Substitute 2 for x and -3 for y in both of the original equations to check.

$$4x + 5y = -7$$
$$4(\mathbf{2}) + 5(\mathbf{-3}) \stackrel{?}{=} -7$$
$$\mathbf{8 - 15} \stackrel{?}{=} -7$$
$$-7 = -7 \textbf{ True}$$

$$6x - 7y = 33$$
$$6(\mathbf{2}) - 7(\mathbf{-3}) \stackrel{?}{=} 33$$
$$\mathbf{12 + 21} \stackrel{?}{=} 33$$
$$33 = 33 \textbf{ True}$$

So the solution of the system of equations is (2, −3).

Solve each system of equations. Check your answer on a separate sheet of paper.

1. $\begin{cases} 3x + 2y = 22 \\ 2x + 4y = 28 \end{cases}$

$$\begin{array}{rl} \mathbf{-2(3x + 2y = 22)} \\ \mathbf{+\ 2x + 4y = 28} \\ \hline \mathbf{-6x - 4y = -44} \\ \mathbf{+\ 2x + 4y = 28} \\ \hline \mathbf{-4x \qquad = -16} \\ \mathbf{x = 4} \\ \mathbf{3(4) + 2y = 22} \\ \mathbf{2y = 10} \\ \mathbf{y = 5;\ (4, 5)} \end{array}$$

2. $\begin{cases} 5x + 3y = 42 \\ 2x + 6y = 60 \end{cases}$ ______

3. $\begin{cases} 3x - 5y = -36 \\ 5x + 2y = 2 \end{cases}$ ______

4. $\begin{cases} 6x + 4y = 30 \\ 2x - 5y = 29 \end{cases}$ ______

5. $\begin{cases} 8c + 2d = 1 \\ 12c + 4d = 1 \end{cases}$ ______

6. $\begin{cases} 9a + 6b = -1 \\ 6a + 9b = 1 \end{cases}$ ______

7. $\begin{cases} 14 - 8s = -10r \\ 5r = 5 - 12s \end{cases}$ ______

8. $\begin{cases} -10 - 12q = -6p \\ 24p + 37 = -18q \end{cases}$ ______

Use with SOURCEBOOK Lesson 6-4, pages 158–159.

Solve each system of equations. Check your answer on a separate sheet of paper.

9. $\begin{cases} 3x - 5y = 12 \\ 12.6x - 21y = 1 \end{cases}$

10. $\begin{cases} 13.8x + 9.2y = -4 \\ 6x + 4y = 8 \end{cases}$

11. $\begin{cases} \frac{1}{2}x - \frac{2}{3}y = 8 \\ \frac{3}{20}x - \frac{1}{5}y = 2\frac{2}{5} \end{cases}$

Solve. Show your work. 3a = 51¢

12. Three apples and 2 oranges cost $0.65. Two apples and 5 oranges cost $0.80. What is the cost of 1 apple and 1 orange?

1 orange is 10¢, 1 apple is 15¢

13. On Monday, Ming works 4 h 30 min, and Dahlia works 3.5 h. Together, they earn $78.15. On Tuesday, Ming works 5 h 12 min, and Dahlia works 4.8 h. Together, they earn $98.92. What is each person's hourly rate?

14. Geometry Two angles are complementary. One angle is 2° less than 3 times the other angle. Find the measure of each angle. (*Hint:* The sum of the measures of complementary angles is 90°.)

23° & 67°

15. Geometry Two angles are supplementary. One angle is 15° less than 2 times the other angle. Find the measure of each angle. (*Hint:* The sum of the measures of supplementary angles is 180°.)

65° & 115°

WRITE ABOUT IT

16. By which variables should you multiply each equation in the system $\begin{cases} ax + by = c \\ dx - ey = f \end{cases}$ of equations to eliminate x? Explain your answer.

6-5 Apply Systems of Linear Equations

Name ______________________________ Date ____________

Juan mixes a 30% acid solution and a 60% acid solution to get 6 quarts of a 50% acid solution. How many quarts of each solution does he use?

Let x = amount of 30% solution. Let y = amount of 60% solution.

	30% Solution	+	60% Solution	=	50% Solution		equation
Amount of solution (qt)	x	+	y	=	6	→	$x + y = 6$
Amount of acid (qt)	$0.3x$	+	$0.6y$	=	0.5(6)	→	$0.3x + 0.6y = 3$

Solve: $\begin{cases} x + y = 6 \\ 0.3x + 0.6y = 3 \end{cases}$

1 Add the equations.

$-0.3(x + y = 6)$ ← Use the Multiplication Property of Equality.

$+\ 0.3x + 0.6y = 3$

$-0.3x - 0.3y = -1.8$

$+\ 0.3x + 0.6y = 3$

$0.3y = 1.2$ ← Use the Addition Property of Equality to combine equations.

$\frac{0.3y}{0.3} = \frac{1.2}{0.3}$ ← Use the Division Property of Equality.

$y = 4$

2 Substitute 4 for y into one of the original equations. Solve for x.

$x + (4) = 6$ ← Solve for x by substituting 4 for y.

$x + 4 - 4 = 6 - 4$ ← Use the Subtraction Property of Equality.

$x = 2$

Check: Substitute 2 for x and 4 for y in both of the original equations to check.

$x + y = 6$

$(\mathbf{2}) + (\mathbf{4}) \stackrel{?}{=} 6$

$6 = 6$ **True**

$0.3x + 0.6y = 3$

$0.3(\mathbf{2}) + 0.6(\mathbf{4}) \stackrel{?}{=} 3$

$\mathbf{0.6} + \mathbf{2.4} \stackrel{?}{=} 3$

$3 = 3$ **True**

So Juan uses 2 quarts of 30% acid solution and 4 quarts of 60% acid solution.

Solve each problem by writing and solving a system of linear equations. Check your answer on a separate sheet of paper.

1. The Drama Club sold 787 tickets to the school play for \$1889. Tickets cost \$3 for adults and \$2 for students. How many adult tickets and how many student tickets did the club sell?

   Let a = number of adult tickets sold.
   Let s = number of student tickets sold.

   Solve: $\begin{cases} a + s = 787 \\ 3a + 2s = 1889 \end{cases}$

   $-2(a + s = 787)$

   $-2a - 2s = -1574$

   $+\ 3a + 2s = 1889$

   $a = 315$

   $a + s = 787$

   $(315) + s = 787$

   $s = 472$

   adult tickets: 315; student tickets: 472

2. A theater sold 925 tickets for \$4725. Tickets cost \$6 for adults and \$3 for children. How many adult tickets and how many children's tickets did the theater sell?

   ____

Solve each problem by writing and solving a system of linear equations. Check your answer on a separate sheet of paper.

3. A boat takes 4 hours to go 44 miles downstream with the current. It takes 8.8 hours to go 44 miles upstream against the current. What is the speed of the current? What is the speed of the boat? (*Hint:* distance = rate • time)

4. A boat takes 3 hours to go 42 miles downstream with the current. It takes 4.2 hours to go 42 miles upstream against the current. What is the speed of the current? What is the speed of the boat?

5. In 4 years, John will be $\frac{4}{3}$ Grace's age. Five years ago, John was 1 year more than twice Grace's age. How old are John and Grace now?

6. In 6 years, Sylvia will be $\frac{6}{5}$ Hue's age. Four years ago, Sylvia was 10 years less than twice Hue's age. How old are Sylvia and Hue now?

7. A gardener mixes a 10% nitrogen solution with a 20% nitrogen solution to make 4 quarts of a 16.25% nitrogen solution. How many quarts of each does he use?

8. A farmer mixes a 20% fertilizer solution with a 40% fertilizer solution to make 8 quarts of a 33.75% fertilizer solution. How many quarts of each does he use?

MENTAL MATH

Multiply.

9. 42(51)

10. $\frac{5}{6}\left(12\frac{1}{2}\right)$

11. −15(29)

12. −9(7.2)

6-6 Graph Systems of Linear Inequalities

Name ________________________________ Date ____________

Solve by graphing: $\begin{cases} 3x + 2y \geq 8 \\ x - 3y > -6 \end{cases}$

Then name two ordered pairs that are solutions and two that are not.

1 Graph the first inequality.

$3x + 2y \geq 8$

$y \geq -\frac{3}{2}x + 4$ ← Solve the inequality for y.

$m = -\frac{3}{2}, b = 4$

This region *includes* the boundary line $y = -\frac{3}{2}x + 4$ and all points *above* it.

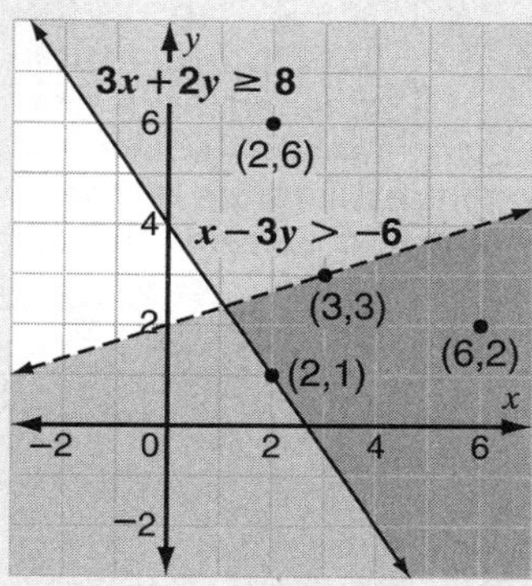

2 Graph the second inequality.

$x - 3y > -6$

$y < \frac{1}{3}x + 2$ ← Solve the inequality for y.

$m = \frac{1}{3}, b = 2$

This region lies *below* the boundary line $y = \frac{1}{3}x + 2$.

3 The solution of the system of inequalities consists of coordinates of all ordered pairs in the area where the shaded regions *intersect.*

(2, 1) and (6, 2) are solutions.
(2, 6) and (3, 3) are not solutions.

On a separate sheet of paper, graph the system of inequalities. Tell if the given ordered pair is a solution of the system.

1. $\begin{cases} x + 2y > -3 \\ 3x + 4y < 12 \end{cases}$ (1, 2)

2. $\begin{cases} 4x - y < -6 \\ x + 3y > 8 \end{cases}$ (−2, 5)

3. $\begin{cases} 3x - 2y \geq -1 \\ 2x + y < 6 \end{cases}$ (10.3, −3.8)

$x + 2y > -3$	$3x + 4y < 12$
$1 + 2(2) \overset{?}{>} -3$	$3(1) + 4(2) \overset{?}{<} 12$
$1 + 4 \overset{?}{>} -3$	$3 + 8 \overset{?}{<} 12$
True: $5 > -3$	True: $11 < 12$

yes

______________ ______________ ______________

4. $\begin{cases} 2x - 5y > 3 \\ 3x + 2y \leq 6 \end{cases}$ (−4.9, 5.1)

5. $\begin{cases} 3x - 8y \geq 7 \\ 6x + 16y \leq -6 \end{cases}$ $\left(\frac{2}{3}, -\frac{5}{8}\right)$

6. $\begin{cases} 4x - 12y \leq -13 \\ 8x + 6y \leq 0 \end{cases}$ $\left(-\frac{3}{4}, \frac{5}{6}\right)$

______________ ______________ ______________

For More Practice Go To:

ONLINE www.progressinmathematics.com Practice/Test Generator

On a separate sheet of paper, graph each system of inequalities. Describe the solution.

7. $\begin{cases} y \le x - 6 \\ y > x - 10 \end{cases}$

8. $\begin{cases} y < x + 4 \\ y \ge x - 4 \end{cases}$

9. $\begin{cases} 0.1x + 0.2y \ge 7 \\ 3.2x + 6.4y \ge -32 \end{cases}$

$y \le x - 6$	$y > x - 10$
$m = 1$; $b = -6$	$m = 1$; $b = -10$
solid line	dashed line
shaded below	shaded above

The solutions are all points on the solid upper line and between the parallel lines.

10. $\begin{cases} 5.2x + 3.6y \le -3 \\ 26x + 18y \le -2 \end{cases}$

11. $\begin{cases} \frac{5}{6} > 3y - \frac{1}{4} \\ \frac{5}{2} + y > \frac{11}{3} \end{cases}$

12. $\begin{cases} \frac{1}{4} > 5x + \frac{2}{3} \\ \frac{3}{2} + x > \frac{8}{5} \end{cases}$

Problem Solving

Graph each system on grid paper to show all possible solutions. Then name three ordered pairs that are solutions.

13. Online shopping An online media company sells customers songs for $1 and TV shows for $2.50. José wants to spend no more than $15 but wants to buy at least 4 items (songs and/or shows).

14. Groceries Toothpaste costs $3.50, and toothbrushes cost $1.25. If Keisha has only $12.50 and needs more than three toothbrushes or toothpastes, how many of each could she buy?

SPIRAL REVIEW

15. Graph: $\begin{cases} 2x + y = 9 \\ 2x + 2y = 8 \end{cases}$
Find and describe the solution.

16. Find the x- and y-intercepts of the equation.
$6x - 9y = 18$

17. Determine whether the sequence could be geometric, arithmetic, or neither. Use a pattern to write the next three terms.
500, 5, 0.05, 0.0005, . . .

6-7 Technology: Graph Systems of Equations

Name ______________________ Date __________

You can use a handheld to graph and solve a system of equations.

$$\begin{cases} y = 2x - 7 \\ y = -4x + 17 \end{cases}$$

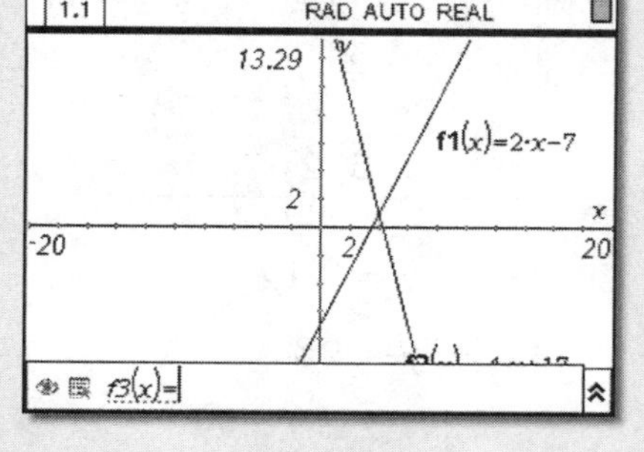

Step 1 Press (home). Then choose (2) to select **Graphs & Geometry**.

Step 2 Input $2x - 7$, then press (enter) to graph the line.

Step 3 Input $-4x + 17$, then press (enter) to graph the line.

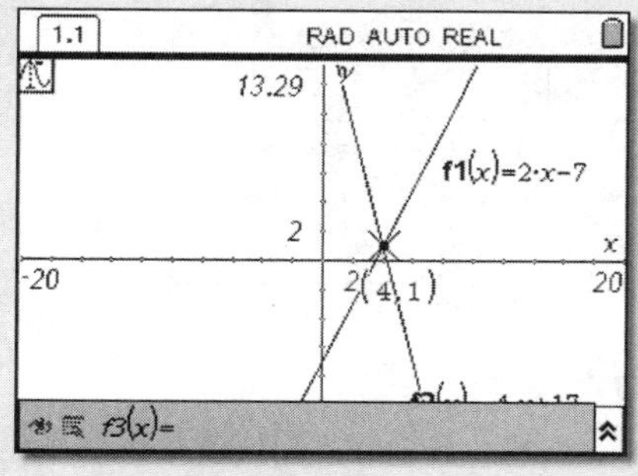

Step 4 Press (menu). Select **Trace**, then **Graph Trace**.

Step 5 Press (menu). Select **Trace**, then **Trace Settings**. Change **Trace Step** to 1, then press (tab) (enter) for **OK**.

Step 6 Press (▶) to move the trace along the line to the intersection of the two lines.

The lines intersect at (4, 1).

Think
Trace shows the coordinates.

Use a handheld to solve the system of linear equations. Check your solutions.

1. $\begin{cases} y = -x + 8 \\ y = x + 4 \end{cases}$ **(2, 6)**

2. $\begin{cases} y = x - 3 \\ y = -x + 13 \end{cases}$ ______

3. $\begin{cases} y = 4x - 5 \\ y = 3x - 3 \end{cases}$ ______

4. $\begin{cases} y = 3x - 8 \\ y = -x + 8 \end{cases}$ ______

5. $\begin{cases} y = -4x - 6 \\ y = 3x + 1 \end{cases}$ ______

6. $\begin{cases} y = -2x + 5 \\ y = 3x - 15 \end{cases}$ ______

7. $\begin{cases} y = -3x + 5 \\ y = 2x - 10 \end{cases}$ ______

8. $\begin{cases} y = 5x - 5 \\ y = 2x + 1 \end{cases}$ ______

9. $\begin{cases} y = 3x - 3 \\ y = -2x + 7 \end{cases}$ ______

10. $\begin{cases} y = 4x - 11 \\ y = -x + 4 \end{cases}$ ______

11. $\begin{cases} y = 5x + 11 \\ y = -3x - 5 \end{cases}$ ______

12. $\begin{cases} y = 2x + 8 \\ y = -4x - 10 \end{cases}$ ______

13. $\begin{cases} y = -\frac{1}{2}x + 8 \\ y = \frac{1}{4}x + 5 \end{cases}$ ______

14. $\begin{cases} y = -\frac{1}{5}x - 1 \\ y = \frac{3}{5}x - 5 \end{cases}$ ______

15. $\begin{cases} y = -\frac{2}{3}x - 10 \\ y = \frac{7}{9}x + 3 \end{cases}$ ______

16. $\begin{cases} y = -\frac{5}{6}x - 13 \\ y = \frac{11}{12}x + 8 \end{cases}$ ______

Use with SOURCEBOOK Lesson 6-7, pages 166–167.

Use a handheld to solve the system of linear equations. Check your solutions. (*Hint:* Solve for y first.)

17. $\begin{cases} 2x + y = 14 \\ x - y = 4 \end{cases}$

(6, 2)

18. $\begin{cases} 3x + y = 22 \\ x - y = -2 \end{cases}$

19. $\begin{cases} x + 3y = 1 \\ x - 2y = 11 \end{cases}$

20. $\begin{cases} x + 2y = -12 \\ x - 3y = 28 \end{cases}$

21. $\begin{cases} 3x + 2y = -24 \\ 2x - 5y = 41 \end{cases}$

22. $\begin{cases} 4x + 3y = -39 \\ 3x - 6y = 12 \end{cases}$

23. $\begin{cases} 2x - 5y = -30 \\ 3x - 2y = -34 \end{cases}$

24. $\begin{cases} 3x - 4y = -34 \\ 5x - 2y = -38 \end{cases}$

25. $\begin{cases} 5x - 10y = 55 \\ 7x + 3y = 111 \end{cases}$

26. $\begin{cases} 9x - 5y = 97 \\ 8x + 4y = 120 \end{cases}$

27. $\begin{cases} 11x + 5y = 92 \\ 7x - 6y = 132 \end{cases}$

28. $\begin{cases} 13x + 5y = 230 \\ 11x - 7y = 262 \end{cases}$

Solve. Show your work.

29. Find the solution of each system of equations. Then write an equation of the line that contains the two points.

$\begin{cases} 2x + 3y = 27 \\ 5x - 2y = 1 \end{cases}$ and $\begin{cases} 4x + y = -11 \\ 3x - y = -3 \end{cases}$

30. Jacob paid \$21.75 for 5 pens and 7 pencils and Leticia paid \$23.25 for 9 of the same pens and 2 of the same pencils. What would one pen and one pencil cost? (*Hint:* Change **Trace Step**.)

CHALLENGE

31. Use a handheld to find the decimal coordinates of the point of intersection of the graphs of $3x - 10y = -50$ and $22x + 10y = 60$.

6-8 Technology: Graph Systems of Inequalities

Name ______________________________ Date ______________

You can use a handheld to graph the system. $\begin{cases} y > 0.5x - 2 \\ y \leq -3x + 5 \end{cases}$

Step 1 Press (home). Then choose (2) to select **Graphs & Geometry.**

Step 2 Use the (clear) key to delete the equal sign. Input $> 0.5x - 2$.
Press (enter) to graph the inequality.

Remember: The dashed line is not part of the solution set.

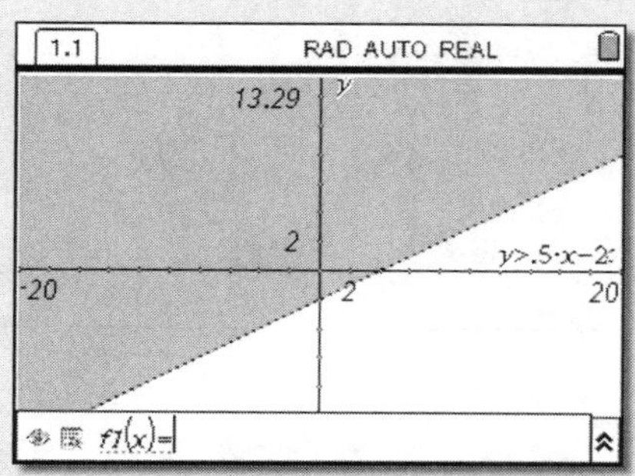

Step 3 Use the (clear) key to delete the equal sign. Input $\leq -3x + 5$. Use (ctrl) (<) to enter this inequality symbol.

Remember: The solid line is part of the solution set.

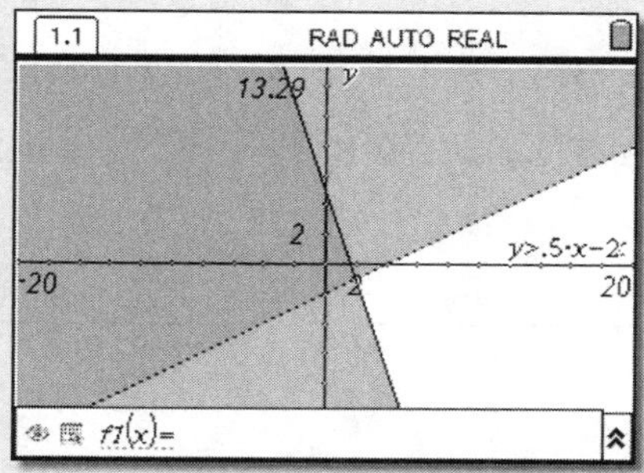

Name two points that are part of the solution set.
Points (0, 1) and (−2, 0) *appear* to be part of the solution set.
Choose test points and check the solution algebraically.

Use a handheld to graph the system. Then name two points that are part of the solution set.

1. $\begin{cases} y < 1 \\ y > 2x + 2 \end{cases}$ ____________

2. $\begin{cases} y \leq -x + 2 \\ y \leq 2 \end{cases}$ ____________

3. $\begin{cases} y > -x \\ y \leq 3 \end{cases}$ ____________

4. $\begin{cases} y \leq -x + 1 \\ y \leq x + 1 \end{cases}$ ____________

5. $\begin{cases} y > 2x + 1 \\ y < -3x + 4 \end{cases}$ ____________

6. $\begin{cases} y > 3x - 1 \\ y < -2x + 4 \end{cases}$ ____________

7. $\begin{cases} y \leq x + 2 \\ y \leq -x \end{cases}$ ____________

8. $\begin{cases} y \leq x \\ y \leq -x - 3 \end{cases}$ ____________

9. $\begin{cases} y \geq -5x + 4 \\ y \geq 2x + 3 \end{cases}$ ____________

10. $\begin{cases} y \geq -4x + 3 \\ y \geq 3x + 7 \end{cases}$ ____________

11. $\begin{cases} y \geq -\frac{1}{3}x - 6 \\ y < \frac{4}{5}x + 9 \end{cases}$ ____________

12. $\begin{cases} y \geq -\frac{1}{3}x - 2 \\ y < \frac{3}{4}x + 11 \end{cases}$ ____________

Use a handheld to graph the system. Then name two points that are part of the solution set. (*Hint*: Solve for *y* first.)

13. $\begin{cases} 2x + y > 10 \\ x - 2y < 8 \end{cases}$

14. $\begin{cases} 3x + y > 8 \\ x - 3y < 9 \end{cases}$

15. $\begin{cases} x + 4y \geq 3 \\ x - 5y > 12 \end{cases}$

16. $\begin{cases} x + 2y \geq 7 \\ x - 6y > 11 \end{cases}$

17. $\begin{cases} 5x + 4y < -24 \\ 3x - 7y > 52 \end{cases}$

18. $\begin{cases} 6x + 5y < -32 \\ 4x - 9y > 64 \end{cases}$

19. $\begin{cases} 4x + 10y \leq 58 \\ 3x + 8y \leq 29 \end{cases}$

20. $\begin{cases} 5x + 2y \leq 27 \\ 4x + 3y \leq -18 \end{cases}$

21. $\begin{cases} 2.1x + 3.4y > 1.5 \\ 1.7x + 5.6y > -9.8 \end{cases}$

22. $\begin{cases} 3.8x + 1.7y > 7.2 \\ 5.2x + 4.8y > -2.3 \end{cases}$

23. $\begin{cases} 4.5x - 6.8y < -12.3 \\ 8.01x + 2.2y > 4.9 \end{cases}$

24. $\begin{cases} 2.1x - 4.3y < -11.5 \\ 7.9x + 4.51y > 7.3 \end{cases}$

Solve.

25. Graph the system on a handheld. Then describe the solution set. Explain your reasoning.

$$\begin{cases} y > -\frac{3}{4}x - 5 \\ y > \frac{4}{3}x + 8 \\ 3x + 4y \leq 4 \\ 4x - 3y \leq 9 \end{cases}$$

26. The school band is selling 280 shirts and 150 shorts stamped with the school logo. They need sales of at least \$2000. A shirt sells for \$19.95 and shorts sell for \$12.95. How many of each do they need to sell to have at least \$2000? (*Hint*: Use (menu): Choose **Window** and **A: Zoom — Fit.**)

CHALLENGE

27. Graph a system of inequalities that has no solution. Explain how you created the system.

6-9 Problem-Solving Strategy: Work Backward

Read › Plan › Solve › Check

Name ______________________________ Date ____________

Work backward to solve.

1. A snail is at the bottom of a 15-foot well. Each day it climbs 7 inches up the well. Each night it slips down 4 inches. How many days will it take for the snail to climb out of the well?

____

2. The Smiths did some baking this week. On Monday, Sally added 12 cookies to the cookie jar. Later, Meg took 6 cookies out. On Tuesday, Lynn added 14 cookies. Later, Sally took 8. Ruth then took twice the number of cookies that were in the jar before Sally added hers. Now the jar holds 8 cookies. How many cookies did Ruth take?

____

3. Lin, Manuel, and Bea are playing a game. The player who wins each round gets half of the losing players' play money. In Round 1, Lin wins; she gets half of each of the other players' money. In round 2, Bea wins; she gets half of each of the other players' money. In round 3, Lin wins again; she gets half of each of each of the other players' money. After round 3, they find Lin has $112.50, Manuel has $12.50 and Bea has $50. How much money did they have at the start?

____

4. Kelly has a 6-L can and a 10-L can. How can she measure out exactly 8 L?

____

Use with SOURCEBOOK Lesson 6-9, pages 170–171.

5. Find the number of different paths an ant can use to advance from point P to point Q if (a) it must stay on the line segments;
(b) it must never backtrack; and
(c) it must only travel on a segment in the direction indicated.

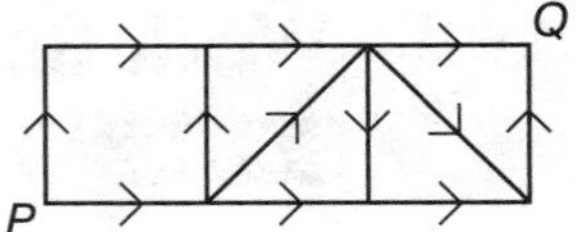

6. Gordon has a 10-min timer and a 7-minute timer. Using both timers, how can Gordon be sure that he leaves his soufflé in the oven for exactly 16 minutes?

7. Jerry accidentally spilled the entire jar of 46 toothpicks he brought for a school project. "Hey," said his friend, Jane, "Let's play a game. We can take 1, 2, 3, or 4 toothpicks at a time. The last one to pick up a toothpick loses. We'll alternate turns. You go first." If Jane wants to win, what should be her strategy?

8. A boy visits the amusement park on Park Island for three days. The island ferry costs \$2 each way. Each day before taking the ferry to the park, he counts his money and decides he will use exactly half of it at the park itself. If after his third trip to the park he has spent all his money, how much did he have at the start of the three days?

Enrichment:
Use Cramer's Rule to Solve Systems of Linear Equations

Name ______________________ Date ____________

Solve using Cramer's Rule: $\begin{cases} 5x = 7 - 2y \\ y = 3x - 13 \end{cases}$

First, rewrite the system in standard form: $\begin{cases} 5x + 2y = 7 \\ 3x - y = 13 \end{cases}$.

Find the following determinants.

$\begin{vmatrix} a & b \\ c & d \end{vmatrix} = ad - bc$ | $\begin{vmatrix} e & b \\ f & d \end{vmatrix} = de - bf$ | $\begin{vmatrix} a & e \\ c & f \end{vmatrix} = af - ce$

$\begin{vmatrix} 5 & 2 \\ 3 & -1 \end{vmatrix} = 5(-1) - 2(3) = -11$ | $\begin{vmatrix} 7 & 2 \\ 13 & -1 \end{vmatrix} = 7(-1) - 2(13) = -33$ | $\begin{vmatrix} 5 & 7 \\ 3 & 13 \end{vmatrix} = 5(13) - 7(3) = 44$

Then apply Cramer's Rule.

$x = \begin{vmatrix} e & b \\ f & d \end{vmatrix} \div \begin{vmatrix} a & b \\ c & d \end{vmatrix} = -33 \div (-11) = 3$ $\qquad$ $y = \begin{vmatrix} a & e \\ c & f \end{vmatrix} \div \begin{vmatrix} a & b \\ c & d \end{vmatrix} = 44 \div (-11) = -4$

So $(3, -4)$ is the solution of the system $\begin{cases} 5x = 7 - 2y \\ y = 3x - 13 \end{cases}$.

Evaluate the determinant.

1. $\begin{vmatrix} 2 & 1 \\ -1 & 3 \end{vmatrix}$

(2 • 3) − (−1 • 1)
6 − (−1)
6 + 1; 7

2. $\begin{vmatrix} 1 & -4 \\ 0 & 3 \end{vmatrix}$ ____________

3. $\begin{vmatrix} 3 & 2 \\ 2 & -1 \end{vmatrix}$ ____________

4. $\begin{vmatrix} -1 & 2 \\ 4 & -1 \end{vmatrix}$ ____________

5. $\begin{vmatrix} 3 & -1 \\ 2 & 4 \end{vmatrix}$ ____________

6. $\begin{vmatrix} 3 & -1 \\ 4 & -1 \end{vmatrix}$ ____________

7. $\begin{vmatrix} 1 & 1 \\ 2 & 1 \end{vmatrix}$ ____________

8. $\begin{vmatrix} 6 & -2 \\ 3 & -1 \end{vmatrix}$ ____________

9. $\begin{vmatrix} -5 & -7 \\ 3 & 2 \end{vmatrix}$ ____________

10. $\begin{vmatrix} -8 & -6 \\ 4 & 3 \end{vmatrix}$ ____________

11. $\begin{vmatrix} 5 & 3 \\ -6 & -9 \end{vmatrix}$ ____________

12. $\begin{vmatrix} 7 & 0 \\ -2 & -5 \end{vmatrix}$ ____________

Use with SOURCEBOOK Enrichment Lesson, pages 172–173.

Solve the system of equations.

13. $\begin{cases} 2x - y = 2 \\ 3x - 2y = 1 \end{cases}$

$\begin{vmatrix} a & b \\ c & d \end{vmatrix} = \begin{vmatrix} 2 & -1 \\ 3 & -2 \end{vmatrix} = -4 - (-3) = -1$

$\begin{vmatrix} e & b \\ f & d \end{vmatrix} = \begin{vmatrix} 2 & -1 \\ 1 & -2 \end{vmatrix} = -4 - (-1) = -3$

$\begin{vmatrix} a & e \\ c & f \end{vmatrix} = \begin{vmatrix} 2 & 2 \\ 3 & 1 \end{vmatrix} = 2 - 6 = -4$

$x = \frac{-3}{-1} = 3;\ y = \frac{-4}{-1} = 4;\ (3, 4)$

14. $\begin{cases} 3x - y = 2 \\ x + y = -6 \end{cases}$

15. $\begin{cases} 2x - y = 9 \\ 3x = -4y - 14 \end{cases}$

16. $\begin{cases} y = 9 - 2x \\ 3y - 2x = 11 \end{cases}$

17. $\begin{cases} 3y = 12 - \frac{3}{2}x \\ y = -2 - \frac{1}{2}x \end{cases}$

18. $\begin{cases} x = \frac{3}{4}y + \frac{25}{4} \\ y = \frac{5}{4} + \frac{3}{8}x \end{cases}$

Problem Solving

19. The sum of the digits of a two-digit number is 8. When the digits are reversed, the number is increased by 36. Find the number.

20. Natural Delights mixes almonds that cost \$3.50/lb with cashews that cost \$6.00/lb to create 20 lb of mixed nuts. The mix is resold for \$4.50/lb. How many lb of each nut are used to make the new mix?

WRITE ABOUT IT

21. Of the methods you have learned in this chapter for solving systems of linear equations, which method do you prefer to use? Explain.

Test Prep: Extended-Response Questions

Strategy: Show All Your Work

Name ______________________________ Date ____________

To organize your thoughts and demonstrate your understanding, **show or describe your steps.**	To solve the problem, try using these strategies: • Reread the item. • Use the Test-Prep strategy. • Apply appropriate rules, definitions, properties, or strategies. • Analyze your answers.

Solve. Show all your work. *TIP: Budget your time carefully.*

1. A class has a total of 28 students. The number of girls is 8 less than twice the number of boys.

Part A
Write a system of equations to find the number of boys and girls in the class.

Answer: ______________________

Part B
How many boys and girls are in the class?

Answer: ______________________

2. A cable company charges a fee of $35.99 per month for service. In addition, you can rent movies for $2.99 each.

Part A
Write an equation to represent the total cost per month, c, to have cable and rent m movies.

Answer: ______________________

Part B
One month, Quan's cable bill was $59.91. How many movies did he rent?

Answer: ______________________

3. Marjorie buys a square table. The perimeter of the table top is 168 in.

Part A
What is the side length of the table?

Answer: ______________________

Part B
Marjorie buys a square tablecloth that has an area of 3600 in.^{2}. How far does the tablecloth hang down from the edge of the table?

Answer: ______________________

Use with SOURCEBOOK Test Prep Lesson, page 174.

Vocabulary Development

Name ______________________ Date __________

Chapter 6 Vocabulary

consistent	inconsistent	point of intersection
dependent	independent	solution of a system of equations
		system of equations

From the vocabulary list above, choose the term(s) that best complete each sentence. Write the term(s) in the space(s) provided.

1. An ordered pair that makes each equation in the system true is a ______________.

2. A point that is on the graph of two different lines is called a ______________ .

3. A system of equations that describes two different intersecting lines is ______________.

4. When there is at least one solution of a system of equations, the system is ______________.

5. A set of two or more equations that have variables in common is a ______________.

6. If two equations in a system describe the same line, the system is ______________.

7. If a system of equations has no solution, the system is ______________.

Tell whether each statement is true or false. If false, rewrite the statement to make it true.

8. The solution of an independent system of equations may be $x = 3$.

____

9. Every system of equations has a solution.

____

10. A system of equations cannot have more than one solution.

____

11. If two lines are parallel, they represent a consistent system of equations.

____

12. If a system of equations describes two lines with different slopes and different y-intercepts, the system is consistent.

____

13. The solution of a system of consistent and independent equations is an ordered pair.

____

Use after SOURCEBOOK Lessons 6-1–6-6, pages 150–165.

Practice Chapter 6 Test

Name ______________________________ Date ______________

On a separate sheet of paper, graph each system of equations. Find the number of solutions and describe the system.

1. $\begin{cases} 3x + 2y = -12 \\ 12x + 8y = 16 \end{cases}$

2. $\begin{cases} y = -\frac{2}{3}x + 1 \\ 4x + 6y = 6 \end{cases}$

3. $\begin{cases} 3x - y = -9 \\ 2x + y = -11 \end{cases}$

Solve each system of equations by substitution. Check your answer.

4. $\begin{cases} y = x + 1 \\ 4x + 3y = 17 \end{cases}$

5. $\begin{cases} x - 2y = 2 \\ 4x + 5y = -18 \end{cases}$

6. $\begin{cases} 4x - 2y = -34 \\ 4x + 7y = 29 \end{cases}$

7. $\begin{cases} 20x - 6y = 0 \\ 3x - 2y = -22 \end{cases}$

Solve each system of equations by elimination. Check your answer.

8. $\begin{cases} 3x + y = 19 \\ 2x + y = 8 \end{cases}$

9. $\begin{cases} 3y - 0.1 = 2x \\ 2x = 4y \end{cases}$

10. $\begin{cases} m + n = \frac{23}{12} \\ m - n = \frac{17}{12} \end{cases}$

11. $\begin{cases} 7c - 9d = -88 \\ 7c - 29 = -4d \end{cases}$

Solve each system of equations by addition or subtraction. Check your answer.

12. $\begin{cases} 9x + 2y = 44 \\ 7x - 5y = 8 \end{cases}$

13. $\begin{cases} 3x + 5y = -34 \\ 5x - 2y = -36 \end{cases}$

14. $\begin{cases} 3y = -5 - x \\ 3x = 10 - 4y \end{cases}$

15. $\begin{cases} 10x + 5y = -8 \\ 4x + 3 = -3y \end{cases}$

Solve each problem by writing and solving a system of linear equations.

16. A jar contains \$16.10 in nickels and quarters. The number of quarters is 6 less than twice the number of nickels. How many nickels and how many quarters are in the container?

17. The sum of two integers is 7. The greater integer is 58 more than twice the lesser integer. What are the integers?

Graph each system of inequalities on a separate sheet of paper. Find whether the given ordered pair is a solution of the system.

18. $\begin{cases} 3x - y < -4 \\ 2x + 3y \geq 18 \end{cases}$ $(-2, 7)$

19. $\begin{cases} 4y \leq 32 - 3x \\ 5x + 2y \geq 24 \end{cases}$ $(8, 2)$

20. $\begin{cases} x + y \leq 6 \\ x + y \geq -6 \end{cases}$ $(-2, -1)$

Problem Solving

21. Cooking You must buy peas and cucumbers for a recipe. Peas cost \$1.25/lb. Cucumbers cost \$1.75/lb. You want to spend less than \$11.25 and need more than 5 lb altogether. If you also need 2 lb of cucumbers, list three amounts of peas you could buy.

22. Watch Production A factory produces both metal and plastic wristwatches. Metal watches take 10.5 h to make. Plastic watches take 6.3 h. The number of work hours at the factory is limited to 945 h per week, and the factory can produce no more than 120 watches per week. What is the greatest number of each type of watch the factory can produce per week?

Tell About It

Explain how you solve the problem. Show all your work.

23. How can you determine, without graphing, whether $(-1, 3)$ and $(1, -3)$ are solutions of the system of inequalities?

$\begin{cases} 3x + 2y \leq 5 \\ 4x - 5y \geq -1 \end{cases}$

Cumulative Review: Chapters 1–6

Name ______________________ Date __________

Circle the best answer.

1. Which number is a perfect square?

A. 80
B. 90
C. 144
D. 200

2. Simplify.

$5^2 \bullet 5^{-5} \bullet 5^7$

F. $\frac{1}{125}$ **G.** $\frac{1}{20}$

H. 20 **J.** 625

3. Which is equivalent to the expression below?

$(2.4 \times 10^{12}) \div (1.2 \times 10^6)$

A. 1.2×10^2 **B.** 2×10^2

C. 1.2×10^6 **D.** 2×10^6

4. Simplify.

$5^2 - |-12| \bullet 2 - (3 - 5)^2$

F. -8 **G.** -3

H. 0 **J.** 5

5. Solve.

$9b + 4 - 3b = 5b + 11$

A. $b = -7$ **B.** $b = 1$

C. $b = \frac{15}{11}$ **D.** $b = 7$

6. Solve.

$5x + 17 = 3x - 11$

F. $x = -14$ **G.** $x = -3$

H. $x = \frac{3}{4}$ **J.** $x = 3$

7. Solve.

$|d - 4| = 6$

A. $d = -2$ or $d = 2$
B. $d = -2$ or $d = 10$
C. $d = -2$ or $d = -10$
D. $d = 2$ or $d = 10$

8. Solve for c.

$6c + 2b - 4c = 3b$

F. $c = \frac{b^2}{2}$ **G.** $c = \frac{5b}{2}$

H. $c = \frac{b}{2}$ **J.** $c = \frac{1}{2}$

9. Which inequality is graphed?

−3 −2 −1 0 1 2 3 4

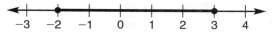

A. $-2 < x < 3$
B. $-2 \le x \le 3$
C. $x < -2$ or $x > 3$
D. $x \le -2$ or $x \ge 3$

10. Solve: $-3 \le 5z - (8z + 9)$

F. $z \ge -2$ **G.** $z \ge 2$

H. $z \le -2$ **J.** $z \le 2$

11. Solve: $|2w + 3| - 4 < 7$

A. $-7 < w < 4$
B. $-4 < w > 7$
C. $w < -7$ or $w > 4$
D. $-4 < w < 7$

12. Solve: $|3b + 1| \ge 8$

F. $-3 \le b \le \frac{7}{3}$

G. $b \le -3$ or $b \ge \frac{7}{3}$

H. $b \le \frac{7}{3}$ or $b \ge \frac{7}{3}$

J. $b \le -\frac{7}{3}$ or $b \ge 3$

13. Which relation contains the ordered pair $(-2, 4)$?

A. $y = x^4$
B. $y = x^2 + 2x - 4$
C. $y = -x + 4$
D. $y = 2x + 8$

14. Find the 8th term of the arithmetic sequence.

$-24, -20, -16, -12, \ldots$

F. -4
G. 0
H. 4
J. 8

15. Which function rule shows the *n*th term of the arithmetic sequence?

$17, 11, 5, -1, \ldots$

A. $a_n = 17 + 6(n - 1)$
B. $a_n = 17 - 6(n - 1)$
C. $a_n = 17 + 6n$
D. $a_n = 6 + 17n$

16. What is the slope of the line that passes through points $(7, 8)$ and $(-9, 11)$?

F. $\frac{3}{16}$ **G.** $\frac{16}{3}$

H. $-\frac{3}{16}$ **J.** $-\frac{16}{3}$

17. What is the point-slope form of the equation of a line that passes through $(1, 2)$ and $(4, 8)$?

A. $y - 1 = -2(x - 2)$
B. $y - 2 = -2(x - 1)$
C. $y - 1 = 2(x - 2)$
D. $y - 2 = 2(x - 1)$

18. Which ordered pair is a solution of the system $\begin{cases} 2x - 3y = -19 \\ 3x - 5y = -31 \end{cases}$?

F. $(2, 5)$ **G.** $(5, 2)$

H. $(-2, 5)$ **J.** $(5, -2)$

19. Which best describes the solution of the system $\begin{cases} x - 5y = 20 \\ 2x - 10y = 15 \end{cases}$?

A. inconsistent
B. inconsistent and dependent
C. consistent and dependent
D. independent

20. Which ordered pair is a solution of the system $\begin{cases} x + y \leq 2 \\ x + y \geq -1 \end{cases}$?

F. $(1, 8)$ **G.** $(3, -1)$

H. $(-2, -1)$ **J.** $(7, 1)$

Tell About It

Explain how you solve the problems. Show all your work.

21. The width of a rectangle is half of the length of the rectangle. If the perimeter is 84 inches, what is the length of the rectangle?

22. A car left town at 6 A.M. going due north at 45 mi/h. Two hours later, another car left town going due north at 50 mi/h. How far apart are the cars at 11 A.M.? (*Hint:* distance = rate × time)

7-1 Introduction to Polynomials

Name ______________________________ Date ______________

Determine whether each is a *monomial*.

$13x^3 - 9x$
No, the expression contains more than one term.

$\sqrt{x}$
No, the variable is under a radical sign.

$29x^3y^4z^6$
Yes, the product of a number and three variables.

d^{-1}
No, the variable has a negative exponent.

Remember: A monomial is an algebraic expression that is a product of a constant and a number of variables, each raised to a nonnegative power.

Are the following monomials *like terms*?

$19x^4$ and $23x^3$
No, the exponents of the variables are not identical.

$3x^2y^5$ and $-29x^2y^5$
Yes, only their numerical coefficients differ.

$-27d^5$ and $27d^5$
Yes, only their numerical coefficients differ.

-18, c^2, and $12c^3$
No, exponents of the variables are not the same. −18 is a constant.

Classify each *polynomial* and state its *degree*.

$g^2 - 4g + 29$
The degree of g^2 is 2.
The degree of $4g$ is 1.
The degree of 29 is 0. ← $29 = 29g^0$
There are 3 terms, so the polynomial is a *trinomial*. The greatest degree of the terms is 2, so the polynomial is quadratic.

$x^3 + 2x^2$
The degree of x^3 is 3.
The degree of $2x^2$ is 2.
There are 2 terms, so the polynomial is a *binomial*. The greatest degree of the terms is 3, so the polynomial is cubic.

Determine whether the expression is a monomial. Explain.

1. $2x + 7y$
No, the expression contains more than one term.

2. $9a - 7b + 3$ ______________

3. $7xy^2$ ______________

4. $-9x^2y^2$ ______________

5. $6a^{-3}$ ______________

6. $11yz^{-8}$ ______________

7. $\frac{2.3}{g}$ ______________

8. $\frac{6.8}{a}$ ______________

Tell whether the monomials are like monomials. If so, combine the like terms.

9. $3a$ and $-9a$
Yes; $3 + (-9) = -6$
$-6a$

10. $11ab$ and $-23ab$ ______________

11. xy and xy^2 ______________

12. x^2y and xy ______________

13. $6d^2e$ and $3d^2e$ ______________

14. $-8fg^2$ and $11fg^2$ ______________

15. $13t$ and $-24v$ ______________

16. $91x$ and $91y$ ______________

17. $3xyz$, $7xz$, and $8yz$ ______________

18. $2ac$, $-5cb$, and $2ab$ ______________

19. $4b^3$, $-9b^3$, and $15b^3$ ______________

20. $-6w^4$, $2w^4$, and $24w^4$ ______________

Use with SOURCEBOOK Lesson 7-1, pages 176–177.

Simplify.

21. $-2a^2b + 9ab^2 - 4a^2b + 3ab$

22. $5m^3n - 5mn^2 + m^3n + mn^2$

23. $15x^2y + x^2y - 2x^2y + 2xy$

24. $3a^2b - a^2b^2 - 2a^2b - 3a^2b^2 + 5a^2b$

25. $4x^2y^3 + 2xy^2 - x^2y^3 + 3x^2y^3 + 5xy^2$

Classify each expression as a *monomial*, *binomial*, or *trinomial* and then state its degree.

26. $9k^4\ell^2$

$4 + 2 = 6$
monomial; degree of 6

27. $17m^5n^{11}$

28. 5

29. -8

30. $7s^4t^2 - 12t^9 + 8$

31. $5m^3n^7 + 4m^2 - 11$

32. $4a^9 - 2a^6b^8$

33. $-7j^4k^2 - 13k^8 + 8j^4k^2$

Write each polynomial in standard form. (*Hint:* Watch for like terms.)

34. $3x^2 + 11 + 2x - 9x^3$

$2x = 2x^1$ and $11 = 11x^0$
$3 > 2 > 1 > 0$
$-9x^3 + 3x^2 + 2x + 11$

35. $8x^2 - 11x^3 + 13x + 1$

36. $9z^4 - 9z^4 - 4z + 24$

37. $11z^5 + 3z^2 - 11z^5 + 31$

38. $2.3m^2 - 5.1m - 1.8 + 6.3m^3$

39. $4.8n - 7.4n^3 - 2.9n + 5.2n^2$

Problem Solving

40. Show four different monomials of degree 3 that use at most two variables, *x* and *y*, all with a coefficient of 1.

41. A trinomial of degree 2 has terms with degree 2, 1 and 0. Give at least two different trinomials that could fit this description.

WRITE ABOUT IT

42. Write the polynomial below in standard form. Explain your reasoning.
$4y^4 + 2x^4 + 6x^3y + 6xy^3 - 9x^2y^2$

7-2 Add and Subtract Polynomials

Name ______________________ Date __________

Add: $5x^2 + 4x - 2x^2 - 6x$

$5x^2 + 4x - 2x^2 - 6x$ ← Identify like terms.

$(5x^2 - 2x^2) + (4x - 6x)$ ← Apply the Commutative and Associative Properties to group like terms.

$3x^2 + (-2x)$ ← Combine like terms.

$3x^2 - 2x$ ← Apply the definition of subtraction.

Subtract: $(11x^2y^2 - 7xy^2 + 13y^4) - (17x^2y^2 - 9xy^2 - 5y^4)$

$(11x^2y^2 - 7xy^2 + 13y^4) + (-17x^2y^2 + 9xy^2 + 5y^4)$ ← Add the opposite of the polynomial being subtracted and identify like terms.

$(11x^2y^2 - 17x^2y^2) + (-7xy^2 + 9xy^2) + (13y^4 + 5y^4)$ ← Apply the Commutative and Associative Properties to group like terms.

$-6x^2y^2 + 2xy^2 + 18y^4$ ← Combine like terms.

Add or subtract like terms to simplify each expression. Use algebra tiles to help.

1. $(9x^2 + 15x) - (12x^2 - 8x)$

$9x^2 + (-12x^2) + 15x + 8x$
$-3x^2 + 23x$

2. $(16y^2 + 21y) - (8y^2 - 3y)$

3. $(5g + 4h + 9gh) + (13h - 8gh - 6g)$

4. $(12t + 8u + 12tu) + (7t - 6u - 4tu)$

5. $21n + 19mn - 15m - 18mn + 16m - 14n$

6. $32k + 16k\ell - 31k - 15k\ell + 19\ell - 17\ell$

7. $1.5x^2 + 3.8x - 4.2x^2 - 6.7 + 3.4x - 9.2$

8. $\frac{1}{2}x + \frac{1}{4}x^2 - \frac{3}{4} + \frac{4}{2}x + \frac{3}{8}x^2 - \frac{1}{8}$

Perform the indicated operations.

9. Subtract $(-2m^4 - 3mn^3 - 2n^4)$ from the sum of $(6m^4 - 2mn^3 + 16n^4)$ and $(6mn^3 + 18n^4)$.

10. Subtract $(-8v^5 - 7v^3w^3 - 8w^6)$ from the sum of $(10v^5 - 6v^3w^3 + 10w^6)$ and $(9v^5 + 14v^3w^3)$.

Use with SOURCEBOOK Lesson 7-2, pages 178–181.

Solve. Show your work.

11. The figure below is a rectangle. Write an expression that represents its perimeter.

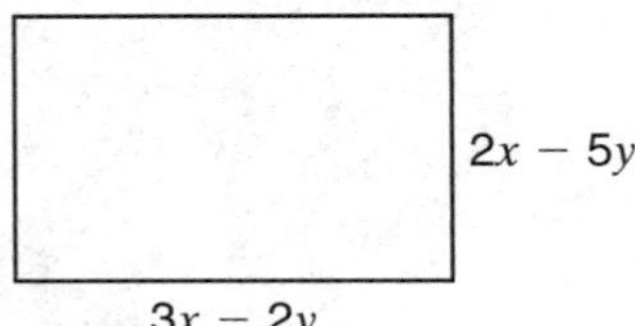

12. The figure below is a square. Write an expression that represents its perimeter.

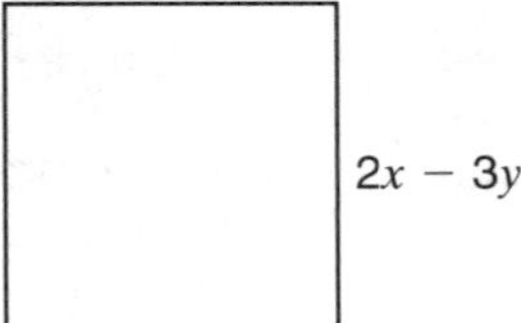

13. The perimeter of the quadrilateral below is $12x + 10$. Find an expression that represents the length of the unmarked side.

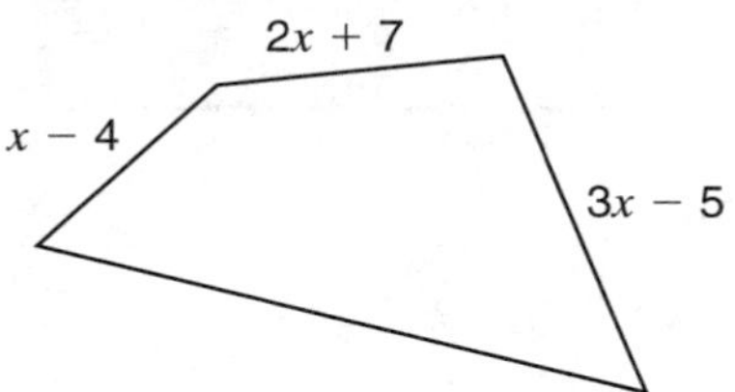

14. The figure below is a regular pentagon. Write an expression that represents its perimeter.

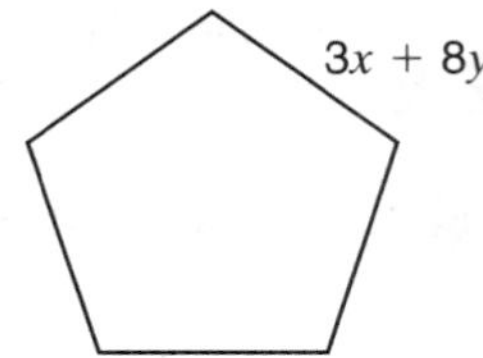

Problem Solving

15. The lengths of the bases of an isosceles trapezoid are $7x + 1$ and $11x + 8$. If the perimeter of the trapezoid is $26x + 15$, what is the length of each leg of the isosceles trapezoid?

16. The length of a side of square *A* is 7 more than the length of a side of square *B*. If the perimeter of square *A* is $8x + 32$, what is the perimeter of square *B*?

TEST PREPARATION

17. Simplify: $(12x^3 + 12x^2 - 9x + 12) - (4x^3 - 2x^2 - 3x - 7)$

A. $8x^3 + 14x^2 - 6x + 5$ **C.** $8x^3 + 14x^2 - 12x + 5$

B. $8x^3 + 14x^2 - 6x + 19$ **D.** $8x^3 + 14x^2 - 12x + 19$

7-3 Multiply a Polynomial by a Monomial

Name ____________________ Date ____________

Use the Laws of Exponents to multiply monomials algebraically.

Multiply: $(5a^4b^5)(-7ab^2)$

$(5a^4b^5)(-7ab^2) = (5)(-7)(a^4 \bullet a)(b^5 \bullet b^2)$ ← Multiply the coefficients and multiply the variables.

$= (-35a^{4+1}b^{5+2})$ ← Apply the Law of Exponents for Multiplication.

$= -35a^5b^7$ ← Simplify.

Remember: Laws of Exponents
Product of Powers: $a^m \bullet a^n = a^{m+n}$
Power of a Power: $(a^m)^n = a^{m(n)}$
Power of a Product: $(ab)^m = a^mb^m$

Simplify: $(-5x^2y^6)^3$

$(-5x^2y^6)^3 = (-5)^3(x^2)^3(y^6)^3$ ← Write out the factors of the power.

$= (-125)x^{2\bullet 3}y^{6\bullet 3}$ ← Apply the Law of Exponents for Power of a Product.

$= -125\,x^6y^{18}$ ← Simplify.

Simplify: $4c^2d^5(-6c^3d^2 + 5c^4d^2)$

$4c^2d^5(-6c^3d^2) + 4c^2d^5(5c^4d^2)$ ← Apply the Distributive Property.

$4(-6)(c^2 \bullet c^3)(d^5 \bullet d^2) + 4(5)(c^2 \bullet c^4)(d^5 \bullet d^2)$ ← Apply the Commutative and Associative Properties.

$-24(c^{2+3})(d^{5+2}) + 20(c^{2+4})(d^{5+2})$ ← Apply the Law of Exponents for Multiplication.

$-24c^5d^7 + 20c^6d^7$ ← Simplify.

Simplify each expression.

1. $(4a^3b^7)(8a^2b^5)$
   $(4)(8)(a^3 \bullet a^2)(b^7 \bullet b^5)$
   $32a^{3+2}b^{7+5}$
   $32a^5b^{12}$

2. $(9c^6d^4)(3c^4d^9)$

3. $(-2x^8y^5)(7x^{10}y^2)$

4. $(12m^9n^8)(-5m^6n^{12})$

5. $(9f^5g^{10})^3\left(-\frac{1}{3}f^5g^4\right)^2$

6. $\left(-\frac{1}{4}t^7u^{14}\right)^2(8t^2u^6)^3$

7. $6x^4y^6 - (12x^2y)^2(3y^4)$

8. $9d^3e^8 - (3de^2)^2(7de^4)$

9. $-15v^8w^7 - (4v^3w^2)^3(2vw^5)$

10. $-23g^6h^4 - (3g^2h^3)^4(4gh^6)$

11. $3a^2b^2(-2a^3b^4 + 4ab^2)$

12. $5x^3y^4(-4x^4y + 7x^2y^7)$

13. $-4a^3b^3\,(-3a^2b^2 - 2ab^3)$

14. $7m^2n^3\,(-5m^2n^3 - 9m^3n^4)$

Simplify.

15. $5d^2f^4(3d^5f^2 - 5d^2f^3 + 7df^5)$

$5d^2f^4(3d^5f^2) + 5d^2f^4(-5d^2f^3) + 5d^2f^4(7df^5)$
$15(d^{2+5})(f^{4+2}) + (-25)(d^{2+2})(f^{4+3}) +$
$35(d^{2+1})(f^{4+5})$
$15d^7f^6 - 25d^4f^7 + 35d^3f^9$

16. $3x^3y^5(9x^6y^4 - 4x^2y^4 + 3xy^6)$

17. $2.4a^7b^2(1.3a^5b + 2.5a^3b^2 + 0.4a^2)$

18. $3.2c^8d^4(0.9c^6d + 1.5c^4d^3 + 0.2d^5)$

19. $\frac{1}{2}x^2y\left(20xy + 8x + \frac{1}{2}y\right) + \left(3x^3y^2 - \frac{3}{4}x^2y^2\right)$

20. $\frac{1}{3}rs^2\left(15r^2s^2 + 12rs + \frac{1}{4}s\right) + \left(8r^2s^3 - \frac{1}{2}rs^3\right)$

Solve. Show your work.

21. Write a polynomial in simplest form to express the shaded area.

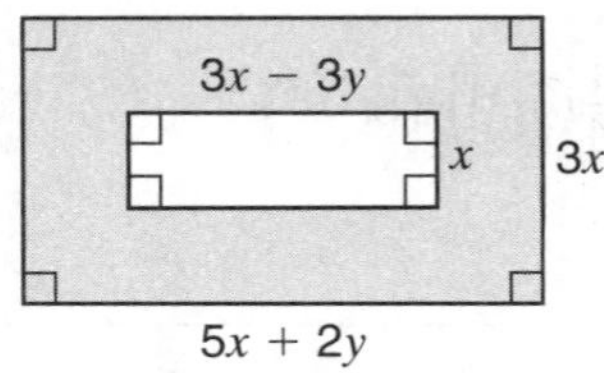

22. Write a polynomial in simplest form to express the shaded area in terms of π.

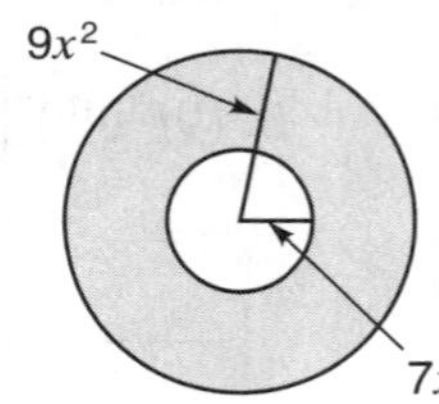

CHALLENGE

23. Simplify.

$(x^{3a})^b(x^{7ab}) + (x^a)^{5a}(x^{2a})$

7-4 Model Binomial Multiplication

Name ______________________________ Date ____________

Find each product using an area model.

$(3x + 4)(2x + 1)$

$2x + 1$; $2x$; 1

$3x + 4$; $3x$; 4

$3x \bullet 2x = 6x^2$ | $3x \bullet 1 = 3x$

$4 \bullet 2x = 8x$ | $4 \bullet 1 = 4$

Find the area of each region:

$3x \bullet 2x = 6x^2$ $\quad$ $3x \bullet 1 = 3x$

$4 \bullet 2x = 8x$ $\quad$ $4 \bullet 1 = 4$

$6x^2 + 3x + 8x + 4$ ← Add the areas of the 4 regions.

$6x^2 + 11x + 4$ ← Combine like terms.

So $(3x + 4)(2x + 1) = 6x^2 + 11x + 4$

$(5x - 3)(3x + 2)$

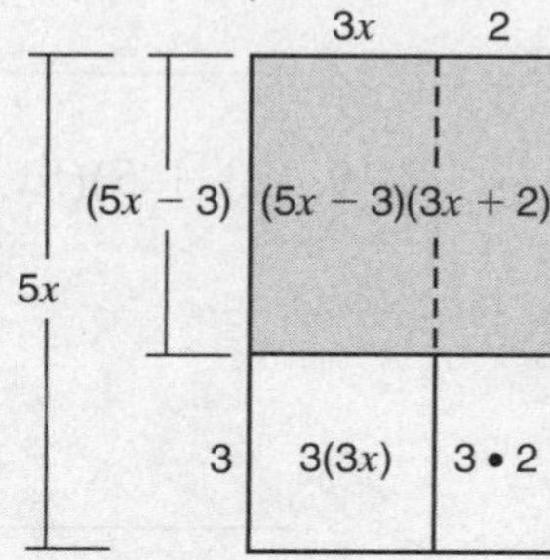

To find $(5x - 3)(3x + 2)$, subtract $(15x^2 + 10x) - (9x + 6)$.

$(5x - 3)(3x + 2) = 15x^2 + 10x - 9x - 6$

$= 15x^2 + x - 6$ ← Combine like terms.

So $(5x - 3)(3x + 2) = 15x^2 + x - 6$

Write the binomial expressions modeled by each diagram. Then find each product.

1.

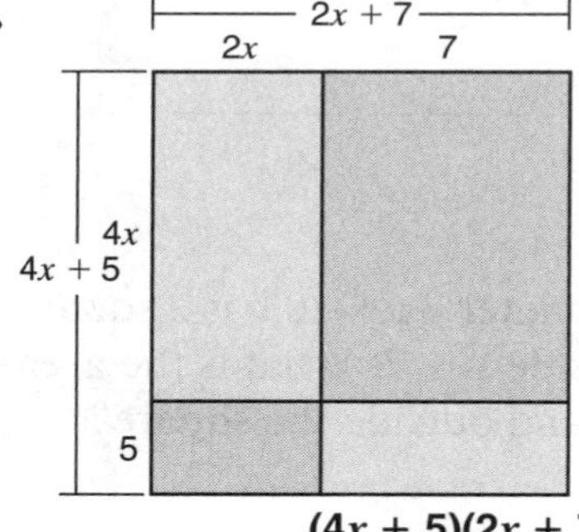

$(4x + 5)(2x + 7)$

$4x \bullet 2x = 8x^2$; $4x \bullet 7 = 28x$

$5 \bullet 2x = 10x$; $5 \bullet 7 = 35$

$8x^2 + 28x + 10x + 35$

$8x^2 + 38x + 35$

2.

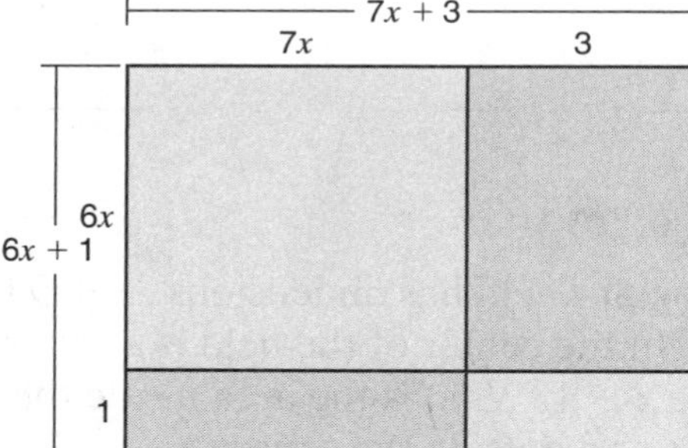

____

3.

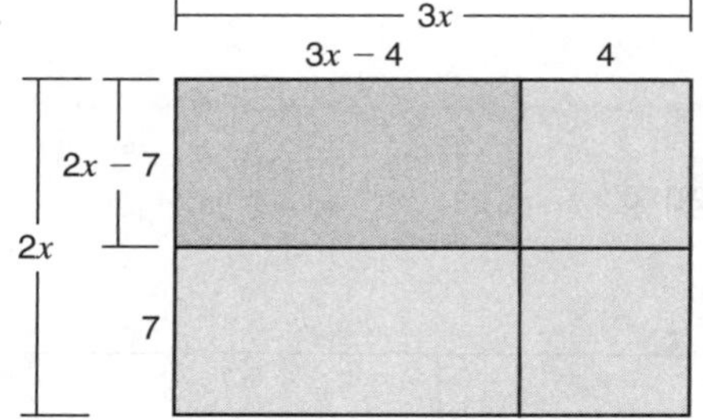

____

4.

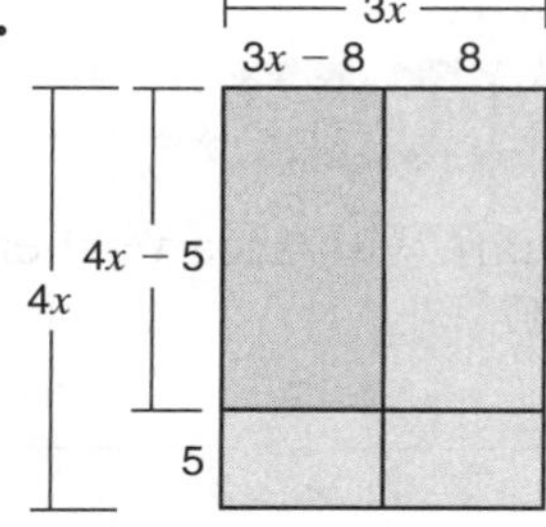

____

Find the product. Sketch an area model on a separate sheet of paper.

5. $(15 + 4)(15 - 4)$
$15 \cdot 15 = 225$
$15 \cdot (-4) = -60$
$4 \cdot 15 = 60$
$4 \cdot (-4) = -16$
$225 - 60 + 60 - 16$
209

6. $(30 + 3)(30 - 3)$

7. $(x + 4)(x + 7)$

8. $(x + 6)(x + 9)$

9. $(2x + 5)(5x - 7)$

10. $(4x + 1)(6x - 1)$

11. $(2x - 3)(3x - 2)$

12. $(4x - 5)(5x - 4)$

13. $(8x - 3)(5x + 2)$

14. $(7x - 2)(10x + 3)$

15. $(5x - 7)(5x + 7)$

16. $(6x + 1)(6x - 1)$

Problem Solving

17. A rectangular field has dimensions $3x + 9$ by $5x + 11$. In the center of the field is a square with side $x + 1$. What is the area inside the rectangle and outside the square?

18. A circle with diameter $8x + 10$ has a square inside of it with side $x + 2$. What is the area inside the circle and outside the square?

CRITICAL THINKING

19. If $x \cdot x$ represents a square with area x^2, then what geometric figure does $x \cdot x \cdot x$ represent?

7-5 Multiply Binomials

Name ______________________________ Date ______________

Multiply: $(2x + 4)(3x - 2)$

Method 1: Multiply horizontally.

$2x(3x - 2) + 4(3x - 2)$ ←Apply the Distributive Property.

$2x(3x) + 2x(-2) + 4(3x) + 4(-2)$ ←Apply Distributive Property again.

$6x^2 - 4x + 12x - 8$ ←Simplify.

$6x^2 + 8x - 8$ ←Combine like terms.

Method 2: Multiply vertically.

$$\begin{array}{r} 2x + 4 \\ \times\ 3x - 2 \\ \hline 6x^2 + 12x \\ -4x - 8 \\ \hline 6x^2 + 8x - 8 \end{array}$$

$6x^2 + 12x$ ←Apply the Distributive Property: $3x(2x + 4) = 3x(2x) + 3x(4)$

$-4x - 8$ ←Apply the Distributive Property: $-2(2x + 4) = -2(2x) + (-2)(4)$

$6x^2 + 8x - 8$ ←Combine like terms.

Method 3: Use FOIL.

F	O	I	L
Multiply the FIRST terms	Multiply the OUTER terms	Multiply the INNER terms	Multiply the LAST terms

$2x(3x) + 2x(-2) + 4(3x) + 4(-2)$

$6x^2 - 4x + 12x - 8$ ←Simplify.

$6x^2 + 8x - 8$ ←Combine like terms.

So $(2x + 4)(3x - 2)$ is $6x^2 + 8x - 8$.

Write each product in simplest form.

1. $(2n + 3)^2$

$(2n + 3)(2n + 3)$
$2n(2n) + 2n(3) + 3(2n) + 3(3)$
$4n^2 + 6n + 6n + 9$
$4n^2 + 12n + 9$

2. $(3m + 1)^2$ ______________

3. $(x + 7)(2x - 5)$ ______________

4. $(3x + 4)(x - 9)$ ______________

5. $(2y - 7z)(5y - 2z)$ ______________

6. $(8c - 3d)(3c - 7d)$ ______________

7. $(d - 2.1e)(d + 1.3e)$ ______________

8. $(r - 3.4s)(r + 4.8s)$ ______________

9. $(3.1m - 6.3n)(5.2m + 7.4n)$ ______________

10. $\left(z - \frac{2}{3}a\right)\left(z - \frac{1}{3}a\right)$ ______________

11. $\left(x - \frac{3}{4}y\right)\left(x + \frac{7}{4}y\right)$ ______________

12. $\left(b + \frac{4}{5}c\right)\left(b - \frac{3}{5}c\right)$ ______________

Find the area of each polygon.

13. square

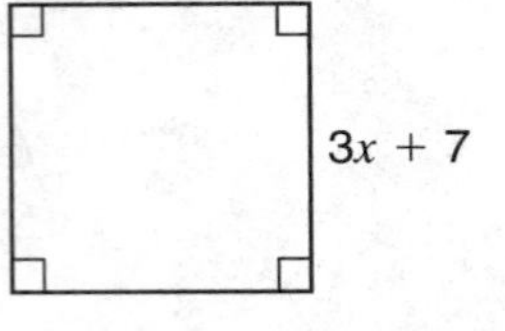

$(3x + 7)(3x + 7)$
$3x(3x) + 3x(7) + 7(3x) + 7(7)$
$9x^2 + 21x + 21x + 49$
$9x^2 + 42x + 49$

14. square

$2x + 9$

15. rectangle

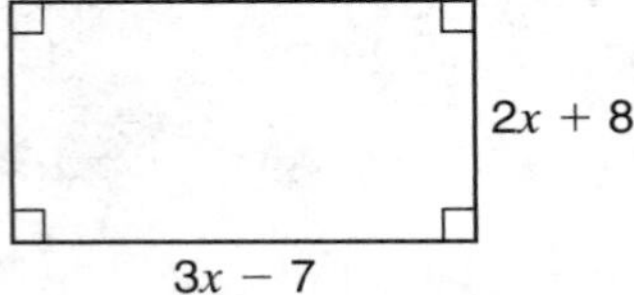

16. rectangle

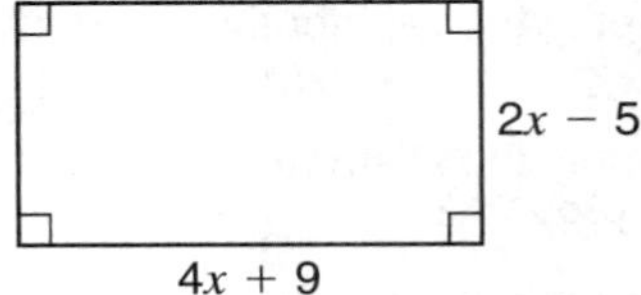

17. parallelogram

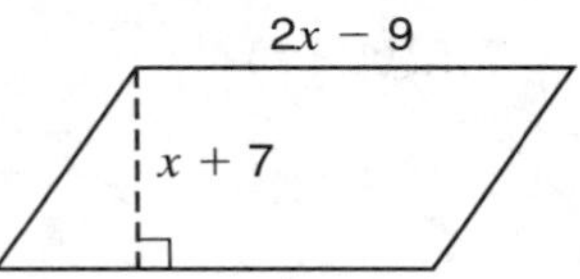

18. parallelogram

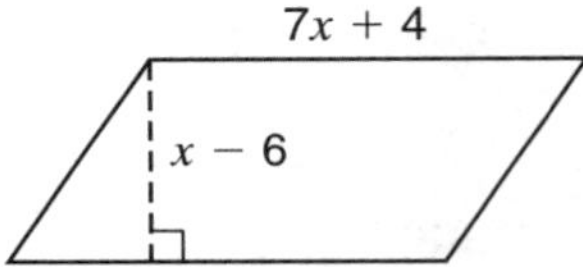

Problem Solving

19. A square grassy park is surrounded by a sidewalk 3 feet wide. If the width of the grassy park is x units, what is the area of the sidewalk?

20. If the area of a rectangle with length $4x + 9$ units is $12x^2 + 59x + 72$ square units, what is its width?

CHALLENGE

21. Use the Distributive Property to find $(x + y + 2)^2$.

7-6 Multiply Polynomials

Name ______________________ Date __________

Use the tabular method to find the product: $(x + 5)(3x^2 + 5x - 1)$

	$3x^2$	$+5x$	-1
x	$3x^3$	$+5x^2$	$-x$
$+5$	$+15x^2$	$+25x$	-5

← Multiply the monomials in the rows and columns to complete the table.

$3x^3 + (5x^2 + 15x^2) + (25x - x) - 5$ ← Find the sum of the monomial terms from the table by combining like terms.

$3x^3 + 20x^2 + 24x - 5$ ← Simplify.

Multiply: $(a^2 - 4)(3a^2 + 4a - 7)$

$(a^2 - 4)(3a^2 + 4a - 7) = a^2(3a^2 + 4a - 7) - 4(3a^2 + 4a - 7)$ ← Apply the Distributive Property.

$= a^2(3a^2) + a^2(4a) - a^2(7) - 4(3a^2) - 4(4a) - 4(-7)$ ← Apply the Distributive Property.

$= 3a^4 + 4a^3 - 7a^2 - 12a^2 - 16a + 28$ ← Simplify.

$= 3a^4 + 4a^3 - (7a^2 + 12a^2) - 16a + 28$ ← Apply the Commutative and Associative Properties.

$= 3a^4 + 4a^3 - 19a^2 - 16a + 28$ ← Combine like terms.

So $(a^2 - 4)(3a^2 + 4a - 7) = 3a^4 + 4a^3 - 19a^2 - 16a + 28$.

Multiply. Use the tabular method.

1. $(x - 4)(4x^2 - 7x + 6)$

	$4x^2$	$-7x$	$+6$
x	$4x^3$	$-7x^2$	$+6x$
-5	$-20x^2$	$+35x$	-30

$4x^3 - 7x^2 + 6x - 20x^2 + 35x - 30$

$4x^3 - (7x^2 + 20x^2) + (6x + 35x) - 30$

$4x^3 - 27x^2 + 41x - 30$

2. $(m - 6)(3m^2 - 4m + 3)$

____

3. $(4n + 3)(5n^2 + 6n - 5)$

____

4. $(3y + 2)(3y^2 + 5y - 6)$

____

5. $(2a^2 + 3a + 1)(3a^2 + 2a + 4)$

____

6. $(4z^2 + 5z + 3)(2z^2 + 3z + 5)$

____

7. $(12c^2 - 5c - 7)(7c^2 + 4c + 9)$

____

8. $(3u + 2v)(4u - 5v + w)$

____

9. $(16d^2 - 9d - 11)(11d^2 + 3d + 5)$

____

Find the product. Multiply horizontally.

10. $(3y^2 - 4)(y^2 - y + 4)$
$3y^2(y^2 - y + 4) - 4(y^2 - y + 4)$
$3y^2(y^2) - 3y^2(y) + 3y^2(4) - 4(y^2) - 4(-y) - 4(4)$
$3y^4 - 3y^3 + 12y^2 - 4y^2 + 4y - 16$
$3y^4 - 3y^3 + 8y^2 + 4y - 16$

11. $(12h^2 - 7)(2h^2 - 3h + 13)$

12. $(b^2 - 1.2b + 3.4)(b^2 - 1.5b + 2.3)$

13. $(c^2 - 3.5c + 5.2)(c^2 - 1.4c + 4.1)$

Find the product. Multiply vertically.

14.
$$\begin{array}{r} f^2 - 7f - 4 \\ \times \quad f - 11 \\ \hline f^3 - 7f^2 - 4f \\ - 11f^2 + 77f + 44 \\ \hline f^3 - 18f^2 + 73f + 44 \end{array}$$

15.
$$\begin{array}{r} j^2 - 11j - 6 \\ \times \quad 2j - 9 \\ \hline \end{array}$$

16.
$$\begin{array}{r} n^2 + n - 6 \\ \times\, n^2 - 2n + 3 \\ \hline \end{array}$$

17.
$$\begin{array}{r} m^2 + 4m - 11 \\ \times\, m^2 - 6m + 11 \\ \hline \end{array}$$

18.
$$\begin{array}{r} 3p^2 + 2p - 5 \\ \times\, 5p^2 - 7p + 12 \\ \hline \end{array}$$

19.
$$\begin{array}{r} 7q^2 + 9q - 12 \\ \times\, 11q^2 - 7q + 10 \\ \hline \end{array}$$

Solve. Show your work.

20. Geometry What is the volume of the rectangular prism? (*Hint:* Volume = length × width × height)

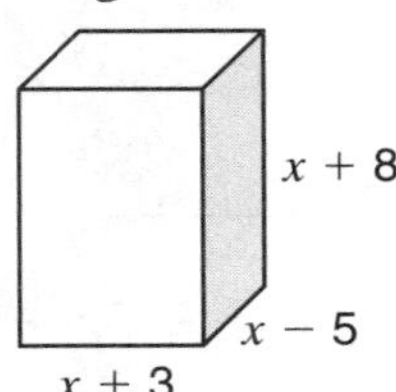

21. Geometry What is the volume of the right triangular prism? (*Hint:* Volume $= \frac{1}{2} \times$ area of base × height)

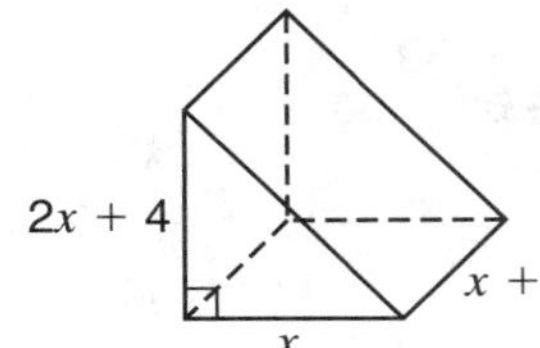

SPIRAL REVIEW

22. What are the x- and y-intercepts of $7x - 2y = -28$?

23. Solve the system of linear equations.
$$\begin{cases} 2x - 3y = -7 \\ 3x + 5y = -1 \end{cases}$$

7-7 Divide a Polynomial by a Monomial

Name ______________________ Date __________

Divide: $(15y^3 + 20y^2 - 30y) \div 5y$

$$\frac{15y^3 + 20y^2 - 30y}{5y} = \left(\frac{15y^3}{5y}\right) + \left(\frac{20y^2}{5y}\right) + \left(\frac{-30y}{5y}\right)$$ ← Divide each term of the polynomial by the monomial divisor.

$$= (3y^{3-1}) + (4y^{2-1}) + (-6y^{1-1})$$ ← Divide the coefficients; apply the Law of Exponents for Division to divide the variables.

$$= 3y^2 + 4y - 6$$ ← Simplify.

So $(15y^3 + 20y^2 - 30y) \div 5y = 3y^2 + 4y - 6$.

Simplify: $\left(\frac{y^{-2}}{z^{-3}}\right)^2$

$$\left(\frac{y^{-2}}{z^{-3}}\right)^2 = \frac{y^{-2(2)}}{z^{-3(2)}}$$ ← Use the Law of Exponents for a Power of a Quotient.

$$= \frac{z^{3(2)}}{y^{2(2)}}$$ ← Use the Law of Exponents for a Negative Power.

$$= \frac{z^6}{y^4}$$ ← Simplify by raising a power to a power.

Divide and check.

1. $12v^7 \div (-6v^5)$ $\left(\frac{12}{-6}\right)\left(\frac{v^7}{v^5}\right)$

$-2v^{7-5}$

$-2v^2$

$12v^7 \stackrel{?}{=} (-6v^5)(-2v^2)$

$12v^7 = 12v^7$ True

2. $40b^9 \div (-5b^3)$ ____________

3. $6x^2y^4 \div 3xy^2$ ____________

4. $60g^3h^6 \div 4gh^4$ ____________

5. $-126a^{11}bc^2 \div 14ab^4c^6$ ____________

6. $-236pq^4r^{11} \div 59p^3q^7r^9$ ____________

7. $(15x^3 + 25x^2 - 2x) \div (-5x)$ ____________

8. $(28y^3 + 12y^2 - 5y) \div (-4y)$ ____________

9. $(4x^4 - 12x^3y^2 - 10x^2y) \div (-2x^2y)$ ____________

10. $(12m^6n^4 - 30m^5n^7 - 42m^4n^6) \div (-6m^4n^6)$ ____________

11. $(52r^7s^5t^4 - 91r^9s^7t^2 + 78r^8s^7t^3) \div (-13r^8s^6t^3)$ ____________

Use with SOURCEBOOK Lesson 7-7, pages 190–191.

Simplify.

12. $\left(\frac{x^3}{y^2}\right)^4$
$= \frac{x^{3(4)}}{y^{2(4)}}$
$= \frac{x^{12}}{y^8}$

13. $\left(\frac{v^5}{w^{11}}\right)^{12}$

14. $\left(\frac{b^{-3}}{c^{-5}}\right)^{-2}$

15. $\left(\frac{d^{-5}}{e^{-8}}\right)^{-13}$

16. $\left(\frac{4w^0}{v^{-6}}\right)^3$

17. $\left(\frac{-2a^0}{b^{-3}}\right)^4$

18. $\left(\frac{-14a^{-2}}{7b^{-3}}\right)^3$

19. $\left(\frac{-36v^{-5}}{-6t^{-8}}\right)^4$

20. $\frac{(-4m^4n^2)^2(2mn)^3}{-20m^5n^{10}}$

21. $\frac{(2x^2y^4)^4(-3xy)^2}{-15x^{12}y^4}$

22. $\frac{(2c^6d^5)^4(1.2c^4d)^2}{(-0.4c^3d^{12})^2}$

23. $\frac{(-3.2x^8y^6)^2(x^3y^4)^3}{(1.6x^{14}y^{10})^2}$

24. $\frac{(3x^2y^2)^{-2}(-xy^3)^4}{(7x^{-3}y^{-2})^{-3}\,(x^3y^2)^{-3}}$

25. $\frac{(2r^2s^2)^{-3}(-rs^7)^2}{-(9r^{-2}s^{-3})^{-2}(r^4s)^{-2}}$

26. $\frac{(-3p^4q^2)^{-2}(p^2q)^3}{(4p^8q^{-3})^{-2}(-p^{-4}q^5)^{-3}}$

Solve.

27. The area of a rectangle with width $3x$ is given by the expression $12x^2 - 15x$. Write a polynomial expression for the length of the rectangle.

28. The area of a triangle with height $4x$ is given by the expression $16x^2 - 4x$. Write a polynomial expression for the base of the triangle.

MENTAL MATH

Compute mentally.

29. (24)(30)

30. (15)(9)(2)

31. $5\frac{2}{3} + 7\frac{1}{8} + 11\frac{1}{3} - 4\frac{1}{8}$

7-8 Divide Polynomials Using Long Division

Name ______________________ Date ____________

Divide: $(6a^2 - a - 10) \div (2a + 3)$

$$\begin{array}{r} 3a - 5 \\ 2a+3\overline{)6a^2 - a - 10} \\ (-)\ \underline{6a^2 + 9a} \\ -10a - 10 \\ (-)\ \underline{-10a - 15} \\ 5 \end{array}$$

- ← $6a^2 \div 2a = 3a$
- ← Multiply $3a(2a + 3)$.
- ← Bring down the -10.
- ← Subtract $-5(2a + 3)$.
- ← Remainder; Express by placing over the divisor, $2a + 3$.

So $(6a^2 - a - 10) \div (2a + 3) = 3a - 5 + \frac{5}{2a+3}$.

Remember:
Dividend = quotient • divisor + remainder

Divide.

1. $(6m^2 + 7m + 2) \div (3m + 2)$

$$\begin{array}{r} 2m + 1 \\ 3m+2\overline{)6m^2 + 7m + 2} \\ (-)\ \underline{6m^2 + 4m} \\ 3m + 2 \\ (-)\ \underline{3m + 2} \\ 0 \end{array}$$

2m + 1

2. $(6n^2 + 51n + 108) \div (2n + 9)$ ____________

3. $(12x^2 + 42x - 24) \div (2x + 8)$ ____________

4. $(27y^2 + 48y - 35) \div (3y + 7)$ ____________

5. $(35y^2 - 6y - 80) \div (5y - 8)$ ____________

6. $(99b^2 - 59b - 14) \div (9b - 7)$ ____________

7. $(60z^2 - 163z + 63) \div (15z - 7)$ ____________

8. $(133a^2 - 265a + 88) \div (19a - 8)$ ____________

9. $(14q^2 - 25q + 10) \div (2q - 3)$ ____________

10. $(15r^2 - 56r + 19) \div (5r - 7)$ ____________

11. $(49b^2 + 14b - 121) \div (7b - 11)$ ____________

12. $(121f^2 + 22f - 196) \div (11f - 14)$ ____________

Divide.

13. $(a^2 - 64) \div (a + 8)$

14. $(b^2 - 100) \div (b + 10)$

15. $(g^3 - 27) \div (g - 3)$

16. $(j^3 - 125) \div (j - 5)$

17. $(h^3 + 64) \div (h + 4)$

18. $(u^3 + 512) \div (u + 8)$

19. $(2e^3 + 28 + 4e^2) \div (2e - 4)$

20. $(60 - 6t^3 + 90t) \div (3t - 15)$

21. $(m^3 + 6m^2 + 11m + 6) \div (m + 3)$

Solve.

22. Geometry The area of a rectangle is $9x^2 - 25$. If the width is $3x - 5$, what is the length?

23. Geometry The volume of a rectangular pool is $20x^2 + 27x - 14$. If the height of the pool is $5x - 2$, what is the area of the base of the pool?

CHALLENGE

24. Divide: $(x^5 - 2x^3 + 7x^2 - 8x - 28) \div (x^2 - 4)$

7-9 Problem-Solving Strategy:
Find a Pattern

Read Plan Solve Check

Name ______________________ Date __________

Find a pattern to solve.

1. What is the sum of the first 35 odd numbers?

____

2. How many diagonals does a regular 12-gon have?

____

3. If the design seen here (made with toothpicks) is extended to 20 triangles, how many toothpicks will it require?

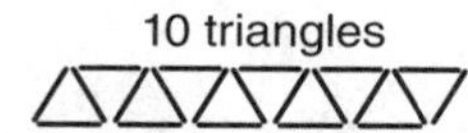

____

4. This design (made with toothpicks) is 4 layers deep. How many toothpicks are required to make a similar design that is 12 layers deep?

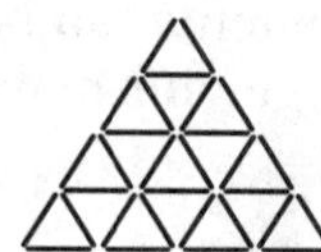

____

Use with SOURCEBOOK Lesson 7-9, pages 194–195.

5. Use a handheld. What digit is in the ones place of the standard form of 7^{42}?

6. The fraction $\frac{1}{7}$ can be represented as a repeating decimal. What is the 87th digit in the decimal expansion of $\frac{1}{7}$?

7. The patterns of dots seen here are the first 5 terms of the sequence of successive "hollow triangles of size *n*." How many dots are there in the hollow triangle of size 30?

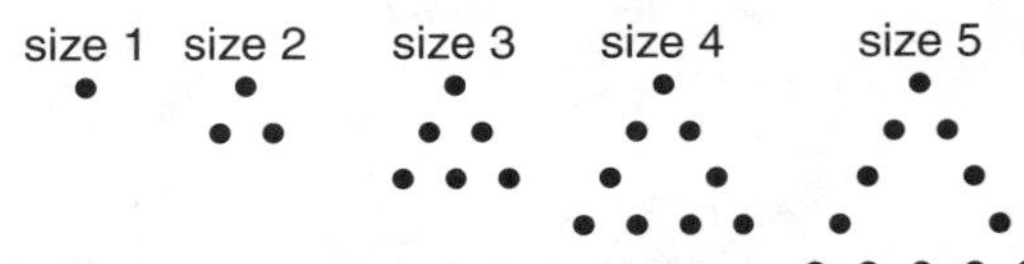

8. Refer to the pattern of dots seen here as a "4-by-3 tree" because it has 4 dots along two lateral sides and 3 dots along its base. How many line segments can be drawn that connect the dots of a 9-by-8 tree? (Segments may cross, but may not overlap.)

Enrichment:
Pascal's Triangle and the Expansion of $(x + y)^n$

Name ______________________________ Date ____________

Find the expansion of $(x + y)^6$.

Think

Each term of the expansion can be written as $x^a y^b$, where a and b are between 0 and n.
The exponents of x begin at n and decrease to 0.
The exponents of y begin at 0 and increase to n.

So the terms of the expansion $(x + y)^6$ are:
$x^6, x^5y^1, x^4y^2, x^3y^3, x^2y^4, x^1y^5$, and y^6.

Remember: The coefficient of each term of the expansion for $(x + y)^n$ are the same as the numbers in Row n of Pascal's Triangle.

1 ← Row 0
1 1
1 2 1
1 3 3 1
1 4 6 4 1
1 5 10 10 5 1 ← Row 5
1 6 15 20 15 6 1
1 7 21 35 35 21 7 1

So the coefficients of the expansion $(x + y)^6$ are 1, 6, 15, 20, 15, 6, 1.

So $(x + y)^6 = x^6 + 6x^5y + 15x^4y^2 + 20x^3y^3 + 15x^2y^4 + 6xy^5 + y^6$.

Use row 8 of Pascal's Triangle as shown below to answer each exercise.

1 8 28 56 70 56 28 8 1

1. Find row 9 of Pascal's Triangle. Then find 2^9.

1 9 36 84 126 126 84 36 9 1
1 + 9 + 36 + 84 + 126 + 126 + 84 + 36 + 9 + 1 = 512

2. Find row 10 of Pascal's Triangle. Then find 2^{10}.

____

3. Find row 11 of Pascal's Triangle. Then find 2^{11}.

____

4. Find row 12 of Pascal's Triangle. Then find 2^{12}.

____

5. Find row 13 of Pascal's Triangle. Then find 2^{13}.

____

6. Find row 14 of Pascal's Triangle. Then find 2^{14}.

____

Find the expansion. (*Hint:* Treat expressions of the form $(x - y)$ as $[x + (-y)]$.)

7. $(x + y)^4$

8. $(m + n)^7$

9. $(f - g)^4$

10. $(a - b)^5$

11. $(3 - 4c)^3$

12. $(x - 3)^6$

13. $(ab + c)^5$

14. $(a^2 + b)^4$

Write briefly on each topic.

15. Explain how to create Pascal's Triangle.

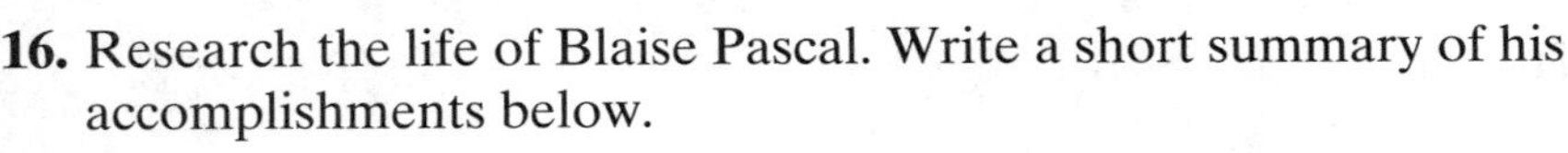

16. Research the life of Blaise Pascal. Write a short summary of his accomplishments below.

WRITE ABOUT IT

17. Research and explain a pattern in the Pascal's Triangle that was not listed in the SourceBook. Patterns listed in the SourceBook include: the Expansion of $(x + y)^n$, Powers of 2, Triangular and Square Numbers, and the Fibanocci Sequence.

Test Prep: Multiple-Choice Questions

Strategy: Apply Mathematical Reasoning

Name ______________________________ Date ____________

Use a diagram to organize the information that you are given. Pay close attention to the labels and scales.

To select the correct answer in a multiple-choice item, try using the following strategies.
- Underline important words.
- Restate the question.
- Use the Test-Prep strategy.
- Analyze and eliminate answer choices.

Choose the correct answer. *TIP: Do not spend too much time on any one question.*

1. Which equation is represented by the graph?

A. $y = -2.5x + 0.5$

B. $y = -2.5x - 0.5$

C. $y = 2.5x + 0.5$

D. $y = 2.5x - 0.5$

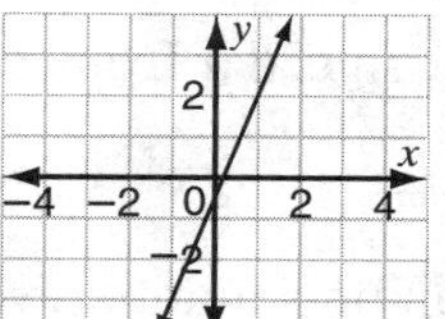

2. Which inequality is represented by the graph?

F. $y > -2x + 4$

G. $y \geq -2x + 4$

H. $y > 2x + 4$

J. $y \geq 2x + 4$

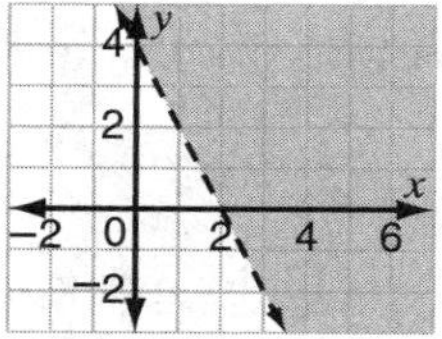

3. What is the area of the shaded region?

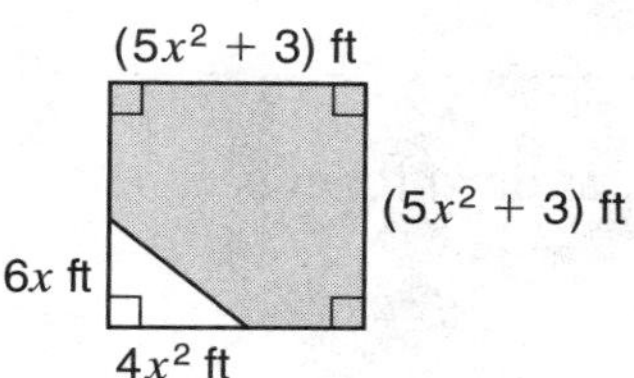

A. $(25x^4 + 18x^2 + 9)$ ft^2

B. $(25x^4 + 42x^2 + 9)$ ft^2

C. $(25x^4 - 12x^3 + 30x^2 + 9)$ ft^2

D. $(25x^4 + 12x^3 + 30x^2 + 9)$ ft^2

4. What is the range of the function shown on the graph?

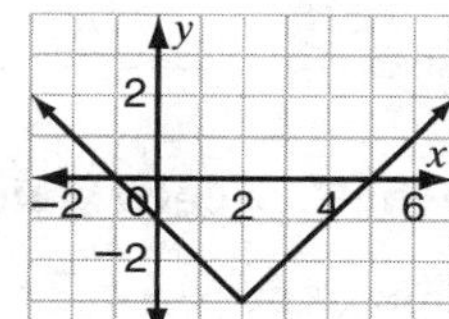

F. $x \geq -3$

G. $y > -3$

H. $y \geq -3$

J. all real numbers

5. If the pattern continues, what will the circumference of the fifth circle be?

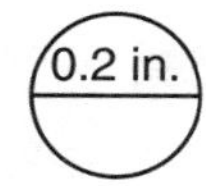

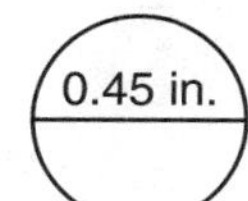

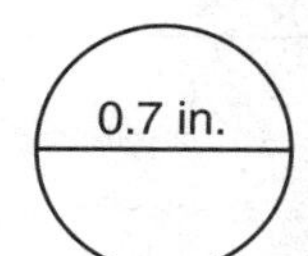

A. 0.95π in. **C.** 1.44π in.

B. 1.2π in. **D.** 2.4π in.

6. The perimeter of the triangle is 44 m. What is the length of the shortest side?

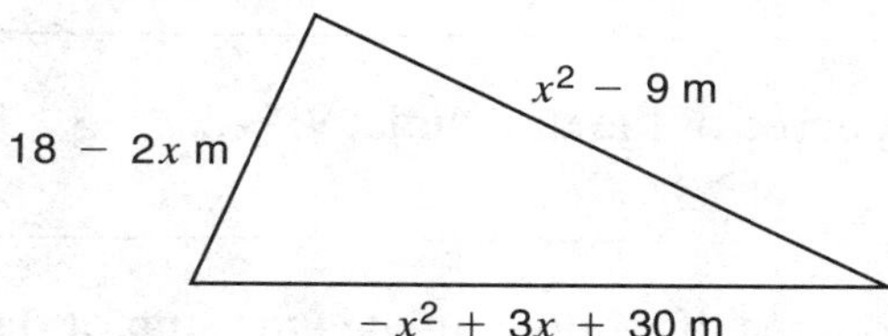

F. 5 m **H.** 16 m

G. 8 m **J.** 20 m

For More Practice Go To:

ONLINE www.progressinmathematics.com

Vocabulary Development

Name ______________________ Date __________

Chapter 7 Vocabulary

constant term	monomial	polynomial
degree of a monomial	leading coefficient	standard form
degree of a polynomial		

From the vocabulary list above, choose the term(s) that best complete each sentence. Write the term(s) in the space(s) provided.

1. The sum of the exponents of a term's variables is the ______________.

2. The sum of monomials is a ______________.

3. The greatest degree of all terms of a polynomial is the ______________.

4. A polynomial in one variable arranged so its terms are in order from greatest degree to least degree is written in ______________.

5. An algebraic expression with exactly one term that can be a number, variable, or product of a number and one or more variable(s) is called a(n) ______________.

6. A term that has no variable part is called a ______________.

7. The coefficient of the first term of a polynomial in standard form is called the ______________.

Tell whether each statement is true or false. If it is false, change it to make it true.

8. The expression $7x + 8$ is a binomial.

____

9. The expression $2x^3 + 6x + 8$ is a trinomial of degree 4.

____

10. The standard form of a polynomial always lists the constant term first.

____

11. The degree of the monomial 9^2 is 2.

____

12. The degree of a polynomial is the sum of the degrees of each term of the polynomial.

____

13. To find the degree of a monomial, multiply the exponents of its variables.

____

Use after SOURCEBOOK Lessons 7-1–7-8, pages 176–193.

Practice Chapter 7 Test

Name ______________________________ Date ______________

Tell whether each expression is a monomial.

1. $3a + 9$ ______

2. $15m^5n^4$ ______

3. $11x^{-8}$ ______

4. $9.6z$ ______

Classify each expression as a *monomial, binomial,* or *trinomial.* Then state its degree.

5. $19a^4b^3 + 1$ ______

6. $2x$ ______

7. $2d^9e - 5d^8 + 13d$ ______

8. $9m^4n^5 + 9m^{12} - 45$ ______

Write each polynomial in standard form.

9. $5y + 13 + 8y^3 - 4y^2$ ______

10. $\frac{5}{16}y - \frac{9}{4}y^3 - \frac{1}{5}y^5 + \frac{5}{8}$ ______

11. $8.6n^5 - 1.9n^7 - 14.2n + 9.8n^6$ ______

Simplify.

12. $19y^2 + 15y - 24y^2 - 6y$ ______

13. $24u + 19t - 15u + 7tu + 8t$ ______

14. $(23y^2 - 12y) - (4y^3 - 21y + 6)$ ______

15. $(5c^8d^9)(-2c^6d^{10})$ ______

16. $8x^6y^8 - (5x^3y)^2(2y^6)$ ______

17. $5x^2y^7(4x^7y^2 - 3x^4y^3 + 7xy^5)$ ______

Multiply.

18. $(7b + 3)^2$ ______

19. $(x + 11)(3x - 4)$ ______

20. $(4x - 1)(3x - 2)$ ______

Find each product.

21. $(3b + 1)(2b^2 + 5b - 3)$ ______

22. $(3x^2 + 2x - 1)(2x^2 - 4x + 3)$ ______

Divide and check.

23. $52x^3y^5 \div 4xy^4$ ______

24. $(16xy^4 - 20x^4y^3 - 8x^3y^2) \div (-4x^5y^2)$ ______

Use after SOURCEBOOK Lessons 7-1–7-8, pages 176–193.

Simplify.

25. $\left(\frac{u^{11}}{y^{19}}\right)^8$

26. $\left(\frac{y^{-5}}{x^{-3}}\right)^7$

27. $\left(\frac{3g^0}{18\ell^5}\right)^{-2}$

28. $\frac{(c^5d^3e^4)^3(2c^2de^5)^2}{(5c^2d^8e^4)^3}$

Divide and check.

29. $(z^2 + 7z - 2) \div (z + 4)$

30. $(a^3 + 4a^2 + 5a + 2) \div (a + 2)$

Problem Solving

31. If the perimeter of a square garden is $12a + 24$ units, what is the area of the garden?

32. The diameter of a circular pool is $5x + 1$ units. What is area of a cover that only fits over the top of the pool?

Tell About It

Explain how you solve the problem. Show all your work.

33. What is area of the shaded region?

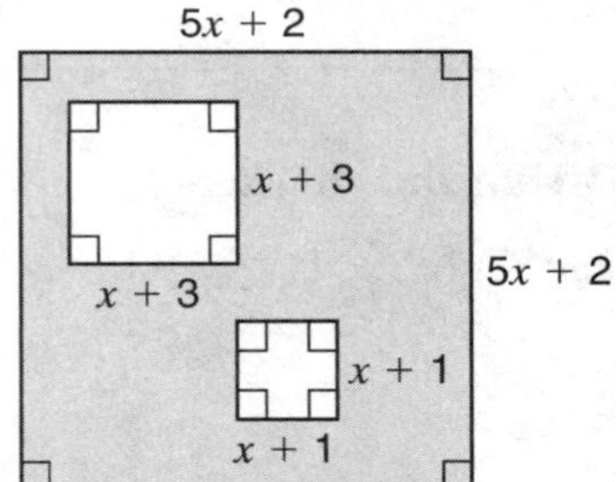

Cumulative Review: Chapters 1–7

Name ______________________ Date ____________

Circle the best answer.

1. If $A = \{2, 12, 19, 23, 29\}$ and $B = \{2, 23, 34, 40, 45\}$, then what is $A \cap B$?

A. $\{2, 12, 19, 34, 40, 45\}$
B. $\{19, 23, 29\}$
C. $\{2, 23\}$
D. $\{34, 40, 45\}$

2. Which set of numbers is *not* closed under addition?

F. $\{-2, -1, 0, 1, 2\}$
G. {whole numbers}
H. {real numbers}
J. {integers}

3. Divide: $\frac{3}{5} \div \left(-\frac{9}{10}\right)$

A. $-\frac{3}{2}$
B. $-\frac{2}{3}$
C. $\frac{2}{3}$
D. $\frac{3}{2}$

4. Solve.

$|d - 5| = 11$

F. $d = -6$ or $d = 16$
G. $d = -16$ or $d = 16$
H. $d = -6$ or $d = -16$
J. $d = 6$ or $d = 16$

5. Solve.

$4(2c + 3) - 1 = 8c + 2$

A. $c = 1$
B. $c = 0$
C. $c =$ all real numbers
D. $\varnothing$

6. Which inequality best matches the statement, "The number of desks in the classroom is at most 12"?

F. $d < 12$
G. $d \leq 12$
H. $d \geq 12$
J. $d > 12$

7. Solve for x:

$-7 < 3x + 5 < 14$

A. $4 < x < -3$
B. $-4 < x < 3$
C. $-4 > x > 3$
D. $4 < x > -3$

8. Solve for b:

$|2b - 1| + 3 > 16$

F. $-12 < b < 14$
G. $-6 < b < 7$
H. $b < -7$ or $b > 6$
J. $b < -6$ or $b > 7$

9. Which recursive formula could be used to generate this sequence?

$2, \frac{1}{2}, \frac{1}{8}, \frac{1}{32}, \ldots$

A. $a_n = \frac{1}{4} \bullet a_{n-1}$
B. $a_n = 2 \bullet a_{n-1}$
C. $a_n = \frac{1}{2} \bullet a_{n-1}$
D. $a_n = 4 \bullet a_{n-1}$

10. Which is the 9th term of the sequence?

$2100, 210, 21, 2.1, \ldots$

F. 0.0021
G. 0.00021
H. 0.000021
J. 0.0000021

11. Which is a direct variation?

A. $y = x^3$
B. $y = 9x^2 + 9x - 3$
C. $y = -15x$
D. $y = 2$

12. Which equation has a slope of 3 and a y-intercept of -9?

F. $y = 3x - 9$
G. $3x + 9y = -1$
H. $y = -9x + 3$
J. $-9y = 3x$

13. What are the x- and y-intercepts of the equation $9x - 3y = -36$?

A. x-intercept: -4; y-intercept: 12
B. x-intercept: 4; y-intercept: -12
C. x-intercept: 12; y-intercept: -4
D. x-intercept: -12; y-intercept: 4

14. Solve: $\begin{cases} 3x + 2y = 9 \\ 2x - 3y = -7 \end{cases}$

F. (1, 3)
G. (3, 1)
H. infinitely many solutions
J. $\varnothing$

15. Solve: $\begin{cases} 5x - y = 10 \\ y = 3x - 8 \end{cases}$

A. $(-1, 5)$
B. $(1, -5)$
C. infinitely many solutions
D. $\varnothing$

16. Solve: $\begin{cases} 7x + 3y = 4 \\ 14x + 6y = 8 \end{cases}$

F. (1, 3) **G.** (3, 1)
H. infinitely many solutions **J.** $\varnothing$

17. Which is a monomial of degree 5?

A. $5x$ **B.** $7x^5$
C. $5x^5y^5$ **D.** $3x^5 + 2$

18. Multiply: $(6c^2d^4)(-4c^3d^5)$

F. $-24c^6d^{20}$
G. $2c^6d^{20}$
H. $-24c^5d^9$
J. $2c^5d^9$

19. Multiply: $(x - 3)^2$

A. $x^2 + 9$
B. $x^2 - 9$
C. $x^2 + 6x + 9$
D. $x^2 - 6x + 9$

20. Divide: $(a^2 - 9) \div (a - 3)$

F. $a + 3$
G. $a - 3$
H. $a - 12$
J. $a + 6$

Tell About It

Explain how you solve the problem. Show all your work.

21. The area of a field with length $8x + 9$ is $56x^2 - 9x - 81$. What is the width of the field?

22. Nancy has 24 nickels and dimes worth \$2.10. How many of each coin does Nancy have?

8-1 Common Monomial Factors

Name ______________________________ Date ______________

Write $20a^4b^2c - 15a^2b^4c^5$ in factored form.

1 Find the greatest common monomial factor.

GCF of 20 and 15: 5 ⟵ $20 = 2^2 \cdot 5$; $15 = 3 \cdot 5$; GCF: 5

GCF of a^4 and a^2: a^2 ⟵ a appears in both monomials; the least power is a^2

GCF of b^2 and b^4: b^2 ⟵ b appears in both monomials; the least power is b^2

GCF of c and c^5: c ⟵ c appears in both monomials; the least power is c

Greatest common monomial factor: $5a^2b^2c$

2 Write each term as a product involving the greatest common monomial factor.

$$20a^4b^2c - 15a^2b^4c^5 = \mathbf{5a^2b^2c}(4a^2) - \mathbf{5a^2b^2c}(3b^2c^4)$$

$$= \mathbf{5a^2b^2c}(4a^2 - 3b^2c^4) \longleftarrow \text{Apply the Distributive Property.}$$

So in factored form, $20a^4b^2c - 15a^2b^4c^5 = 5a^2b^2c(4a^2 - 3b^2c^4)$.

Find the greatest common monomial factor of the terms.

1. $8x^2, 12x, 24$

$8x^2 = 2^3 \cdot x^2$
$12x = 2^2 \cdot 3 \cdot x$
$24 = 2^3 \cdot 3$
$\longrightarrow 2^2$

4

2. $22a^3, 121a^2, 33$

______

3. $18d^2e^3, 81d^2e^4, 36d^2e^5$

______

4. $21x^5y^3, 42x^4y^3, 63x^3y^3$

______

5. $-12m^2n^4p^6, -36m^3n^2p^7, -48m^2n^3p^5$

______

6. $-45a^3b^5c^8, -30a^2b^3c^6, -60a^3b^4c^9$

______

7. $34t^5uv, -22tuv^4, -30t^2u^5v^8$

______

8. $24d^2ef^4, 21def^2, 39d^3ef$

______

9. $48x^2y^3z^{10}, 96x^3y^4z^{11}, 48x^4y^5z^{12}$

______

10. $72u^8v^6w^3, 36u^3v^5w^2, 36u^6v^4w^2$

______

11. $40a^4b^2, 120a^3c^2, 60b^3c^2$

______

12. $60d^2e^4, 90d^4f^6, 120e^2f^8$

______

Use with SOURCEBOOK Lesson 8-1, pages 200–201.

Factor the polynomial by finding the greatest common monomial factor. Check your answer on a separate sheet of paper.

13. $7x^5 + 14x^3$

GCF 7 and 14: 7
GCF x^5 and x^3: x^3
$7x^3(x^2) + 7x^3(2)$
$7x^3(x^2 + 2)$

14. $11y^4 + 22y^2$

15. $-16d^7 - 16d^4$

16. $-24e^5 - 24e^2$

17. $4x^7y + 8x^6y - 12x^4y$

18. $30wu^4 - 10wu^6 - 25wu^5$

19. $24ab + 8ab^2 - 4$

20. $18d^2e + 27d^2 - 9$

21. $-q^5r - 3q^3r^3 - qr$

22. $-12x^3y^3z^3 + 12x^3y^2z^3 - 36x^3y^3z^4$

23. $-9a^4b^2c^4 - 18a^3b^2c^4 + 9a^4b^3c^4$

Problem Solving

24. The area of a rectangular playground is represented by the binomial $9x^3 + 12x^2$. The length is represented by $3x^2$. If the length is 192 feet, what is the width of the playground?

25. Suppose the area of a circle is represented by the expression $16\pi x^4$. What expression could represent the radius? (*Hint:* $A = \pi r^2$)

CRITICAL THINKING

26. One factor of the polynomial $\frac{5}{8}a^4b^3 - \frac{15}{8}a^6b^9 + \frac{25}{8}a^4b^{10}$ is the polynomial $1 - 3a^2b^6 + 5b^7$. What is the monomial factor?

8-2 Factor Trinomials $ax^2 + bx + c$ with $a = 1$

Name ______________________ Date __________

Factor: $x^2 + 14x + 24$

Think

$b = 14$, $c = 24$.
What factors have a product of 24 and a sum of 14?

Factors of 24	Sum of 14
1, 24	25
2, 12	14 ←
3, 8	11
4, 6	10

The factors of 24 whose sum is 14 are 2 and 12.

So in factored form,
$x^2 + 14x + 24 = (x + 12)(x + 2)$.

Multiply to check:
$(x + 12)(x + 2) = x^2 + 2x + 12x + 24$
$= x^2 + 14x + 24$ ✓

Factor $x^2 - 18xy - 40y^2$.

Think

$b = -18y$, $c = -40y^2$.
What factors have a product of $-40y^2$ and a sum of $-18y$?

Factors of $-40y^2$	Sum of $-18y$
$y, -40y$	$-39y$
$2y, -20y$	$-18y$ ←
$4y, -10y$	$-6y$
$5y, -8y$	$-3y$

The factors of $-40y^2$ whose sum is $-18y$ are $2y$ and $-20y$.

So in factored form,
$x^2 - 18xy - 40y^2 = (x + 2y)(x - 20y)$.

Multiply to check:
$(x + 2y)(x - 20y) = x^2 - 20xy + 2xy - 40y^2$
$= x^2 - 18xy - 40y^2$ ✓

Factor each trinomial. Check by multiplying the factors. If the polynomial cannot be factored, write *prime*.

1. $x^2 + 5x + 4$

1, 4: sum 5
2, 2: sum 4
$(x + 4)(x + 1)$
Check: $(x + 4)(x + 1)$
$= x^2 + x + 4x + 4$
$= x^2 + 5x + 4$

2. $x^2 + 7x + 6$ __________

3. $y^2 - 6y + 8$ __________

4. $m^2 - 9m + 8$ __________

5. $x^2 + 5x - 14$ __________

6. $p^2 + p - 30$ __________

7. $r^2 - 3r - 54$ __________

8. $x^2 - 21x - 100$ __________

9. $b^2 - 12b + 32$ __________

10. $w^2 - 23w + 60$ __________

11. $g^2 + 20g - 36$ __________

12. $c^2 + 14c - 24$ __________

Use with SOURCEBOOK Lesson 8-2, pages 202–205.

Factor each trinomial. Check by multiplying the factors. If the polynomial cannot be factored, write *prime*.

13. $-16 - x^2 - 10x$
$-x^2 - 10x - 16$
$-(x^2 + 10x + 16)$
1 and 16: sum 17
4 and 4: sum 8
8 and 2: sum 10
$-(x + 8)(x + 2)$

14. $-12 - y^2 - 8y$ __________

15. $14d - 45 - d^2$ __________

16. $14z - 33 - z^2$ __________

17. $-7x + 2 - x^2$ __________

18. $-5y + 3 - y^2$ __________

19. $-7\ell + 60 - \ell^2$ __________

20. $-2k + 63 - k^2$ __________

21. $-h^2 - 2h + 143$ __________

22. $-n^2 - 5n + 300$ __________

23. $-s^2 + 4s + 396$ __________

24. $-w^2 + 17w + 480$ __________

25. $a^2 + 14ab - 32b^2$ __________

26. $-f^2 + 13fg - 42g^2$ __________

27. $70y^2 - x^2 - 9xy$ __________

Solve. Show your work.

28. The trinomial $x^2 + 30x + 161$ represents the area of a rectangle. If $x + 23$ represents the length of the rectangle, what binomial represents the width?

____

29. The trinomial $x^2 + x + \frac{1}{4}$ represents the area of a square. What binomial represents the measure of one side?

____

SPIRAL REVIEW

30. Factor the binomial by finding the greatest common monomial factor.
$24y^6 + 8y^4$

____

31. Write the product in simplest form.
$(3a + 1)(4a^2 + 7a - 2)$

____

8-3 Factor Trinomials $ax^2 + bx + c$ with $a \neq 1$

Name ______________________ Date ____________

Factor: $5a^2 + 16a + 3$

Think
$a = 5, b = 16, c = 3; ac = 15$

Find two positive factors of 15 that sum to 16.

Factors of 15	Sum of factors
1, 15	16 ←
3, 5	8

$5a^2 + 16a + 3 = 5a^2 + (15 + 1)a + 3$ ← Select the factors 15 and 1.

$= 5a^2 + 15a + a + 3$ ← Use the Distributive Property.

$= (5a^2 + 15a) + (a + 3)$ ← Group terms that have a common monomial factor.

$= 5a(a + 3) + 1(a + 3)$ ← Factor each binomial using the greatest common monomial factor.

$= (5a + 1)(a + 3)$ ← Use the Distributive Property.

So in factored form, $5a^2 + 16a + 3 = (5a + 1)(a + 3)$.

Multiply to check: $(5a + 1)(a + 3) = 5a^2 + 15a + a + 3$
$= 5a^2 + 16a + 3$ ✓

Factor each trinomial. Check by multiplying the factors.
If the polynomial cannot be factored, write *prime*.

1. $2x^2 + 11x + 5$
$ac = 10$; $1 + 10 = 11$
$2x^2 + 10x + x + 5$
$2x(x + 5) + 1(x + 5)$
$(2x + 1)(x + 5)$
Check:
$= 2x^2 + 10x + x + 5$
$= 2x^2 + 11x + 5$

2. $2r^2 + 15r + 7$

3. $2c^2 - 5c + 3$

4. $2p^2 - 9p + 7$

5. $3t^2 + 14t - 8$

6. $4q^2 + 29q - 25$

7. $5a^2 + 13a - 6$

8. $11x^2 + 9x - 2$

9. $3n^2 - n - 10$

10. $7x^2 - 5x - 12$

11. $19y^2 - 138y + 35$

12. $19a^2 - 82a + 24$

Factor each trinomial. Check by multiplying the factors. If the polynomial cannot be factored, write *prime*.

13. $5x^2 + 12x + 7$

Find the value of the linear term:

$(5x + 7)(x + 1) \longrightarrow 12x$

$(5x + 1)(x + 7) \longrightarrow 36x$

$(5x + 7)(x + 1)$

Check: $= 5x^2 + 5x + 7x + 7$

$= 5x^2 + 12x + 7$

14. $3a^2 + 34a + 11$

15. $11g^2 - 36g + 9$

16. $13c^2 - 70c + 25$

17. $8n^2 + 10n - 3$

18. $12b^2 + 17b - 7$

19. $8x^2 - 2x - 15$

20. $12z^2 - 16z - 16$

21. $10m^2 - 31m + 63$

22. $45y^2 + 56y - 45$

23. $15t^2 + 13t - 72$

24. $39s^2 + 19s + 2$

Write the polynomial shown by each area model, and then factor.

25.

$8g^2$	$12g$
$6g$	9

$8g^2 + 12g + 6g + 9$

$8g^2 + 18g + 9$

$ac = 72$; $6 + 12 = 18$

$8g^2 + 12g + 6g + 9$

$4g(2g + 3) + 3(2g + 3)$

$(4g + 3)(2g + 3)$

26.

$12b^2$	$18b$
$10b$	15

27.

$11m^2$	$4m$
$77m$	28

CHALLENGE

28. Factor the trinomial $8y^4 + 32y^3 + 30y^2$. Explain your steps.

8-4 Special Product and Factoring: $(a \pm b)^2 = a^2 \pm 2ab + b^2$

Name ______________________ Date __________

Evaluate: $(3m + 8)^2$

Square the first term.		Twice the product of the terms		Square the last term.
↓		↓		↓
$(3m)^2$	+	$2(3m)(8)$	+	$(8)^2$
$9m^2$	+	$48m$	+	64

So $(3m + 8)^2 = 9m^2 + 48m + 64$.

Remember:
The square of a binomial is the *square of the first term*, plus or minus *twice* the *product of both its terms*, plus the *square of the last term*.

$(a + b)^2 = a^2 + 2ab + b^2$
$(a - b)^2 = a^2 - 2ab + b^2$

Determine if $49q^2 - 28q + 16$ is a perfect square trinomial.

$49q^2 - 28q + 16$

$7q \bullet 7q - 2(7q)(4) + 4 \bullet 4$ ← Write the trinomial in the form $a^2 - 2ab + b^2$, where $a = 7q$, and $b = 4$.

Think
$-2(7q)(4) \stackrel{?}{=} -28q$
$-56q = -28q$ **False**

So $49q^2 - 28q + 16$ is *not* a perfect square trinomial.

Square each binomial.

1. $(x + 15)^2$

   $(x)^2 + 2(x)(15) + (15)^2$
   $x^2 + 30x + 225$

2. $(r + 20)^2$ ______________

3. $(t - 14)^2$ ______________

4. $(y - 25)^2$ ______________

5. $(2x - 11)^2$ ______________

6. $(3h - 2)^2$ ______________

7. $(7b + 5)^2$ ______________

8. $(8g + 3)^2$ ______________

9. $(5x + 9y)^2$ ______________

10. $(7u + 3v)^2$ ______________

11. $(11r - 7s)^2$ ______________

12. $(12a - 5b)^2$ ______________

13. $(0.2x - 0.3y)^2$ ______________

14. $(0.5q - 0.4r)^2$ ______________

15. $\left(\frac{1}{3}d + \frac{1}{5}e\right)^2$ ______________

Determine if each trinomial is a perfect square. If so, factor it. If not, explain why not.

16. $121b^2 + 22b + 1$

$11b \cdot 11b + 2(11b)(1) + 1 \cdot 1$

$2(11b)(1) \stackrel{?}{=} 22b$

$22b = 22b$ True

$(11b + 1)^2$

17. $64x^2 + 16x + 1$

18. $36c^2 + 30c + 25$

19. $49g^2 + 56g + 64$

20. $16t^2 - 40t + 25$

21. $36r^2 - 84r + 49$

22. $25x^2 - 110xy + 121y^2$

23. $81v^2 - 90vw + 25w^2$

24. $m^2 - m + 0.25$

25. $y^2 - 1.2y + 0.36$

26. $q^2 - \frac{3}{2}q + \frac{9}{16}$

27. $z^2 - \frac{10}{9}z + \frac{25}{81}$

Solve. Show your work.

28. The trinomial $4x^2 - 52x + 169$ represents the area of a square. What binomial represents the measure of each side of the square?

29. Nancy is making a square garden with side $23v - 4w$. What trinomial represents the area of the garden?

TEST PREPARATION

30. Which trinomial is a perfect square?

A. $16x^2 - 150x + 625$

B. $81x^2 - 126x + 49$

C. $100x^2 - 100x + 81$

D. $36x^2 - 25x + 64$

31. Evaluate: $\left(\frac{1}{2}x - \frac{2}{5}y\right)^2$

F. $x^2 + \frac{4}{5}y^2$

G. $x^2 - \frac{4}{5}y^2$

H. $\frac{1}{4}x^2 - \frac{1}{5}xy + \frac{4}{25}y^2$

J. $\frac{1}{4}x^2 - \frac{2}{5}xy + \frac{4}{25}y^2$

8-5 Special Product and Factoring: $(a + b)(a - b) = a^2 - b^2$

Name ______________________ Date __________

Multiply: $(2x + 15)(2x - 15)$

Think
$(a + b)(a - b) = a^2 - b^2$

$(2x + 15)(2x - 15) = (2x)^2 - (15)^2$
$= 4x^2 - 225$

Factor: $25x^2 - 144$

$25x^2 - 144 = (5x)^2 - (12)^2$ ← The binomial can be expressed as the difference of two perfect squares.

$= (5x + 12)(5x - 12)$

Check: $25x^2 - 144 \stackrel{?}{=} (5x + 12)(5x - 12)$
$\stackrel{?}{=} 25x^2 - 60x + 60x - 144$
$= 25x^2 - 144$ **True**

Multiply.

1. $(b + 17)(b - 17)$

   $(b)^2 - (17)^2$
   $b^2 - 289$

2. $(a + 21)(a - 21)$

   $(a)^2 - (35)^2$
   $a^2 - 441$

3. $(r - 35)(r + 35)$

   $(r)^2 + (35)^2$
   $r^2 + 1225$

4. $(g - 40)(g + 40)$

   $g^2 - 1600$

5. $(4x - 3)(4x + 3)$

   $(4x)^2 - (3)^2$
   $16x^2 - 9$

6. $(7h - 5)(7h + 5)$

   $49h^2 - 25$

7. $(9x + 7y)(9x - 7y)$

   $81x^2 - 49y^2$

8. $(8m + 13n)(8m - 13n)$

   $64m^2 - 169n^2$

9. $(10t + 9u)(10t - 9u)$

   $100t^2 - 81u^2$

10. $(20b + 7c)(20b - 7c)$

    $400b^2 - 49c^2$

11. $(q - 0.8)(q + 0.8)$

    $q^2 - 0.64$

12. $(d - 0.9)(d + 0.9)$

    $d^2 - 0.81$

13. $(3.2r + 1.1s)(3.2r - 1.1s)$

    $10.24r^2 - 1.21s^2$

14. $(2.6v + 2.1w)(2.6v - 2.1w)$

    $4.36v^2 - 4.2w^2$

15. $\left(f - \frac{1}{3}\right)\left(f + \frac{1}{3}\right)$

    $f^2 - \frac{1}{9}$

16. $\left(k - \frac{1}{8}\right)\left(k + \frac{1}{8}\right)$

    $k^2 - \frac{1}{64}$

17. $\left(\frac{3}{5}p + \frac{7}{3}q\right)\left(\frac{3}{5}p - \frac{7}{3}q\right)$

    $\frac{9}{25}p^2 - \frac{49}{9}q^2$

18. $\left(\frac{5}{4}x + \frac{5}{6}y\right)\left(\frac{5}{4}x - \frac{5}{6}y\right)$

    $\frac{25}{16}x^2 - \frac{25}{36}y^2$

Use with SOURCEBOOK Lesson 8-5, pages 212–213.

Factor. Then check your answer.

19. $x^2 - 324$

$(x)^2 - (18)^2$

$(x + 18)(x - 18)$

Check:

$= x^2 - 18x + 18x - 324$

$= x^2 - 324$ ✓

20. $b^2 - 900$

(b+30)(b-30)

21. $121 - 64d^2$

(11+8d)(11-8d)

22. $169 - 100m^2$

(13+10m)(13-10m)

23. $25r^2 - 256s^2$

24. $49f^2 - 361g^2$

25. $h^2 - 1.44$

26. $k^2 - 2.25$

27. $p^2 - \frac{25}{9}$

28. $w^2 - \frac{36}{49}$

29. $\frac{1}{4}\ell^2 - \frac{1}{9}m^2$

30. $\frac{1}{25}x^2 - \frac{1}{16}y^2$

31. $0.25b^2 - 0.36c^2$

32. $0.16p^2 - 0.25q^2$

33. $6.25v^2 - 0.49w^2$

34. $0.01j^2 - 0.04k^2$

Problem Solving

35. The sum of two numbers times the difference of the same two numbers is 32. What are the numbers?

36. One number is 3 more than a second number. The product of their sum and their difference is 45. What are the numbers?

CRITICAL THINKING

37. Can the binomial $5y^2 - 125$ be factored as the difference of two perfect squares? Explain your answer.

8-6 Factor by Grouping

Name ______________________ Date ____________

Factor: $4r^5 + 4 + r^3 + 16r^2$

$(4r^5 + 4) + (r^3 + 16r^2)$ ← Arrange in groups with common factors.

$4(r^5 + 1) + r^2(r + 16)$ ← Factor the GCF from each group.

Think

There is no common binomial factor. Use the Commutative and Associative Properties of Equality to rearrange and regroup the terms differently.

$(4r^5 + 16r^2) + (r^3 + 4)$ ← Group the first and fourth terms.

$4r^2(r^3 + 4) + 1(r^3 + 4)$ ← Factor the GCF from each group.

$(4r^2 + 1)(r^3 + 4)$ ← Apply the Distributive Property.

Remember: When a polynomial contains four or more terms and two groups have the same binomial factor, factor by grouping.

Check:

$4r^5 + 4 + r^3 + 16r^3 \stackrel{?}{=} (4r^2 + 1)(r^3 + 4)$

F O I L

$\stackrel{?}{=} 4r^5 + 16r^2 + r^3 + 4$

$= 4r^5 + 4 + r^3 + 16r^2$ **True**

Factor each polynomial by grouping. Check your answer.

1. $21b^3 + 133b^2 + 3b + 19$

$7b^2(3b + 19) + 1(3b + 19)$
$(7b^2 + 1)(3b + 19)$
Check:
$= 21b^3 + 133b^2 + 3b + 19$

2. $55a^3 + 5a^2 + 22a + 2$

3. $7a^3 + 5a + 28a^2 + 20$

4. $9c^3 + 4c + 18c^2 + 8$

5. $12m^3 - 8m - 10 + 15m^2$

6. $12p^3 - 14p - 63 + 54p^2$

7. $-65w + 78w^4 - 6w^3 + 5$

8. $-11z^3 + 264z^4 - 48z + 2$

9. $21x^2 + 14x^2y - 2xy - 3x$

10. $32b^2 - 3ab - 4b + 24ab^2$

11. $14c^3 - 35c^2d + 6cd^3 - 15d^4$

12. $95a^2 - 57ab + 10ab - 6b^2$

Use with SOURCEBOOK Lesson 8-6, pages 214–215.

Factor each polynomial by grouping. Check your answer.

13. $m^2 + np - mp - mn$

14. $2ab + bc - b^2 - 2ac$

15. $3a^2 + 2bc + 6ac + ab$

16. $5m^2 + 7np + 35mn + mp$

17. $gj - hk + gk - hj$

18. $fm - tz + ft - mz$

19. $3ac - 8bd - 4ad + 6bc$

20. $10ce - 18df - 12cf + 15de$

21. $x^2z + w^2y + x^2w^2 + yz$

22. $ip + j^3q^2 + iq^2 + j^3p$

23. $-28r^2u + 12su + 14r^2t - 6st$

24. $10x^3z - 14w^2z - 15x^3y + 21w^2y$

25. $\frac{5}{12}jk - \frac{5}{32}k\ell - \frac{7}{9}j\ell + \frac{7}{24}\ell^2$

26. $\frac{1}{10}p^2 - \frac{2}{45}pq - \frac{5}{24}pr + \frac{5}{54}qr$

27. $1.14ax - 0.54bx + 0.76ay - 0.36by$

Solve. Show your work.

28. The area of a rectangle is represented by $a^2b + 2a + ab^2 + 2b$. If $a + b$ represents the length, what binomial represents the width?

29. The area of a rectangle is represented by $x^3 - xy + 2x^2y^2 - 2y^3$. If $x + 2y^2$ represents the length, what binomial represents the width?

CHALLENGE

30. Factor by grouping: $a^2 - b^2 + ax + bx$. Explain your steps.

8-7 Factor Completely

Name ____________________ Date __________

Factor completely: $3x^3 - 24x^2 + 48x$

$3x(x^2 - 8x + 16)$ ← The GCF is $3x$.

$3x(x - 4)^2$ ← $x^2 - 8x + 16$ is a perfect-square trinomial.

Check: $3x^3 - 24x^2 + 48x \stackrel{?}{=} 3x(x - 4)^2$

$\stackrel{?}{=} 3x(x^2 - 8x + 16)$

$= 3x^3 - 24x^2 + 48x$ **True**

Factor completely: $9v^3 - 2$

$9v^3 - 2$ ← No GCF
Not the difference of two perfect squares

$9v^3 - 2$ cannot be factored.
It is prime.

Factor completely. Check using multiplication. If the polynomial *cannot* be factored using integers, label it *prime.*

1. $2a^2 - 162$

$2(a^2 - 81)$

$2(a + 9)(a - 9)$

Check:

$2a^2 - 162 \stackrel{?}{=} 2(a + 9)(a - 9)$

$\stackrel{?}{=} (2a + 18)(a - 9)$

$= 2a^2 - 162$ True

2. $3b^2 - 48$

____

3. $8c^3 - 80c^2 + 200c$

____

4. $2f^3 - 28f^2 + 98f$

____

5. $3ab^2 + 21ab - 54a$

____

6. $5vw^2 + 20vw - 160v$

____

7. $-5x^2y - 25xy - 15y$

____

8. $-2hj^2 - 18hj - 2h$

____

9. $8x^2y - 4x^2 + 19y$

____

10. $4a^3b - 9b^2 + 4a$

____

11. $48t^3 + 88t^2 + 24t$

____

12. $140m^3 + 133m^2 + 21m$

____

Factor completely. Check using multiplication. If the polynomial *cannot* be factored using integers, label it *prime*.

13. $7d^4 - 7$

14. $8c^4 - 128$

15. $c^4d - 13c^2d + 36d$

16. $a^4b - 5a^2b + 4b$

17. $27a^4 + 27a^3 - 12a^2 - 12a$

18. $64x^4 + 64x^3 - 324x^2 - 324x$

19. $a^4 - 2a^2b^2 + b^4$

20. $16x^4 - 72x^2y^2 + 81y^4$

21. $x^8 - 1$

Problem Solving

22. A rectangular prism has a volume of $x^3y + xy^3 - 2x^2y^2$ with a square base. If it has a lateral area of 30 in.^{2}, what is the volume in cubic inches?

23. A rectangular prism has a volume of $x^3 - y^3 + x^2y - xy^2$, and a square base. If a lateral side has an area of 16 cm^2, what is the volume in cubic centimeters?

MENTAL MATH

Multiply.

24. (24)(36)

25. (91)(89)

26. (74)(66)

27. $(29)^2$

28. $(63)^2$

8-8 Technology: Factor Polynomials Using a Graph

Name ______________________ Date ______________

You can use a handheld to find the x-intercepts and factor the polynomial $x^2 - 16$.

Step 1 Press (home). Then choose (2) to select **Graphs & Geometry**.

Step 2 Input $x^2 - 16$, then press (enter) to graph the parabola.

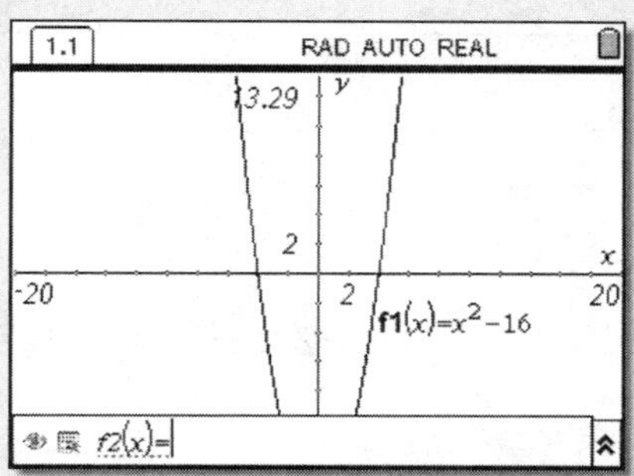

Step 3 Press (menu). Select **Window**, then select **Zoom – Box**.

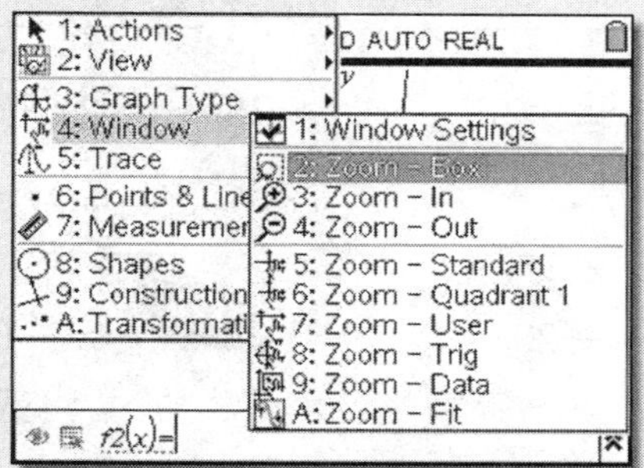

Step 4 Move the cursor to select a box that contains the x-intercepts.

Choose integers for the corners. Press (enter) at each corner.

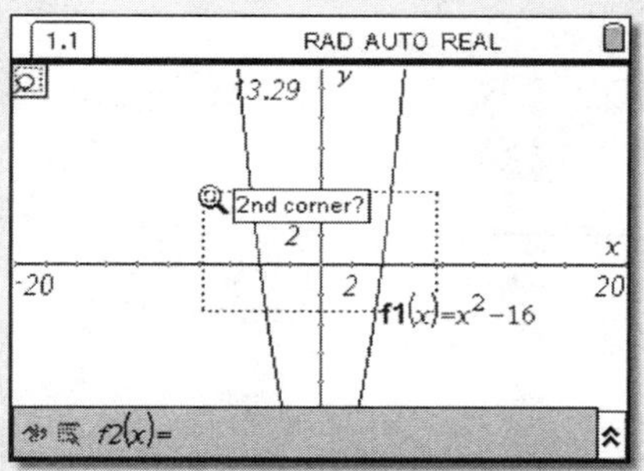

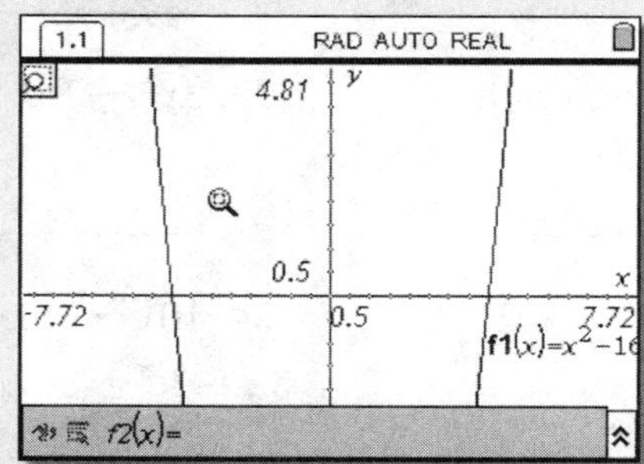

It appears that the x-intercepts are at -4 and 4. You may want to repeat Steps 3 and 4 to zoom in closer.

Then $(x + 4)$ and $(x - 4)$ are factors.

Check: You can verify the answer found by multiplying the two binomials.

$$(x + 4)(x - 4) = x^2 - 4x + 4x - 16$$
$$= x^2 - 16$$

So the factored form of $x^2 - 16$ is $(x + 4)(x - 4)$.

Use a handheld to factor the polynomial.

1. $x^2 - 4$ **$(x + 2)(x - 2)$**

2. $x^2 - 1$ ______

3. $x^2 - 36$ ______

4. $x^2 - 49$ ______

5. $x^2 - 100$ ______

6. $x^2 - 144$ ______

7. $x^2 - 400$ ______

8. $x^2 - 225$ ______

Use a handheld to factor the polynomial.

9. $x^2 + 2x - 3$

$(x + 3)(x - 1)$

10. $x^2 + 2x - 8$

11. $x^2 + 10x + 9$

12. $x^2 + 7x + 12$

13. $x^2 - 9x + 18$

14. $x^2 - 8x + 7$

15. $x^2 - x - 30$

16. $x^2 - 3x - 28$

17. $x^2 + 6x - 16$

18. $x^2 + 2x - 15$

19. $x^2 - 10x + 24$

20. $x^2 - 11x + 10$

21. $x^2 - x - 20$

22. $x^2 - x - 6$

23. $x^2 - 9x + 20$

24. $x^2 - 17x + 72$

25. $2x^2 + 7x + 3$

26. $2x^2 + 11x + 5$

27. $2x^2 + 9x - 5$

28. $2x^2 + 15x - 8$

29. $3x^2 - 10x + 8$

30. $3x^2 - 16x + 16$

31. $3x^2 - 20x - 32$

32. $3x^2 - 26x - 40$

33. $10x^2 - x - 2$

34. $10x^2 - 11x - 6$

35. $4x^2 + 8x + 3$

36. $4x^2 + 16x + 15$

Solve.

37. For which trinomials in questions 9–36 does the graph cross the positive x-axis twice? Describe the factors.

38. Factor $f(x) = 2x^4 + x^3 - 29x^2 - 34x + 24$ using a handheld. (*Hint*: There are four unique binomial factors.)

CHALLENGE

39. The factors of $f(x) = x^2 - 5x + 3$ are not rational numbers. Use a handheld to approximate the factors to the nearest tenth.

8-9 Problem-Solving Strategy: Review of Strategies

Read Plan Solve Check

Name ______________________ Date __________

Solve using a strategy that you have used before.

1. In each of the past four years, the scholarship endowment at Valleyview College has doubled. Today, it holds $4,000,000. What was the initial amount that the fund began with four years earlier?

2. Can you time a 7-minute event with only two timers: A 3-minute timer and a 5-minute timer? Explain.

3. The fraction $\frac{1}{13}$ can be represented as a repeating decimal. What is the 200th digit in the decimal expansion of $\frac{1}{13}$?

4. What is the ones digit for the sum $5^{34} + 2^{98} + 3^{110}$?

5. Find the sum of $\frac{1}{2} + \frac{1}{2^2} + \frac{1}{2^3} + \frac{1}{2^4} + \ldots + \frac{1}{2^{16}}$.

Use with SOURCEBOOK Lesson 8-9, pages 220–221.

6. The divisors of 1001 add up to 1344. What is the sum of the *reciprocals* of the divisors of 1001?

7. Regardless of where the point T is placed along the base of PS the ratio of the area of the shaded region to the trapezoid's area is the same. What is that ratio?

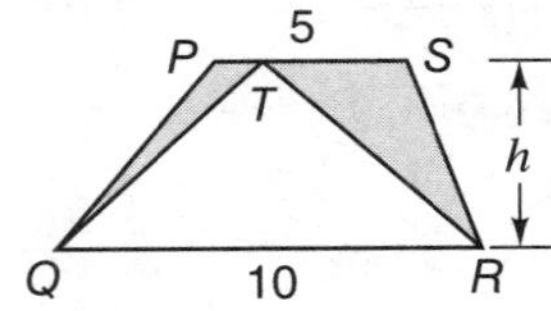

8. Suppose $\overline{XY}$ is tangent to inner circle P and a chord of the larger circle P. Find the area of the shaded region between the two circles if $XY = 36$.

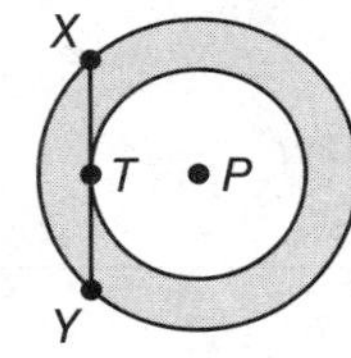

9. Subtract: $4 - 1.\overline{23456}$

10. Solve the following equation for a and b, where a and b are rational:

$$(2a^2 + 3b - 4)^2 + (2a + 3b)^2 = 0$$

Enrichment:
Factor Sums and Differences of Cubes

Name ______________________________ Date ______________

Factor: $\frac{8}{27}x^3 + 125y^3$

$$\frac{8}{27}x^3 + 125y^3 = \left(\frac{2}{3}x\right)^3 + (5y)^3$$
$$= \left(\frac{2}{3}x + 5y\right)\left[\left(\frac{2}{3}x\right)^2 - 2\left(\frac{2}{3}x\right)5y + (5y)^2\right]$$
$$= \left(\frac{2}{3}x + 5y\right)\left(\frac{4}{9}x^2 - \frac{20}{3}xy + 25y^2\right)$$

Remember:
Sum of two cubes:
$a^3 + b^3 = (a + b)(a^2 - ab + b^2)$
Difference of two cubes:
$a^3 - b^3 = (a - b)(a^2 + ab + b^2)$

Multiply: $(x^2 + 3y)^3$

$$(x^2 + 3y)^3 = (x^2)^3 + 3(x^2)^2(3y) + 3(x^2)(3y)^2 + (3y)^3$$
$$= x^6 + 9x^4y + 9x^2y^2 + 27y^3$$

Remember:
Cube of a Sum:
$(a + b)^3 = a^3 + 3a^2b + 3ab^2 + b^3$
Cube of a Difference:
$(a - b)^3 = a^3 - 3a^2b + 3ab^2 - b^3$

Factor each polynomial.

1. $8p^3 + q^3$

$(2p)^3 + (q)^3$
$(2p + q)[(2p)^2 - (2p)q + q^2]$
$(2p + q)(4p^2 - 2pq + q^2)$

2. $s^3 + 216$

____

3. $8z^3 - m^6$

____

4. $8x^3 - 27y^3$

____

5. $27w^6 + 64z^3$

____

6. $125h^9 + 512k^3$

____

7. $\frac{1}{8}q^3 - r^3$

____

8. $m^3 - \frac{8}{27}$

____

9. $\frac{1}{343}h^3 + 64$

____

10. $\frac{125}{216} - b^3d^3$

____

11. $m^3n^6 - \frac{1}{1000}$

____

12. $\frac{3}{32}r^2t^3 - \frac{3}{4}r^2v^3w^6$

____

Simplify.

13. $(2m - n)^3$

$(2m)^3 - 3(2m)^2n + 3(2m)n^2 - n^3$
$8m^3 - 12m^2n + 6mn^2 - n^3$

14. $(x - 3y)^3$

15. $(4p + 2q)^3$

16. $(7a + 6b)^3$

17. $\left(\frac{1}{4}c + \frac{2}{3}\right)^3$

18. $\left(\frac{2}{5} + \frac{1}{8}e\right)^3$

19. $\left(\frac{1}{2}t - \frac{3}{5}\right)^3$

20. $\left(\frac{5}{6} - \frac{1}{3}d\right)^3$

21. $(h^2k + r^3t^2)^3$

22. $(g^2n^3 + a^9b^8)^3$

23. $(a^4 - 7m^2n^5)^3$

24. $(2b^{10} - 5x^5y^4)^3$

CHALLENGE

25. Simplify the expression, $(x - 2)^5$, using the rule for the cube of a difference.

Test Prep: Multiple-Choice Questions

Strategy: Try All the Answers

Name ______________________ Date __________

When solving a multiple-choice problem, you can sometimes work backward by **testing the answers** in the original problem.

To select the correct answer in a multiple-choice item, try using the following strategies.

- Underline important words.
- Restate the question.
- Use the Test-Prep strategy.
- Apply appropriate rules, definitions, properties, or strategies.
- Analyze and eliminate answer choices.

Choose the correct answer. *TIP: Work easier problems first.*

1. What is the factored form of $10x^2 + 3x - 18$?

A. $(2x - 3)(5x + 6)$

B. $(2x + 3)(5x - 6)$

C. $(2x - 6)(5x + 3)$

D. $(2x + 6)(5x - 3)$

2. The difference of $3x^3 - 5x^2 + 1$ and another polynomial is $x^3 - 2x^2 - 5x - 5$. What is the other polynomial?

F. $-4x^3 + 7x^2 + 5x + 4$

G. $-2x^3 + 3x^2 - 5x - 6$

H. $2x^3 - 3x^2 + 5x + 6$

J. $4x^3 - 7x^2 - 5x - 4$

3. Which function describes the data in the table?

x	−2	0	2	4
$f(x)$	10	6	10	22

A. $f(x) = -5x$ **C.** $f(x) = -x^2 + 6$

B. $f(x) = 5x$ **D.** $f(x) = x^2 + 6$

4. What is the solution of the system of equations?

$$\begin{cases} y = 4x - 9 \\ x + y = 1 \end{cases}$$

F. $(-1, 2)$ **H.** $(-2, 1)$

G. $(1, -2)$ **J.** $(2, -1)$

5. Which value of x is in the solution set of the inequality $x - 12 > -4x + 8$?

A. −5 **C.** 4

B. −4 **D.** 5

6. Which binomial is a factor of $2x^3 - 4x^2 + 2x$?

F. $2x$ **H.** $x + 1$

G. $x - 1$ **J.** $x - 2$

7. The circumference of a circular rug is 1.44π m. What is the radius of the rug?

A. 0.36 m

B. 0.72 m

C. 1.2 m

D. 2.88 m

8. Jeremy mows lawns to earn money. He wants to buy a concert ticket that costs \$65. He starts with \$15 and earns \$12 for each lawn he mows. What is the least number of lawns he must mow in order to buy the ticket?

F. 4 **H.** 6

G. 5 **J.** 7

Use with SOURCEBOOK Test Prep Lesson, pages 244.

For More Practice Go To:
ONLINE www.progressinmathematics.com

Vocabulary Development

Name ______________________________ Date ______________

Chapter 8 Vocabulary

difference of two squares	prime polynomial
factorable	special product
greatest common monomial factor	square of a binomial
perfect-square trinomial	

From the vocabulary list above, choose the terms that best complete(s) each sentence. Write the term(s) in the space(s) provided.

1. The square of a binomial is called a ______________________.

2. The product of the sum and the difference of the same two terms is called the ______________________.

3. The ______________________ of two or more monomials is the product of all the integer and variable factors that are common to those monomials.

4. If a polynomial can be written as a product of factors, then it is ______________________.

5. A polynomial whose terms do not have a common factor other than 1 is called a ______________________.

6. The difference of two squares and perfect-square trinomials are both examples of ______________________.

Tell whether each statement is *true* or *false*. If false, rewrite the statement to make it true.

7. The expression $9x^2 + 16$ is a perfect-square trinomial.

____

8. The difference of two squares can be factored as the square of the difference of two terms.

____

9. The factors of a perfect-square trinomial are two different binomials.

____

10. The greatest common monomial factor for the binomial $12x^4 - 24x^2y^2$ is $4x^2$.

____

Use after SOURCEBOOK Lessons 8-1–8-7, pages 200–217.

Practice Chapter 8 Test

Name ______________________________ Date ______________

Find the GCF of the terms.

1. $-16d^2, -24d^4, -32$

2. $21m^4n^4, 28m^3n^3, 35m^3n^2$

3. $60x^6y^5, 30x^4y^5, 45x^7y^5$

Factor the polynomial by finding the greatest monomial factor. Check your answer.

4. $12y^7 + 12y^3$

5. $-34g^6 - 68g^2$

6. $20x^4y^2 - 15x^3y^3 - 30x^2y^2$

Factor each trinomial. Check by multiplying. If the polynomial cannot be factored, write *prime*.

7. $x^2 + 8x + 15$

8. $y^2 - 6y - 55$

9. $b^2 - 16b + 48$

10. $r^2 - 2f + 13$

11. $3r^2 - 20r - 63$

12. $12q^2 - 37q + 11$

13. $10p^2 + p - 21$

14. $45n^2 - 26n - 8$

15. $f^2 - 4fg + 4g^2$

16. $r^2 - 10rs + 25s^2$

17. $c^2 - 19cd + 70d^2$

18. $m^2 + 14mn - 49n^2$

Square each binomial.

19. $(w + 28)^2$

20. $(\ell - 33)^2$

21. $(5y - 11)^2$

22. $(4x + 7y)^2$

23. $(6v + 9w)^2$

24. $(10a - 8b)^2$

25. $(0.11y - 0.12z)^2$

26. $\left(\frac{1}{2}w - \frac{1}{3}x\right)^2$

Determine if each trinomial is a perfect square. If so, factor. If not, explain why not.

27. $25b^2 + 60b + 144$

28. $36t^2 - 156t + 169$

29. $144x^2 + 24xy + y^2$

Multiply.

30. $(s - 1.7)(s + 1.7)$

31. $(5v + 11w)(5v - 11w)$

32. $\left(t - \frac{1}{7}\right)\left(t + \frac{1}{7}\right)$

Factor, if possible. Check your answer. If not possible, explain why not.

33. $r^2 - 2500$

34. $z^2 - 13$

35. $49m^2 - 16$

36. $16h^2 - 21$

Factor each polynomial by grouping. Check your answer.

37. $15y(7y + 19) + 3(7y + 19)$

38. $8c^3 + 88c^2 - c - 11$

Factor completely. Check your answer. If the polynomial cannot be factored, write *prime*.

39. $11v^2 - 44$

40. $7g^3 - 56g^2 + 112g$

41. $25x^3y - 30xy - 17y + 3$

Problem Solving

42. The trinomial $25a^2 + 60a + 36$ represents the area of a square. What expression represents the perimeter of the square?

43. If the trinomial $x^2 + 4x + 4$ represents the area of a triangle and the binomial $x + 2$ represents the base, what expression represents the height of the triangle?

Tell About It

Explain how you solve each problem. Show all your work.

44. Factor completely: $x^2 + 6x + 9 - y^2$

45. Multiply: $(x + 3)^2(x - 3)^2$

Cumulative Review: Chapters 1–8

Name ______________________________ Date ____________

Circle the best answer.

1. $\begin{bmatrix} 6 & -5 \\ -3 & 2 \end{bmatrix} + \begin{bmatrix} 8 & -3 \\ 1 & -5 \end{bmatrix} =$

A. $\begin{bmatrix} 14 & -8 \\ -2 & -3 \end{bmatrix}$ **B.** $\begin{bmatrix} 14 & -5 \\ -3 & 2 \end{bmatrix}$

C. $\begin{bmatrix} 48 & 15 \\ -3 & -10 \end{bmatrix}$ **D.** $\begin{bmatrix} 3 & 3 \\ -8 & 3 \end{bmatrix}$

2. In U, which describes the set $\{1, 8\}$?

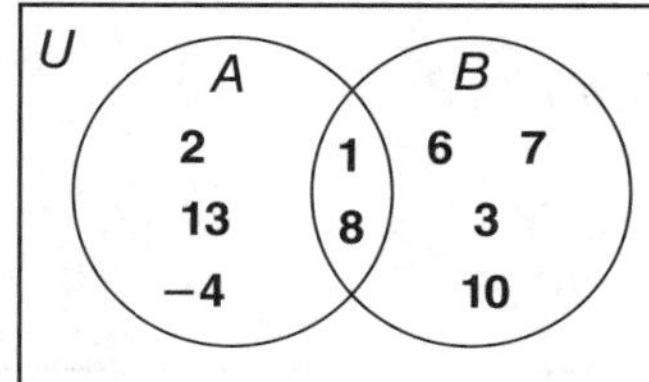

F. $A \cup B$ **G.** $A \cap B$
H. A' **J.** B'

3. Solve.

$|h + 8| = 9$

A. $h = -17$ or $h = 17$
B. $h = -1$ or $h = 1$
C. $h = 17$ or $h = -1$
D. $h = -17$ or $h = 1$

4. Which interval shows the inequality $\{x \mid x \geq 9.5\}$?

F. $(9.5, \infty)$
G. $(-\infty, 9.5]$
H. $[9.5, \infty)$
J. $(-\infty, 9.5)$

5. Solve.

$15a + 8 - 7a = 8a + 8$

A. $\{a \mid a = 1\}$
B. $\{a \mid a = -1\}$
C. $\{a \mid a \text{ is any real number}\}$
D. $\varnothing$

6. What is the domain of the relation in the table?

x	y
−4	−7
−2	−3
0	1
2	5
4	9

F. $\{-7, -3, 1, 5, 9\}$
G. $\{-4, -2, 0, 2, 4\}$
H. $\{-7, -4, -3, -2, 0, 1, 2, 4, 5, 9\}$
J. $\varnothing$

7. Which inequality is best represented by the graph below?

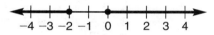

−4 −3 −2 −1 0 1 2 3 4

A. $v < -2$ or $v \geq 0$
B. $v \leq -2$ or $v \geq 0$
C. $v < -2$ or $v > 0$
D. $-2 < v \leq 0$

8. Solve for v.

$|2v - 1| \geq -3$

F. $-2 \leq v \leq 4$
G. $-1 \leq v \leq 2$
H. $v \leq -2$ or $v \geq 4$
J. $v \leq -1$ or $v \geq 2$

9. What is the slope of the line that connects the points $(-4, 8)$ and $(3, 1)$?

A. -9
B. -1
C. 1
D. 9

10. Which equation is a direct variation?

F. $y + 2x = 0$
G. $3y + x = 1$
H. $y + x^2 = 0$
J. $y = 2$

11. What is the slope of the line with equation $2x + 7y = 14$?

A. 7 **B.** $\frac{2}{7}$

C. $-\frac{2}{7}$ **D.** $-\frac{7}{2}$

12. Which ordered pair is the solution of the system $\begin{cases} 5x - 2y = 11 \\ 4x + 6y = -14 \end{cases}$?

F. $(-1, -3)$
G. $(1, 3)$
H. $(-1, 3)$
J. $(1, -3)$

13. Which polynomial has degree 4?

A. $4x$
B. $x + y + z + 4$
C. $9x^2yz + 1$
D. $8x^4y + 19x$

14. Multiply $(6c^2 + 5)^2$.

F. $12c^4 + 10$
G. $36c^4 + 25$
H. $36c^4 + 30c^2 + 25$
J. $36c^4 + 60c^2 + 25$

15. Factor $25c^2 + 20c^5$ completely.

A. $5(5c^2 + 4c^5)$
B. $5c(5c + 4c^4)$
C. $5c^2(5 + 4c^3)$
D. $c^2(25 + 20c^3)$

16. Which is a factor of $x^2 + 16x - 36$?

F. $(x + 2)$
G. $(x + 18)$
H. $(x + 6)$
J. $(x - 9)$

17. Which statement best describes the system $\begin{cases} 7x - 2y = 0 \\ x - y = 1 \end{cases}$?

A. inconsistent
B. inconsistent and dependent
C. consistent and independent
D. independent

18. Simplify $(5a^3b^2)^3$.

F. $125a^9b^6$
G. $15a^9b^6$
H. $125a^6b^5$
J. $15a^6b^5$

19. Multiply $(3x - 11)(3x + 11)$.

A. $9x^2 + 121$
B. $9x^2 - 66x - 121$
C. $9x^2 - 121$
D. $9x^2 - 66x + 121$

20. Which is a factor of $6a^2 + 11a - 35$?

F. $(2a - 7)$
G. $(3a + 5)$
H. $(3a - 5)$
J. $(3a - 7)$

Tell About It

Explain how you solve each problem. Show all your work.

21. The area of a rectangle is represented by the expression $x^3 + 5x^2 + 3x + 15$. What binomials represent the length and width of the rectangle?

22. It takes a boat 3 hours to travel 33 mi of a river with the current. It takes the same boat $4\frac{5}{7}$ hours to travel the same distance against the current. What is the boat's speed? What is the speed of the current? (*Hint:* distance = rate × time)

9-1 Simplify Radical Expressions

Name ______________________________ Date ______________

Simplify: $-12\sqrt{45}$

$= -12\sqrt{9 \bullet 5}$ ← Factor out the greatest perfect square.

$= -12\sqrt{9}\sqrt{5}$ ← Use the Product Property of Square Roots: $\sqrt{ab} = \sqrt{a} \bullet \sqrt{b}$, where $a \geq 0$ and $b \geq 0$.

$= -12(3\sqrt{5})$ ← Simplify.

$= -36\sqrt{5}$ ← Simplify.

So in simplest form, $-12\sqrt{45} = -36\sqrt{5}$.

Simplify: $8\sqrt{72x^7y^8z}$

$= 8\sqrt{9 \bullet 4 \bullet 2 \bullet x^6 \bullet x \bullet y^8 \bullet z}$ ← Factor out perfect squares.

$= 8\sqrt{36x^6y^8 \bullet 2xz}$ ← Use the Commutative Property.

$= 8\sqrt{36x^6y^8}\sqrt{2xz}$ ← Use the Product Property of Square Roots.

$= 8(6|x^3|y^4\sqrt{2xz})$ ← Simplify.

$= 48|x^3|y^4\sqrt{2xz}$ ← Simplify.

So in simplest form, $8\sqrt{72x^7y^8z} = 48|x^3|y^4\sqrt{2xz}$.

Simplify the expression.

1. $\sqrt{27}$

$\sqrt{9 \bullet 3}$

$\sqrt{9} \bullet \sqrt{3}$

$3\sqrt{3}$

2. $\sqrt{44}$

3. $\sqrt{700}$

4. $\sqrt{20{,}000}$

5. $-\sqrt{18}$

6. $-\sqrt{48}$

7. $-12\sqrt{54}$

8. $-11\sqrt{20}$

9. $7\sqrt{441}$

10. $9\sqrt{625}$

11. $23\sqrt{92}$

12. $15\sqrt{261}$

13. $\sqrt{0.72}$

14. $\sqrt{1.25}$

15. $\sqrt{0.4}$

$\sqrt{0.1}$

16. $\sqrt{0.9}$

17. $8\sqrt{1.44}$

18. $6\sqrt{1.21}$

19. $-11\sqrt{2.56}$

20. $-13\sqrt{3.24}$

Simplify the expression. (*Hint:* Expressions of the form $\sqrt{x^{2m}}$, where *m* is odd, must be written in the form $|x^m|$, after simplification.

21. $6\sqrt{25x^2y}$

$6\sqrt{25x^2 \bullet y}$

$6\sqrt{25x^2} \bullet \sqrt{y}$

$6(5|x|\sqrt{y})$

$30|x|\sqrt{y}$

22. $9\sqrt{81ab^2}$

23. $4\sqrt{120x^4y^5}$

24. $3\sqrt{60x^7y^6}$

$3\sqrt{4x^6y^6 \bullet 15x}$

$\sqrt{15x}$

25. $-4\sqrt{180a^5b^2c^{10}}$

26. $-2\sqrt{98m^3n^8p^2}$

27. $\sqrt{350t^8u^{12}v^{10}}$

$\sqrt{25t^8u^{12}v^{10} \bullet 14}$

$\sqrt{14}$

28. $\sqrt{320a^{14}b^6c^{20}}$

$\sqrt{5}$

29. $-15\sqrt{540k^6\ell m}$

30. $-20\sqrt{272fg^8h}$

31. $3\sqrt{2400x^{30}y^{16}}$

32. $7\sqrt{2700a^{100}b^{18}}$

33. $4x\sqrt{32x^4y^3}$

34. $3a\sqrt{125a^6b^5}$

35. $-2m^3\sqrt{315m^8}$

36. $-5a^4\sqrt{124a^{10}}$

Problem Solving

37. Seven more than 3 times the square root of a number is 19. What is the number?

38. The sum of the square roots of two integers is 7. What are two such integers?

CRITICAL THINKING

39. A radical expression, simplified, equals $15|x^5y^7z|\sqrt{3xy}$. If the original expression was all part of the radicand, what was the original radical expression? Explain your work.

9-2 Add and Subtract Radical Expressions

Name ______________________ Date ____________

Simplify: $-7\sqrt{2} + 8\sqrt{11} + 16\sqrt{2} - 13\sqrt{11}$

$-7\sqrt{2} + 8\sqrt{11} + 16\sqrt{2} - 13\sqrt{11}$ ← Identify like radicands.

$(-7\sqrt{2} + 16\sqrt{2}) + (8\sqrt{11} - 13\sqrt{11})$ ← Use the Commutative and Associative Properties of Equality.

$(-7 + 16)\sqrt{2} + (8 - 13)\sqrt{11}$ ← Apply the Distributive Property.

$9\sqrt{2} - 5\sqrt{11}$ ← These terms have unlike radicands. Do not combine.

Simplify: $11\sqrt{50x^2} + 4x^3\sqrt{8x^4} - 7x\sqrt{28x^8} - 3\sqrt{32x^2}$

$11\sqrt{25x^2 \bullet 2} + 4x^3\sqrt{4x^4 \bullet 2} - 7x\sqrt{4x^8 \bullet 7} - 3\sqrt{16x^2 \bullet 2}$ ← Factor out perfect squares in the radicand, wherever possible.

$11\sqrt{25x^2} \bullet \sqrt{2} + 4x^3\sqrt{4x^4} \bullet \sqrt{2} - 7x\sqrt{4x^8} \bullet \sqrt{7} - 3\sqrt{16x^2} \bullet \sqrt{2}$ ← Use the Product Property of Square Roots.

$11(5|x|\sqrt{2}) + 4x^3(2x^2\sqrt{2}) - 7x(2x^4\sqrt{7}) - 3(4|x|\sqrt{2})$ ← Simplify.

$55|x|\sqrt{2} + 8x^5\sqrt{2} - 14x^5\sqrt{7} - 12|x|\sqrt{2}$ ← Identify like radicands *and* like terms.

$8x^5\sqrt{2} - 14x^5\sqrt{7} + (55|x|\sqrt{2} - 12|x|\sqrt{2})$ ← Use the Commutative Property of Equality.

$8x^5\sqrt{2} - 14x^5\sqrt{7} + (55|x| - 12|x|)\sqrt{2}$ ← Apply the Distributive Property.

$8x^5\sqrt{2} - 14x^5\sqrt{7} + 43|x|\sqrt{2}$ ← Simplify.

Simplify each expression. (*Hint:* $a\sqrt{x} \pm b\sqrt{x} = (a \pm b)\sqrt{x}$, where a and $b \geq 0$.)

1. $6\sqrt{7} - 4\sqrt{13} + 9\sqrt{7} + 11\sqrt{13}$

$(6\sqrt{7} + 9\sqrt{7}) - (4\sqrt{13} - 11\sqrt{13})$

$(6 + 9)\sqrt{7} - (4 - 11)\sqrt{13}$

$15\sqrt{7} + 7\sqrt{13}$

2. $5\sqrt{14} - 2\sqrt{10} + 3\sqrt{14} + 14\sqrt{10}$

$\sqrt{10}$

$\sqrt{10}$

3. $26 - 3\sqrt{21} + 7\sqrt{2} + 18$

____

4. $15 - 4\sqrt{30} + 22 + 8\sqrt{3}$

____

5. $9\sqrt{12} - 7\sqrt{63} + 8\sqrt{75} + 3\sqrt{28}$

____

6. $5\sqrt{18} - 11\sqrt{125} + 4\sqrt{98} + 2\sqrt{180}$

____

7. $-9\sqrt{448} - 5\sqrt{1300} + 8\sqrt{325} + 6\sqrt{700}$

____

8. $-6\sqrt{405} - 7\sqrt{1500} + 4\sqrt{735} + 2\sqrt{500}$

____

9. $\sqrt{2366} + \sqrt{1183} - \sqrt{847} - \sqrt{686}$

____

10. $\sqrt{6615} - \sqrt{6250} + \sqrt{3840} - \sqrt{2890}$

____

Use with SOURCEBOOK Lesson 9-2, pages 228–229.

Simplify each expression.

11. $3\sqrt{a} - 2\sqrt{5} + \sqrt{a} - 7\sqrt{5}$

$3\sqrt{a} + \sqrt{a} - 2\sqrt{5} - 7\sqrt{5}$

$(3 + 1)\sqrt{a} + (-2 - 7)\sqrt{5}$

$4\sqrt{a} - 9\sqrt{5}$

12. $6\sqrt{b} - 8\sqrt{3} + \sqrt{b} - 11\sqrt{3}$

13. $2d - 11\sqrt{99} - 5d + 4\sqrt{704}$

14. $8f - 6\sqrt{288} - 17f + 3\sqrt{800}$

15. $9|n|\sqrt{17} - 5\sqrt{17n^2} + 11|n|\sqrt{272}$

16. $12|m|\sqrt{19} - 6\sqrt{19m^2} + 8|m|\sqrt{1216}$

17. $3y^2\sqrt{25} - 12|y|\sqrt{24y} + 9|y|\sqrt{54}$

$\sqrt{6y}$

18. $11|x|\sqrt{36} - 4x^2\sqrt{63x} + 10|x|\sqrt{72x}$

19. $\frac{2}{3}\sqrt{189} + 0.2\sqrt{450x^2} + 8|x|\sqrt{128}$

20. $\frac{4}{5}\sqrt{1250} + 0.4\sqrt{300a^2} + 7|a|\sqrt{147}$

Problem Solving

21. Geometry The perimeter of a rectangle is $42\sqrt{2} + 18\sqrt{5}$. If the width of the rectangle is $7\sqrt{2} + 3\sqrt{5}$, what is the length?

22. Two numbers have a sum of $17\sqrt{11}$ and a difference of $\sqrt{11}$. What are the numbers?

TEST PREPARATION

23. Which radical expression is equivalent to $4\sqrt{3x} + 8$?

A. $2\sqrt{12x} + \sqrt{16}$ **B.** $\sqrt{36x} + \sqrt{16}$

C. $\sqrt{36x} + \sqrt{64}$ **D.** $2\sqrt{12x} + \sqrt{64}$

9-3 Multiply and Divide Radical Expressions

Name ______________________ Date __________

Multiply: $-3\sqrt{5a}\,(2\sqrt{3a^2})(-4\sqrt{8a})$

$-3(2)(-4)\sqrt{5a} \bullet \sqrt{3a^2} \bullet \sqrt{8a}$ ← Use the Commutative and Associative Properties of Equality.

$24\sqrt{5a \bullet 3a^2 \bullet 8a}$ ← Use the Product Property of Square Roots.

$24\sqrt{120a^4}$ ← Multiply.

$24\sqrt{4a^4 \bullet 30}$ ← Factor out perfect squares.

$24\sqrt{4a^4} \bullet \sqrt{30}$ ← Use the Product Property of Square Roots.

$24(2a^2)\sqrt{30}$ ← Simplify.

$48a^2\sqrt{30}$ ← Simplify.

Simplify: $\sqrt{\frac{7}{6}}$

Think

$\sqrt{\frac{a}{b}} = \frac{\sqrt{a}}{\sqrt{b}}$, where $a \geq 0$ and $b > 0$.

So $\sqrt{\frac{7}{6}} = \frac{\sqrt{7}}{\sqrt{6}}$

$= \frac{\sqrt{7}}{\sqrt{6}} \bullet \frac{\sqrt{6}}{\sqrt{6}}$ ← Multiply by 1 in the form of $\frac{\sqrt{6}}{\sqrt{6}}$.

$= \frac{\sqrt{42}}{\sqrt{36}}$ ← Simplify.

$= \frac{\sqrt{42}}{6}$ ← Simplify.

Simplify each radical expression. Assume that all variables represent nonnegative numbers.

1. $3\sqrt{8} \bullet 2\sqrt{5} \bullet 4\sqrt{6}$

$3(2)(4)\sqrt{8} \bullet \sqrt{5} \bullet \sqrt{6}$

$24\sqrt{8(5)(6)}$

$24\sqrt{240}$

$24\sqrt{16(15)}$

$24\sqrt{16} \bullet \sqrt{15}$

$24(4)\sqrt{15}$

$96\sqrt{15}$

2. $2\sqrt{12} \bullet 4\sqrt{7} \bullet 5\sqrt{15}$

____

3. $-5x\sqrt{2} \bullet 6\sqrt{10} \bullet 3\sqrt{6x^2}$

____

4. $-2\sqrt{3y^2} \bullet 5y\sqrt{8} \bullet 9\sqrt{14}$

____

5. $-3\sqrt{3x}\,(2\sqrt{5x} + 6\sqrt{6x})$

$\sqrt{18x^2}$

____

6. $-2\sqrt{2a}\,(3\sqrt{12a} + 8\sqrt{5a})$

____

7. $(\sqrt{3} + 4\sqrt{7})(5\sqrt{3} - 2\sqrt{7})$

____

8. $(\sqrt{5} + 3\sqrt{3})(2\sqrt{5} - 4\sqrt{3})$

____

9. $(7\sqrt{2} - x\sqrt{5})^2$

____

For More Practice Go To:

www.progressinmathematics.com

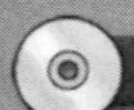

Practice/Test Generator

Simplify each radical expression. Assume that all variables represent nonnegative numbers.

10. $\frac{\sqrt{5}}{\sqrt{3}}$

$\frac{\sqrt{5}}{\sqrt{3}} \cdot \frac{\sqrt{3}}{\sqrt{3}}$

$\frac{\sqrt{15}}{\sqrt{9}}$

$\frac{\sqrt{15}}{3}$

11. $\frac{\sqrt{11}}{\sqrt{7}}$

$\frac{\sqrt{77}}{7}$

12. $\frac{\sqrt{24}}{\sqrt{8}}$

13. $\frac{\sqrt{42}}{\sqrt{7}}$

14. $\frac{7a}{\sqrt{8}}$

$\frac{7a\sqrt{2}}{\sqrt{16}}$

15. $\frac{5b}{\sqrt{27}}$

16. $\sqrt{\frac{12}{5}}$

17. $\sqrt{\frac{20}{7}}$

18. $\sqrt{\frac{6x}{7}}$

19. $\sqrt{\frac{5a}{11}}$

20. $\frac{2\sqrt{2a} + 4\sqrt{a}}{\sqrt{8a}}$

21. $\frac{5\sqrt{b} + 10\sqrt{b}}{\sqrt{5b}}$

Problem Solving

22. Geometry The length of a side of a square is $3\sqrt{8} + 6$. What is the area of the square? (*Hint:* Area = s^2)

23. Geometry The base of a triangle is $5\sqrt{2} + \sqrt{3}$ and the height is $5\sqrt{2} - \sqrt{3}$. What is the area of the triangle? $\left(\textit{Hint: } \text{Area} = \frac{1}{2}bh\right)$

CHALLENGE

24. Simplify: $\frac{3\sqrt{2} + 6}{2\sqrt{5} + 3}$

(*Hint:* Multiply both numerator and denominator by $2\sqrt{5} - 3$.)

9-4 Solve Radical Equations

Name ______________________ Date __________

Solve: $\sqrt{y-5}+7=21$

$\sqrt{y-5}=14$ ← Use the Subtraction Property of Equality to isolate the radicand.

$(\sqrt{y-5})^2=14^2$ ← Square both sides of the equation.

$y-5=196$ ← Simplify.

$y=201$ ← Use the Addition Property of Equality.

Check: $\sqrt{y-5}+7\stackrel{?}{=}21$

$\sqrt{201-5}+7\stackrel{?}{=}21$

$\sqrt{196}+7\stackrel{?}{=}21$

$14+7\stackrel{?}{=}21$

$21=21$ **True**

Solve: $5\sqrt{y+2}-3=-28$

$5\sqrt{y+2}=-25$ ← Use the Addition Property of Equality to isolate the radicand.

$\sqrt{y+2}=-5$ ← Use the Division Property of Equality.

$(\sqrt{y+2})^2=(-5)^2$ ← Square both sides of the equation.

$y+2=25$ ← Simplify.

$y=23$ ← Use the Subtraction Property of Equality.

Check: $5\sqrt{y+2}-3=-28$

$5\sqrt{23+2}-3\stackrel{?}{=}-28$

$5\sqrt{25}-3\stackrel{?}{=}-28$

$5(5)-3\stackrel{?}{=}-28$

$25-3\stackrel{?}{=}-28$

$22=-28$ **False**

The solution, $y=23$, is an extraneous solution.
There is no real number solution for $5\sqrt{y+2}-3=-28$.

Solve each equation. Check your solution. If there is no solution, write *no real solution*.

1. $2\sqrt{x}-4=2$

$2\sqrt{x}=6$

$\sqrt{x}=3$

$(\sqrt{x})^2=3^2$

$x=9$

Check:

$2\sqrt{9}-4\stackrel{?}{=}2$

$2(3)-4\stackrel{?}{=}2$

True: $2=2$

2. $3\sqrt{a}-7=11$ ______________

3. $10+4\sqrt{d}=38$ ______________

4. $24+6\sqrt{h}=90$ ______________

5. $\sqrt{x+9}=4$ ______________

6. $\sqrt{w+4}=5$ ______________

7. $\sqrt{28-p}=-6$ ______________

8. $\sqrt{89-w}=-10$ ______________

9. $\sqrt{\frac{p}{3}}=2$ ______________

10. $\sqrt{\frac{g}{5}}=3$ ______________

11. $-3\sqrt{28x}=52$ ______________

12. $-5\sqrt{72k}=60$ ______________

Solve each equation. Check your solution. If there is no solution, write *no real solution.*

13. $5 + \sqrt{s - 2} = 6$

14. $9 + \sqrt{m - 5} = 12$

15. $\frac{\sqrt{b + 1}}{3} = -5$

16. $\frac{\sqrt{h + 2}}{4} = -2$

17. $\frac{\sqrt{s - 4}}{5} = 3$

18. $\frac{\sqrt{v - 11}}{7} = 3$

19. $\sqrt{2x + 1} = 3$

20. $\sqrt{7z + 4} = 9$

21. $6\sqrt{5n - 3} = 42$

22. $10\sqrt{7f - 1} = 50$

23. $2 + 5\sqrt{3k + 18} = 32$

24. $7 + 3\sqrt{3g + 1} = 22$

Solve.

25. The skid-to-stop formula, $S = \sqrt{30Df}$, relates speed, S, in miles per hour to distance, D, in feet and to drag factor, f.

a. If a car travels at 70 mi/h and skids 500 feet, what is the drag factor of the road? Round to the nearest tenth.

b. If a car travels at 45 mi/h and the drag factor is 0.2, how long are the skid marks?

SPIRAL REVIEW

26. Simplify: $-\sqrt{2178}$

27. Multiply: $(r + 12)^2$

9-5 The Pythagorean Theorem

Name ______________________ Date ____________

A diagonal fence creates two triangular fields. Each field has a height of 240 ft and a base of 380 ft. What is the length of the diagonal fence? Write the answer in simplest radical form.

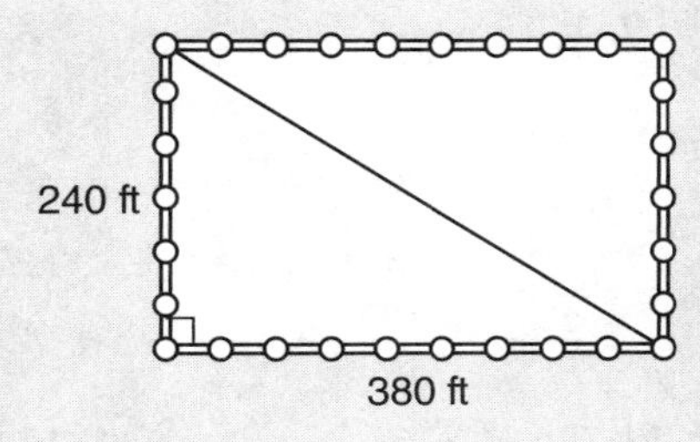

$a^2 + b^2 = c^2$ ← Use the Pythagorean Theorem.

$240^2 + 380^2 = c^2$ ← Substitute values into the Pythagorean Theorem.

$57{,}600 + 144{,}400 = c^2$ ← Simplify.

$202{,}000 = c^2$ ← Simplify.

$\sqrt{202{,}000} = c$ ← Take the square root of both sides.

$20\sqrt{505} = c$ ← Write in simplest radical form: $\sqrt{202{,}000} = \sqrt{400 \bullet 505}$

The length of the diagonal fence is $20\sqrt{505}$ feet.

Find the length of the third side of each right triangle. Give your answer in simplest radical form.

1.

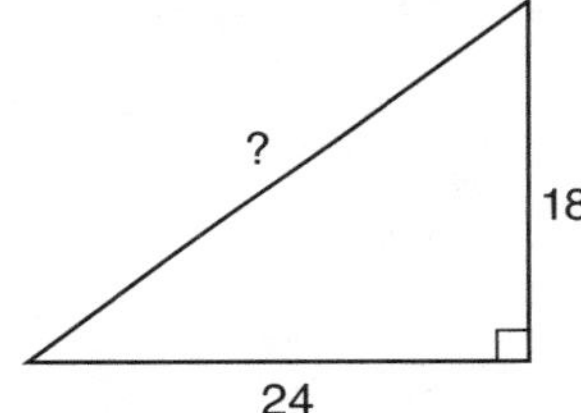

$a^2 + b^2 = c^2$
$24^2 + 18^2 = c^2$
$576 + 324 = c^2$
$900 = c^2$
$\sqrt{900} = c$
$c = 30$

____

2.

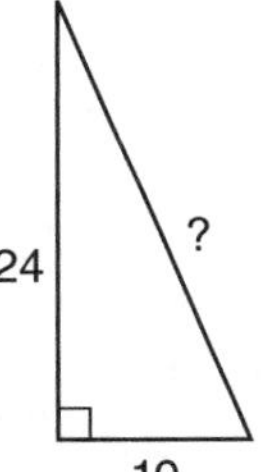

____

3.

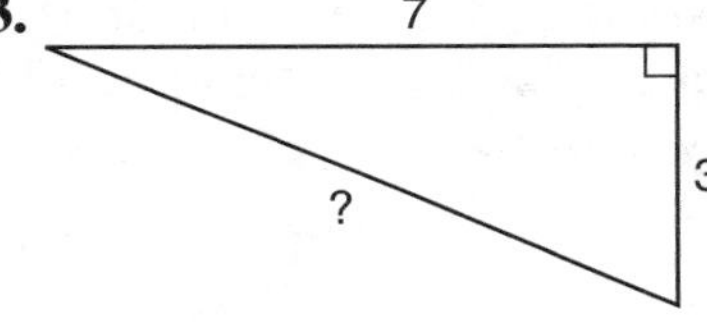

____

4.

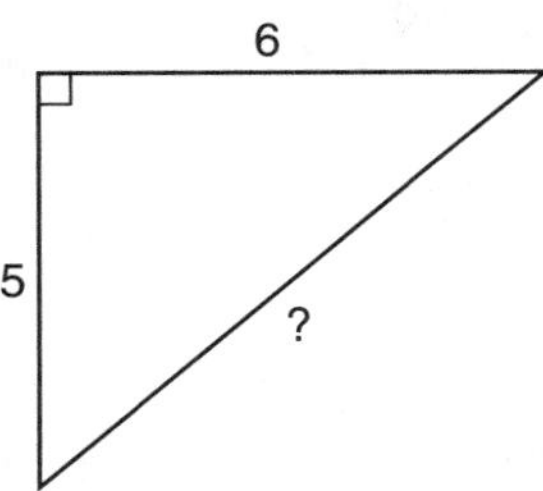

____

5.

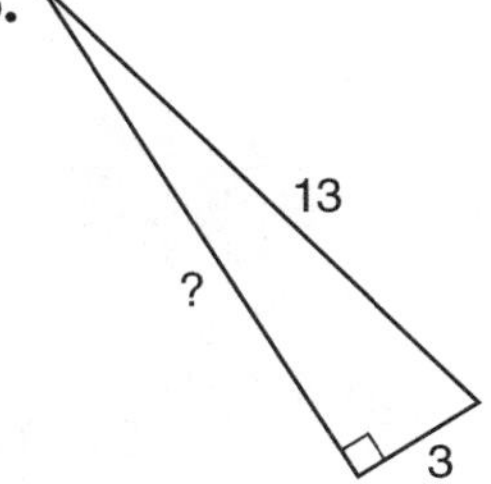

____

6.

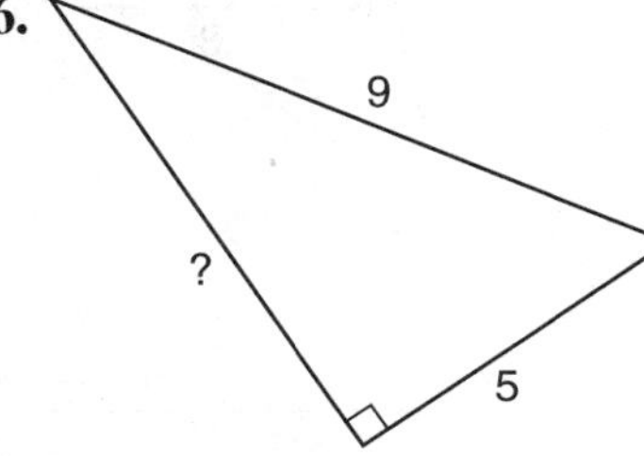

____

Determine whether or not a right triangle can have sides of the given lengths.

7. 1, 1, 5
$a^2 + b^2 = c^2$
$1^2 + 1^2 \stackrel{?}{=} 5^2$
$1 + 1 \stackrel{?}{=} 25$
$2 = 25$ False
no

8. 5, 5, 7

9. 2, $4\sqrt{2}$, 6

10. 3, $6\sqrt{2}$, 9

11. 3.6, 4.8, 6

12. 4.5, 6, 7.5

13. $\frac{3}{4}$, $\frac{1}{4}$, 1

14. $\frac{5}{3}$, $\frac{1}{3}$, 2

Problem Solving

15. Bill traveled due north for 5 miles, then 7 miles due west, and then $\sqrt{74}$ miles southeast towards his starting point. Did Bill arrive at his starting point? Explain how you know.

16. The side of a square is 9 inches. What is the length of each diagonal?

17. What is the length of the unknown side of the figure?

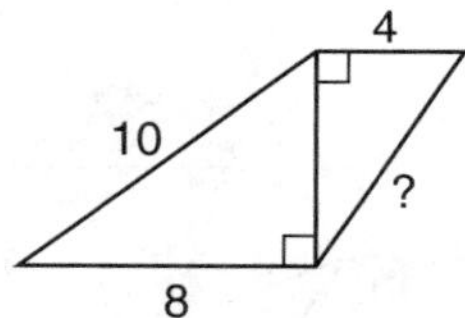

18. What is the perimeter of the square?

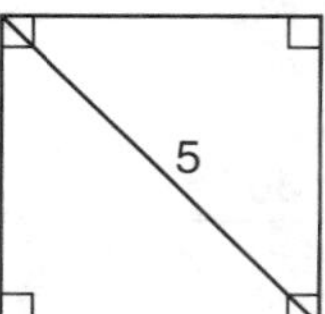

MENTAL MATH

19. $(\sqrt{15} + 12)(\sqrt{15} - 12)$

20. $(\sqrt{21} + 16)(\sqrt{17} - \sqrt{17})$

9-6 Distance in the Coordinate Plane

Name ______________________ Date __________

Find the distance between the points. Write the answer in simplest radical form.

(5, 6) and point (5, −3)

Think
x-values are equal, but y-values are not. This is a vertical line; use $|y_2 - y_1|$.

$|-3 - 6|$ ← Substitute the given values into the formula.

$|-9|$ ← Simplify.

9 ← Find the absolute value.

(−3, 2) and point (2, 2)

Think
y-values are equal, but x-values are not. This is a horizontal line; use $|x_2 - x_1|$.

$|2 - (-3)|$ ← Substitute the given values into the formula.

$|5|$ ← Simplify.

5 ← Find the absolute value.

(2, 7) and point (9, 8)

Think
x-values are not equal; y-values are not equal. Use the distance formula.

$d = \sqrt{(9-2)^2 + (8-7)^2}$

$= \sqrt{(7)^2 + (1)^2}$ ← Simplify.

$= \sqrt{50}$ ← Simplify.

$= 5\sqrt{2}$ ← Simplify.

Remember: Distance Formula
The distance, d, between any two points, (x_1, y_1) and (x_2, y_2), can be found using the formula:
$d = \sqrt{(x_2 - x_1)^2 + (y_2 - y_1)^2}$.

Find the distance between the points. Write your answer in simplest radical form.

1. (−5, 12) and (−5, 15)
x-values are equal
vertical line
$|15 - 12| = |3| = 3$
3

2. (11, −7) and (5, −7) ____________

3. (10, 2) and (7, 5) ____________

4. (12, 4) and (6, 8) ____________

5. (−2, 1) and (0, 3) ____________

6. (−3, 2) and (0, 7) ____________

7. (−1, –8) and (−7, −3) ____________

8. (−2, −5) and (−9, −2) ____________

9. (2, −13) and (10, 8) ____________

10. (1, −15) and (8, 2) ____________

11. $\left(\frac{2}{3}, \frac{1}{5}\right)$ and $\left(\frac{1}{3}, \frac{2}{5}\right)$ ____________

12. $\left(\frac{1}{4}, \frac{2}{7}\right)$ and $\left(\frac{1}{2}, \frac{1}{7}\right)$ ____________

Use the graph to solve each problem.

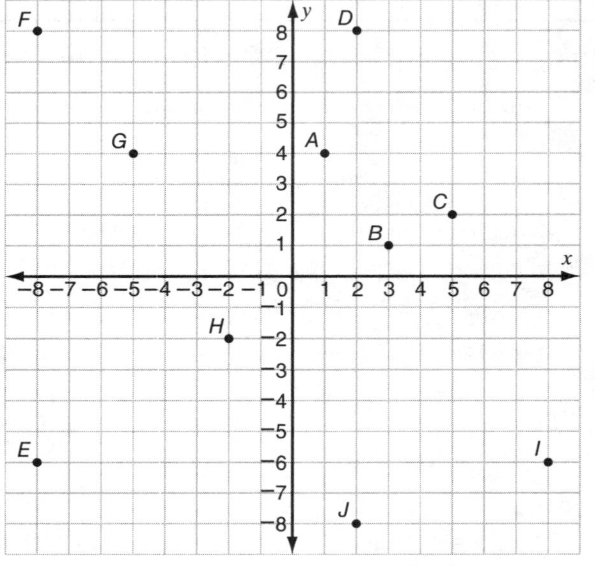

13. What is the perimeter of quadrilateral *EFGH*?

14. What is the perimeter of triangle *AIJ*?

15. What is the perimeter of quadrilateral *ABCD*?

Problem Solving

16. Prove that points $A(1, 1)$, $B(4, 2)$, and $C(0, 4)$ form a right triangle.

17. A quadrilateral is formed by points $A(-1, 1)$, $B(2, 2)$, $C(3, 0)$, and $D(0, -1)$. Prove that *ABCD* is not a rectangle.

WRITE ABOUT IT

18. What possible values of a will make the distance between points $(a, 2)$ and $(0, 0)$ $\sqrt{29}$ units? Explain your steps. (*Hint: a* can be positive *or* negative.)

9-7 Problem-Solving Strategy: Account for All Possibilities

Read › Plan › Solve › Check

Name ______________________________ Date ____________

Account for all possibilities to solve.

1. There are four players left in a table tennis tournament. Trophies are awarded to the 1st, 2nd, and 3rd place winners. In how many different ways can the trophies be awarded?

____

2. Three Green Company taxis and two Orange Company taxis are heading for a 5-cab stand. By company, in how many different ways can they line up?

____

3. Consider two number-cubes, each numbered 1 through 6. The sum 7 has the best chance of being formed when they are rolled together. Suppose on each cube, the numbers 5 and 6 are both replaced by 0. What sum has the greatest chance of being rolled by the two affected number cubes?

____

4. Stephen invited 15 guests to a charity event at his house last Saturday evening. He gave each guest a card with a number from 1 through 16, except the number 4 which he reserved for himself. After pairing his guests off, he realized that the sum of each couple's numbers formed a square number. What number did Stephen's partner have?

____

Use with SOURCEBOOK Lesson 9-7, pages 240–241.

5. Determine the fewest U.S. coins (pennies, nickels, dimes, quarters, and half-dollars) you would need to carry in order to be able to make any value from 1¢ to 99¢.

6. Given that the number 13, $x2y$ is divisible by 15, what are the possible values for x and y?

7. Two friends are comparing the sizes of their rectangular backyards. Yusef and Alia discover that both of their yards have an area of 36 ft^2, but that the perimeter of Alia's yard is 4 ft longer than Yusef's. What are the perimeters of the two yards? (Consider only integral answers.)

8. Find all pairs of consecutive whole odd numbers less than 100, such that their squares differ by a perfect cube.

Enrichment:
Extending the Pythagorean Theorem to Three Dimensions

Name ______________________________ Date ______________

Find the length of the diagonal of the prism.
Round to the nearest hundredth of a foot.

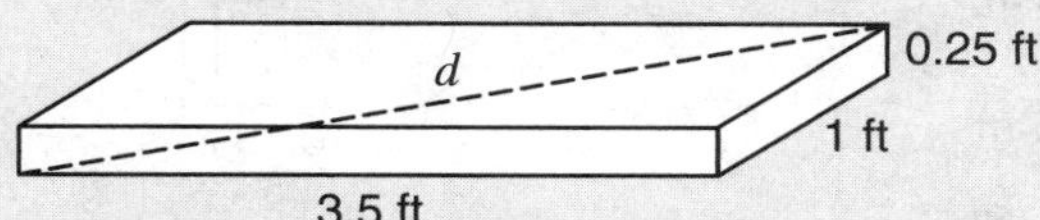

$$d = \sqrt{(3.5)^2 + (1)^2 + (0.25)^2}$$
$$= \sqrt{12.25 + 1 + 0.0625}$$
$$= \sqrt{13.3125}$$
$$\approx 3.65 \text{ ft}$$

← The length of a diagonal of a rectangular prism is:
$d = \sqrt{(\text{length})^2 + (\text{width})^2 + (\text{height})^2}$

Find the distance between points (3, −4, 7) and (2, 1, 5).
Round to the nearest hundredth of a foot.

$$d = \sqrt{(2-3)^2 + [1-(-4)]^2 + (5-7)^2}$$
$$= \sqrt{(-1)^2 + (5)^2 + (-2)^2}$$
$$= \sqrt{1 + 25 + 4}$$
$$= \sqrt{30} \approx 5.48$$

← The distance d between points $P_1(x_1, y_1, z_1)$ and $P_2(x_2, y_2, z_2)$ is
$d = \sqrt{(x_2 - x_1)^2 + (y_2 - y_1)^2 + (z_2 - z_1)^2}$

Find the length of the diagonal in each rectangular prism.
Round to the nearest hundredth, if necessary.

1.

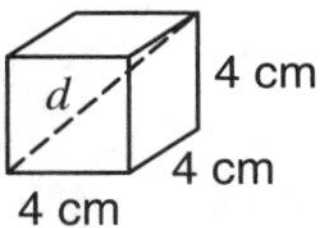

$d = \sqrt{(4)^2 + (4)^2 + (4)^2}$
$d = \sqrt{16 + 16 + 16}$
$d = \sqrt{48}$
$d \approx$ **6.93 cm**

2.

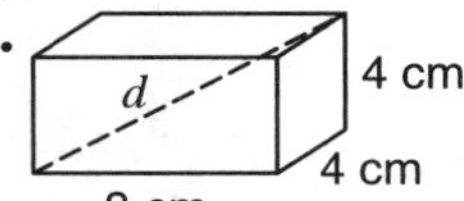

____

3.

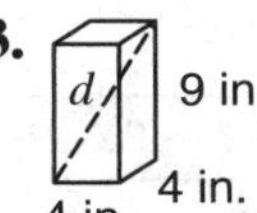

____

4.

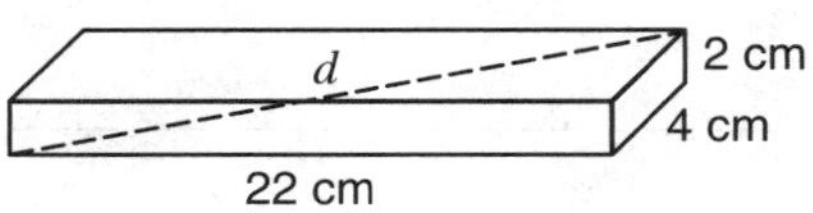

____

5.

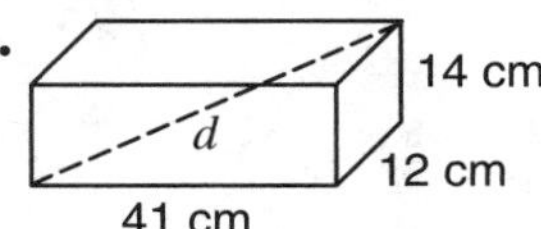

____

6.

d
3.2 m
3 m
3 m

____

Use with **SOURCEBOOK Enrichment Lesson, pages 242–243.**

Find the length of the diagonal in each rectangular prism. Round to the nearest hundredth, if necessary.

7.

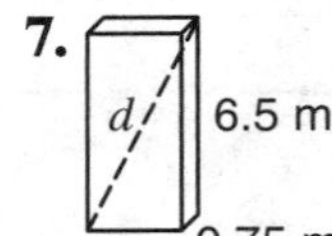

8.

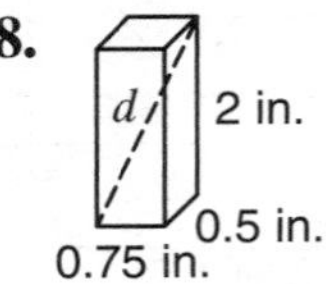

9.

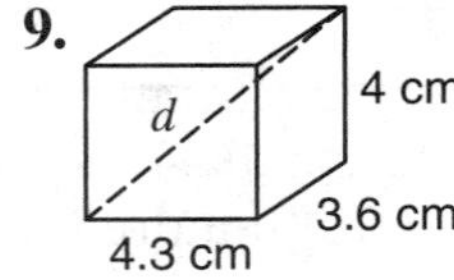

10.

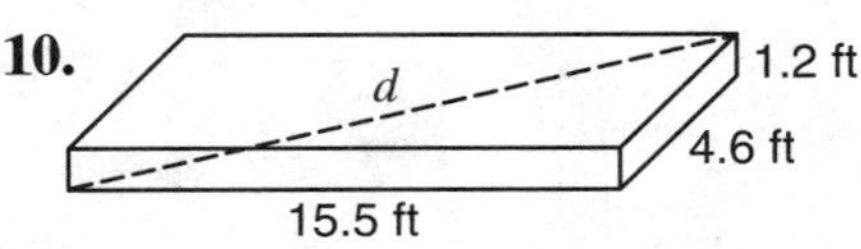

11.

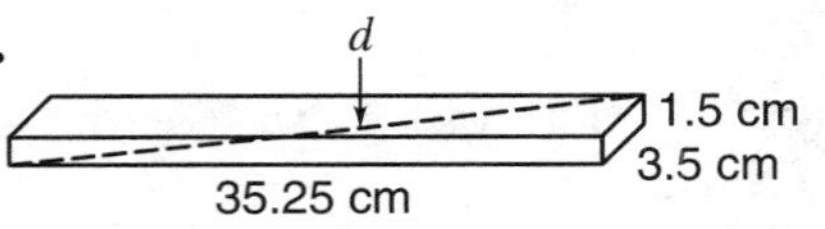

12.

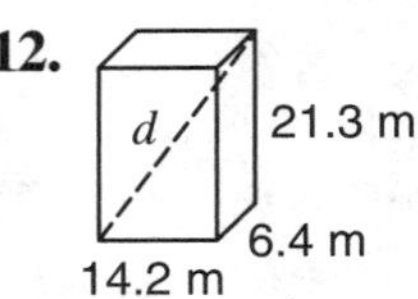

Find the distance between each pair of points. Round to the nearest hundredth, if necessary.

13. $(4, 0, -3)$ and $(2, -7, 6)$

$d = \sqrt{(2-4)^2 + (-7-0)^2 + [6-(-3)]^2}$
$= \sqrt{(-2)^2 + (-7)^2 + (9)^2}$
$= \sqrt{4 + 49 + 81}$
$= \sqrt{134} \approx 11.58$

14. $(5, 2, 8)$ and $(6, 9, -12)$

15. $(-3, 7, 9)$ and $(13, 4, 5)$

16. $(6, -2, 11)$ and $(3, 7, 15)$

MENTAL MATH

Solve.

17. $3x + 5 = 14$

18. $5 - 4x = 21$

19. $14x + 24 = 2x$

Test Prep: Multiple-Choice Questions

Strategy: Try All the Answers

Name ______________________________ Date ____________

When solving a multiple-choice question, **an estimate** of the answer can help to eliminate unreasonable choices.

To select the correct answer in a multiple-choice item, try using the following strategies.

- Underline important words.
- Restate the question.
- Use the Test-Prep strategy.
- Analyze and eliminate answer choices.

Sample Test Item

The hypotenuse of a right triangle measures 6 m. One leg measures 4.8 m. What is the length of the other leg? Round to the nearest tenth.

$b^2 = 6^2 - 4.8^2$ ← $4.8^2 \approx 23$

$\approx 36 - 25$

≈ 13

so $b \approx \sqrt{13}$, which is between 3 and 4.

A. 2.9 m ← This is less than 3. Eliminate this choice.

(B.) 3.6 m ← This is the correct choice.

C. 3.9 m ← This is much greater than $\sqrt{13}$. Eliminate this choice.

D. 4.2 m ← This is greater than 4. Eliminate this choice.

Choose the correct answer. *TIP: Recognize that there may be several ways to solve the same problem.*

1. The expression $\sqrt{8} - \sqrt{12}$ is between which pair of numbers?

A. −2 and −1 **C.** 0 and 1

B. −1 and 0 **D.** 1 and 2

2. Solve: $\sqrt{3x} = 9.9$

F. $x = 5.72$ **H.** $x = 32.67$

G. $x = 10.89$ **J.** $x = 98.01$

3. Charlene buys a jacket that is on sale for $47.16. The original price was $58.95. What was the percent discount?

A. 20% **C.** 80%

B. 25% **D.** 125%

4. Approximate the distance between the points (1, 6) and (4, −3).

F. 3 **H.** 9.5

G. 8.5 **J.** 12

5. A box has length 1.75 ft, width 1 ft, and height 0.5 ft. What is its volume?

A. 0.5 ft^3

B. 0.875 ft^3

C. 3.25 ft^3

D. 3.5 ft^3

6. When an object is dropped from a height s, in ft, the formula $s = 16t^2$ relates the height to the time, in sec, that it takes the object to hit the ground. Jackson drops a ball from a height of 48 ft. How long does it take the ball to hit the ground?

F. about 0.12 sec **H.** about 3 sec

G. about 1.73 sec **J.** about 3.46 sec

Use with SOURCEBOOK Test Prep Lesson, page 244.

Vocabulary Development

Name ______________________________ Date ____________

Chapter 9 Vocabulary

Distance Formula	Pythagorean triple
extraneous solution	Quotient Property of Square Roots
Product Property of Square Roots	radical equation
Pythagorean Theorem	rationalizing the denominator

From the vocabulary list above, choose the term(s) that best complete each sentence. Write the term(s) in the space(s) provided.

1. A(n) ______________________ is any set of positive whole numbers, *a*, *b*, and *c*, that can be the lengths of the sides of a right triangle.

2. According to the ______________________, the square root of a product of two nonnegative numbers equals the product of the square root of each nonnegative number ($\sqrt{ab} = \sqrt{a} \bullet \sqrt{b}$, where $a \geq 0$ and $b \geq 0$).

3. An equation that contains a variable within a radical is called a(n) ______________________.

4. When solving a radical equation, always check your answer to eliminate ______________________; these are not solutions to the original equation.

5. According to the ______________________, if a triangle is a right triangle, then the sum of the squares of the legs, *a* and *b*, equals the square of the hypotenuse, *c*.

6. According to the ______________________, the square root of a quotient of a nonnegative number and a number greater than 0 equals the quotient of the square root of the nonnegative number and the square root of the number greater than zero $\left(\sqrt{\frac{a}{b}} = \frac{\sqrt{a}}{\sqrt{b}},\right.$ where $a \geq 0$ and $\left. b > 0\right)$.

Tell whether each statement is true or false. If it is false, change it to make it true.

7. To rationalize the denominator in the fraction $\frac{2}{\sqrt{2}}$, multiply by $\sqrt{2}$.

____

8. If you know the coordinates of the vertices of a triangle on the coordinate plane, you can prove whether or not the triangle is a right triangle by using the Pythagorean Theorem.

____

Use after SOURCEBOOK Lessons 9-1–9-6, pages 226–239.

Practice Chapter 9 Test

Name ______________________ Date __________

Simplify each expression. Assume that all variables represent nonnegative numbers.

1. $\sqrt{300}$ **2.** $4\sqrt{729}$ **3.** $-7\sqrt{63}$ **4.** $-8\sqrt{84}$

5. $2\sqrt{45x^8y^9}$ **6.** $-2\sqrt{20a^6b^3c^2}$ **7.** $11m^2\sqrt{250m^{10}np^{24}}$

8. $2\sqrt{5} - 8\sqrt{6} + 13\sqrt{5} + 15\sqrt{6}$ **9.** $51 - 2\sqrt{8} + 11\sqrt{2} + 34$

10. $13\sqrt{a} - 11\sqrt{2a} + \sqrt{a} - 12\sqrt{2a}$ **11.** $15r - 2\sqrt{343} - 23r + 8\sqrt{175}$

12. $5\sqrt{6} \bullet 2\sqrt{3} \bullet 4\sqrt{27}$ **13.** $-2\sqrt{2a}\,(5\sqrt{7a} + 5a\sqrt{3a})$

14. $(-3\sqrt{2} + 9\sqrt{5})(2\sqrt{2} + \sqrt{5})$ **15.** $(3\sqrt{6} - 5)^2$

16. $\frac{\sqrt{15}}{\sqrt{3}}$ **17.** $\frac{\sqrt{3}}{\sqrt{8}}$ **18.** $\frac{3x}{\sqrt{12}}$ **19.** $\sqrt{\frac{45}{11x}}$

Solve each equation. Check your solution. If there is no solution, write *no real solution*.

20. $5\sqrt{a} - 8 = 17$

21. $\sqrt{2b - 1} + 3 = 8$

22. $11 + 7\sqrt{3k + 18} = -31$

Find the length of the third side of each triangle. Give your answer in simplest radical form.

23.

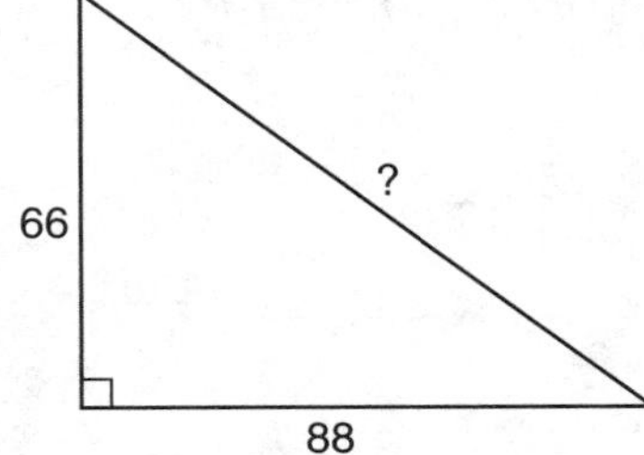

24.

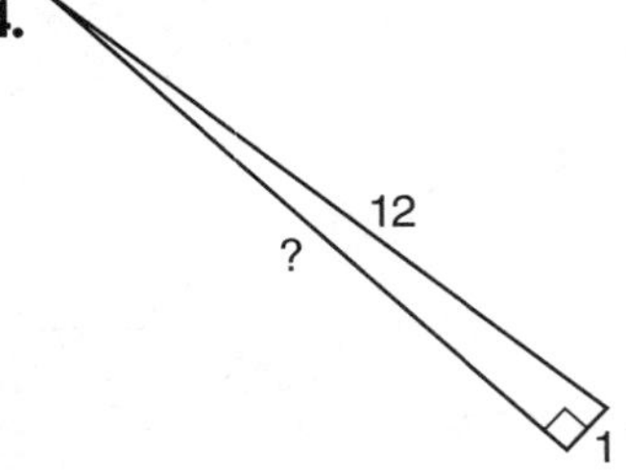

Find the distance between the points. Write your answer in simplest radical form.

25. $(-6, 0)$ and $(2, 6)$

26. $(-1, -5)$ and $(8, -14)$

Problem Solving

27. The length of a side of a square is $4\sqrt{3} - 1$. What is the area of the square?

28. A rectangle has a width of $12\sqrt{5} - 3\sqrt{7}$ and a length of $12\sqrt{5} + 3\sqrt{7}$. What is the area of the rectangle?

Tell About It

Explain how you solve the problem. Show all your work.

29. Train A leaves the station at noon going due north at 50 mi/h. Train B leaves the station 1 hour later going due east at 60 mi/h. About how far apart are the trains at 3 P.M.? (*Hint:* distance = rate × time)

Cumulative Review: Chapters 1–9

Name ______________________________ Date ____________

Circle the best answer.

1. Which numbers are ordered from least to greatest?

A. $-\frac{1}{2}, |-0.7|, -1.1, -0.65, -\sqrt{4}, -0.\overline{5}$
B. $-\sqrt{4}, -1.1, -0.65, -0.\overline{5}, -\frac{1}{2}, |-0.7|$
C. $-\sqrt{4}, -1.1, |-0.7|, -0.65, -0.\overline{5}, -\frac{1}{2}$
D. $-\sqrt{4}, -1.1, -0.65, -\frac{1}{2}, -0.\overline{5}, |-0.7|$

2. Evaluate: $\frac{(5-2)^2 + 4^3 \div 16}{[2(8-5)]^2 - 3^2}$

F. $\frac{7}{3}$ **G.** $\frac{13}{27}$
H. $\frac{67}{432}$ **J.** $\frac{4}{27}$

3. Which is an open sentence?

A. $9 \bullet (-23)$
B. $15 + 2a$
C. $18 - 23 = 21$
D. $3x + 1 = 8$

4. Solve: $-\frac{5}{3} = a - \frac{1}{2}$

F. $a = -\frac{4}{3}$ **G.** $a = -\frac{7}{6}$
H. $a = -\frac{4}{5}$ **J.** $a = -\frac{2}{3}$

5. Solve: $21d + 11 - 4d = 17d + 1$

A. $d = 1$
B. $d = -1$
C. all real numbers
D. $\varnothing$

6. Which is the same as $\{x \mid x < -1.5\}$?

F. $(-\infty, -1.5)$
G. $(-\infty, -1.5]$
H. $[-1.5, \infty)$
J. $(-1.5, \infty]$

7. Which equation gives the nth term of the sequence?

7, 5, 3, 1, −1, …

A. $a_n = 2n + 7$
B. $a_n = -2n - 5$
C. $a_n = -2n + 9$
D. $a_n = 2n - 9$

8. Which is an arithmetic sequence?

F. 2, −4, 8, −16, 32, …
G. −10, −9, −11, −10, −12, …
H. 23, 28, 33, 38, 43, …
J. 1, −1, 1, −1, 1, …

9. Solve: $-2r + 3 < 4 - 7$

A. $r > 3$
B. $r < 3$
C. $r > -3$
D. $r < -3$

10. Solve: $2\,|2t - 1| \geq 10$

F. $-5 \leq t \leq 5$
G. $-2 \leq t \leq 3$
H. $t \leq -2$ or $t \geq 3$
J. $t \geq -1$ or $t \leq 2$

11. A line through which points slopes up from left to right?

A. (−2, 1) and (3, 6)
B. (3, 5) and (−1, 9)
C. (0, 0) and (6, −10)
D. (1, 7) and (2, 4)

12. Which is an equation of a line with slope 2?

F. $2y + 2x = 0$
G. $2x + y = 2$
H. $x - 2y = 2$
J. $4x - 2y = 7$

13. Which statement best describes this system? $\begin{cases} 5x - 3y = 11 \\ 5x - 3y = 5 \end{cases}$

A. inconsistent
B. inconsistent and dependent
C. consistent and independent
D. independent

14. Which is a solution of this system? $\begin{cases} x + 2y \leq 3 \\ x + y \geq -2 \end{cases}$

F. $(-7, 1)$
G. $(5, 6)$
H. $(1, 1)$
J. $(12, -1)$

15. Which is a solution of this system? $\begin{cases} 7x - 2y = 0 \\ x - y = 5 \end{cases}$

A. $(2, -7)$ **B.** $(-2, 7)$
C. $(-2, -7)$ **D.** $(2, 7)$

16. Multiply: $(3x - 2)^2$

F. $9x^2 + 4$
G. $9x^2 - 6x + 4$
H. $9x^2 - 12x - 4$
J. $9x^2 - 12x + 4$

17. Divide. $(2a^3 + 6a^2 - 2a - 6) \div (a + 3)$

A. $2(a - 1)(a - 1)$
B. $2(a + 1)(a - 1)$
C. $2a^2 - 1$
D. $2a^2 + 1$

18. Factor completely: $12b^3 + 24b$

F. $12(b^3 + 2b)$
G. $12b(b^2 + 2)$
H. $3b(4b^2 + 8)$
J. $4b(3b^2 + 6)$

19. Which is a factor of $x^2 - 12x - 45$?

A. $(x + 45)$
B. $(x - 3)$
C. $(x + 15)$
D. $(x - 15)$

20. Simplify: $\sqrt{48}$

F. $4\sqrt{3}$
G. $3\sqrt{4}$
H. 6
J. 24

21. Simplify: $11\sqrt{2} - 15\sqrt{11} + 8\sqrt{2} + 6\sqrt{11}$

A. $10\sqrt{22}$
B. $10\sqrt{9}$
C. $19\sqrt{2} - 9\sqrt{11}$
D. $3\sqrt{2} + 21\sqrt{11}$

22. Solve: $\sqrt{5w - 4} = 2$

F. $w = \frac{8}{5}$ **G.** $w = \frac{6}{5}$
H. $w = 0$ **J.** no real solution

Tell About It

Explain how you solve the problem. Show all your work.

23. The lengths of the sides of a triangle are 20, 48, and 52. Is the triangle a right triangle?

24. A rectangle has a width of $7\sqrt{2}$ units and a length of $4\sqrt{6} + 8$ units. What is the area of the rectangle? (*Hint:* $A = \ell w$)

10-1 Identify Quadratic Functions and Their Graphs

Name ______________________________ Date ______________

For the parabola shown, identify the vertex, axis of symmetry, x-intercepts, maximum or minimum value of the function, and the domain and range of the function.

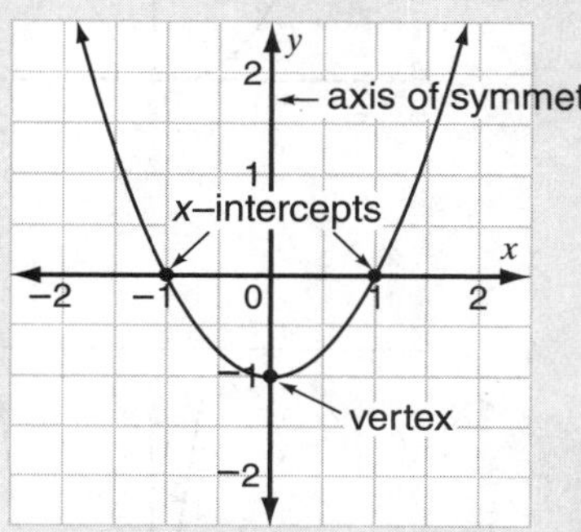

vertex: $(0, -1)$
axis of symmetry: $x = 0$
x-intercepts: -1 and 1.

Think
$f(x) = x^2 - 1$ opens *upward*, so the y-value of the vertex is the *minimum* value of the function.

minimum value: -1
domain: all real numbers
range: $\{y \mid y \geq -1\}$

Tell whether the graph of the quadratic function opens upward or downward. Explain.

1. $y = -2 + 3x - x^2$

$y = -x^2 + 3x - 2$
$a = -1;\ -1 < 0$
The parabola opens downward.

2. $y = -6 + x - 5x^2$

____

3. $y - 7 = 5x + 4x^2$

____

4. $y - 8 = -x + 10x^2$

____

5. $y + 4 = x^2$

____

6. $y + 5 = 3x^2$

____

7. $2y + x^2 = -3$

____

8. $8y + 3x^2 = 4$

____

9. $0.2y - x = -2x - 0.6x^2$

____

For each parabola shown, identify the vertex. Then give the minimum or maximum value of the function. Explain.

10.

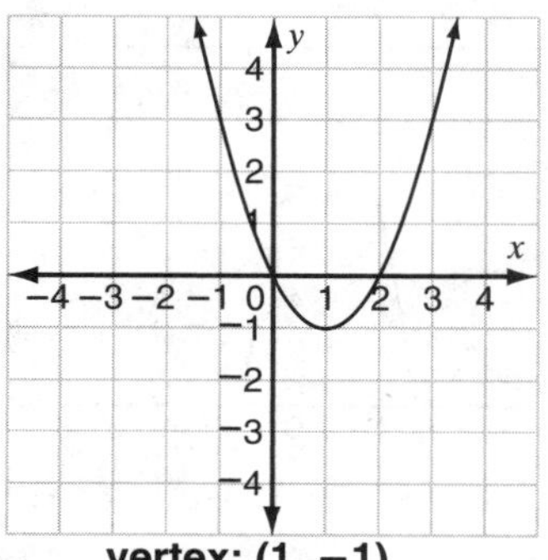

vertex: $(1, -1)$
parabola opens upward
minimum of the function is -1

11.

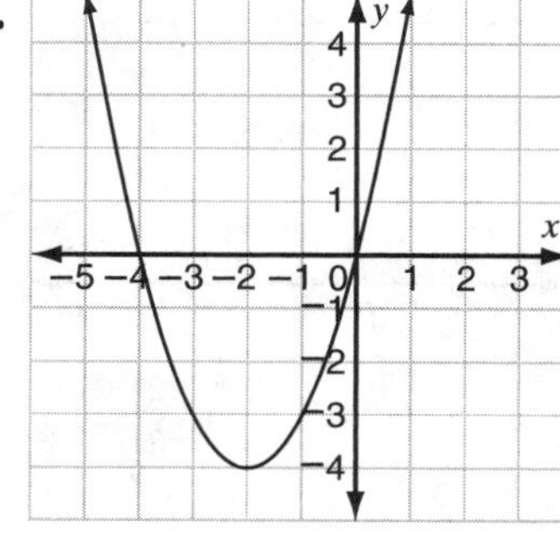

____

12.

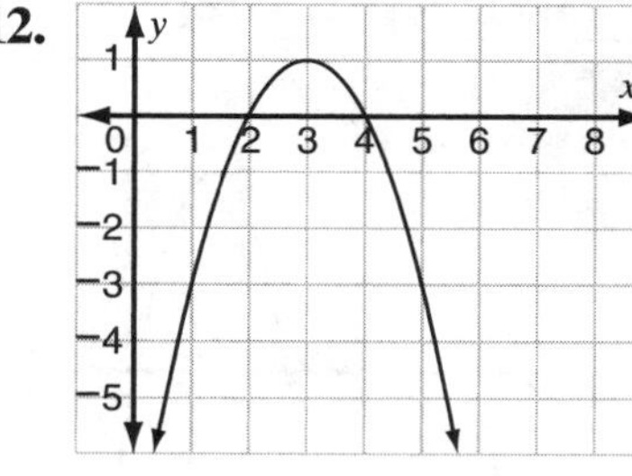

____

For each parabola shown, identify the vertex. Then give the minimum or maximum value of the function. Explain.

13.

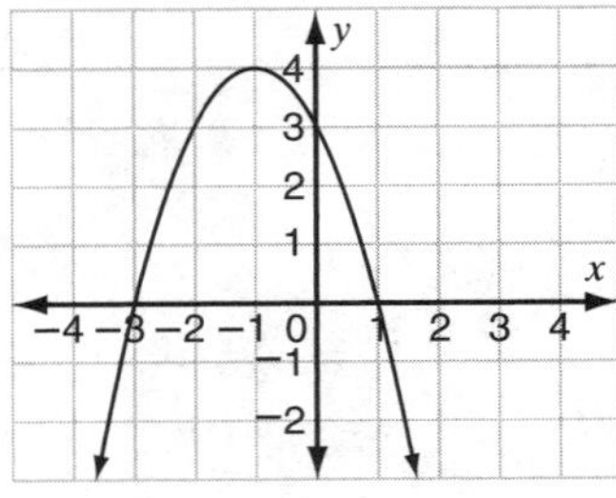

14.

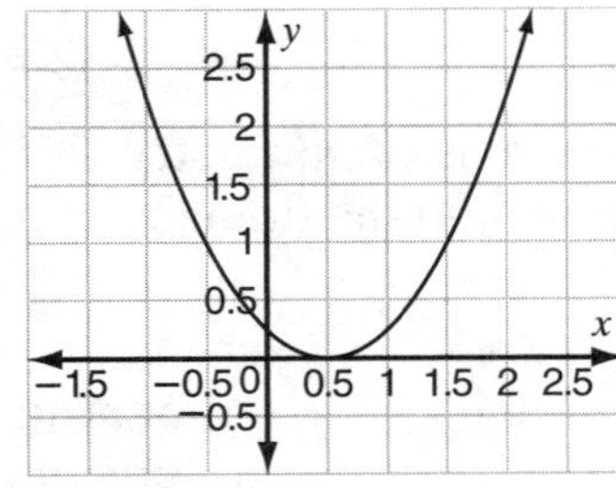

15.

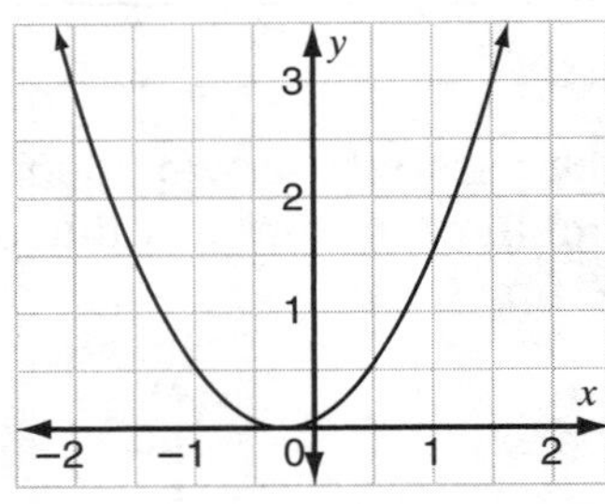

16.

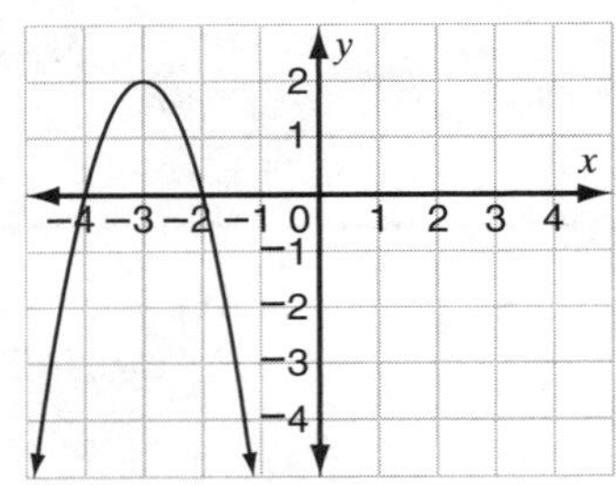

17.

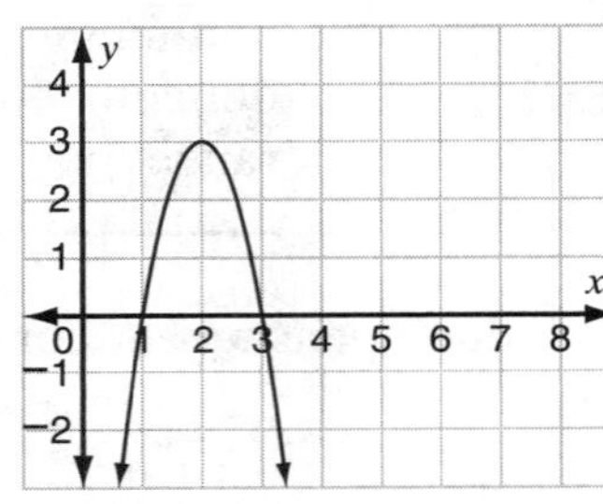

18.

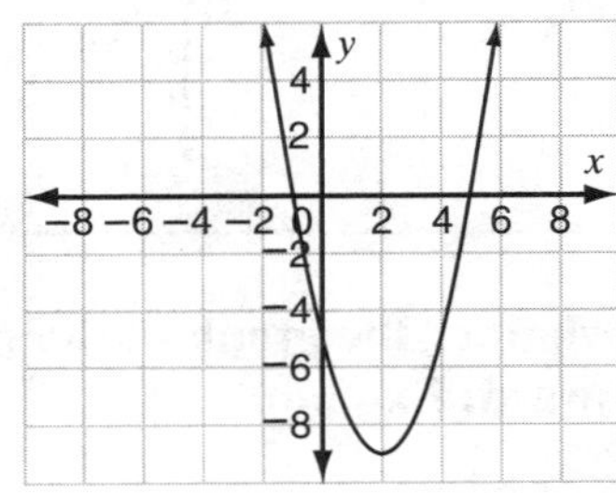

For each parabola shown, identify the domain and range.

19.

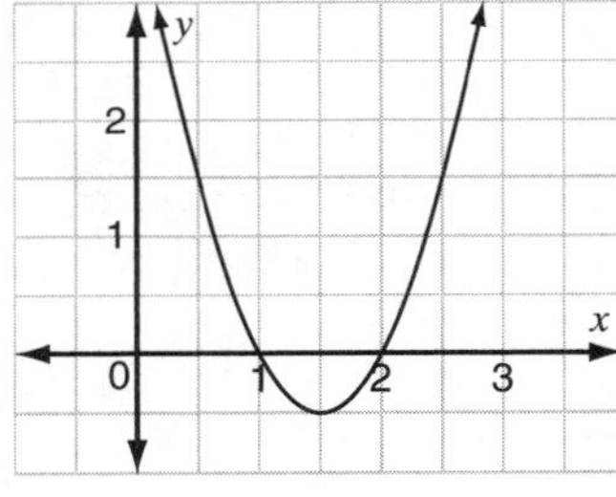

domain: All real numbers
range: $\{y \mid y \geq -0.5\}$

20.

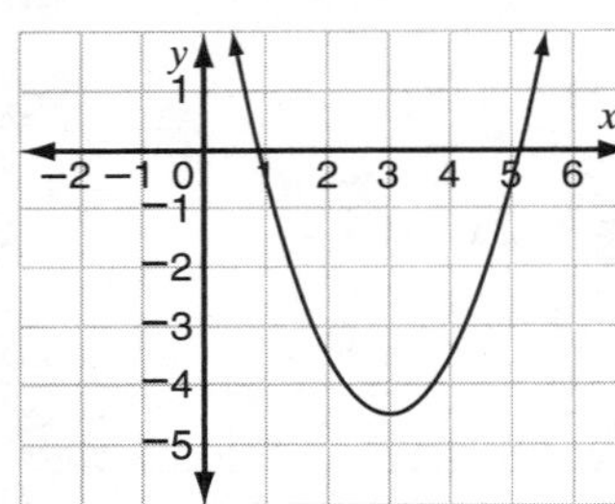

21.

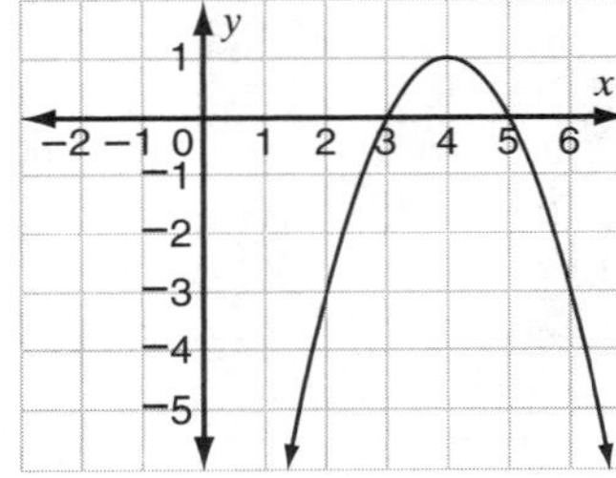

22.

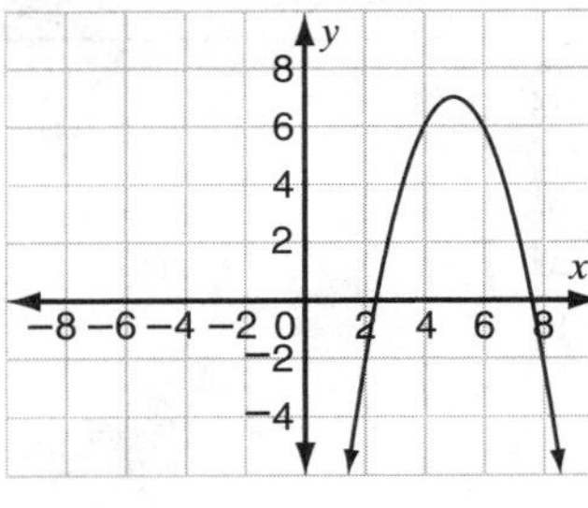

23.

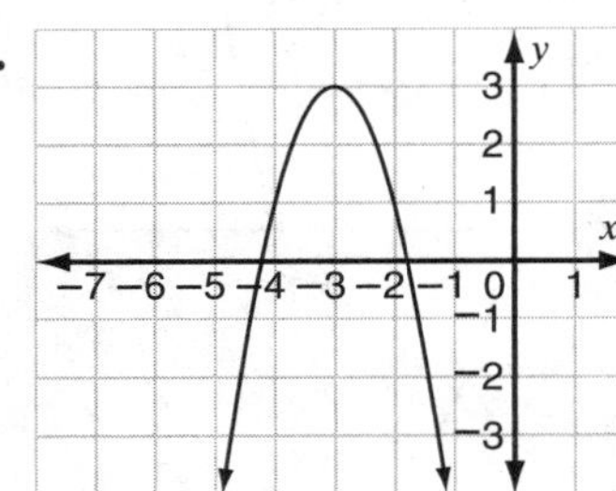

24.

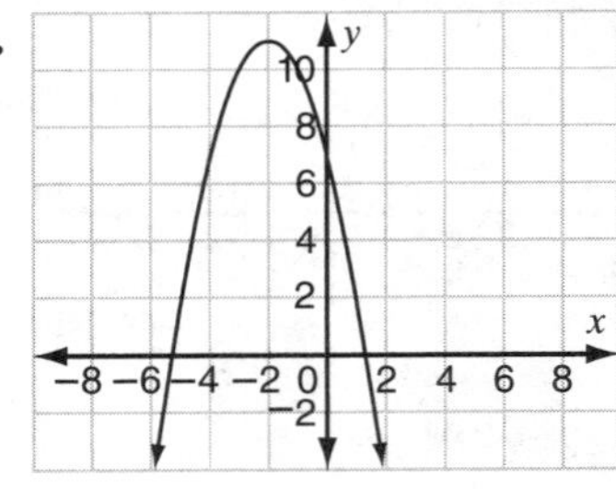

For each parabola shown, identify the axis of symmetry.

25.

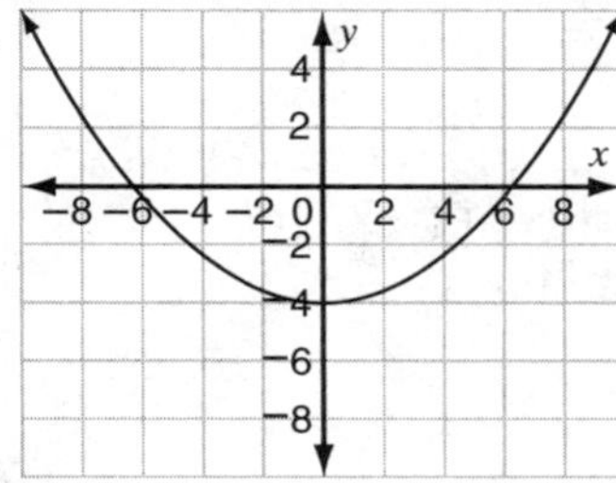

26.

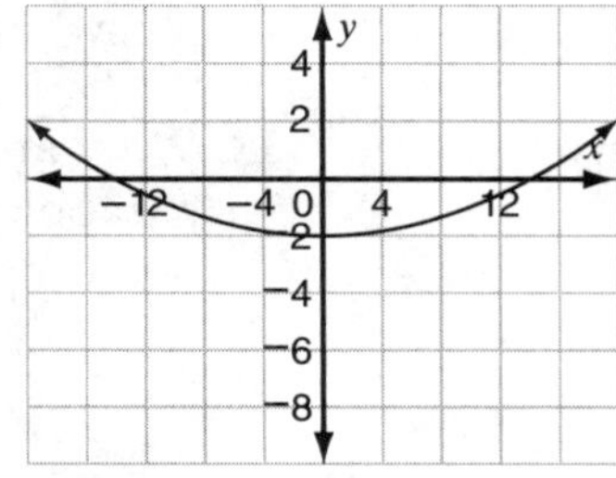

27.

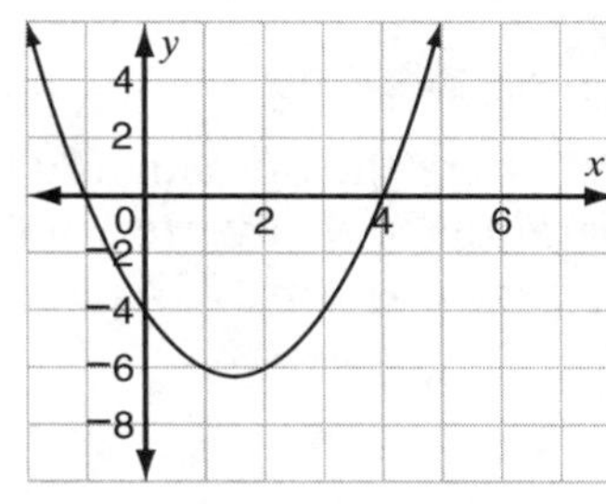

28.

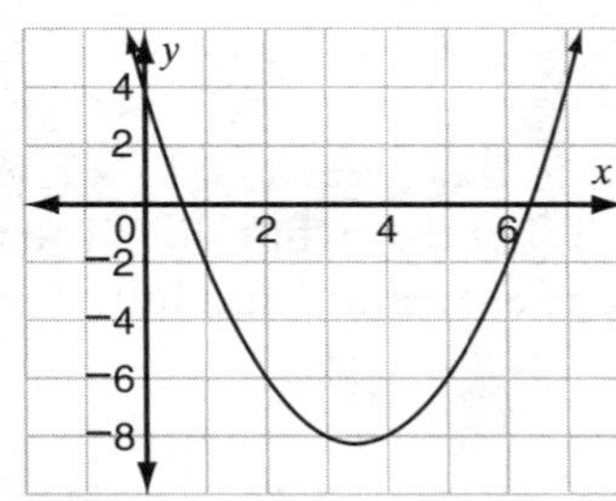

29.

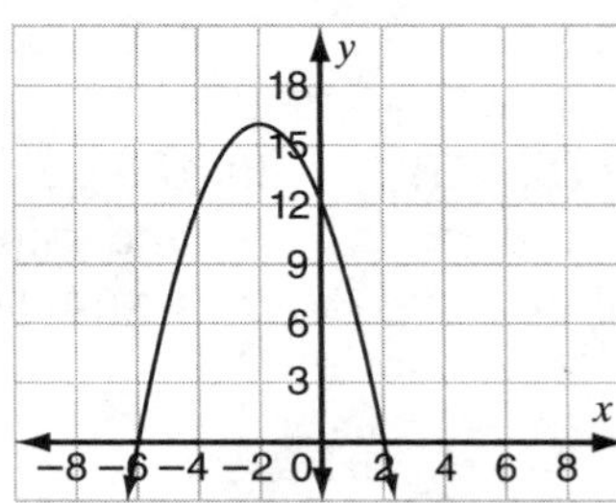

30.

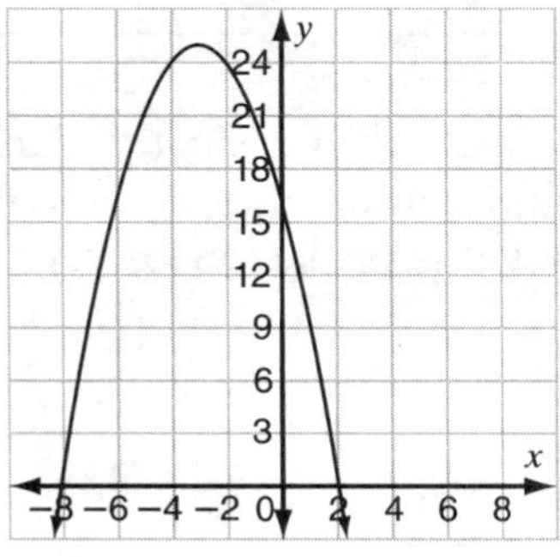

For each parabola shown, identify the *x*-intercepts.

31.

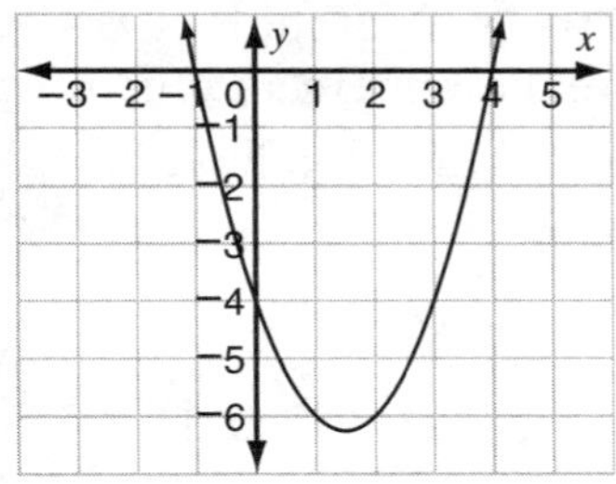

x-intercepts: −1 and 4

32.

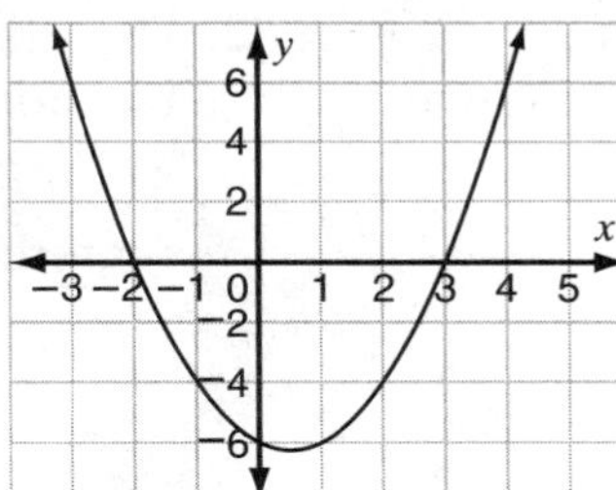

33.

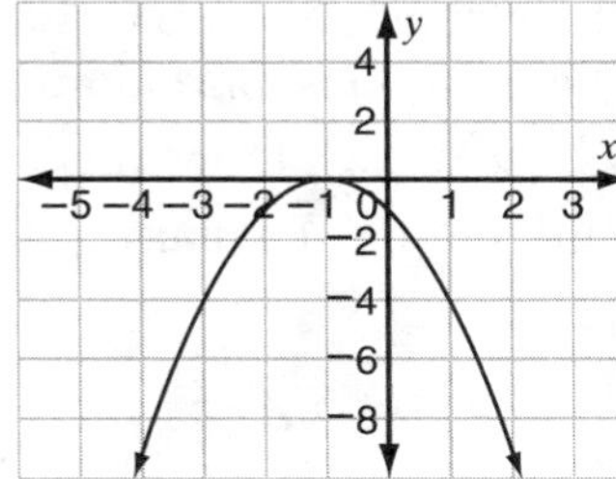

34.

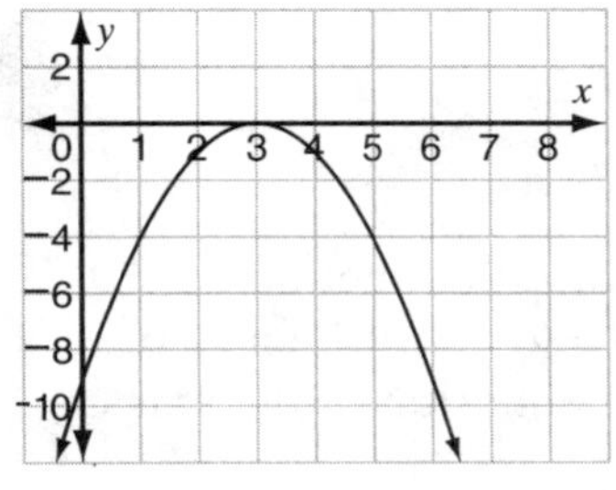

35.

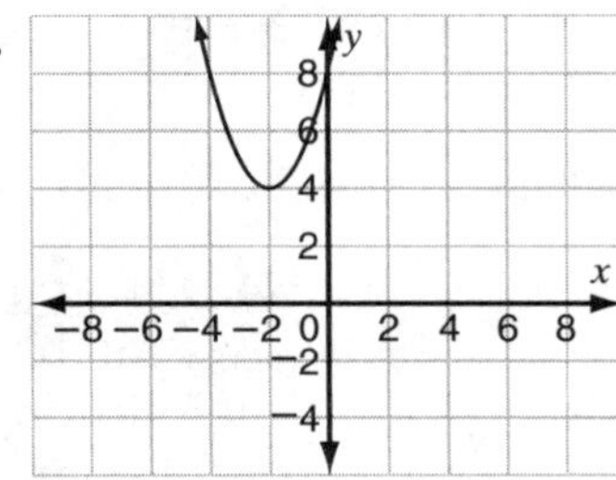

36.

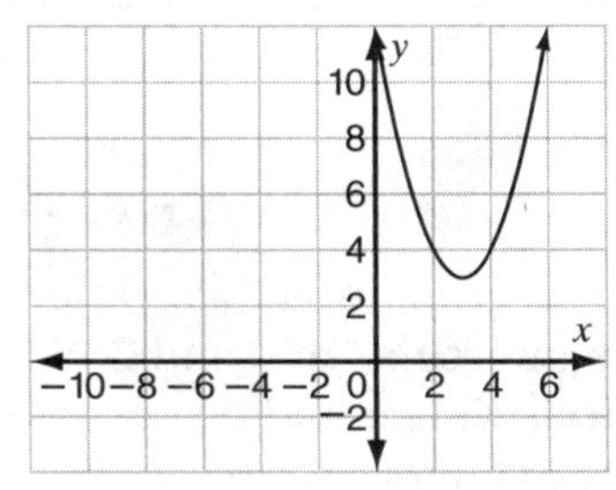

Problem Solving

37. What are the domain and range of any parabola with a vertex of (4, 8) that opens downward? Explain.

38. What are the domain and range of any parabola with a vertex of $(-2, 11)$ that opens upward? Explain.

39. If a quadratic function has a vertex at $(5, -3)$ and x-intercepts at 4 and 6, what does the y-value of the vertex represent? Explain.

40. If a quadratic function has a vertex at $(-1, 8)$ and x-intercepts at -3 and 1, what does the y-value of the vertex represent? Explain.

41. The axis of symmetry of a parabola is $x = \frac{2}{3}$. The domain is all real numbers and the range is $\{y \mid y \leq -\frac{1}{2}\}$. Does this function have x-intercepts? Explain.

42. The axis of symmetry of a parabola is $x = \frac{2}{3}$. The domain is all real numbers and the range is $\{y \mid y \geq \frac{11}{9}\}$. Does this function have x-intercepts? Explain.

TEST PREPARATION

43. The graph of a quadratic function has x-intercepts at 0 and 2. Which of the following could be equation of the axis of symmetry?

A. $x = 0$ **C.** $x = 2$

B. $x = 1$ **D.** $x = 3$

44. The graph of a quadratic function has x-intercepts at -8 and -4. Which of the following could be equation of the axis of symmetry?

A. $x = -8$ **C.** $x = -4$

B. $x = -6$ **D.** $x = -2$

10-2 Graph Quadratic Functions: Parabola

Name ______________________ Date __________

Graph: $y = x^2 + 2x - 8$

1 Find the equation of the axis of symmetry.

$a = 1$ and $b = 2$ ← Identify the values of a and b in $y = ax^2 + bx + c$.

$x = \frac{-b}{2a} = \frac{-(2)}{2(1)} = -1$ ← Substitute 1 for a and 2 for b in $x = \frac{-b}{2a}$.

The axis of symmetry is $x = -1$.

2 Find the coordinates of the vertex.
The x-coordinate of the vertex is -1.

$y = x^2 + 2x - 8$
$= (-1)^2 + 2(-1) - 8$ ← Substitute -1 for x.
$= 1 - 2 - 8$ ← Simplify.
$= -9$ ← Simplify.

The vertex is at $(-1, -9)$

3 Select two x-values greater than -1 and two x-values less than -1 and make a function table. Then graph the ordered pairs in the table on a coordinate plane and draw a smooth curve through them.

x	y	(x, y)
-3	$(-3)^2 + 2(-3) - 8 = -5$	$(-3, -5)$
-2	$(-2)^2 + 2(-2) - 8 = -8$	$(-2, -8)$
-1	$(-1)^2 + 2(-1) - 8 = -9$	$(-1, -9)$
0	$(0)^2 + 2(0) - 8 = -8$	$(0, -8)$
1	$(1)^2 + 2(1) - 8 = -5$	$(1, -5)$

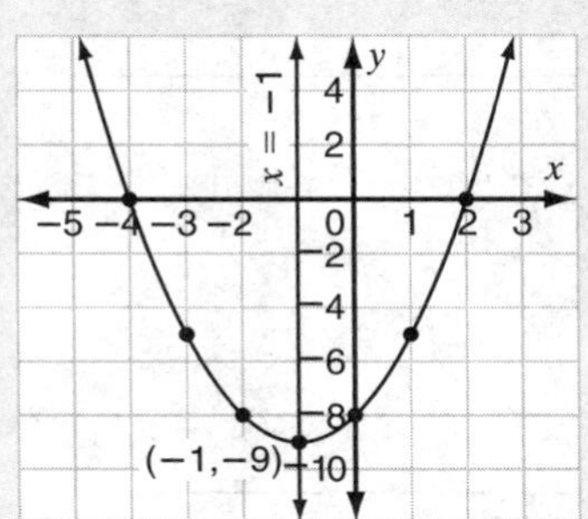

The parabola opens upward because $a = 1$ and $1 > 0$.

Write the equation of the axis of symmetry, and find the coordinates of the vertex of the parabola. Use a separate sheet of paper to make a function table and graph each function.

1. $y = x^2 + 2x - 10$

$x = -\frac{b}{2a} = -\frac{2}{2(1)} = -1$
$y = (-1)^2 + 2(-1) - 10 = -11$
vertex: (−1, −11)

2. $y = x^2 + 4x - 3$

____

3. $y = 4x^2 + 8x - 7$

____

4. $y = 3x^2 + 12x - 2$

____

5. $y = -5x^2 + 10x - 1$

____

6. $y = -3x^2 + 18x - 20$

____

7. $y = -6x^2 + 36x - 40$

____

8. $y = -5x^2 + 40x - 60$

____

9. $y = 6x^2 - 24$

____

Write the equation of the axis of symmetry, and find the coordinates of the vertex of the parabola. Use a separate sheet of paper to make a function table and graph each function.

10. $y = 4x^2 + 64$

11. $y = 2x^2 + 98$

12. $y = -5x^2 + 1.2$

13. $y = -3x^2 + 6.75$

14. $y = x^2 - 9x - 1$

15. $y = x^2 - 5x - 10$

16. $y = \frac{1}{4}x^2 - 2x + 1$

17. $y = \frac{1}{3}x^2 - 6x + 8$

18. $y = -\frac{1}{8}x^2 + x - 1$

Problem Solving

19. Using a handheld, graph the equations $f(x) = (x - 3)^2$, $f(x) = (x - 5)^2$, and $f(x) = (x - 7)^2$. Examine how these graphs differ from $f(x) = x^2$. Then explain how the graph of $f(x) = (x - a)^2$ differs from the graph of $f(x) = x^2$.

20. Using a handheld, graph the equations $f(x) = (x + 2)^2$, $f(x) = (x + 4)^2$, and $f(x) = (x + 8)^2$. Examine how these graphs differ from $f(x) = x^2$. Then explain how the graph of $f(x) = (x + a)^2$ differs from the graph of $f(x) = x^2$.

CHALLENGE

21. Using a handheld, find the equation of a parabola that opens upward with a vertex of (3, 4) and is as wide as the parabola $f(x) = x^2$. Give the equation in the form $y = ax^2 + bx + c$.

10-3 Solve Quadratic Equations by Factoring

Name ____________________ Date __________

Solve: $3x^2 = -20x + 63$

$3x^2 + 20x - 63 = 0$ ← Write the equation in standard form.

$(x + 9)(3x - 7) = 0$ ← Factor.

$x + 9 = 0$ or $3x - 7 = 0$ ← Apply the Zero-Product Property.

$x = -9$ or $3x = 7$ ← Apply the Addition and Subtraction Properties of Equality.

$x = \frac{7}{3}$ ← Use the Division Property of Equality.

Check:

$3x^2 = -20x + 63$	$3x^2 = -20x + 63$
$3(-9)^2 \stackrel{?}{=} -20(-9) + 63$	$3\left(\frac{7}{3}\right)^2 \stackrel{?}{=} -20\left(\frac{7}{3}\right) + 63$
$3(81) \stackrel{?}{=} 180 + 63$	$3\left(\frac{49}{9}\right) \stackrel{?}{=} \frac{-140}{3} + 63$
$243 = 243$ **True**	$\frac{49}{3} = \frac{49}{3}$ **True**

So -9 and $\frac{7}{3}$ are the roots of the equation.

Solve: $x = \sqrt{14x - 45}$

$x^2 = (\sqrt{14x - 45})^2$ ← Square both sides of the equation.

$x^2 = 14x - 45$ ← Simplify.

$x^2 - 14x + 45 = 0$ ← Write in standard form.

$(x - 9)(x - 5) = 0$ ← Factor.

$x - 9 = 0$ or $x - 5 = 0$ ← Use the Zero-Product Property.

$x = 9$ or $x = 5$ ← Use the Addition Property of Equality.

Check:

$x = \sqrt{14x - 45}$	$x = \sqrt{14x - 45}$
$9 \stackrel{?}{=} \sqrt{14(9) - 45}$	$5 \stackrel{?}{=} \sqrt{14(5) - 45}$
$9 \stackrel{?}{=} \sqrt{126 - 45}$	$5 \stackrel{?}{=} \sqrt{70 - 45}$
$9 \stackrel{?}{=} \sqrt{81}$	$5 \stackrel{?}{=} \sqrt{25}$
$9 = 9$ **True**	$5 = 5$ **True**

So 5 and 9 are the roots of the equation.

Solve each equation by factoring. Check the solution on a separate sheet of paper.

1. $x^2 + 9x = 10$

$x^2 + 9x - 10 = 0$
$(x + 10)(x - 1) = 0$
$x + 10 = 0$ or $x - 1 = 0$
$x = -10$ or $x = 1$
$\{-10, 1\}$

2. $x^2 + 8x = 20$ ____________

3. $7x = -11x^2 - 1$ ____________

4. $3x = -2x^2 - 7$ ____________

5. $-6x = x^2 - 91$ ____________

6. $8x = x^2 - 48$ ____________

7. $25x^2 - 64 = 0$ ____________

8. $64x^2 - 121 = 0$ ____________

9. $-10x^2 = 19x - 15$ ____________

10. $-21x^2 = -22x - 8$ ____________

11. $25x^2 = 70x - 49$ ____________

12. $8x^2 = 72x - 162$ ____________

Use with SOURCEBOOK Lesson 10-3, pages 254–257.

**Solve each equation by factoring, if possible.
Check the solution on a separate sheet of paper.**

13. $49 = x^2$

14. $225 = x^2$

15. $2x^2 + 5x = 3$

16. $3x^2 - 4x = 4$

17. $5x^2 = 35x - 50$

18. $4x^2 = 44x - 112$

19. $3x^2 + 66 = -39x$

20. $7x^2 + 140 = -84x$

21. $12x^2 = -60x - 72$

22. $7x^2 = -63x - 56$

23. $8x^2 - 64x = 56$

24. $11x^2 - 154x = 165$

25. $1 - 144x^2 = 0$

26. $9 - 400x^2 = 0$

27. $0 = 15 + 5x^2$

28. $0 = 7 + 28x^2$

29. $36x^2 = 132x - 121$

30. $-18x^2 = 60x + 50$

31. $72 = 8x^2 + 36x$

32. $105 = 12x^2 - 69x$

Solve each equation by factoring. Then check the solution on a separate sheet of paper.

33. $x = \sqrt{7x - 6}$

$x^2 = (\sqrt{7x-6})^2$
$x^2 = 7x - 6$
$0 = x^2 - 7x + 6$
$0 = (x - 6)(x - 1)$
$x - 6 = 0$ or $x - 1 = 0$
$x = 6$ or $x = 1$
$\{6, 1\}$

34. $x = \sqrt{7x - 12}$

35. $\sqrt{3x + 10} = x$

36. $\sqrt{2x + 48} = x$

37. $x = \sqrt{11x - 24}$

38. $x = \sqrt{17x - 30}$

39. $x = \sqrt{8 - 2x}$

40. $x = \sqrt{17 - 16x}$

41. $x = \sqrt{-8x - 7}$

42. $x = \sqrt{-13x - 36}$

43. $\sqrt{15 - 4x} = 2x$

44. $\sqrt{4 - 9x} = 3x$

45. $5x = \sqrt{1 - 2x}$

46. $4x = \sqrt{7 - 34x}$

47. $2x = \sqrt{14 + 10x}$

48. $3x = \sqrt{8 + 21x}$

49. $7x = \sqrt{49x - 10}$

50. $5x = \sqrt{60x - 27}$

51. $x - 2 = \sqrt{x - 2}$

52. $x - 5 = \sqrt{x - 5}$

Solve.

53. The product of two consecutive integers is 42. What are the integers?

54. The product of two consecutive integers is 156. What are the integers?

55. The product of two consecutive positive integers is 110. What are the integers?

56. The product of two consecutive negative integers is 420. What are the integers?

Problem Solving

57. Solve for x: $(x - 4)^2 + (x + 5)^2 = (2x + 1)^2$

58. Solve for x: $(2x + 5)^2 - (x - 11)^2 = (3x - 6)^2$

SPIRAL REVIEW

Solve each problem.

59. Simplify: $9\sqrt{2} - 7\sqrt{3} + 11\sqrt{2} + 15\sqrt{3}$

60. Find the distance between points $(-7, -1)$ and $(4, -3)$.

61. Multiply: $(3n + 1)(4n^2 + 8n - 2)$

62. Is $(9, 1)$ a solution of the inequality $y > -3x + 4$?

10-4 Solve Verbal Problems Involving Quadratic Equations

Name ______________________ Date __________

Ms. White had a square garden. She added 7 ft to the length and 3 ft to the width. The area of the new garden is 140 ft^2. What was the width of the square garden?

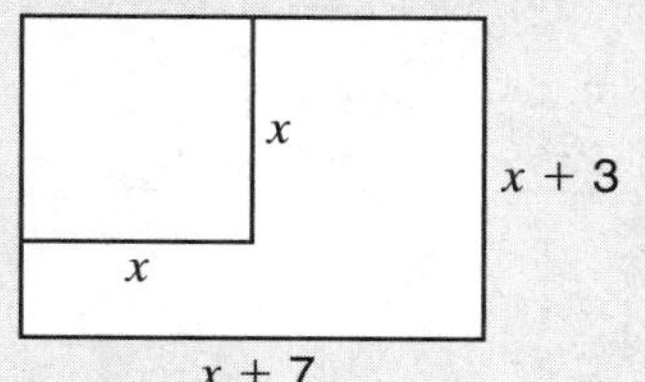

Let x = the width of the square garden.
So $x + 3$ = the width of the new garden, and
$x + 7$ = the length of the new garden.

$(x + 3)(x + 7) = 140$ ← Use the formula for area, $A = \ell w$.

$x^2 + 7x + 3x + 21 = 140$ ← Use the Distributive Property.

$x^2 + 10x + 21 = 140$ ← Simplify.

$x^2 + 10x - 119 = 0$ ← Write in standard form.

$(x - 7)(x + 17) = 0$ ← Factor.

$x - 7 = 0$ or $x + 17 = 0$ ← Use the Zero-Product Property.

$x = 7$ or $x = -17$ ← Use Addition and Subtraction Properties of Equality.

Because the width cannot be negative, $x \neq -17$.
So the width of the square garden was 7 feet.

Solve and check.

1. Bob wants to fence 72 ft^2 for a rectangular chicken pen, with the length twice the width. Find the dimensions of the pen.

   Let x = width and $2x$ = length; $x(2x) = 72$; $2x^2 = 72$; $x^2 = 36$; $x^2 - 36 = 0$; $(x + 6)(x - 6) = 0$; $x = -6$ or $x = 6$; distance cannot be negative, so $x = 6$ and $2x = 12$; The pen has a width of 6 ft and a length of 12 ft.

2. Mr. Yau uses 88 m of fence to enclose 384 m^2 of a rectangular plot of lawn. Find the dimensions of the lawn.

   ____

3. Mindy drops a rock from a cliff 256 ft above the beach. After how many seconds does the rock hit the beach? (*Hint:* $d = 16t^2$, where d = distance, and t = time.)

   ____

4. Carlos drops a ball from a glider 81 ft above a lake. After how many seconds does the ball hit the lake?

   ____

5. The number of yd^2 in the area of a square is twice the number of yd in its perimeter. What is the measure of one side of the square, in yd?

   ____

6. The length of a rectangle is 3 cm longer than the width. If the area of the rectangle is 70 cm^2, what are the dimensions?

   ____

Use with SOURCEBOOK Lesson 10-4, pages 258–259.

Write a quadratic equation with the given roots.

7. $\left\{11, \frac{1}{2}\right\}$

$x = 11$ or $x = \frac{1}{2}$

$x - 11 = 0$ or $2x - 1 = 0$

$(x - 11)(2x - 1) = 0$

$2x^2 - x - 22x + 11 = 0$

$2x^2 - 23x + 11 = 0$

8. $\left\{9, \frac{1}{3}\right\}$

9. $\{-2, 14\}$

10. $\{-5, 11\}$

11. $\{-3, 3\}$

12. $\{-5, 5\}$

13. $\left\{-\frac{2}{3}, \frac{2}{3}\right\}$

14. $\left\{-\frac{5}{2}, \frac{5}{2}\right\}$

15. $\{0, -15\}$

16. $\{-8, 0\}$

17. $\left\{\frac{7}{2}, \frac{5}{4}\right\}$

18. $\left\{\frac{5}{3}, \frac{3}{2}\right\}$

Problem Solving

19. The length of a rectangular flower bed is 5 ft longer than its width. A sidewalk with a width of 3 ft surrounds the bed. If the total area of the bed and sidewalk is 546 ft^2, what are the dimensions of the flower bed?

20. Ali dropped an eraser from a window 171 ft above the ground. It hit a bird feeder 27 ft above the ground. How many seconds after Ali dropped the eraser did it hit the bird feeder?

WRITE ABOUT IT

21. Suppose a quadratic equation has the roots $\sqrt{3}$ and $-\sqrt{3}$. Explain how you would find the equation from these roots. Then find the equation.

10-5 Solve Quadratic Equations by Completing the Square

Name ______________________________ Date ______________

Solve: $2x^2 + 3x + 1 = 0$ Use completing the square.

$x^2 + \frac{3}{2}x = -\frac{1}{2}$ ← Write in the form $x^2 + \frac{b}{a}x = -\frac{c}{a}$

$x^2 + \frac{3}{2}x + \left(\frac{3}{4}\right)^2 = -\frac{1}{2} + \left(\frac{3}{4}\right)^2$ ← Add $\left(\frac{3}{4}\right)^2$ to each side to complete the square.

$\left(x + \frac{3}{4}\right)^2 = \frac{1}{16}$ ← Write $x^2 + \frac{3}{2}x + \frac{9}{16}$ as the square of a binomial.

$x + \frac{3}{4} = \pm\frac{1}{4}$ ← Take the square root of both sides.

$x + \frac{3}{4} = \frac{1}{4}$ or $x + \frac{3}{4} = -\frac{1}{4}$ ← Write and solve two equations.

$x = -\frac{1}{2}$ or $x = -1$ ← Apply the Subtraction Property of Equality; simplify.

Check: $2x^2 + 3x + 1 \stackrel{?}{=} 0$ | $2x^2 + 3x + 1 \stackrel{?}{=} 0$

$2\left(-\frac{1}{2}\right)^2 + 3\left(-\frac{1}{2}\right) + 1 \stackrel{?}{=} 0$ | $2(-1)^2 + 3(-1) + 1 \stackrel{?}{=} 0$

$\frac{1}{2} - \frac{3}{2} + 1 \stackrel{?}{=} 0$ | $2 - 3 + 1 = 0$

$0 = 0$ **True** | $0 = 0$ **True**

Solve each equation by completing the square. Then check.

1. $x^2 + 2x - 35 = 0$

$x^2 + 2x = 35$
$x^2 + 2x + 1 = 35 + 1$
$(x + 1)^2 = 36$
$x + 1 = \pm 6$
$x + 1 = 6$ or $x + 1 = -6$
$x = 5$ or $x = -7$

2. $x^2 + 4x - 96 = 0$

____

3. $x^2 + 4x + 1 = 0$

____

4. $x^2 + 6x + 2 = 0$

____

5. $x^2 - 11x + 30 = 0$

____

6. $x^2 - 13x + 22 = 0$

____

7. $x^2 - 9x - 36 = 0$

____

8. $x^2 - 11x - 102 = 0$

____

9. $2x^2 + 5x - 3 = 0$

____

Use with SOURCEBOOK Lesson 10-5, pages 260–261.

Solve each equation by completing the square. Then check.

10. $3x^2 - 4 + 11x = 0$

11. $5x^2 - 6 + 13x = 0$

12. $25x^2 + 21 = 50x$

13. $15x^2 + 16 = 34x$

14. $3x^2 = 6x - 2$

15. $9x^2 = 36x - 31$

16. $-8x = 16x^2 - 27$

17. $-48x = 36x^2 + 11$

18. $-12x = 7x^2 + 5$

Solve.

19. Ten less than three times the square of a number is 0. Which numbers are possible?

20. The lengths of the sides of a square are increased by 5 in. If the new area of the square is 39 in.², what was the original length of the square?

MENTAL MATH

21. (123)(98)

22. (23.4)(0.9)

23. 59.8 − 17.9 + 13.2 − 9.1

10-6 The Quadratic Formula and the Discriminant

Name ______________________ Date ____________

Use the discriminant to describe the root(s) of each equation.

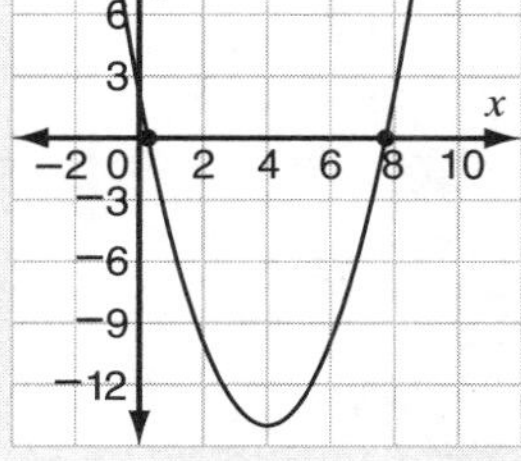

1 $x^2 - 8x + 2 = 0$

$a = 1, b = -8$, and $c = 2$ ← Identify a, b, and c.

$b^2 - 4ac = (-8)^2 - 4(1)(2) = 64 - 8 = 56$ ← Substitute into $b^2 - 4ac$ and simplify.

The discriminant is 56, which is positive but not a perfect square. The equation has two irrational roots.

Remember: If the discriminant is positive *and* a perfect square, the equation will have two *rational* roots.

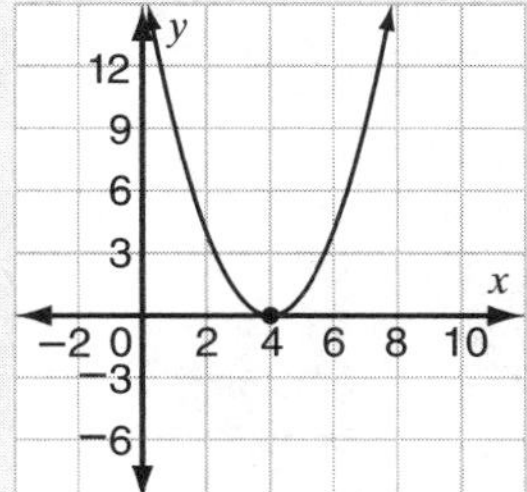

2 $x^2 - 8x + 16 = 0$

$a = 1, b = -8$, and $c = 16$ ← Identify a, b, and c.

$b^2 - 4ac = (-8)^2 - 4(1)(16) = 64 - 64 = 0$ ← Substitute into $b^2 - 4ac$ and simplify.

The discriminant is 0. There is one rational root.

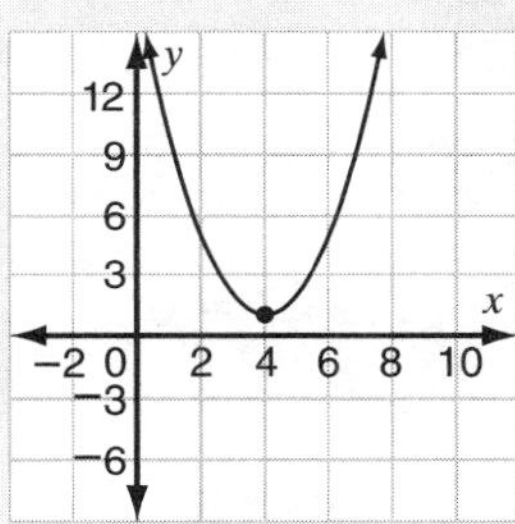

3 $x^2 - 8x + 17 = 0$

$a = 1, b = -8$, and $c = 17$ ← Identify a, b, and c.

$b^2 - 4ac = (-8)^2 - 4(1)(17) = 64 - 68 = -4$ ← Substitute into $b^2 - 4ac$ and simplify.

The discriminant is -4, which is less than zero. There are no real roots.

Find the discriminant of each quadratic equation. Then describe the number and type of roots of the equation.

1. $x^2 + 5x + 7 = 0$

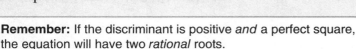

$a = 1, b = 5, c = 7$
$b^2 - 4ac = (5)^2 - 4(1)(7)$
$25 - 28 = -3$
no real roots

2. $x^2 + 2x + 6 = 0$ ____________

3. $x^2 - 5x + 2 = 0$ ____________

4. $x^2 - 3x + 1 = 0$ ____________

5. $2x^2 - 19x + 35 = 0$ ____________

6. $3x^2 - 14x + 8 = 0$ ____________

7. $9x^2 - 6x + 1 = 0$ ____________

8. $25x^2 - 10x + 1 = 0$ ____________

9. $3x^2 - 7x + 11 = 0$ ____________

10. $4x^2 - 3x + 5 = 0$ ____________

11. $4x^2 + 12x + 9 = 0$ ____________

12. $5x^2 + 10x + 5 = 0$ ____________

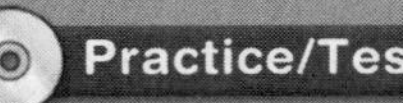

Find the discriminant of each quadratic equation. Describe the number and type of roots of the equation.

13. $10x^2 + 11x - 6 = 0$

14. $14x^2 + 19x - 3 = 0$

15. $-3x^2 + 7x + 2 = 0$

16. $-5x^2 + 9x + 3 = 0$

17. $-16x^2 + 24x - 9 = 0$

18. $-121x^2 + 110x - 25 = 0$

19. $-\frac{1}{4}x^2 - \frac{2}{3}x - \frac{1}{2} = 0$

20. $-\frac{5}{2}x^2 - \frac{3}{4}x - \frac{6}{5} = 0$

21. $\frac{2}{9}x^2 - \frac{3}{5}x - 2 = 0$

22. $\frac{5}{11}x^2 - \frac{8}{3}x - 7 = 0$

23. $-1.4x^2 - 0.5x + 0.9 = 0$

24. $-2.1x^2 - 1.6x + 0.5 = 0$

Problem Solving

25. For what values of k will the equation $kx^2 + 3x + 2 = 0$ have no real roots?

26. For what values of k will the equation $2x^2 - kx + 4 = 0$ have 1 real root?

CRITICAL THINKING

27. The graph of a quadratic function goes through the points $(-5, 2)$ and $(3, -1)$. How many solutions does the related equation have? Explain your answer.

10-7 Solve Quadratic Equations with the Quadratic Formula

Name ______________________ Date __________

Solve: $28x^2 - 95x - 750 = 0$

$a = 28, b = -95$, and $c = -750$ ← Identify a, b, and c.

$$x = \frac{-(-95) \pm \sqrt{(-95)^2 - 4(28)(-750)}}{2(28)}$$ ← Substitute the values a, b, and c in the Quadratic Formula.

$$x = \frac{95 \pm \sqrt{93{,}025}}{56}$$ ← Simplify

$$x = \frac{95 + 305}{56} \text{ or } x = \frac{95 - 305}{56}$$ ← Write as two solutions.

$$= \frac{400}{56} \quad \text{or} \quad = \frac{-210}{56}$$ ← Simplify.

$$= \frac{50}{7} \quad \text{or} \quad = -\frac{15}{4}$$ ← Simplify.

The solutions of $28x^2 - 95x - 750 = 0$ are $\frac{50}{7}$ and $-\frac{15}{4}$.

Remember:
The Quadratic Formula
If $ax^2 + bx + c = 0$, where $a \neq 0$, then $x = \dfrac{-b \pm \sqrt{b^2 - 4ac}}{2a}$.

Solve by using the Quadratic Formula. Write answers in simplest radical form.

1. $6x^2 + x = 15$

$6x^2 + x - 15 = 0$

$a = 6, b = 1, c = -15$

$$x = \frac{-1 \pm \sqrt{1^2 - 4(6)(-15)}}{2(6)}$$

$$x = \frac{-1 \pm \sqrt{361}}{12}$$

$$x = \frac{-1+19}{12} \text{ or } x = \frac{-1-19}{12}$$

$$x = \frac{18}{12} \text{ or } x = \frac{-20}{12}$$

$$\left\{-\frac{5}{3}, \frac{3}{2}\right\}$$

2. $6x^2 + 7x = 20$

3. $5x^2 - 2x + 3 = 0$

4. $6x^2 - 5x + 9 = 0$

5. $2x^2 = 15$

6. $3x^2 = 31$

Solve by using the Quadratic Formula. Write answers in simplest radical form.

7. $2x^2 = 5x + 2$

8. $3x^2 = 5x + 1$

$$\frac{\pm\sqrt{(-5)^2 - 4(3)(-1)}}{2(3)}$$

9. $11x^2 + 5x = 0$

10. $21x^2 + 4x = 0$

11. $-8x - 2 = 3x^2$

12. $-6x - 3 = 2x^2$

Solve. Show all your work.

13. Geometry The area of a rectangle is 299 cm^2. The length is 3 cm less than twice the width. What are the dimensions of the rectangle? (*Hint:* $A = lw$)

14. A bird drops a seed from 40 ft above the ground. How many seconds does it take for the seed to hit the ground? (*Hint:* $d = 16t^2$)

TEST PREPARATION

15. What are the solutions of the quadratic equation $x^2 = -4x - 2$?

A. $x = -4 + \sqrt{2}$ and $x = -4 - \sqrt{2}$

B. $x = 2 + \sqrt{2}$ and $x = 2 - \sqrt{2}$

C. $x = -2 + \sqrt{2}$ and $x = -2 - \sqrt{2}$

D. no real solution

10-8 Solve Linear-Quadratic Systems

Name ______________________ Date ____________

Solve: $\begin{cases} x + y = 11 \\ y = x^2 - 2x + 5 \end{cases}$

$y = -x + 11$ ← Solve $x + y = 11$ for y using the Subtraction Property of Equality.

$-x + 11 = x^2 - 2x + 5$ ← Substitute $-x + 11$ for y in $y = x^2 - 2x + 5$.

$x^2 - x - 6 = 0$ ← Use Addition and Subtraction Properties of Equality to write the resulting quadratic equation in standard form.

$(x - 3)(x + 2) = 0$ ← Factor.

$x - 3 = 0$ or $x + 2 = 0$ ← Apply the Zero-Product Property.

$x = 3$ or $x = -2$ ← Use the Addition and Subtraction Properties of Equality.

To find y, substitute the values of x in either equation.

If $x = 3$, then $y = -3 + 11 = 8$.
(3, 8) is a solution.

If $x = -2$, then $y = -(-2) + 11 = 13$.
(−2, 13) is a solution.

Check: (3, 8)

$y = x^2 - 2x + 5$

$8 \stackrel{?}{=} (3)^2 - 2(3) + 5$

$8 \stackrel{?}{=} 9 - 6 + 5$

$8 = 8$ **True**

$x + y = 11$

$3 + 8 \stackrel{?}{=} 11$

$11 = 11$ **True**

Check: (−2, 13)

$y = x^2 - 2x + 5$

$13 \stackrel{?}{=} (-2)^2 - 2(-2) + 5$

$13 \stackrel{?}{=} 4 + 4 + 5$

$13 = 13$ **True**

$x + y = 11$

$-2 + 13 \stackrel{?}{=} 11$

$11 = 11$ **True**

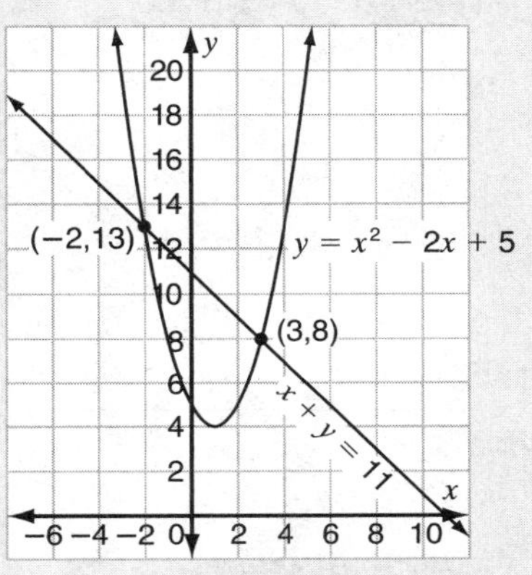

Solve each system of equations. Check your solutions on a separate sheet of paper.

1. $\begin{cases} y = 4 \\ y = 3x^2 + 5x + 4 \end{cases}$

$3x^2 + 5x + 4 = 4$

$3x^2 + 5x = 0$

$x(3x + 5) = 0$

$x = 0$ or $3x + 5 = 0$

$x = -\frac{5}{3}$

$\left(-\frac{5}{3}, 4\right)$, (0, 4)

2. $\begin{cases} y = 2 \\ y = 5x^2 + 3x + 2 \end{cases}$

____

3. $\begin{cases} y = -1 \\ y = -x^2 - 4x - 6 \end{cases}$

____

4. $\begin{cases} y = 1 \\ y = -x^2 - 4x - 4 \end{cases}$

____

5. $\begin{cases} x + y = -1 \\ y = x^2 + 5x + 7 \end{cases}$

____

6. $\begin{cases} x - y = 2 \\ y = x^2 - 6x + 8 \end{cases}$

____

Solve each system of equations. Check your solutions on a separate sheet of paper.

7. $\begin{cases} 9x + y = 4 \\ y = 3x^2 - 15x + 7 \end{cases}$

8. $\begin{cases} 6x - y = 12 \\ y = 4x^2 - 10x + 4 \end{cases}$

9. $\begin{cases} 3x + y = -12 \\ y = 3x^2 + 11x + 16 \end{cases}$

10. $\begin{cases} 4x + 2y = -16 \\ y = 4x^2 + 8x + 20 \end{cases}$

11. $\begin{cases} 4x - y = -25 \\ y + 5 + 3x = 5x^2 - 3x - 10 \end{cases}$

12. $\begin{cases} 5x - y = -20 \\ y + 3x + 5 = 3x^2 + 2x - 20 \end{cases}$

Problem Solving

13. The length of a rectangle is 1 foot more than twice the width. The area of the rectangle is two times the square of the width, plus three times the width, less 14 square feet. What is the width of the rectangle?

14. The equation of a line is $y = k$. The equation of a parabola is $y = 2x^2 + 4x + 7$. What value of k will give the system of equations exactly one solution? two solutions? no solutions?

CHALLENGE

15. Find the x-coordinates of the points of intersection of the system: $\begin{cases} y = 2x^2 - 3x - 8 \\ y = -x^2 + 2x + 6 \end{cases}$

10-9 Technology: Find the Zeros of Polynomial Functions

Name ______________________ Date ____________

You can use the **Solve** function of a handheld to find the zeros, or roots, of the equation $x^2 - 5x - 84 = 0$.

Step 1 Press (home). Then choose (1) to select **Calculator**.

Step 2 Press (menu). Select **Algebra**, then select **Solve**.

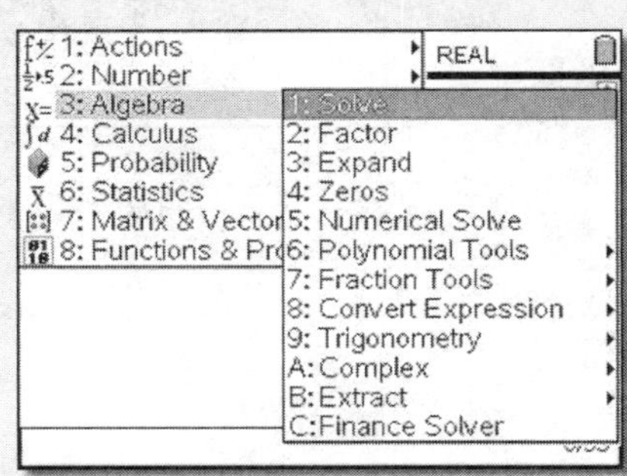

Step 3 Input $x^2 - 5x - 84 = 0, x$ and press (enter). The ", x" means solve for x.

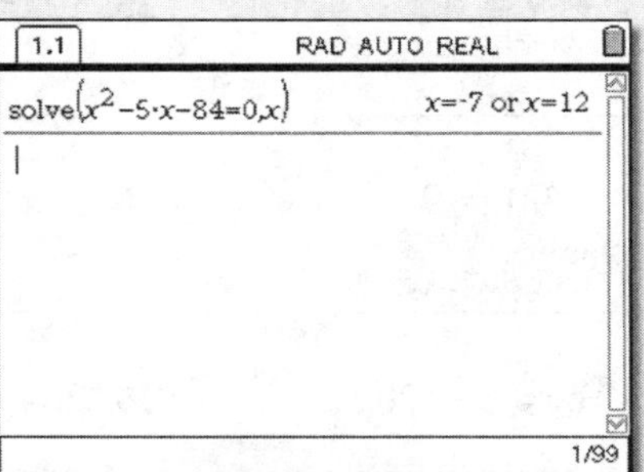

Solution: $\{-7, 12\}$

Check: To verify the answer found, substitute the values into the polynomial equation.

$$(-7)^2 - 5(-7) - 84 \stackrel{?}{=} 0$$
$$49 + 35 - 84 \stackrel{?}{=} 0$$
$$84 - 84 \stackrel{?}{=} 0$$
$$0 = 0 \text{ True}$$

$$(12)^2 - 5(12) - 84 \stackrel{?}{=} 0$$
$$144 - 60 - 84 \stackrel{?}{=} 0$$
$$84 - 84 \stackrel{?}{=} 0$$
$$0 = 0 \text{ True}$$

Use a handheld to find the roots of the equation.

1. $x^2 - 5x - 35 = 0$

{−4, 9}

2. $x^2 - 3x - 54 = 0$ ______

3. $x^2 - 22x + 105 = 0$ ______

4. $x^2 - 2x - 143 = 0$ ______

5. $x^2 + 4x - 140 = 0$ ______

6. $x^2 - 23x + 120 = 0$ ______

7. $x^2 - 29x + 180 = 0$ ______

8. $x^2 + 57x + 800 = 0$ ______

9. $x^2 + 80x + 1584 = 0$ ______

10. $x^2 - 55x + 754 = 0$ ______

11. $x^2 - 40x + 399 = 0$ ______

12. $x^2 + 19x - 2072 = 0$ ______

13. $x^2 + 47x - 1704 = 0$ ______

14. $x^2 - 9x - 2236 = 0$ ______

15. $x^2 - 14x - 3672 = 0$ ______

Use a handheld to find the roots of the equation.

16. $x^2 + x - 1 = 0$

$x = \frac{-1 \pm \sqrt{5}}{2}$

17. $x^2 + x - 3 = 0$

18. $2x^2 - 3x - 1 = 0$

19. $5x^2 - 3x - 1 = 0$

20. $2x^2 + x - 15 = 0$

21. $3x^2 + 8x - 35 = 0$

22. $6x^2 - 13x + 5 = 0$

23. $12x^2 - 17x + 6 = 0$

24. $15x^2 - 23x - 24 = 4$

25. $8x^2 - 26x - 90 = 9$

26. $35x^2 - 70x + 24 = 6x - 8$

27. $12x^2 - 33x + 16 = 28x - 61$

28. $130x^2 - 13x = 2 - 20x$

29. $204x^2 + 85x = 5 + 12x$

30. $89x^2 + 64x = 0$

31. $123x^2 + 79x = 0$

32. $81x^2 - 529 = 0$

33. $625x^2 - 5041 = 0$

Solve. Show your work.

34. The area of the shaded region is 111 square inches. What are the dimensions of the large rectangle?

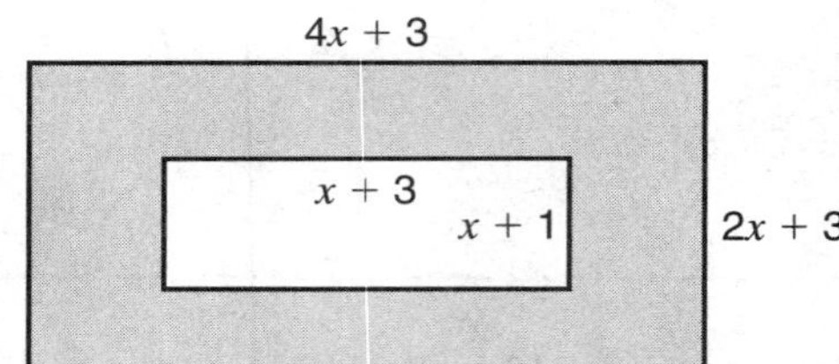

35. One number is 1 less than twice another number. Their product is 241 more than their sum. What are the numbers?

WRITE ABOUT IT

36. Solve the equation $x^2 - 66x + 1089 = 0$. Explain why there is only one solution. How does the one solution relate to the graph of $y = x^2 - 66x + 1089$? Explain.

10-10 Technology: Families of Quadratic Functions

Name ______________________ Date ____________

You can use a handheld to graph the equations $y = x^2$ and $y = -7x^2$ and examine how the value and sign of a affect the graph of $y = ax^2$.

Step 1 Press (home). Then choose (2) to select **Graphs & Geometry**.

Step 2 Input x^2, then press (enter) to graph the parabola.

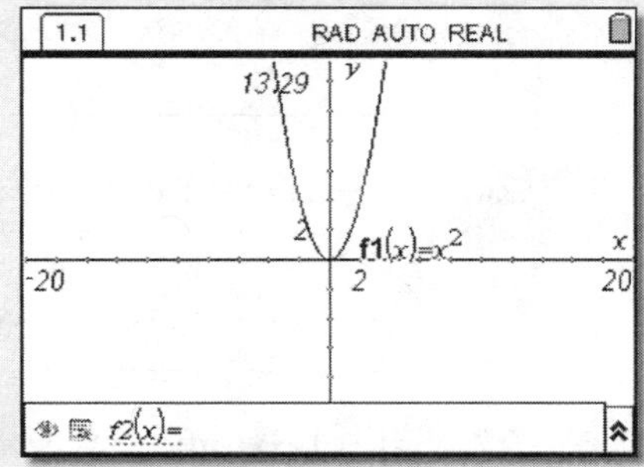

Step 3 Input $-7x^2$, then press (enter) to graph the parabola.

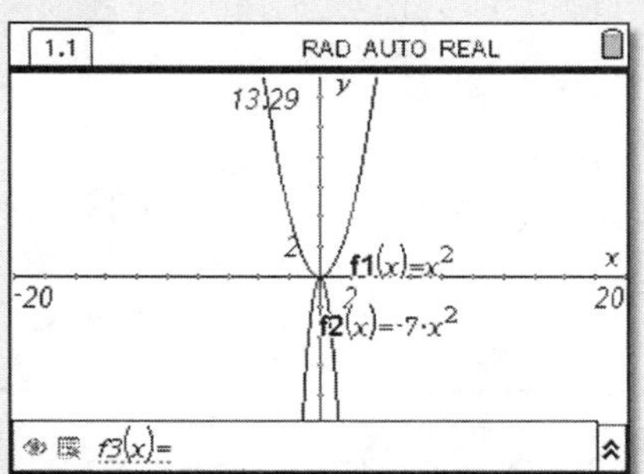

The second function is narrower and opens downward.

Predict how the graph of the second function will compare to that of the first function. Then use a handheld to verify your prediction.

1. $y = x^2$ and $y = 8x^2$

second will be narrower

2. $y = x^2$ and $y = 12x^2$

____

3. $y = x^2$ and $y = -x^2$

____

4. $y = 2x^2$ and $y = -2x^2$

____

5. $y = x^2$ and $y = -4x^2$

____

6. $y = x^2$ and $y = -12x^2$

____

7. $y = x^2$ and $y = 0.2x^2$

____

8. $y = x^2$ and $y = 0.05x^2$

____

9. $y = 3x^2$ and $y = -3x^2$

____

10. $y = 6x^2$ and $y = -6x^2$

____

11. $y = 4x^2$ and $y = -4x^2$

____

12. $y = 5x^2$ and $y = -5x^2$

____

13. $y = -x^2$ and $y = -12x^2$

____

14. $y = -2x^2$ and $y = -10x^2$

____

15. $y = 5x^2$ and $y = 0.07x^2$

____

Predict how the graph of the second function will compare to that of the first function. Then use a handheld to verify your prediction.

16. $y = 5x^2$ and $y = 0.004x^2$

second will be wider

17. $y = 3x^2$ and $y = \frac{2}{3}x^2$

18. $y = 2x^2$ and $y = \frac{2}{5}x^2$

19. $y = -5x^2$ and $y = \frac{3}{4}x^2$

20. $y = -7x^2$ and $y = \frac{5}{9}x^2$

21. $y = \frac{1}{12}x^2$ and $y = -\frac{2}{3}x^2$

22. $y = \frac{1}{8}x^2$ and $y = -\frac{3}{4}x^2$

23. $y = -2x^2$ and $y = \frac{9}{2}x^2$

24. $y = -3x^2$ and $y = \frac{19}{3}x^2$

25. $y = \frac{5}{4}x^2$ and $y = 1.25x^2$

26. $y = \frac{7}{10}x^2$ and $y = 0.7x^2$

27. $y = -1.9x^2$ and $y = \sqrt{9}x^2$

28. $y = -3.04x^2$ and $y = \sqrt{16}x^2$

29. $y = 1.99x^2$ and $y = -1.08x^2$

30. $y = 2.88x^2$ and $y = -2.026x^2$

Solve.

31. Predict how the graph of $y = 3(x - 2)^2$ will compare to the graph of $y = x^2$, then use a handheld to verify your prediction. Use your observation to compare the graph of $y = a(x - b)^2$ for $a > 1$ and $b > 0$ to the graph of $y = x^2$.

32. Predict how the graph of $y = \frac{3}{4}x^2 + 5$ will compare to the graph of $y = x^2$, then use a handheld to verify your prediction. Use your observation to compare the graph of $y = ax^2 + b$ for $0 < a < 1$ and $b > 0$ to the graph of $y = x^2$.

CRITICAL THINKING

33. Predict how the graph of $y = 5(2^x)$ will compare to the graph of $y = 2^x$, then use a handheld to verify your prediction. Use your observation to compare the graph of $y = a(2^x)$ to the graph of $y = 2^x$.

10-11 Problem-Solving Strategy:
Adopt a Different Point of View

Read · Plan · Solve · Check

Name ______________________________ Date ______________

Solve by adopting a different point of view.

1. The circle seen here has center at C and radius r and passes through the origin. Perpendicular lines have been drawn from C to the axes, and the intersection points have been labeled A and B. What is the length of x?

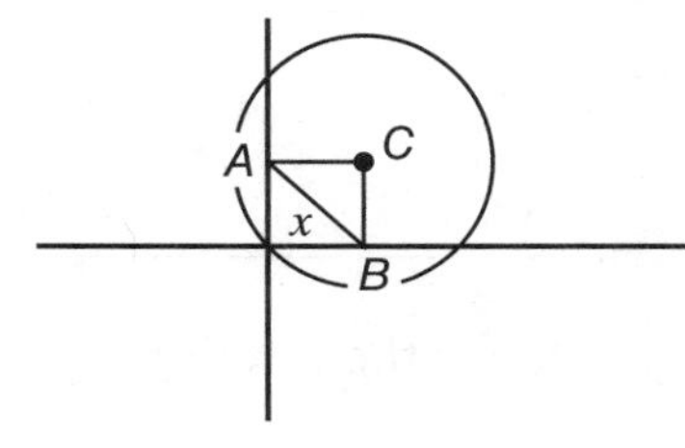

____

2. What is the greatest value of the expression

$$wy + wz + xy + xz$$

if w, x, y, and z have values 5, 7, 9, and 11, though not necessarily in this order?

____

3. For a and b with $1 \leq a \leq 5 \leq b \leq 9$, what is the greatest value $\frac{a+b}{ab}$ can have?

____

4. Suppose this pattern of 0s and 1s is continued through 225 places:
1 1 0 1 1 0 0 0 1 1 0 0 0 0 0 1 1 0 0 0 0 0 0 0 1 1 0 0 0 0 0 0 0 0 0 1 . . .
How many 1s are there?

____

5. What is the area of the kite seen here, which is 40 in. tall by 14 in. across?

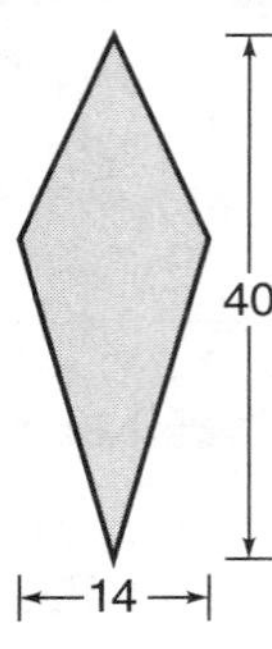

6. What is the fraction equivalent of $0.42\overline{333}$?

7. The figure at the right is "4 squares tall." How many squares would be in a similar figure that is "20 squares tall"?

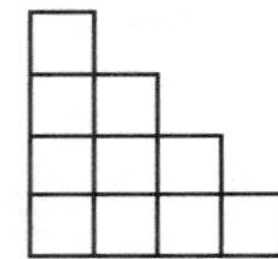

8. Without using a calculator, determine the sum:

$$2 + 4 + 6 + 8 + 10 + 12 + \ldots + 994 + 996 + 998 + 1000$$

Enrichment:
Reflective Properties of Parabolic Surfaces

Name ______________________________ Date ______________

A point on a parabola is 3.25 in. from the focus of the parabola. How far is the point from the directrix?

Think

A point, which is 3.25 in. from the focus of a parabola, must also be 3.25 in. from the directrix.

So the point is 3.25 in. from the directrix.

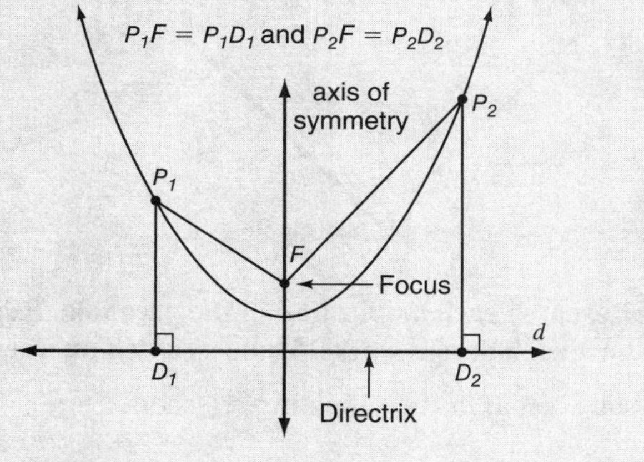

Fill in the blanks.

1. A ______________________ is the set of all points in a plane whose distance from a fixed point F is the same as their distance from a fixed line d.

2. The Law of ______________________ states that the angle of ______________________ equals the angle of reflection.

3. A point on a parabola is 12 m from the focus of the parabola. How far is the point from the directrix? ______________________

4. A point on a parabola is 3.5 mm from the focus of the parabola. How far is the point from the directrix? ______________________

5. A point on a parabola is $8\frac{1}{5}$ ft from the directrix of the parabola. How far is the point from the focus? ______________________

6. A point on a parabola is $x + 6.2$ cm from the focus of the parabola. How far is the point from the directrix? ______________________

7. A ray strikes a surface with an angle of incidence of 38.4°. What is the angle of reflection? ______________________

8. A ray is reflected off a surface with an angle of reflection of 88.03°. What is the angle of incidence? ______________________

9. A ray hits and reflects off a surface at a combined angle of 56.5°. What is the angle of incidence? ______________________

Use with SOURCEBOOK Enrichment Lesson, pages 276–277.

10. A ray hits and reflects off a surface at a combined angle of 175.25°.

What is the angle of reflection? ______________________

A ray is pictured striking a surface. Draw the reflected ray.

11. 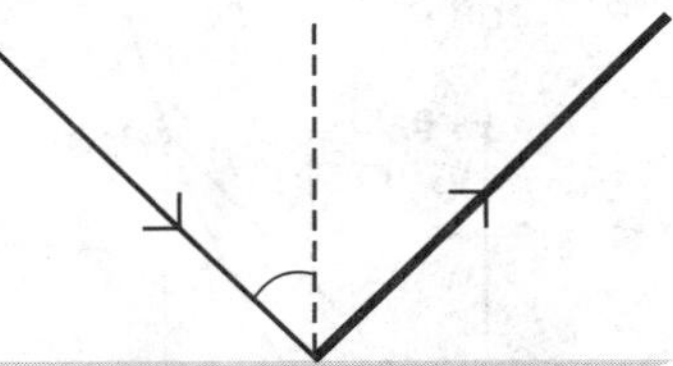

12. 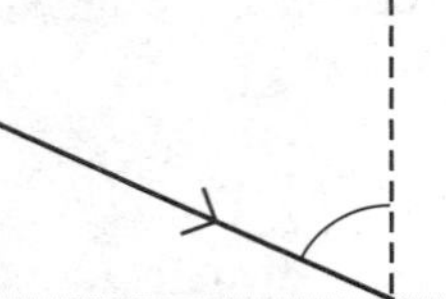

13. 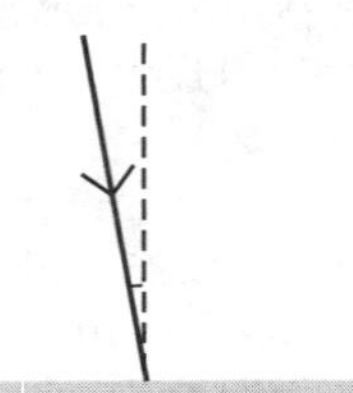

Research each application of the parabola. Report your findings. Describe how each design works. Make a sketch on a separate sheet of paper.

14. Research the reflecting telescope.

____

____

____

15. Research parabolic receivers.

____

____

____

16. Research and describe how electric heaters work.

____

____

____

SPIRAL REVIEW

Solve.

17. $x^2 - 10x = -24$

18. $x^2 = 16$

19. $3x^2 = 28 - 17x.$

______________ ______________ ______________

Test Prep: Short-Answer Questions

Strategy: Show All Your Work

Name ____ Date ______________

When answering a short-answer question, be sure to **explain your thinking** in order to demonstrate your understanding of how to solve the problem.	To solve the problem, try using these strategies: • Reread the test item. • Use the Test-Prep strategy. • Identify key ideas. • Apply appropriate rules, definitions, properties, or strategies. • Analyze your answers.

Solve. Show all your work. *TIP Write or print neatly and legibly.*

1. Graph the equation $y = \frac{1}{2}x^2 - 3x + 1$ on a coordinate plane and identify its vertex and axis of symmetry.

Answer: ______________________

2. Miranda is 4 years older than her brother Brendan. The product of their ages is 165. Write and solve an equation to find each sibling's age.

Answer: ______________________

3. Write a rule for the function shown in the input-output table. Then find $f(32)$.

x	0	2	4	6
$f(x)$	−7	−3	1	5

Answer: ______________________

4. A taxi driver charges a fixed rate of $5, plus $0.75 per mi. Write an equation that can be used to find the cost of a taxi ride of *m* miles. Then find the number of miles traveled if the cost of a ride was $12.50.

Answer: ______________________

5. The prefered slope of a wheelchair ramp is no less than $\frac{1}{20}$ and no greater than $\frac{1}{16}$. Write an inequality showing the prefered horizontal lengths of a ramp with a height of 3 ft. Then use a separate sheet of paper to graph the inequality.

Answer: ______________________

6. Solve the system of equations.

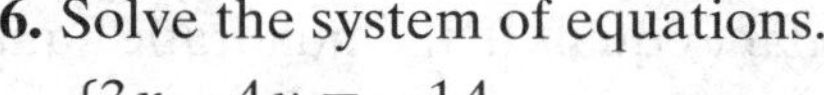

$$\begin{cases} 3x - 4y = -14 \\ 2y = x + 8 \end{cases}$$

Answer: ______________________

Use with SOURCEBOOK Test Prep Lesson, page 278.

Vocabulary Development

Name ______________________ Date ____________

Chapter 10 Vocabulary

axis of symmetry	parabola	roots of the equation
completing the square	parent function	vertex
discriminant	Quadratic Formula	Zero-Product Property
maximum value	quadratic equation	Zeros of the Function
minimum value	quadratic function	

From the vocabulary list above, choose the term(s) that best complete each sentence. Write the term(s) in the space(s) provided.

1. The vertical line that passes through the vertex of a parabola is called the ______________.

2. A formula that can be used to solve any quadratic equation is the ______________.

3. A U-shaped curve is called a ______________.

4. The point at which a parabola changes direction is the ______________.

5. Solving a quadratic equation by adding a term to make a perfect-square trinomial is called ______________.

6. The part of the quadratic formula that provides information about the roots of a quadratic equation is the ______________.

7. The simplest function with the defining characteristics of a family of functions is called the ______________.

8. According to the ______________ if a and b are real numbers and $ab = 0$, then either $a = 0$ or $b = 0$.

Tell whether each statement is true or false. If it is false, change it to make it true.

9. If the discriminant equals 0, the quadratic equation has one real root.

____

10. The expression $\frac{-b}{2a}$ is the discriminant for the equation $ax^2 + bx + c = 0$.

____

11. If the discriminant is greater than 0 and is a perfect square, the quadratic equation has 2 irrational roots.

____

Use after SOURCEBOOK Lessons 10-1–10-8, pages 246–269.

Practice Chapter 10 Test

Name ______________________________ Date ____________

Tell whether the graph of the quadratic function opens upward or downward. Explain.

1. $y = -2 - x^2 + 5x$

2. $y - 9x^2 = 0$

3. $6y - 2x = 12 - 4x^2$

For each parabola shown, identify the following:

- **vertex**
- **axis of symmetry**
- **x-intercept(s)**
- **maximum or minimum value of the function**
- **domain and range of the function**

4.

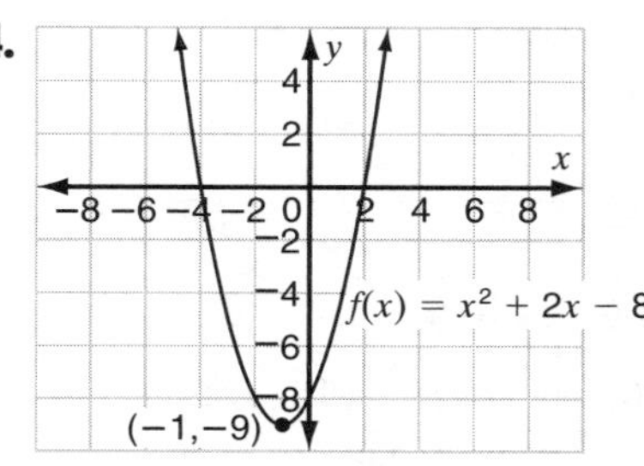

5.

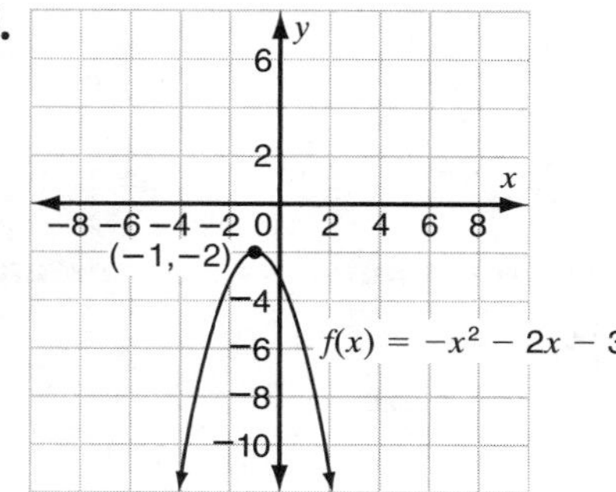

6.

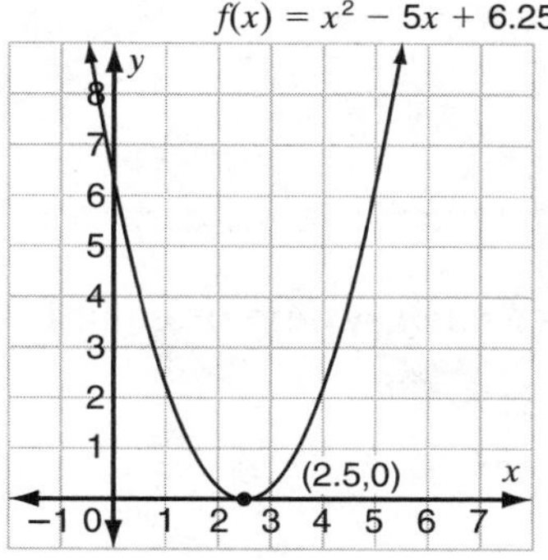

Solve each equation by factoring.

7. $x^2 - 8x = 33$

8. $3x^2 - 5x = 28$

9. $25x^2 - 1 = 0$

10. $12x = -7x^2 - 15$

Write an equation with the given roots.

11. $\{-3, 7\}$

12. $\{7, 6\}$

13. $\left\{\frac{3}{2}, -\frac{7}{4}\right\}$

14. $\left\{-\frac{11}{4}, -\frac{6}{7}\right\}$

Solve each equation by completing the square.

15. $x^2 = 10x - 9$

16. $x^2 - 8x + 3 = 0$

17. $18x^2 - 24x = -1$

Find the discriminant of each quadratic equation. Use it to describe the number and type of roots of the equation.

18. $2x^2 - x + 1 = 0$

19. $100x^2 - 60x + 9 = 0$

20. $3x^2 - 5x + 1 = 0$

Solve using the quadratic formula. Write answers in simplest radical form.

21. $2x^2 + 5x = 7$

22. $x^2 = 63 - 2x$

23. $4x^2 = 3x + 2$

Solve each system of equations. Check your solutions on a separate sheet of paper.

24. $\begin{cases} y = 2 \\ y = 3x^2 + 4x - 5 \end{cases}$

25. $\begin{cases} y = -7x + 13 \\ y = 5x^2 - 7x + 8 \end{cases}$

26. $\begin{cases} y = 3x - 14 \\ y = \frac{1}{2}x^2 - 3x + 4 \end{cases}$

Problem Solving

27. Samantha wants to enclose 1680 ft^2 for a rectangular horse pen. The length will be 2 ft longer than the width. Find the dimensions of the pen. (*Hint:* $A = \ell w$)

28. Devon dropped a dime from a cliff 320 ft above the ground. After how many seconds did the dime hit the ground? (*Hint:* $d = 16t^2$)

Tell About It

Explain how you solve the problem. Show all your work.

29. Solve: $\begin{cases} y = 35 \\ y = -x^2 + 13x + 60 \end{cases}$

Cumulative Review: Chapters 1–10

Name ______________________________ Date ____________

Circle the best answer.

1. Which integer is a perfect square?

A. 50 **B.** 71
C. 81 **D.** 120

2. If $U = \{-2, -1, 0, 1, 2, 3, 4\}$ and $A = \{0, 1, 2, 3, 4\}$, what is A'?

F. $\{-2, -1, 0, 1, 2, 3, 4\}$
G. $\{-2, -1, 0, 1, 2\}$
H. $\{0, 1, 2\}$
J. $\{-2, -1\}$

3. Solve: $-|5f| = -25$

A. $\{f \mid f = -5 \text{ or } 5\}$
B. $\{f \mid f = -5\}$
C. $\{f \mid f = 5\}$
D. $\varnothing$

4. Solve for b: $5b - 7c = 12b$

F. $b = -1$ **G.** $b = -c$
H. $b = c$ **J.** $b = -7c + 7$

5. Solve: $-17 < 3a + 4 < 13$

A. $-\frac{13}{3} < a < \frac{17}{3}$ **B.** $-16 < a < 14$
C. $-7 < a < 3$ **D.** $a > -7$ or $a < 9$

6. Which value of x makes this relation a function? $L = \{(-4, 3), (x, 5), (-2, 6), (3, 2)\}$

F. -4 **G.** -3
H. -2 **J.** 3

7. Which ordered pair belongs to the function $y = -3x^2$?

A. $(1, 1)$ **B.** $(-1, 3)$
C. $(-1, 9)$ **D.** $(-1, -3)$

8. What is the slope of a line that connects points $(2, 9)$ and $(-1, 5)$?

F. $-\frac{4}{3}$ **G.** $-\frac{3}{4}$
H. $\frac{3}{4}$ **J.** $\frac{4}{3}$

9. Which equation is a direct variation?

A. $y = -5x$
B. $y = -3x + 2$
C. $y = x^3$
D. $y = -11$

10. Which equation has a y-intercept of 2?

F. $y = 2x + 8$ **G.** $2y = x + 1$
H. $4x + 2y = 4$ **J.** $4x - 2y = 4$

11. Solve by substitution: $\begin{cases} y = -x + 6 \\ x + 2y = 13 \end{cases}$

A. $(-1, 7)$ **B.** $(7, -1)$
C. $(1, 7)$ **D.** $(7, 1)$

12. Which ordered pair is a solution of this system? $\begin{cases} x + 3y \le 4 \\ x - y \ge 1 \end{cases}$

F. $(-3, 5)$ **G.** $(1, -2)$
H. $(3, 3)$ **J.** $(-2, 4)$

13. Which is a binomial of degree 5?

A. $5x^5 + 9x + 7$ **B.** $2x^4y + 3xyz$

C. $11x^5y - 12yz^4$ **D.** $5x + 5$

14. Simplify.
$(6y^3 + 17y^2 - 11y + 3) - (4y^3 - 6y^2 - 9y - 3)$

F. $2y^3 + 23y^2 - 2y + 6$

G. $2y^3 + 23y^2 - 2y$

H. $2y^3 + 11y^2 - 20y$

J. $2y^3 + 11y^2 - 20y + 6$

15. Factor completely: $10a^3 + 20a^2$

A. $2(5a^3 + 10a^2)$ **B.** $5a(2a^2 + 4a)$

C. $10a(a^2 + 2a)$ **D.** $10a^2(a + 2)$

16. Which is a factor of $7x^2 + 33x - 10$?

F. $7x - 5$ **G.** $x - 5$

H. $7x + 5$ **J.** $7x - 2$

17. What is $\sqrt{150}$ written in simplest form?

A. 75 **B.** $6\sqrt{25}$

C. $5\sqrt{6}$ **D.** $25\sqrt{3}$

18. Multiply: $(-4\sqrt{2} + 3\sqrt{5})(-4\sqrt{2} - 3\sqrt{5})$

F. -13 **G.** $-8\sqrt{2}$

H. -161 **J.** $-13 - 24\sqrt{10}$

19. Which is the vertex of the quadratic function $f(x) = x^2 - 14x - 2$?

A. $(7, -51)$

B. $(-7, 145)$

C. $(14, -2)$

D. $(0, -2)$

20. Solve: $2x^2 - 17x = -21$

F. $\frac{2}{3}, 7$ **G.** $\frac{3}{2}, 7$

H. $-\frac{3}{2}, -7$ **J.** $-\frac{2}{3}, -7$

21. To complete the square in the equation $x^2 - 24x = 16$, which number should be added to both sides of the equation?

A. 8 **B.** 12

C. 64 **D.** 144

22. Which is the discriminant of the equation $5x^2 - 7x = 2$?

F. 89 **G.** 9

H. -54 **J.** -89

Tell About It

Explain how you solve each problem. Show all your work.

23. The product of two consecutive odd positive integers is 1023. What are the integers?

24. The number of ft^2 in the area of a square is three times the number of ft in the perimeter of the square. What is the length of the square?

11-1 Ratios and Rates

Name ______________________ Date ____________

A bag of marbles contains 28 red marbles, 30 green marbles, and 24 yellow marbles. What is the ratio of red marbles to yellow marbles, written as a fraction in simplest form?

Remember: A ratio is a comparison of two numbers by division. The ratio a to b can also be written $a : b$ and $\frac{a}{b}$, where $b \neq 0$.

$\frac{28}{24}$ ← $\frac{\text{number of red marbles}}{\text{number of yellow marbles}}$

$\frac{28 \div 4}{24 \div 4} = \frac{7}{6}$ ← Simplify.

The ratio of red marbles to yellow marbles is $\frac{7}{6}$.

Lois walked 12 mi in 5 h. What is her unit rate?

Remember: A rate compares quantities with different types of units. A unit rate is a rate in which the denominator is 1.

$\frac{12 \text{ mi}}{5 \text{ h}}$ ← Write as a fraction.

$\frac{12 \text{ mi} \div 5}{5 \text{ h} \div 5} = \frac{2.4 \text{ mi}}{1 \text{ h}}$ ← Divide the numerator and denominator by 5.

The unit rate is 2.4 miles per hour or 2.4 mi/h.

A classroom has 15 boys and 20 girls. Write each ratio as a fraction in simplest form.

1. girls to boys

$\frac{20}{15} = \frac{20 \div 5}{15 \div 5}$

$\frac{4}{3}$

2. boys to girls

3. boys to the entire class

4. girls to the entire class

A car dealer has 15 red, 22 blue, 8 black, and 30 white cars for sale. Write each ratio as a fraction in simplest form.

5. red cars to white cars

$\frac{15}{30} = \frac{15 \div 15}{30 \div 15}$

$\frac{1}{2}$

6. blue cars to white cars

7. red cars to blue cars

8. red cars to black cars

9. white cars to all cars

10. blue cars to all cars

11. all cars to black cars

12. all cars to red cars

Use with SOURCEBOOK Lesson 11-1, pages 280–283.

Write each situation as a unit rate.

13. 620 mi in 8 h

$$\frac{620 \text{ mi} \div 8}{8 \text{ h} \div 8} = \frac{77.5 \text{ mi}}{1 \text{ h}}$$

77.5 mi/h

14. 750 mi in 12 h

15. 675 words in 30 min

16. 1300 words in 40 minutes

17. \$2.25 for 12.5 oz

18. \$3.92 for 24.5 ounces

Convert the units of measure as indicated.

19. 90 km per h to m per min

$$\frac{90 \text{ km}}{1 \text{ h}} \bullet \frac{1 \text{ h}}{60 \text{ min}} \bullet \frac{1000 \text{ m}}{1 \text{ km}} = \frac{1500 \text{ m}}{1 \text{ min}}$$

1500 m/min

20. 120 km per h to m per min

21. 58 oz per min to lb per h

22. 74 oz per min to lb per h

23. 0.5 mm per s to m per h

24. 0.1 km per h to cm per s

Solve. Show your work.

25. Shanille bought 4.5 yd of fabric for \$28.95 and John bought 2.5 yd of the same fabric for \$14.25. Who spent less per yard of fabric?

26. Nancy drove 451.5 mi on 14 gal of gas. Luis drove 382.2 mi on 12 gal of gas. Whose gas mileage was better?

CHALLENGE

27. A kilometer is about $\frac{5}{8}$ mi. About how many ft per min is 110 km per h?

11-2 Apply Proportion to Scale Models

Name ______________________________ Date ______________

A map of New York has a scale of 2 in. : 25 mi. Albany is about 135 mi from New York City. About how far apart are the cities on the map?

Let x = the map distance between New York City and Albany.

$$\frac{\text{map distance (in.)}}{\text{actual distance (mi)}} \; \frac{2 \text{ in.}}{25 \text{ mi}} = \frac{x \text{ in.}}{135 \text{ mi}}$$

Solve:

$270 = 25x$ ← Use cross products.

$\frac{270}{25} = \frac{25x}{25}$ ← Use the Division Property of Equality.

$10.8 = x$ ← Simplify.

Albany is about 10.8 in. from New York City on the map.

Check:

$\frac{2}{25} = \frac{x}{135}$

$\frac{2}{25} \stackrel{?}{=} \frac{10.8}{135}$

$270 \stackrel{?}{=} 25(10.8)$

$270 = 270$ True

Use a proportion to solve. Check your work on a separate sheet of paper.

A map of the United States has a scale of 2 inches : 225 miles.

1. Wichita, Kansas is shown 5.5 in. from Baton Rouge, Louisiana. What is the actual distance between the two cities?

   $\frac{\text{map (in.)}}{\text{actual (mi)}} = \frac{2}{225}; \frac{2}{225} = \frac{5.5}{x}$

   $2x = 1237.5$

   $x = 618.75$

   618.75 mi

2. Chicago, Illinois is shown 7.2 in. from Dallas, Texas. What is the actual distance between the two cities?

   ____

3. Salt Lake City, Utah is about 1390 miles from Nashville, Tennessee. About how far apart are they on the map, to the nearest tenth?

   ____

4. Seattle, Washington is about 2010 miles from Columbus, Ohio. About how far apart are they on the map, to the nearest tenth?

   ____

5. Phoenix, Arizona is about 1095 miles from Bismarck, North Dakota. About how far apart are they on the map, to the nearest tenth?

   ____

6. Atlanta, Georgia is about 735 miles from Maine, New York. About how far apart are they on the map, to the nearest tenth?

   ____

A blueprint of a house has a scale of 5 centimeters : 4 meters.

7. The house on the blueprint is 30.5 cm long. What is the actual length of the house?

8. The house on the blueprint is 28.5 cm wide. What is the actual width of the house?

9. The dimensions of the kitchen are 4.5 m by 3 m. What are the dimensions in the drawing?

10. The dimensions of the family room are 10 m by 5.5 m. What are the dimensions in the drawing?

11. An island for the kitchen is 2.5 m long. The space allowed for the island on the scale drawing is 3.2 cm long. Will the island fit?

12. An entertainment center has a length of 3.1 meters. The space allowed for the entertainment center on the scale drawing is 3.9 centimeters long. Will the entertainment center fit?

Solve. Show your work.

13. An artist uses the scale of 2 in. : 1.5 ft to paint a mural on the outside wall of a business. The scale drawing is 30 in. by 45 in.. What are the dimensions of the mural?

14. May uses the scale of 3 cm : 2 m to make a scale model of her city hall. City Hall is 30.5 m by 60 m by 24.5 m. What are the dimensions of her model?

CRITICAL THINKING

15. Jaime is making a scale drawing of his room on a sheet of paper that is 8.5 in. by 11 in. He wants to leave 0.5 in. of blank space around the drawing. His room is 14 ft by 12 ft. What is the largest scale drawing Jaime can fit onto his sheet of paper given his restrictions?

11-3 Calculate Relative Error

Name ______________________________ Date ______________

Find the percent of error and the relative error of the area.

measured dimensions: $58\frac{1}{4}$ ft by 78 ft

actual dimensions: $57\frac{3}{4}$ ft by $78\frac{1}{4}$ ft

Remember: Percent of error describes the accuracy of a measurement.

$$\text{percent of error} = \frac{|\text{measured value} - \text{actual value}|}{\text{actual value}} \cdot 100$$

$58.25 \text{ ft} \cdot 78 \text{ ft} = 4543.5 \text{ ft}^2$ ← Use the formula: length × width = area to find each area.

$57.75 \text{ ft} \cdot 78.25 \text{ ft} = 4518.9375 \text{ ft}^2$

$\frac{4543.5 - 4518.9375}{4518.9375} \cdot 100$ ← Substitute the appropriate values into the formula.

0.5% ← Simplify and round to the nearest tenth of a percent.

0.5% = 0.005 ← The relative error is the percent of error written as a decimal.

The percent of error is 0.5%. The relative error is 0.005.

Find the percent of error and the relative error of the area.

1. measured dimensions: 12 m by 15 m
actual dimensions: 12.1 m by 14.6 m

12 • 15 = 180
12.1 • 14.6 = 176.66
$\frac{|180 - 176.66|}{176.66} \cdot 100 \approx 1.9\%$
percent of error: 1.9%
relative error: 0.019

2. measured dimensions: 18 m by 20 m
actual dimensions: 18.4 m by 20.8

____

3. measured dimensions: 26 in. by $38\frac{1}{2}$ in.
actual dimensions: $25\frac{1}{2}$ in. by 38 in.

____

4. measured dimensions: 42 in. by $46\frac{3}{4}$ in.
actual dimensions: 43 in. by $46\frac{1}{2}$ in.

____

5. measured dimensions: 18.2 cm by 19.5 cm
actual dimensions: 18.6 cm by 18.7 cm

____

6. measured dimensions: 22.5 cm by 34.2 cm
actual dimensions: 22 cm by 35.3 cm

____

Find the percent of error and the relative error of the volume.

7. measured dimensions:
3 cm by 6 cm by 5.5 cm
actual dimensions:
2.9 cm by 5.5 cm by 5.1 cm

$3 \cdot 6 \cdot 5.5 = 99$
$2.9 \cdot 5.5 \cdot 5.1 = 81.345$
$\frac{|99 - 81.345|}{81.345} \cdot 100 \approx 21.7\%$
percent of error: 21.7%
relative error: 0.217

8. measured dimensions:
4 cm by 7.2 cm by 8 cm
actual dimensions:
3.8 cm by 7 cm by 7.5 cm

______

9. measured dimensions:
4 yd by $2\frac{1}{4}$ yd by 3 yd
actual dimensions:
$3\frac{3}{4}$ yd by 2 yd by $3\frac{1}{4}$ yd

______

10. measured dimensions:
6 ft by $5\frac{1}{4}$ ft by $4\frac{1}{4}$ ft
actual dimensions:
$6\frac{1}{4}$ ft by 5 ft by $4\frac{3}{4}$ ft

______

11. measured dimensions:
12 m by 11.6 m by 9.7 m
actual dimensions:
12.4 m by 11.1m by 10.3 m

______

12. measured dimensions:
15 m by 16.8 m by 12.9 m
actual dimensions:
15.5 m by 16 m by 13.5 m

______

Solve. Show your work.

13. A builder is ordering bricks for a walkway. He measured the length and width of the walk as 268.5 ft by 4.5 ft. What is the percent of error of the area if the actual measurements are 274 ft by 4.5 ft?

______

14. A storage shed is advertised as having a volume of 932.96 ft^2. What is the relative error of the volume if the actual dimensions of the shed are 10 ft by 11 ft by 8 ft?

______

TEST PREPARATION

15. Pauline measured her room and got a floor area of 184.8 ft^2. What is the approximate relative error of the area if the actual measurements of her room are 12.5 ft by 13.5 ft?

A. 9.5% **C.** −0.095
B. 0.095 **D.** −9.5%

16. Jovito measures and finds the volume of a cylinder to be 65 cubic centimeters. What is the approximate percent of error if the cylinder actually has a diameter of 2.6 cm and a height of 12.75 cm?

A. −3.9% **C.** 0.039
B. −0.039 **D.** 3.9%

11-4 Apply Percents to Algebraic Problems

Name ______________________ Date __________

Find the total cost of a $54.86 jacket after a 7.1% sales tax is added.

7.1% of $54.86 ← Find the sales tax.

Think

$7.1\% = \frac{7.1}{100} = \frac{71}{1000} = 0.071$

0.071 • 54.86 = 3.89506 ← Write the percent as a decimal and multiply.

The sales tax rounded to the nearest cent is $3.90.

54.86 + 3.90 = 58.76 ← Find the cost of the jacket plus tax.

The total cost of the jacket plus tax is $58.76.

Solve each problem.

1. Find the sale price of a $15.95 book that is discounted 20%.

0.2 • 15.95 = 3.19; 15.95 − 3.19 = 12.76

$12.76

2. Find the sale price of a $36.10 tool that is discounted 30%.

____

3. Find the total cost of a $125.65 pair of boots after an 8.5% sales tax is added.

____

4. Find the total cost of a $102.38 pair of shoes after a 7.5% sales tax is added.

____

5. Megan earns a 1.5% commission on her total sales. One day her total sales were $6258.95. How much was her commission?

____

6. Jeremiah earns a 2.5% commission on his total sales. Last month his total sales were $186,915. How much was his commission?

____

7. Find the amount of simple interest $1500 would earn in 4 years if deposited in an account that paid 2.8% interest. (*Hint:* $I = Prt$)

____

8. Find the amount of simple interest $3100 would earn in 3 years if deposited in an account that paid 4.1% interest.

____

9. Lionel was charged 6.1% simple interest on a loan of $6000. He paid the money plus interest after 3 years. How much did he pay altogether?

____

10. Melissa was charged 4.9% simple interest on a loan of $8000. She paid the money plus interest after 4 years. How much did she pay altogether?

____

11. Tony buys a $980 printer on sale for 25% off. What is the total cost of the printer, including a sales tax of 5.8% of the discounted price?

____

12. Maria buys a $1240 computer on sale for 40% off. What is the total cost of the computer, including a sales tax of 6.5% of the discounted price?

____

Use with SOURCEBOOK Lesson 11-4, pages 288–289.

Solve each problem. Show your work. (*Hint:* percent of change $= \frac{\text{amount of change}}{\text{original amount}} \times 100$)

13. Kirk's starting wage was \$12 per hour. One year later he earns \$13.50 per hour. What is the percent of increase in his hourly wage?

14. Jennifer's starting wage was \$15 per hour. One year later she earns \$18.75 per hour. What is the percent of increase in her hourly wage?

15. Lisa bought a boat for \$34,850. She sold it three years later for \$23,698. What was the percent of decrease in the value of the boat?

16. Janice bought a motorcycle for \$12,900. She sold it two years later for \$5,805. What was the percent of decrease in the value of the motorcycle?

17. Store A buys saws for \$8.50 and sells them for \$21.25. Store B buys saws for \$7.50 and sells them for \$20.25. Which store has a greater percent markup?

18. Store A buys hats for \$22 and sells them for \$77. Store B buys hats for \$24 and sells them for \$84. Which store has a greater percent markup?

Problem Solving

19. Oscar bought a game that was discounted by 20%. To pay for the game plus a 10% sales tax on the discounted price, he used a coupon for \$5 and gave the cashier \$17. What was the original price of the game?

20. Geometry Martina increased the length and width of her rectangular garden by 15%. By what percent is the *area* of her garden increased? (*Hint:* $A = \ell w$)

SPIRAL REVIEW

21. Write a quadratic equation with roots 15 and 4.

22. What is the distance between point (9, 3) and point (8, 2)?

11-5 The Trigonometric Ratios

Name ______________________ Date __________

Find the sine, cosine, and tangent of $\angle A$ to the nearest ten-thousandth.

$$\sin A = \frac{\text{length of leg opposite } \angle A}{\text{length of hypotenuse}} = \frac{21}{29} \approx 0.7241$$

$$\cos A = \frac{\text{length of leg adjacent to } \angle A}{\text{length of hypotenuse}} = \frac{20}{29} \approx 0.6897$$

$$\tan A = \frac{\text{length of leg opposite } \angle A}{\text{length of leg adjacent to } \angle A} = \frac{21}{20} = 1.0500$$

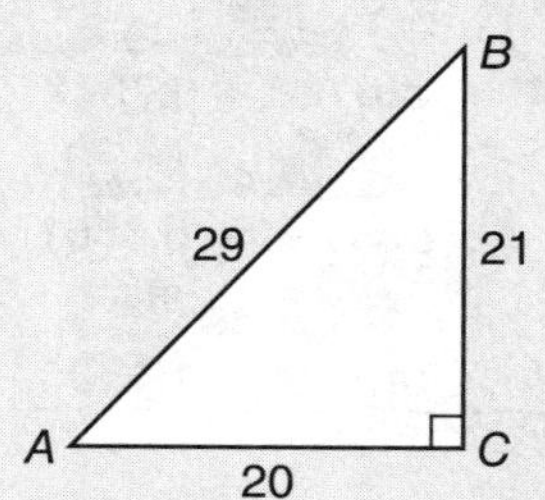

Find the sine, cosine, and tangent of the indicated angle to the nearest ten-thousandth.

1. $\angle A$

$\sin A = \frac{117}{125} = 0.9360$

$\cos A = \frac{44}{125} = 0.3520$

$\tan A = \frac{117}{44} \approx 2.6591$

2. $\angle B$

______

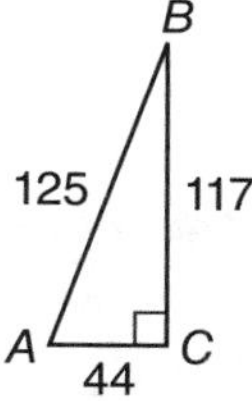

3. $\angle F$ ______

4. $\angle G$ ______

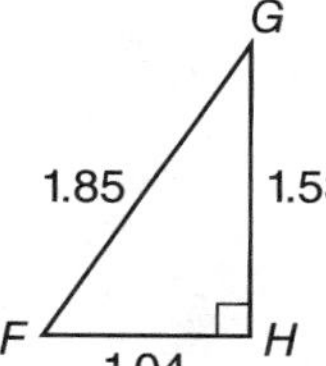

5. $\angle X$ ______

6. $\angle Y$ ______

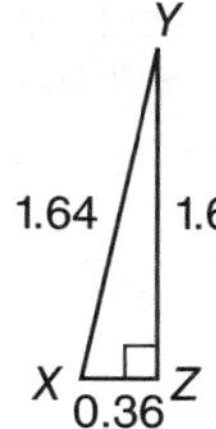

7. $\angle L$ ______

8. $\angle M$ ______

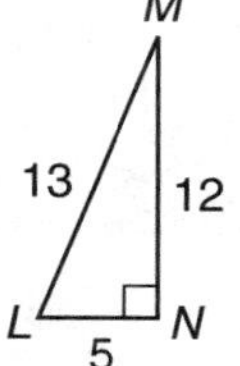

You can use a handheld device to find the sine, cosine, and tangent of the given angle to the nearest ten-thousandth.

9. 49°

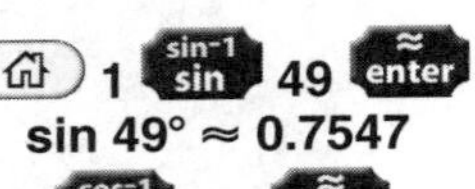

1 sin 49 enter
sin 49° ≈ 0.7547
cos 49 enter
cos 49° ≈ 0.6561
tan 49 enter
tan 49° ≈ 1.1504

10. 84°

11. 12°

12. 45°

13. 23.5°

14. 76.8°

Use a handheld to find the measure of ∠*A* to the nearest degree.

15. sin *A* = 0.5624

 1  

ctrl sin 0.5624 enter
34°

16. sin *A* = 0.9253

17. cos *A* = 0.4836

18. cos *A* = 0.0025

19. tan *A* = 3.5123

20. tan *A* = 8.9652

Problem Solving

21. Manny is making a corner shelf. The legs of the right triangle are 17 cm and 20 cm. What is the measure of the smallest angle of the triangle?

22. A rectangular playground is 25 ft long. Josh constructs a 30-foot fence along its diagonal. What is the measure of the angle between the fence and the side that represents the length of the playground?

WRITE ABOUT IT

23. On paper or a handheld, compare sin 75° with cos 15°. Then compare the sine and cosine of other angles that have a sum of 90°. Explain what you discover.

11-6 Use Trigonometric Ratios to Solve Right Triangles

Name ______________________ Date __________

Solve $\triangle ABC$. Round the length of the side to the nearest tenth.

$m\angle A = 22°$

$m\angle B = 90° - 22°$ ⟵ The acute angles of a right triangle are complementary.

$= 68°$

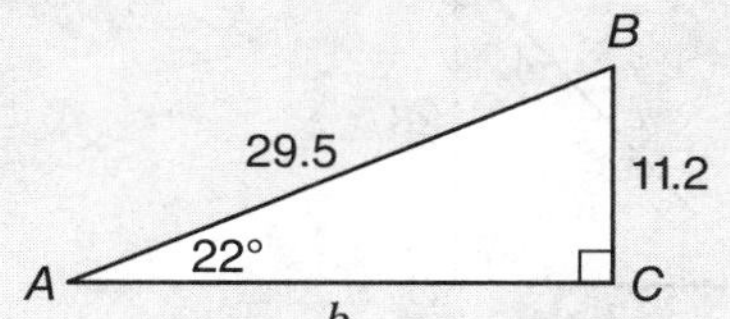

Find the measure of b to the nearest tenth.

$\cos A = \dfrac{\text{length of adjacent leg}}{\text{length of hypotenuse}}$ ⟵ Decide which ratio to use.

$\cos 22° = \dfrac{b}{29.5}$ ⟵ Substitute the given values.

$0.9272 \approx \dfrac{b}{29.5}$ ⟵ Use a handheld to find cos 22°.

$b \approx 0.9272(29.5)$ ⟵ Use the cross products.

$b \approx 27.4$

Remember: The handheld must be in the degree mode and in the approximate mode.

Solve each right triangle. Round the lengths of the sides to the nearest tenth and the angle measures to the nearest degree.

1.

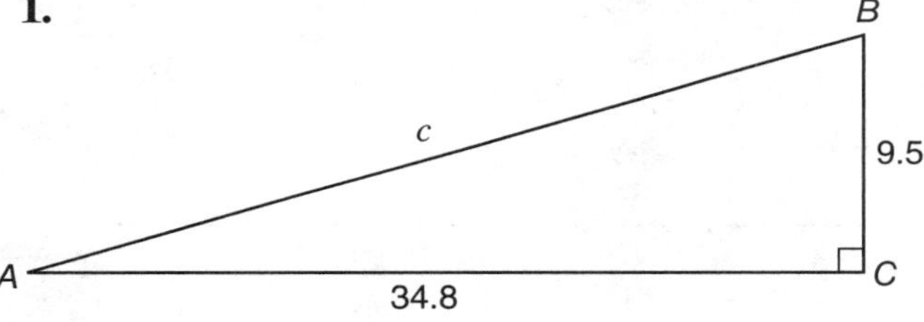

$\tan A = \dfrac{9.5}{34.8} \approx 0.2730$

$\angle A \approx 15°$; $m\angle B \approx 75°$

$(9.5)^2 + (34.8)^2 = c^2$

$1301.29 = c^2$

$36.1 \approx c$

$m\angle A \approx 15°$; $m\angle B \approx 75°$; $c \approx 36.1$

2.

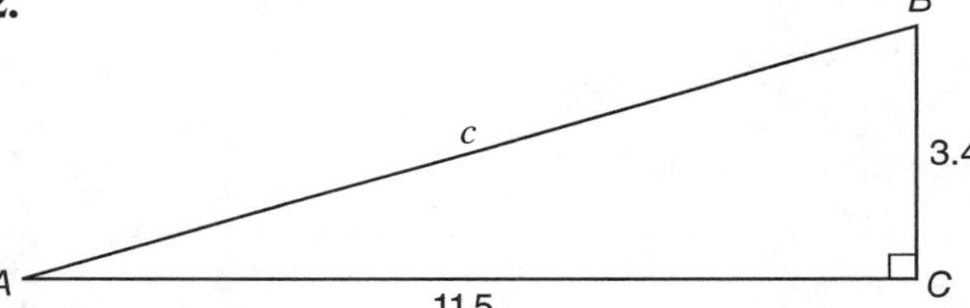

3.

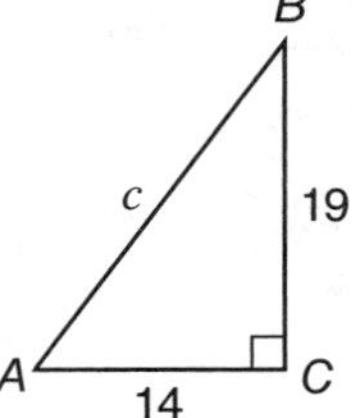

4.

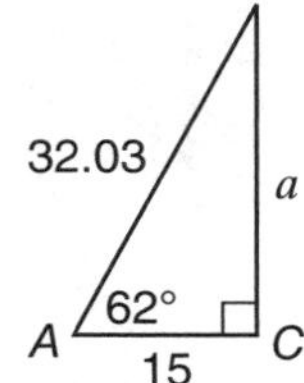

Solve each right triangle. Round the lengths of the sides to the nearest tenth and the angle measures to the nearest degree.

5.

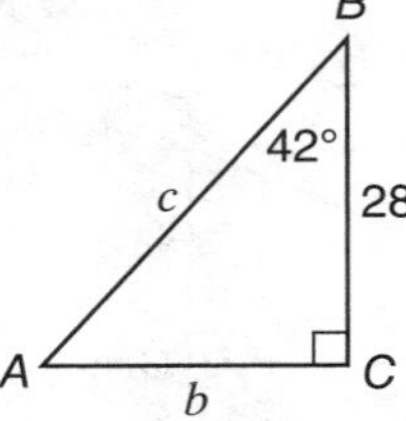

6.

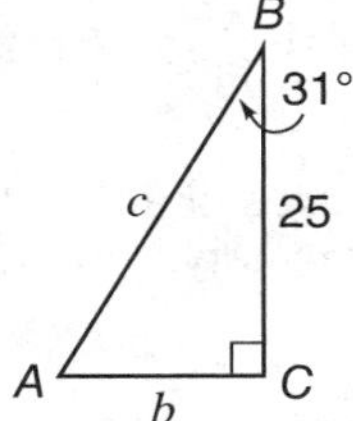

7.

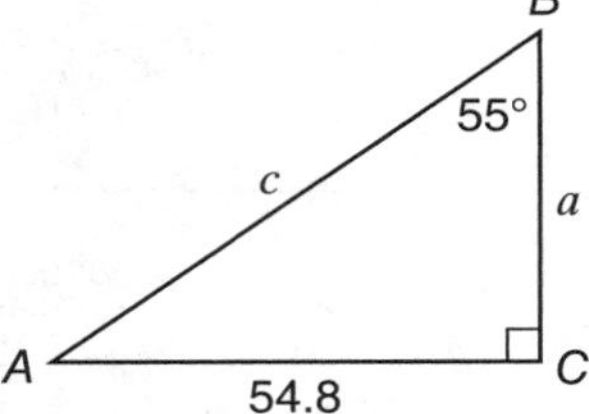

8.

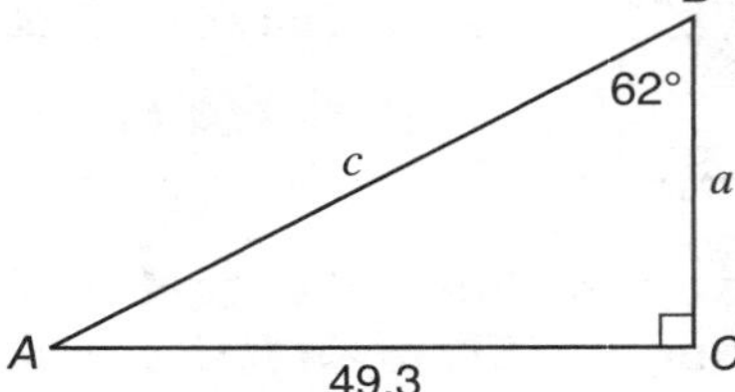

Problem Solving

9. Parag folds paper to make figures. He made a boat shaped like a right triangle with $\frac{5}{8}$-ft and 1-ft legs. What are the measures of the triangle's acute angles? Round to the nearest degree.

10. Ted cuts a rectangular board that is 131 in. long and 75 in. wide along the diagonal to make supports for a table. What are the measures of the angles along the cut?

MENTAL MATH

11. Solve: $\frac{1}{4} = \frac{2}{x}$

12. Solve: $\frac{5}{x} = \frac{1}{9}$

13. Solve: $\frac{3}{x} = \frac{2}{5}$

14. Solve: $\frac{11}{7} = \frac{8}{x}$

11-7 Use Trigonometric Ratios to Solve Verbal Problems

Name ______________________________ Date ______________

A 32-ft telephone pole is anchored to the ground with a wire that starts 8 ft below the top of the pole. The wire makes a 45° angle with the ground. To the nearest foot, how long is the wire?

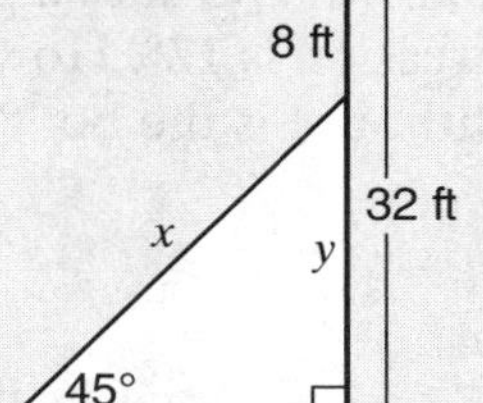

Sketch a diagram to model the situation.
$y = 32 - 8 = 24$ ⟵ To find y, subtract.

To find x, use the sine ratio.

$\sin 45° = \frac{24}{x}$ ⟵ Use the ratio of the opposite side to the hypotenuse.

$0.7071 \approx \frac{24}{x}$ ⟵ Use a handheld to find sin 45°.

$0.7071x \approx 24$ ⟵ Use cross products.

$x \approx \frac{24}{0.7071} \approx 34$ ⟵ Use the Division Property of Equality. Simplify.

The wire is about 34 feet long.

Solve each problem. Round the lengths to the nearest whole number. Show your work.

1. The base of a 20-ft ladder makes a 75° angle with the ground. How far up the wall does the ladder reach?

Let x = height that ladder reaches
$\sin 75° = \frac{x}{20}$; $0.9659 \approx \frac{x}{20}$; $19 \approx x$;
The ladder reaches about 19 ft.

2. The base of a 24-ft ladder makes a 70° angle with the ground. How far up the wall does the ladder reach?

____

3. Ali is standing 100 ft from the base of a tower. Her eye level is 6 ft above the base of the tower. If the angle of elevation from her eyes to the top of the tower is 19°, what is the height of the tower?

____

4. Hans is standing 80 ft from the base of a building. His eye level is 5 ft above the base of the building. If the angle of elevation from his eyes to the top of the building is 24°, what is the height of the building?

____

5. To measure the height of a mountain, a surveyor took two sightings, one 1000 feet farther from the mountain than the other. The first angle of elevation was 85° and the second was 83°. What is the mountain's height?

____

6. To measure the height of a pole, a man took two sightings, one 10 feet farther from the pole than the other. The first angle of elevation was 70° and the second was 64°. What is the pole's height?

____

Solve each problem. Round the lengths to the nearest whole number.

7. George is in a lighthouse 25 ft above sea level. He looks out and sees a boat. The angle of depression is 12°. How far from the lighthouse is the boat?

8. Ruth and Dontay are in a tower 100 m above the street. Using binoculars, they see a bike at a 9° angle of depression. How far from the tower is the bike?

9. A builder is making a ramp that rises 6 ft. If the angle of elevation is 5°, how long must the ramp be?

10. Carla is making a slide that is 460 cm long. If the slide has a 35° angle of elevation, what will be the height?

Problem Solving

11. Shara is making a corner shelf shaped like a right isosceles triangle with a hypotenuse of 42 cm. Without using the Pythagorean theorem, what is the approximate length of each leg?

12. Ted is setting up a tent. He connects two 1.8-m poles at a 52° angle to make a side of the tent. What is the length of the base of this side?

CHALLENGE

13. Ken is near a hill. The angle of elevation from Ken's location to the hill's top is 3.4°. Ken bikes towards the hill at 8 miles per hour. Thirty minutes later, the angle of elevation from Ken's new location is 5.1°. What is the height of the hill in feet?

11-8 Technology: Graph the Sine and Cosine Functions

Name ______________________________ Date ______________

You can use a handheld to graph the equation $y = -3\cos(x)$.

Step 1 Change the calculator settings to degrees. Press (home). Then choose (8) for **System Info** and (2) for **System Settings**. Change **Angle** to degree.

Step 2 Press (home) then choose (2) for **Graphs & Geometry**.

Step 3 Change the window size to see the graph better. Press (menu). Select **Window**, then select **Window Settings**. Change XMin to -90 and XMax to 720. Change YMin to -6 and YMax to 6.

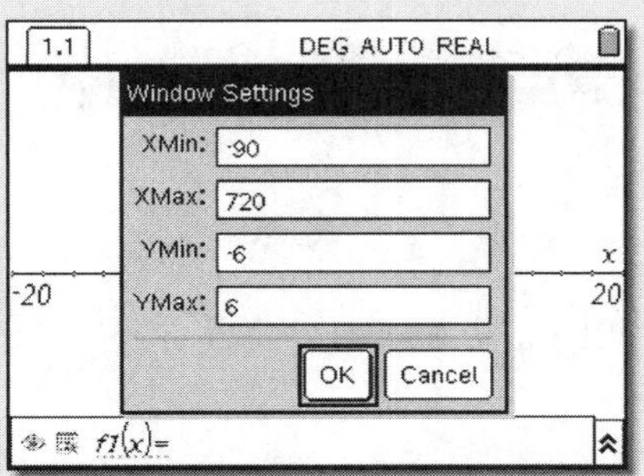

Step 4 Press -3 (cos) x. Then press (enter) to graph the function.

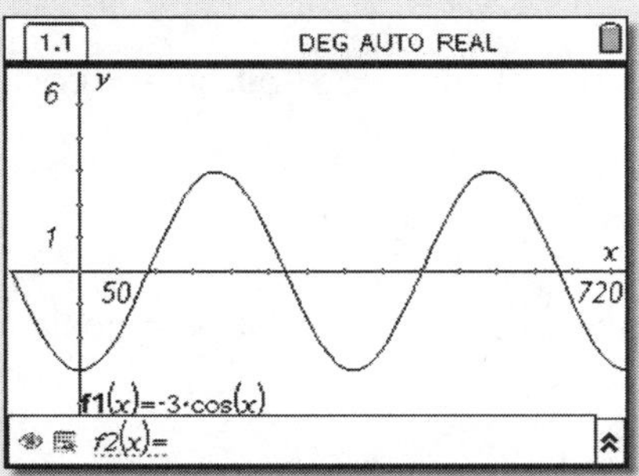

Notice that the graph is a repeating pattern of curves with y-values between -3 and 3. The graph shows that the cosine function is continuous for negative angle measures as well as for angles greater than 90°.

Think
There is a y-value for every x-value.

Use a handheld to graph the trigonometric function. Choose an appropriate window size.

1. $y = 4\sin(x)$ **2.** $y = 4\cos(x)$ **3.** $y = -2\sin(x)$ **4.** $y = -2\cos(x)$

5. $y = 7\sin(x)$ **6.** $y = 7\cos(x)$ **7.** $y = -5\sin(x)$ **8.** $y = -5\cos(x)$

9. $y = \frac{1}{2}\sin(x)$ **10.** $y = \frac{1}{2}\cos(x)$ **11.** $y = -\frac{1}{2}\sin(x)$ **12.** $y = -\frac{1}{2}\cos(x)$

13. $y = \frac{3}{4}\sin(x)$ **14.** $y = \frac{3}{4}\cos(x)$ **15.** $y = -\frac{3}{4}\sin(x)$ **16.** $y = -\frac{3}{4}\cos(x)$

Use a handheld to graph the trigonometric function. Choose an appropriate window size.

17. $y = \sin(2x)$ **18.** $y = \cos(2x)$ **19.** $y = -\sin(2x)$ **20.** $y = -\cos(2x)$

21. $y = -\sin(-2x)$ **22.** $y = -\cos(-2x)$ **23.** $y = -\sin(4x)$ **24.** $y = -\cos(4x)$

25. $y = \sin(3x)$ **26.** $y = \cos(3x)$ **27.** $y = \sin(10x)$ **28.** $y = \cos(10x)$

29. $y = -\sin\left(\frac{1}{2}x\right)$ **30.** $y = -\cos\left(\frac{1}{2}x\right)$ **31.** $y = \sin\left(\frac{1}{4}x\right)$ **32.** $y = \cos\left(\frac{1}{4}x\right)$

33. $y = \sin\left(-\frac{1}{2}x\right)$ **34.** $y = \cos\left(-\frac{1}{2}x\right)$ **35.** $y = -\sin\left(-\frac{1}{4}x\right)$ **36.** $y = -\cos\left(-\frac{1}{4}x\right)$

37. $y = -\sin\left(\frac{3}{4}x\right)$ **38.** $y = -\cos\left(\frac{3}{4}x\right)$ **39.** $y = -\sin\left(-\frac{3}{4}x\right)$ **40.** $y = -\cos\left(-\frac{3}{4}x\right)$

Solve.

41. Use a handheld to graph $y = \sin(x)$ and $y = \cos(x)$. Then solve the equation $\sin(x) = \cos(x)$ for $0° \leq x \leq 360°$.

____

42. Use a handheld to graph $y = \sin(x)$ and $y = -\cos(x)$. Then solve the equation $\sin(x) = -\cos(x)$ for $0° \leq x \leq 360°$.

____

CHALLENGE

43. Use a handheld to graph $y = \sin(x)$, $y = \sin(x - 5)$, $y = \sin(x - 45)$, $y = \sin(x - 90)$, $y = \sin(x - 180)$, $y = \sin(x - 270)$, and $y = \sin(x - 360)$. Explain how each graph differs from the graph of $y = \sin(x)$.

____

11-9 Problem-Solving Strategy:
Guess and Test

Read Plan Solve Check

Name ______________________ Date __________

Use Guess and Test to solve each problem.

1. Find all pairs of positive integers A and B for which $\frac{A}{4} + \frac{B}{6} = \frac{19}{12}$.

2. A box has a square base, but the height is 4 in. more than twice the length of the base. If the box has volume 1280 in.^{3}, what is the measure of a side of its base?

3. The sum of the cubes of two consecutive positive integers is 559. What are the two integers?

4. A 60-cm wire is cut into two pieces that are then used to make two squares, each with a side length that is a whole number of centimeters. The sum of the areas of the squares is 137 cm^2. How was the wire cut?

5. Ms. Johnson asked the class for coins to do a probability demonstration. In all, she obtained the same number of quarters as dimes, and six fewer nickels than either. If the coins total \$6.90, how many coins did she have altogether?

6. Find a pair of positive numbers a and b having the property that *they* differ by a half, and *their squares* differ by a half as well.

7. When a number is subtracted from its own cube the result is 32,736. What is this number?

8. Raffle tickets for a school fundraiser were sold for \$5 each by the school's 5th through 8th grade classes. The 8th grade sold 20 more tickets than the 7th grade. The 7th grade sold four more tickets than the 6th grade. The 5th grade sold exactly half the number of tickets that the 8th grade sold. In all, \$1250 worth of tickets were sold. How many tickets did each grade sell?

Enrichment:
The Law of Sines

Name ______________________________ Date ______________

Find all the unknown side lengths and angle measures of the triangle. Round lengths to the nearest tenth.

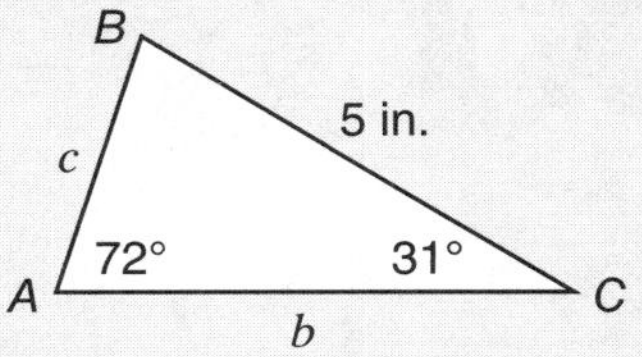

Remember: The Law of Sines
In $\triangle ABC$, where a, b, and c are lengths of the sides opposite $\angle A$, $\angle B$, and $\angle C$, respectively,

$$\frac{a}{\sin A} = \frac{b}{\sin B} = \frac{c}{\sin C}$$

$180° = 72° + m\angle B + 31°$ ⟵ Substitute 72° for m$\angle A$ and 31° for m$\angle C$.

$77° = m\angle B$ ⟵ Use the Addition Property of Equality; Simplify.

$\frac{b}{\sin B} = \frac{a}{\sin A}$ ⟵ Use the Law of Sines. ⟶ $\frac{c}{\sin C} = \frac{a}{\sin A}$

$\frac{b}{\sin 77°} = \frac{5}{\sin 72°}$ ⟵ Substitute into each equation. ⟶ $\frac{c}{\sin 31°} = \frac{5}{\sin 72°}$

$\frac{b}{0.9744} = \frac{5}{0.9511}$ ⟵ Evaluate the Trigonometric Functions. ⟶ $\frac{c}{0.5150} = \frac{5}{0.9511}$

$b \approx 5.1$ ⟵ Use the Cross-Products Rule; Simplify. ⟶ $c \approx 2.7$

So $m\angle B = 77°$, $b \approx 5.1$ in., and $c \approx 2.7$ in.

Find all the unknown side lengths and angle measures.

1.

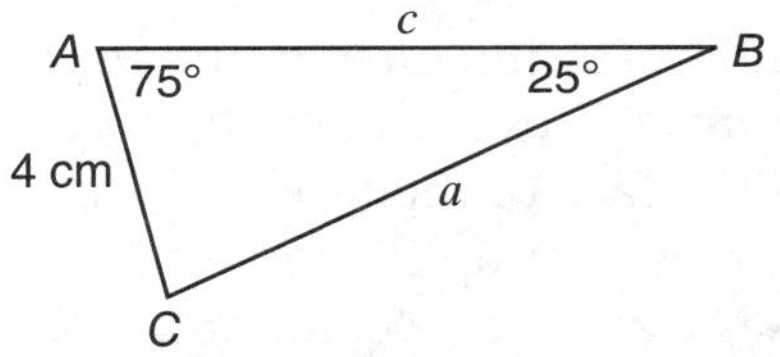

$m\angle C = 180° - 100° = 80°$

$\frac{4}{\sin 25} = \frac{a}{\sin 75}$; $\frac{4\sin 75}{\sin 25}$

$\frac{4}{\sin 25} = \frac{c}{\sin 80}$; $\frac{4\sin 80}{\sin 25}$

$a \approx 9.1$ cm; $c \approx 9.3$ cm

2.

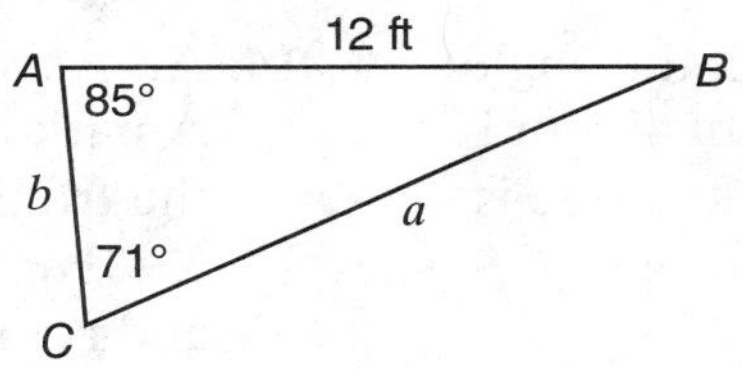

____

3.

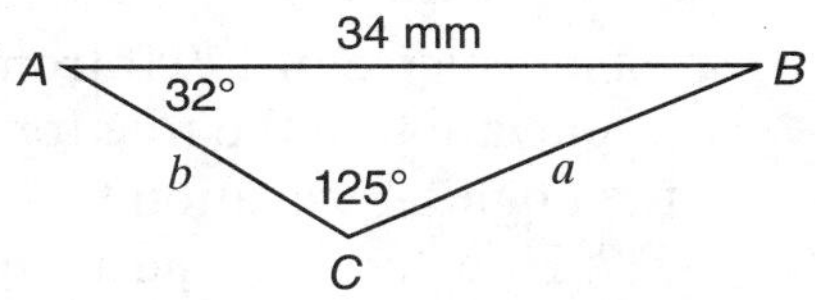

____

4.

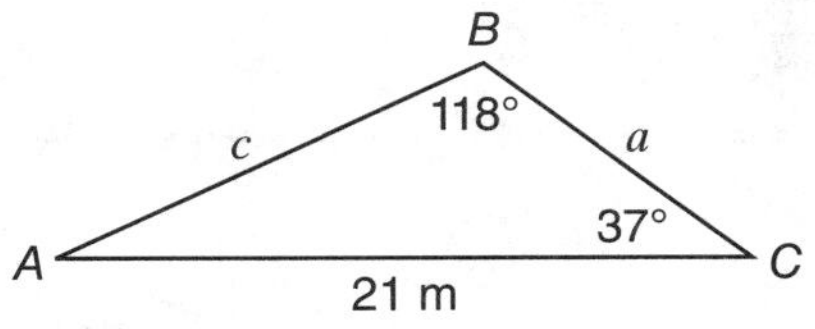

____

5.

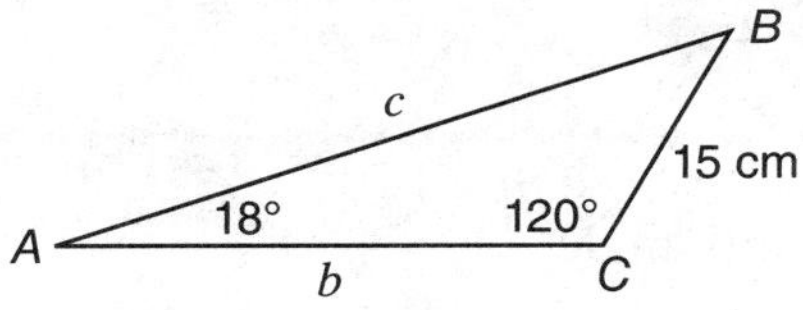

____

6.

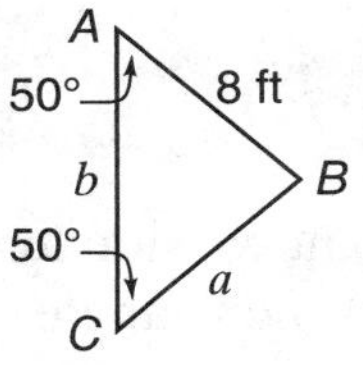

____

Find all the unknown side lengths and angle measures. Round answers to the nearest tenth.

7.

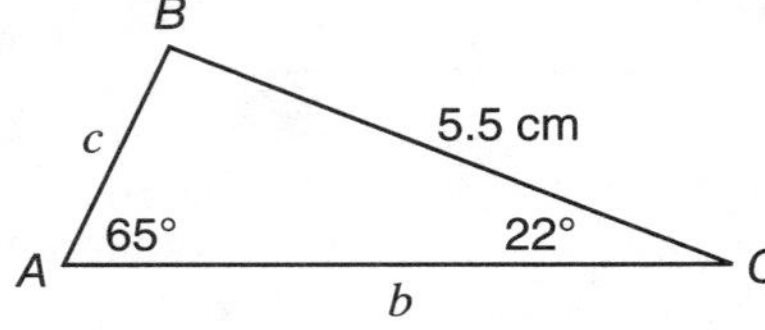

8.

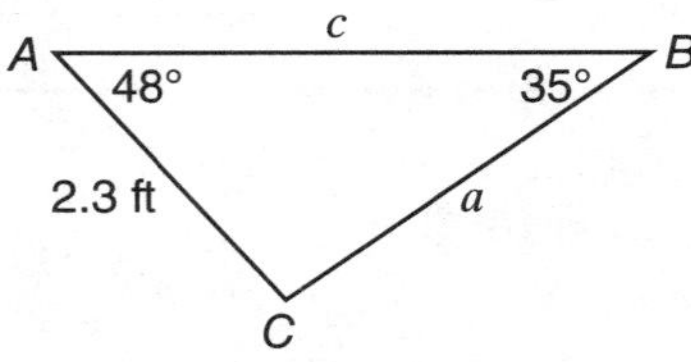

9.

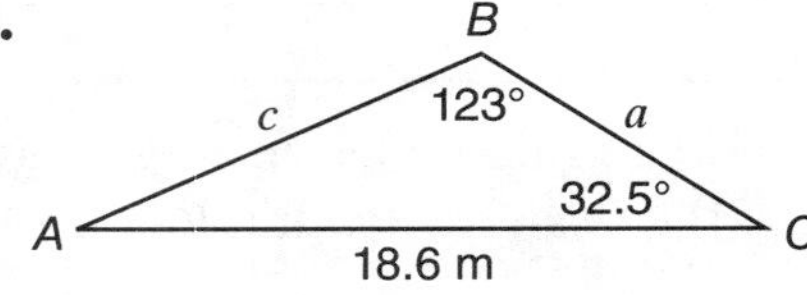

10.

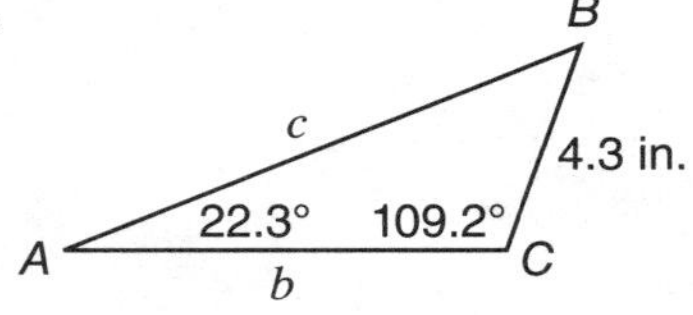

11.

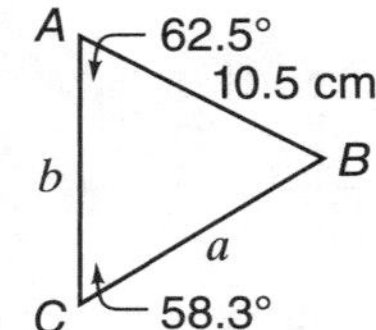

12.

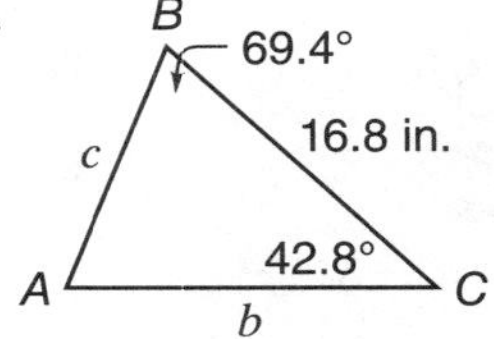

Problem Solving

13. At a distance of 120 ft from a tree, the angle of elevation to the tree top is about 40° and the angle of elevation to a nest in the tree is 21°. How far is the nest from the tree top?

14. An Aspen tree is growing on a mountain. A park ranger measures the angle between the trunk and the face of the mountain as 63°. He then hikes 50 ft up the mountain and measures the angle of elevation to the tree top as 54°. What is the approximate height of the tree?

CHALLENGE

15. Find all unknown side lengths and angle measures of the triangle.

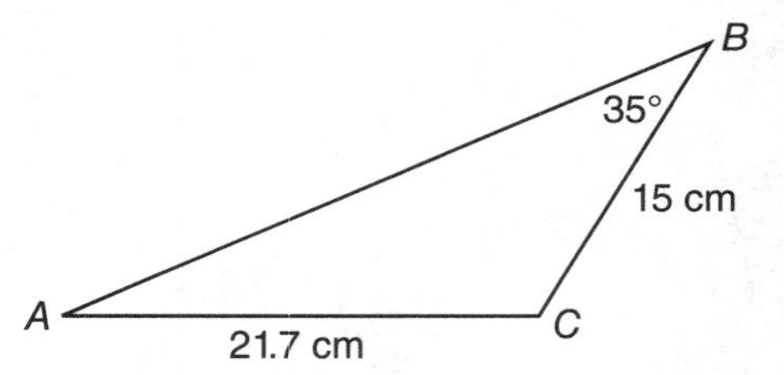

Test Prep: Short-Answer Questions

Strategy: Organize Information

Name ______________________________ Date ____________

When a short-answer question involves objects or figures, **sketch a diagram** to help visualize the problem and organize the information given.

To solve the problem, try using these strategies:

- Reread the test item.
- Use the Test-Prep strategy.
- Apply appropriate rules, definitions, properties, or strategies.
- Analyze your answers.

Solve. Show all your work. *TIP: Use another solution method to check your answers.*

1. Two sailboats leave from the same spot. One travels 8 mi west then 4 mi north to its destination. The other travels 3 mi west then 8 mi south. How far apart are the boats?

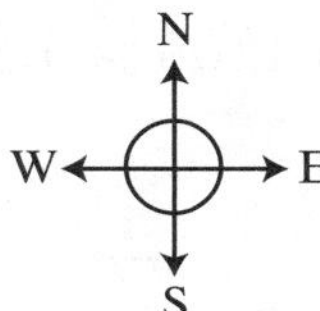

Answer: ______________________

2. The legs of a right triangle measure $x + 3$ cm and $x - 1$ cm. The hypotenuse measures $2\sqrt{10}$ cm. Find the lengths of the legs.

Answer: ______________________

3. A target consists of 4 concentric circles. The radius of each circle is 0.5 ft less than twice the radius of the one directly inside of it. The radius of the center circle is 0.75 ft. What is the circumference of the target? Use 3.14 for π.

Answer: ______________________

4. A surveying instrument is 5 ft off the ground, 22 ft from the base of a building. The angle of elevation from the top of the instrument is 60°. How tall is the building? Round to the nearest tenth.

Answer: ______________________

Use with SOURCEBOOK Test Prep Lesson, page 304.

Vocabulary Development

Name ______________________ Date __________

Chapter 11 Vocabulary

constant of proportionality	proportion	scale model
conversion factors	rate	sine
cosine	ratio	tangent
percent	relative error	trigonometric ratios
percent of change	scale	unit rate
percent of error	scale drawing	

From the vocabulary list above, choose the term(s) that best complete each sentence. Write the term(s) in the space(s) provided.

1. The ratio of the distances on a map to the actual distances is a ______________.

2. A ______________ is an equation that states that two ratios are equal.

3. A rate that has a denominator of 1 is a ______________.

4. A ______________ is a comparison of two numbers a and b by division.

5. A ratio that compares a number to 100 is a ______________.

6. The ratios of the lengths of two sides of a right triangle are called ______________.

7. A ______________ uses a scale to represent an enlarged or reduced model that is similar to the actual object.

8. Three examples of trigonometric ratios are ______________.

9. When there is a relation between two variables, x and y, such that $y = ax$ and $a \neq 0$, a is called the ______________.

Choose three terms from the list that you did not use in Questions 1–9. For each term, write a definition in your own words and give an example.

10. ____

____

____

____

Use after SOURCEBOOK Lessons 11-1–11-7, pages 280–297.

Practice Chapter 11 Test

Name ______________________________ Date ____________

A class has 22 boys and 8 girls.
Write each ratio as a fraction in simplest form.

1. boys to girls

2. girls to boys

3. boys to the entire class

4. girls to the entire class

Write each situation as a unit rate.

5. 1260 miles in 25 hours

6. $1.88 for 23.5 ounces

Convert the units of measure as indicated.

7. 11 ft/s to mi/h

8. 45 cups per minute to gallons per day

A map of California has a scale of 2 inches : 75 miles.

9. Temecula is shown as 11 in. from San Francisco. What is the actual distance between the cities?

10. San Diego is about 210 mi from Bakersfield. About how far apart are they on the map?

Find the percent of error and the relative error of the areas.

11. measured dimensions: 3 cm by 8 cm
actual dimensions: 3.1 cm by 7.9 cm

12. measured dimensions: 2.8 m by 4.1 m
actual dimensions: 2.9 m by 4 m

Solve.

13. Find the sale price of a $64.15 car battery that is discounted 20%.

14. Find the total cost of a $19.95 shovel after a 7.5% sales tax is added.

15. Tom bought a used car for $7500. One year later it was worth $7200. What was the percent of decrease in value of the car?

16. Hideko's starting wage was $23 per hour. Now she earns $26.45 per hour. What is the percent of increase in her hourly wage?

Find the sine, cosine, and tangent of the indicated angle to the nearest ten-thousandth.

17. $\angle X$

18. $\angle Y$

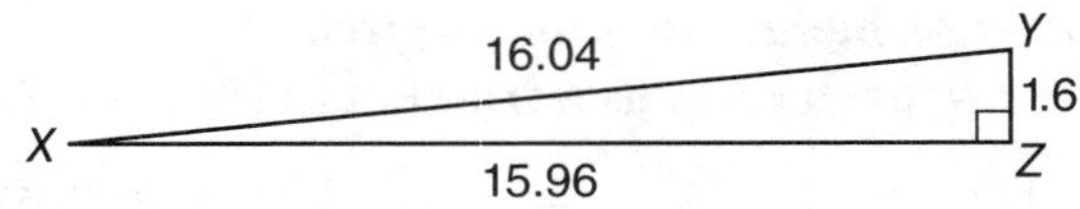

You may use a handheld to find the sine, cosine, and tangent of the given angle to the nearest ten-thousandth.

19. 48.3°

20. 2.5°

21. 77.6°

Solve each right triangle. Round the lengths of the sides to the nearest tenth and angle measures to the nearest degree.

22.

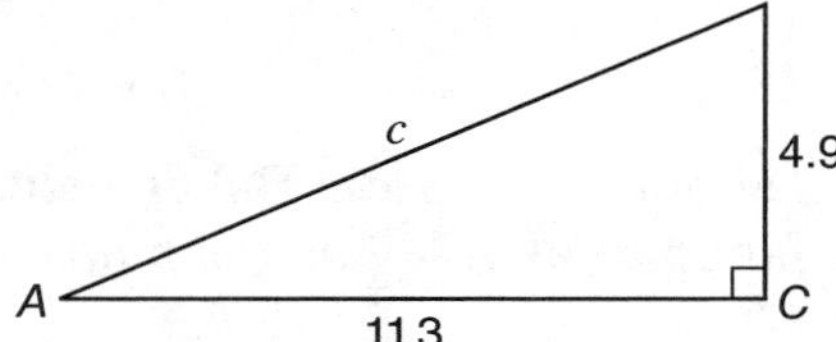

23.

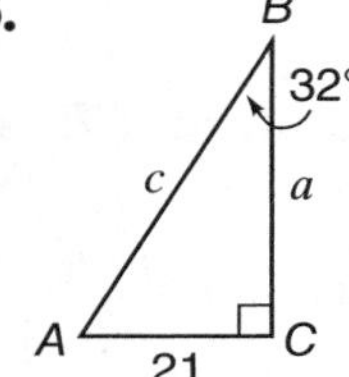

Solve.

24. The base of a 32-ft ladder makes a 65° angle with the ground. How far up the wall does the ladder reach?

25. A man lying on at the top of a 200-ft cliff spots a boat on the water below. The angle of depression is 32°. How far is the man from the boat?

Tell About It

Explain how you solve the problem. Show all your work.

26. Solve the equation $6[\sin(2x)] = 3$.

Cumulative Review: Chapters 1–11

Name ______________________________ Date ______________

Circle the best answer.

1. Which number is irrational?

A. $\sqrt{5}$ **B.** $2.\overline{3}$
C. $\sqrt{121}$ **D.** -2.35

2. Which is equivalent to this expression?
$(3.6 \times 10^{12}) \div (1.2 \times 10^{9})$

F. 2.4×10^{108} **G.** 3.0×10^{21}
H. 3.0×10^{3} **J.** 2.4×10^{3}

3. Solve for d: $7d + 11b = 15b$

A. $d = -3b$ **B.** $d = \frac{4}{7}b$
C. $d = \frac{7}{4}b$ **D.** $d = \frac{26}{7}b$

4. Solve: $|d - 5| = 11$

F. $d = -16$ or $d = 16$
G. $d = -16$ or $d = 55$
H. $d = -6$ or $d = 6$
J. $d = -6$ or $d = 16$

5. Which inequality best matches this sentence? "The number of pencils in the pencil box is at most 51."

A. $p > 51$ **B.** $p < 51$
C. $p \leq 51$ **D.** $p \geq 51$

6. Solve: $-3|2f - 1| \geq -21$

F. $-3 \leq f \leq 4$
G. $-3 \geq f \geq 4$
H. $f \leq -3$ or $f \geq 4$
J. $f \geq -3$ or $f \leq 4$

7. Which is a function rule for the sequence?
$-2, 1, 4, 7, 10, \ldots$

A. $a_n = -3n - 5$ **B.** $a_n = 3n - 5$
C. $a_n = 3n + 5$ **D.** $a_n = -3n + 5$

8. What is a_{10} in the sequence?
0.0095, 0.095, 0.95, 9.5, …

F. 95,000 **G.** 950,000
H. 9,500,000 **J.** 95,000,000

9. Which relation is a linear function?

A. $y = -\frac{5}{x}$

B. $y = -11x - 7.9$

C. $y = x^8$

D. $y = 2x + 7x^2$

10. Which equation contains points $(2, -8)$ and $(5, 7)$?

F. $5x - 5y = -18$ **G.** $x + 5y = 18$
H. $5x + y = 18$ **J.** $5x - y = 18$

11. Solve: $\begin{cases} y = x + 5 \\ 4x + 3y = 1 \end{cases}$

A. $(-2, -3)$ **B.** $(3, -2)$
C. $(-2, 3)$ **D.** $(2, 3)$

12. Which is a solution of this system? $\begin{cases} x - 2y > 7 \\ 5x - y < 12 \end{cases}$

F. $(4, 12)$ **G.** $(-1, 5)$
H. $(-1, -5)$ **J.** $(8, -2)$

13. Which polynomial is in standard form?

A. $24 + 11y^2 - 9y^3 - 13y$
B. $11y^2 + 24 - 9y^3 - 13y$
C. $11y^2 - 9y^3 - 13y + 24$
D. $-9y^3 + 11y^2 - 13y + 24$

14. Multiply: $(5b - 2)^2$

F. $25b^2 - 10b + 4$
G. $25b^2 - 20b + 4$
H. $25b^2 - 20b - 4$
J. $25b^2 + 4$

15. Which is a factor of $16x^2 - 25$?

A. $(8x - 5)$
B. $(8x + 5)$
C. $(4x + 5)$
D. $16x^2 - 25$ is prime.

16. Factor completely: $16h^3 - 48h^2 + 36h$

F. $4h(4h^2 - 12h + 9)$
G. $2h(2h - 3)^2$
H. $h(4h - 6)^2$
J. $4h(2h - 3)^2$

17. Simplify: $6b^3\sqrt{16a^9b^{16}}$

A. $24a^4b^{11}\sqrt{a}$ **B.** $48a^4b^{11}\sqrt{a}$
C. $48a^4b^7\sqrt{a}$ **D.** $24a^4b^7\sqrt{a}$

18. Multiply: $(-5\sqrt{2} + 6)^2$

F. 2
G. 86
H. $186 - 30\sqrt{2}$
J. $86 - 60\sqrt{2}$

19. To complete the square in the equation $x^2 - 8x = 2$, add what value to both sides of the equation?

A. 8 **B.** 16
C. 32 **D.** 64

20. Solve: $36x^2 - 1 = 0$

F. $-6, 6$ **G.** 6
H. $-\frac{1}{6}, \frac{1}{6}$ **J.** $-1, 1$

21. If $\sin A = 0.3854$, what is the measure of angle A, rounded to the nearest degree?

A. 67° **B.** 66°
C. 23° **D.** 22°

22. What is cos 59° to the nearest ten-thousandth?

F. 1.6643 **G.** 0.8572
H. 0.5150 **J.** −0.7711

Tell About It

Explain how you solve the problem. Show all your work.

23. The length of a leg of a right triangle is 3.8 cm and the hypotenuse is 7.2 cm. What is the measure of the angle opposite the 3.8-cm leg?

24. A building casts a 45-ft shadow when the sun's rays make a 72° angle with the ground. How tall is the building?

12-1 Introduction to Rational Expressions

Name ______________________________ Date ______________

Simplify the rational expression. Identify any excluded values.

$\frac{2x + 8}{2x + 4}$ ← Rational expression

$\frac{2(x + 4)}{2(x + 2)}$ ← Factor the numerator and denominator.

$\frac{\overset{1}{\cancel{2}}(x + 4)}{\underset{1}{\cancel{2}}(x + 2)}$ ← Divide out a common factor.

$\frac{x + 4}{x + 2}$ ← Simplify.

The simplest form of $\frac{2x + 8}{2x + 4}$ is $\frac{x + 4}{x + 2}$.

To find the excluded values:

$2x + 4 = 0$ ← Set the denominator of the *original rational expression* equal to 0.

$2(x + 2) = 0$ ← Factor the denominator.

$2 = 0$ or $x + 2 = 0$ ← Use the Zero Product Property.

$x + 2 - 2 = 0 - 2$ ← Solve for x, using the Subtraction Property of Equality.

$x = -2$

So the excluded value is -2 (or $x \neq -2$).

Simplify each rational expression. Identify any excluded values.

1. $\frac{a + 4}{a - 4}$

$\frac{a + 4}{a - 4}$; $a - 4 = 0$

$a = 4$

$\frac{a + 4}{a - 4}$; $a \neq 4$

2. $\frac{b + 6}{b - 3}$ ________

3. $\frac{5c}{5c - 10}$ ________

4. $\frac{8n}{8n + 32}$ ________

5. $\frac{2x + 9}{5x}$ ________

6. $\frac{7y + 11}{11y}$ ________

7. $\frac{12v + 24}{6v}$ ________

8. $\frac{15u + 45}{3u}$ ________

9. $\frac{8x^2}{4x^3 + 2x^2}$ ________

10. $\frac{6b^2}{6b^3 + 2b^2}$ ________

11. $\frac{10d^2 - 4d}{5d - 2}$ ________

12. $\frac{9h^2 - 15h}{3h - 5}$ ________

Simplify. State the excluded value(s) of the variable(s).

13. $\frac{x^2 - x}{x^3 - 7x^2 + 6x}$

$\frac{x(x - 1)}{x(x^2 - 7x + 6)}$

$\frac{\cancel{x}^{1}\cancel{(x-1)}^{1}}{\cancel{x}_{1}\cancel{(x-1)}_{1}(x - 6)}; \frac{1}{x - 6}$

$x = 0$ or $x - 1 = 0$ or $x - 6 = 0$

undefined for $x = 0, 1, 6$

$\frac{1}{x - 6}; x \neq 0, x \neq 1, x \neq 6$

14. $\frac{y^2 - y}{y^3 + 3y^2 - 4y}$

15. $\frac{z^4 + z^3}{z^6 - z^5}$

16. $\frac{p^5 - p^4}{p^8 + p^7}$

17. $\frac{ac + 11ac^2}{abc + 9abc^2}$

18. $\frac{vw - 8vw^2}{uvw - 5uvw^2}$

Problem Solving

19. If both the length and width of a rectangle are tripled, what is the ratio of the area of the original rectangle to the area of the new rectangle?

20. A store sells balloons for advertising. Which has a greater ratio of surface area to volume, balloons with a 10-in. radius or a 12-in. radius? (*Hint: SA* $= 4\pi r^2$ and $V = \frac{4}{3}\pi r^3$)

WRITE ABOUT IT

21. Explain how to find the values where the expression $\frac{1}{x^3 + 3x^2 - x - 3}$ is undefined.

12-2 Simplify Rational Expressions

Name ______________________ Date __________

Simplify $\frac{x^2 + 8x + 12}{x^2 + 4x + 4}$. Identify the excluded values.

$\frac{(x + 6)(x + 2)}{(x + 2)(x + 2)}$ ← Factor the numerator and denominator.

$\frac{(x + 6)\cancel{(x + 2)}^{1}}{(x + 2)\cancel{(x + 2)}_{1}} = \frac{x + 6}{x + 2}$ ← Divide out common factors.

So in simplest form, $\frac{x^2 + 8x + 12}{x^2 + 4x + 4}$ is $\frac{x + 6}{x + 2}$.

Excluded values:

$(x + 2)(x + 2)$ ← Factor the denominator.

$x + 2 = 0$ ← Apply the Zero-Product Property.

$x = -2$ ← Simplify.

The excluded value is -2.

Simplify. Identify excluded values.

1. $\frac{x^2 - 1}{x^2 + 4x + 3}$

   $\frac{(x - 1)(x + 1)}{(x + 1)(x + 3)} = \frac{(x - 1)\cancel{(x + 1)}^{1}}{\cancel{(x + 1)}_{1}(x + 3)}$

   $\frac{x - 1}{x + 3}$; $x + 1 = 0$, $x + 3 = 0$

   $\frac{x - 1}{x + 3}$; $x \neq -3$, $x \neq -1$

2. $\frac{y^2 - 4}{y^2 + 6y + 8}$ ______

3. $\frac{5b + 10b^2}{6b^2 + 7b + 2}$ ______

4. $\frac{8c + 24c^2}{9c^2 + 15c + 4}$ ______

5. $\frac{x^2 - 16}{x^2 - 10x + 24}$ ______

6. $\frac{x^2 - 9}{x^2 - 9x + 18}$ ______

7. $\frac{4x^2 + 4x - 3}{4x^2 + 8x - 5}$ ______

8. $\frac{18m^2 + 60m + 18}{9m^2 + 21m + 6}$ ______

9. $\frac{w^4 - w^3}{w^8 - w^6}$ ______

10. $\frac{q^7 + q^6}{q^9 - q^7}$ ______

11. $\frac{9y^2 - 9y - 10}{9y^2 - 12y - 5}$ ______

12. $\frac{8a^2 - 4a - 24}{16a^2 + 8a - 24}$ ______

Use with SOURCEBOOK Lesson 12-2, pages 308–309.

Simplify each expression. Identify excluded values.

13. $\frac{-m-1}{m^2-1}$

$\frac{-(m+1)}{(m-1)(m+1)}$

$\frac{-1}{m-1}$; $m+1=0$; $m-1=0$

$\frac{-1}{m-1}$; $m \neq -1$, $m \neq 1$

14. $\frac{-y+4}{y^2-16}$

15. $\frac{r^2-r+5}{r^2-3r-4}$

16. $\frac{b^2-3b+1}{b^2-7b-8}$

17. $\frac{3n^3+14n^2-5n}{2n^3+11n^2+5n}$

18. $\frac{4m^3-7m^2-2m}{3m^3-4m^2-4m}$

19. $\frac{3z^2-7z-6}{3z^2-z-2}$

20. $\frac{c^2-c-2}{c^2+3c+2}$

21. $\frac{2d^2-5d-3}{4d^2+12d+5}$

Problem Solving

22. The length of Tom's business card is 2 cm more than the width. Anne's business card is 2 cm wider and 4 cm longer than Tom's business card. What is the ratio of the area of Tom's business card to Anne's business card?

23. Let s represent the length of an edge of a cube. If the lengths of the edges are all increased by 3, what will the ratio of surface area to volume of the new cube be? If the original length was 10 cm, what will the ratio of surface area to volume be? (*Hint:* $SA = 6s^2$)

CHALLENGE

24. The ratio of the area of a square to the area of a right triangle is 1. The height of the right triangle is 3 times the length of the side of the square. What is the ratio of the length of the side of the square to the base of the triangle?

12-3 Multiply Rational Expressions

Name ______________________ Date __________

Multiply. Write the product in simplest form.

$$\frac{x^2 + 7x + 10}{3x^3 + 15x^2 + 18x} \bullet \frac{6x^3 + 42x^2 + 72x}{x^2 + 9x + 20}$$

$$\frac{(x + 2)(x + 5)}{3x(x + 3)(x + 2)} \bullet \frac{6x(x + 3)(x + 4)}{(x + 5)(x + 4)}$$ ← Factor the numerators and denominators.

$$\frac{\overset{1}{\cancel{(x+2)}}\overset{1}{\cancel{(x+5)}}}{\underset{1}{\cancel{3}}\underset{1}{\cancel{x}}\underset{1}{\cancel{(x+3)}}\underset{1}{\cancel{(x+2)}}} \bullet \frac{\overset{2}{\cancel{6}}\overset{1}{\cancel{x}}\overset{1}{\cancel{(x+3)}}\overset{1}{\cancel{(x+4)}}}{\underset{1}{\cancel{(x+5)}}\underset{1}{\cancel{(x+4)}}}$$ ← Divide out the common factors; then simplify.

$\frac{2}{1} = 2$ ← simplest form

Multiply. Write the product in simplest form.

1. $\frac{12a^2}{3a - 15} \bullet (-8a + 40)$

$$\frac{12a^2}{3a - 15} \bullet \frac{-8a + 40}{1}$$

$$\frac{12a^2}{3(a - 5)} \bullet \frac{-8(a - 5)}{1}$$

$$\frac{\overset{4}{\cancel{12}}a^2}{\underset{1}{\cancel{3}}\underset{1}{\cancel{(a-5)}}} \bullet \frac{-8\overset{1}{\cancel{(a-5)}}}{1}$$

$-32a^2$

2. $\frac{20n^2}{4n + 8} \bullet (-6n - 12)$

____

3. $\frac{x^3 - x^2 - 56x}{11x^2} \bullet \frac{22x^3}{x^2 - 2x - 63}$

____

4. $\frac{2n^3 + 4n^2 - 96n}{5n^4} \bullet \frac{15n^3}{n^2 + 13n + 40}$

____

5. $\frac{10t^4 + 9t^3 - 9t^2}{4t^2 + 12t + 9} \bullet \frac{28t^6 + 26t^5 - 24t^4}{20t^5 - 17t^4 + 3t^3}$

____

6. $\frac{9p^3 - 6p^2}{9p^2 - 12p + 4} \bullet \frac{12p^4 + 64p^3 - 48p^2}{2p^2 + 14p}$

____

Multiply. Write the product in simplest form.

7. $\frac{x^2 - y^2}{x^2 - 2xy + y^2} \bullet \frac{-x + y}{-2x - 2y}$

$\frac{(x + y)(x - y)}{(x - y)(x - y)} \bullet \frac{-(x - y)}{-2(x + y)}$

$\frac{\overset{1}{\cancel{(x + y)}}\overset{1}{\cancel{(x - y)}}}{\underset{1}{\cancel{(x - y)}}\underset{1}{\cancel{(x - y)}}} \bullet \frac{-\overset{1}{\cancel{(x - y)}}}{-2\underset{1}{\cancel{(x + y)}}}$

$\frac{-1}{-2} = \frac{1}{2}$

8. $\frac{3m + 3n}{-m - n} \bullet \frac{m^2 + 2mn + n^2}{m^2 - n^2}$

9. $\frac{-21ab}{7a^3b^2} \bullet 14a^4bc^3 \bullet \frac{-3a^2c}{6b^7c^2}$

10. $\frac{15xy^2}{-4xz^3} \bullet 6x^2yz^2 \bullet \frac{2x^3y}{-5x^4y^3}$

Problem Solving

11. The nth term of sequence A can be represented by the expression $\frac{1}{n^2 + 2n + 1}$. The nth term of sequence B is the product of the nth term of sequence A and $\frac{n + 1}{n^2}$. What is the simplest form of the nth term of sequence B? Write the first four terms of both sequences.

12. When the length of an edge of a cube is increased by 8, the ratio of the volumes of the original to the new cube is a factor of $x + 8$. What is the other factor? If $x = 12$ cm, what is the volume of each cube?

TEST PREPARATION

13. Multiply $\frac{5x + 10y}{-4x + 2y} \bullet \frac{16x^2 - 16xy + 4y^2}{5x^2 + 20xy + 20y^2}$.

A. $-\frac{2(x + 2y)}{2x - y}$

B. $-\frac{2(2x - y)}{x + 2y}$

C. $-\frac{(5x + 10y)(2x - y)}{2(x + 2y)(x + 2y)}$

D. $-\frac{(x + 5y)(2x - y)}{2(x + 2y)(x + 2y)}$

12-4 Divide Rational Expressions

Name ______________________ Date ____________

Divide. Write the quotient in simplest form.

$$\frac{x^2 + 9x + 8}{32x^4} \div \frac{x^2 + 2x + 1}{24x^3}$$

$$\frac{x^2 + 9x + 8}{32x^4} \bullet \frac{24x^3}{x^2 + 2x + 1}$$ ⟵ Multiply by the reciprocal of the divisor.

$$\frac{(x + 8)(x + 1)}{32x^4} \bullet \frac{24x^3}{(x + 1)(x + 1)}$$ ⟵ Factor.

$$\frac{(x + 8)\overset{1}{\cancel{(x + 1)}}}{\underset{4}{\cancel{32}}\,\underset{x}{\cancel{x^4}}} \bullet \frac{\overset{3}{\cancel{24}}\,\overset{1}{\cancel{x^3}}}{\underset{1}{\cancel{(x + 1)}}(x + 1)}$$ ⟵ Divide out common factors; then simplify.

$$\frac{3(x + 8)}{4x(x + 1)}$$ ⟵ simplest form

Divide. Write the quotient in simplest form.

1. $\frac{11b - 22}{b^2 - 4} \div (33b + 66)$

   $\frac{11b - 22}{b^2 - 4} \bullet \frac{1}{33b + 66}$

   $\frac{11(b - 2)}{(b - 2)(b + 2)} \bullet \frac{1}{33(b + 2)}$

   $\frac{\overset{1}{\cancel{11}}\overset{1}{\cancel{(b - 2)}}}{\underset{1}{\cancel{(b - 2)}}(b + 2)} \bullet \frac{1}{\underset{3}{\cancel{33}}(b + 2)}$

   $\frac{1}{3(b + 2)(b + 2)}$

2. $\frac{30x^2y^4}{26xz} \div \frac{12xyz}{13x^4y^2}$ ____________

3. $\frac{7c + 21}{c^2 - 9} \div (14c - 42)$ ____________

4. $\frac{16a^3c^2}{15b^4c} \div \frac{24b^2c^3}{20a^5b}$ ____________

5. $\frac{5}{x^2 - 4x - 21} \div \frac{15}{x + 3}$ ____________

6. $\frac{12}{x^2 - 6x - 16} \div \frac{6}{x^2 - 4x - 32}$ ____________

7. $\frac{ab^2 + cb^2}{b^4} \div \frac{a^2 - c^2}{b^8}$ ____________

8. $\frac{x^6}{x^2 - y^2} \div \frac{x^7}{x^2y - xy^2}$ ____________

9. $\frac{p^3qr^2}{p^5 - p^3r^2} \div \frac{p^2q^3r}{2p - 2r}$ ____________

Use with SOURCEBOOK Lesson 12-4, pages 312–313.

Divide. Write the quotient in simplest form.

10. $\frac{k^2 + \ell^2}{7k^2 - 7\ell^2} \div \frac{14k^2 + 14\ell^2}{9k - 9\ell}$

$\frac{k^2 + \ell^2}{7k^2 - 7\ell^2} \cdot \frac{9k - 9\ell}{14k^2 + 14\ell^2}$

$\frac{k^2 + \ell^2}{7(k - \ell)(k + \ell)} \cdot \frac{9(k - \ell)}{14(k^2 + \ell^2)}$

$\frac{\overset{1}{\cancel{(k^2 + \ell^2)}}}{7\underset{1}{\cancel{(k - \ell)}}(k + \ell)} \cdot \frac{9\overset{1}{\cancel{(k - \ell)}}}{14\underset{1}{\cancel{(k^2 + \ell^2)}}}$

$\frac{9}{98(k + \ell)}$

11. $\frac{6m^2 - 6n^2}{12m^2 + 4n^2} \div \frac{m - n}{3m^2 + n^2}$

12. $\frac{6x^2 + 11x - 10}{2x^2 - x - 15} \div \frac{6x^2 + 23x - 18}{x^2 + 5x - 24}$

13. $\frac{4x^2 + 11x - 3}{9x^2 + 9x + 2} \div \frac{4x^2 - 21x + 5}{3x^2 - 13x - 10}$

Problem Solving

14. May says that the graphs of the equations $y = \left(\frac{p^2 - 49}{3p^2 + 19p - 14}\right)x - 3$ and $y = \left(\frac{2 - 3p}{p - 7}\right)x + 8$ are parallel lines. Carlos says they are perpendicular lines. Who is correct? (*Hint*: The slope-intercept form of a linear equation is $y = mx + b$.)

15. Joanne says that the base of a triangle with height $3x + 7$ and area $6x^2 + 29x + 35$ is $2x + 5$. Is she correct? If not, explain her error.

MENTAL MATH

Multiply or divide.

16. $\frac{5}{12} \div \frac{1}{24}$

17. $\frac{2}{3} \div \frac{11}{7} \cdot \frac{3}{4}$

18. $28 \cdot 32$

19. $54 \cdot 46$

12-5 Combine Rational Expressions with Like Denominators

Name ____________________ Date __________

Add: $\frac{5x + 3}{10x^2 + 35x} + \frac{4 - 3x}{10x^2 + 35x}$

Remember: $\frac{a}{c} + \frac{b}{c} = \frac{a + b}{c}$ and $\frac{a}{c} - \frac{b}{c} = \frac{a - b}{c}$, $c \neq 0$.
Write the sum in simplest form and identify any excluded values.

$\frac{5x + 3 + (4 - 3x)}{10x^2 + 35x}$ ← Add the numerators.

$\frac{2x + 7}{10x^2 + 35x}$ ← Combine like terms.

$\frac{\overset{1}{\cancel{(2x + 7)}}}{5x\underset{1}{\cancel{(2x + 7)}}}$ ← Factor the denominator and divide out common factors.

$\frac{1}{5x}$ ← simplest form

$5x = 0 \longrightarrow x = 0$

$2x + 7 = 0 \longrightarrow x = -\frac{7}{2}$

Remember: Set the common denominator equal to zero to find excluded values.

So the excluded values are 0 and $-\frac{7}{2}$ $\left(\text{or } x \neq 0, -\frac{7}{2}\right)$.

Add or subtract. Write the result in simplest form and identify any excluded values.

1. $\frac{3b + 1}{7b + 28} - \frac{2b - 3}{7b + 28}$

$\frac{3b + 1 - (2b - 3)}{7b + 28}$

$\frac{3b + 1 - 2b + 3}{7b + 28}$

$\frac{b + 4}{7b + 28}$

$\frac{\overset{1}{\cancel{(b + 4)}}}{7\underset{1}{\cancel{(b + 4)}}}$

$\frac{1}{7}$; $b \neq -4$

2. $\frac{15}{11d} + \frac{3a}{11d}$

3. $\frac{4m + 7}{5m + 15} - \frac{3m + 4}{5m + 15}$

4. $\frac{9}{f^2 - f} + \frac{8k}{f^2 - f}$

5. $\frac{27}{9x^2 + 12x} - \frac{30}{9x^2 + 12x}$

6. $\frac{11}{6x^2 - 24} - \frac{23}{6x^2 - 24}$

Add or subtract. Write the result in simplest form and identify any excluded values.

7. $\frac{3y+1}{27y+36} + \frac{3}{27y+36}$

$\frac{3y+1+3}{27y+36}$

$\frac{3y+4}{27y+36}; \frac{3y+4}{9(3y+4)}$

$\frac{\overset{1}{\cancel{(3y+4)}}}{9\underset{1}{\cancel{(3y+4)}}}$

$\frac{1}{9}; y \neq -\frac{4}{3}$

8. $\frac{2k+1}{10k+45} + \frac{8}{10k+45}$

______

9. $\frac{16}{3t+15} - \frac{4}{3t+15}$

______

10. $\frac{23}{4r+32} - \frac{3}{4r+32}$

______

11. $\frac{d^2-2d-8}{2d-6} - \frac{21-6d-8}{2d-6}$

______

12. $\frac{m^2-5m+3}{3m-12} - \frac{28-8m+3}{3m-12}$

______

Problem Solving

13. Will subtracted $\frac{3x-1}{x+2} - \frac{2x-5}{x+2}$ and got $\frac{x-6}{x+2}$. Is Will correct? If not, what is his error?

______

14. Troy drove y miles at $x + 10$ miles per hour. Then he drove 10 miles less than twice his previous mileage at two times his previous rate. Write an expression for his total driving time. (*Hint:* $d = rt$)

______

CRITICAL THINKING

15. Explain the error. Give a numerical example to show why it does not work.

$$\frac{3}{x+3} + \frac{6}{x+3} = \frac{\overset{1}{\cancel{3}}}{x+\underset{1}{\cancel{3}}} + \frac{\overset{2}{\cancel{6}}}{x+\underset{1}{\cancel{3}}} = \frac{3}{x+1}$$

______

12-6 Combine Rational Expressions with Unlike Denominators

Name ______________________ Date ________

Add: $\frac{3}{5b + 10} + \frac{4}{b^2 + 2b}$

Write the sum in simplest form and identify any excluded values.

$\frac{3}{5(b + 2)} + \frac{4}{b(b + 2)}$ ← Factor the denominators to identify the LCD.

Think
LCD: $5 \cdot b \cdot (b + 2)$

$\frac{3}{5(b + 2)}\left(\frac{b}{b}\right) + \frac{4}{b(b + 2)}\left(\frac{5}{5}\right)$ ← Multiply by a form of 1.

$\frac{3b}{5b(b + 2)} + \frac{20}{5b(b + 2)}$ ← Write over the LCD.

$\frac{3b + 20}{5b(b + 2)}$ ← Add the numerators; combine like terms.

$5b(b + 2) = 0 \rightarrow b = 0$ or $b = -2$

So in simplest form, $\frac{3}{5b + 10} + \frac{4}{b^2 + 2b} = \frac{3b + 20}{5b(b + 2)}$

and the excluded values are 0 and −2 (or $b \neq 0, -2$).

Find the least common multiple (LCM) of the expressions.

1. $3x^2y$ and $15xy^2$

$3x^2y = 3 \cdot x \cdot x \cdot y$
$15xy^2 = 3 \cdot 5 \cdot x \cdot y \cdot y$
$\text{LCM} = 3 \cdot 5 \cdot x \cdot x \cdot y \cdot y$
$15x^2y^2$

2. $6ab^3$ and $2a^3b$

____

3. $5d^2$ and $15d^2 + 20d$

____

4. $7g^2$ and $42g^2 + 35g$

____

5. $r^2 + 7r$ and $r^2 - 49$

____

6. $h^2 + 11h$ and $h^2 - 121$

____

Find the sum or difference. Write the result in simplest form and identify any excluded values.

7. $\frac{11}{45y^3} + \frac{11}{30y^4}$

$\text{LCD} = 2 \cdot 3^2 \cdot 5 \cdot y^4 = 90y^4$

$\frac{11}{45y^3}\left(\frac{2y}{2y}\right) + \frac{11}{30y^4}\left(\frac{3}{3}\right)$

$\frac{22y}{90y^4} + \frac{33}{90y^4}$

$\frac{22y + 33}{90y^4}$; $90y^4 = 0$; $y = 0$

$\frac{22y + 33}{90y^4}$; $y \neq 0$

8. $\frac{9}{16x^2} + \frac{7x}{12x^3}$

____

9. $\frac{7}{f + 4} - \frac{2}{f - 3}$

____

Find the sum or difference. Write the result in simplest form and identify any excluded values.

10. $\frac{x}{x-2} - \frac{12}{x^2+2x-8}$

$\frac{x}{x-2} - \frac{12}{(x-2)(x+4)}$

LCD = $(x-2)(x+4)$

$\frac{x}{x-2}\left(\frac{x+4}{x+4}\right) - \frac{12}{(x-2)(x+4)}\left(\frac{1}{1}\right)$

$\frac{x^2+4x}{(x-2)(x+4)} - \frac{12}{(x-2)(x+4)}$

$\frac{x^2+4x-12}{(x-2)(x+4)} = \frac{(x+6)\overset{1}{\cancel{(x-2)}}}{\underset{1}{\cancel{(x-2)}}(x+4)}$

$\frac{(x+6)}{(x+4)}$; $x \neq -4, 2$

11. $\frac{x}{x+5} - \frac{10}{x^2+8x+15}$

12. $\frac{2}{(4c-16)} - \frac{2}{(c^2-4c)}$

13. $\frac{1}{k-5} + \frac{2k-19}{k^2-k-20}$

Problem Solving

14. Tyler can build a fence in 12 hours. Toby can build the same fence in 18 hours. Write an expression for how much fence they can build together in x hours.

15. Kiesha rowed downstream for 5 miles and back upstream for 3 miles. She rowed an average of 3 times the rate of the current. Write an expression for her total time. (*Hint:* distance = rate • time)

SPIRAL REVIEW

16. Find the sale price of a $59.62 jacket that is discounted 20%.

17. Solve $2\sqrt{b} - 4 = 8$.

12-7 Mixed Expressions and Complex Fractions

Name ______________________ Date ____________

Simplify: $\dfrac{a + \dfrac{4a}{a-4}}{a - \dfrac{4a}{a+4}}$

Remember: Any complex fraction $\dfrac{\frac{a}{b}}{\frac{c}{d}}$, where $b, c, d \neq 0$, can be expressed as $\dfrac{ad}{bc}$.

$$\dfrac{a + \dfrac{4a}{a-4}}{a - \dfrac{4a}{a+4}} = \dfrac{\dfrac{a(a-4)}{a-4} + \dfrac{4a}{a-4}}{\dfrac{a(a+4)}{a+4} - \dfrac{4a}{a+4}} = \dfrac{\dfrac{a^2 - 4a + 4a}{a-4}}{\dfrac{a^2 + 4a - 4a}{a+4}}$$ ← Add the numerators.

$$\dfrac{\dfrac{a^2}{a-4}}{\dfrac{a^2}{a+4}} = \dfrac{a^2}{a-4} \div \dfrac{a^2}{a+4}$$ ← Simplify. Then write as a division expression.

$$\dfrac{a^2}{a-4} \bullet \dfrac{a+4}{a^2}$$ ← Multiply by the reciprocal of the divisor.

$$\dfrac{\overset{1}{\cancel{a^2}}}{a-4} \bullet \dfrac{a+4}{\underset{1}{\cancel{a^2}}} = \dfrac{a+4}{a-4}$$ ← Divide out common factors. Then multiply.

Simplify.

1. $5 + \dfrac{3}{x-2}$

$\dfrac{5(x-2)}{x-2} + \dfrac{3}{x-2}$

$\dfrac{5x-10}{x-2} + \dfrac{3}{x-2}$

$\dfrac{5x - 10 + 3}{x-2}$

$\dfrac{5x-7}{x-2}$

____

2. $7 + \dfrac{2}{x-4}$

____

3. $a - \dfrac{8}{a+2}$

____

4. $n - \dfrac{2}{n+5}$

____

5. $r - 2 + \dfrac{3r}{r+4}$

____

6. $f - 5 + \dfrac{7f}{f+6}$

____

Simplify.

7. $\dfrac{3 + \frac{2}{g}}{4 + \frac{5}{g}}$

$\dfrac{\frac{3g}{g} + \frac{2}{g}}{\frac{4g}{g} + \frac{5}{g}} = \dfrac{\frac{3g+2}{g}}{\frac{4g+5}{g}}$

$\dfrac{3g+2}{g} \bullet \dfrac{g}{4g+5} = \dfrac{3g+2}{\not{g}_1} = \dfrac{\not{g}^1}{4g+5}$

$\dfrac{3g+2}{4g+5}$

8. $\dfrac{2 + \frac{7}{h}}{5 + \frac{2}{h}}$

9. $\dfrac{x - \frac{x-7}{x+9}}{x+7}$

10. $\dfrac{y - \frac{3y+4}{y+6}}{y+4}$

11. $\dfrac{b - 3 - \frac{40}{b-6}}{b + 2 + \frac{b+2}{b+8}}$

12. $\dfrac{x + 1 + \frac{x+1}{x+3}}{x - 2 + \frac{2x+5}{x+2}}$

Problem Solving

13. The area of a rectangular field is $x - \dfrac{9}{x}$ square yards and its length is $x - \dfrac{18}{x+3}$ yards. What is the width of the field?

TEST PREPARATION

14. Simplify: $\dfrac{8a}{16b^2 - c^2} \bullet \dfrac{16b^2 + 8bc + c^2}{24a^2} \bullet \dfrac{8b - 2c}{b + c}$

A. $\dfrac{8}{3(b+c)}$

B. $\dfrac{2(4b+c)}{3a(b+c)}$

C. $\dfrac{2(4b+c)}{3(b+c)}$

D. $\dfrac{4b+c}{3a(b+c)}$

15. Simplify: $\dfrac{2 - \frac{1}{2x}}{1 - \frac{x}{4x^2}}$

F. $\dfrac{(4x-1)^2}{8x^2}$

G. $\dfrac{1}{1-x}$

H. 2

J. $2x$

12-8 Solve Rational Equations Resulting in Linear Equations

Name ______________________________ Date ____________

Solve: $\frac{a}{3a+6} - \frac{2}{a+2} = 1$

$\frac{a}{3(a+2)} - \frac{2}{a+2} = 1$ ⟵ Factor the denominators.

Think LCD: $3(a + 2)$

$3(a+2)\left(\frac{a}{3(a+2)} - \frac{2}{a+2}\right) = 3(a+2)(1)$ ⟵ Multiply by the LCD.

$\frac{\cancel{3}\cancel{(a+2)}a}{\cancel{3}\cancel{(a+2)}} - \frac{3\cancel{(a+2)}2}{\cancel{(a+2)}} = 3(a+2)$ ⟵ Simplify.

$a - 6 = 3a + 6$ ⟵ Simplify.

$-12 = 2a$ ⟵ Use the Subtraction Property of Equality.

$-6 = a$ ⟵ Use the Division Property of Equality.

Check:

$\frac{a}{3a+6} - \frac{2}{a+2} = 1$

$\frac{-6}{3(-6)+6} - \frac{2}{-6+2} \stackrel{?}{=} 1$

$\frac{-6}{-18+6} - \frac{2}{-4} \stackrel{?}{=} 1$

$\frac{-6}{-12} - \frac{2}{-4} \stackrel{?}{=} 1$

$\frac{1}{2} + \frac{1}{2} \stackrel{?}{=} 1$

$1 = 1$ **True**

Solve. Check your solutions on a separate sheet of paper.

1. $\frac{7}{5p} = \frac{2}{p-6}$

$7(p-6) = 5p(2)$
$7p - 42 = 10p$
$-42 = 3p$
$-14 = p$

2. $\frac{9}{4t} = \frac{3}{t-2}$

3. $\frac{6}{2c} = \frac{3}{2c+3}$

4. $\frac{a+4}{2a+8} = \frac{3}{10}$

5. $\frac{c+11}{5c+55} = \frac{2}{7}$

6. $\frac{1}{3} = \frac{2g-15}{g-5}$

7. $\frac{t}{3} + \frac{t}{2} = 1$

8. $\frac{3x}{5} + \frac{3}{2} = \frac{7x}{10}$

9. $\frac{2k}{3} + \frac{1}{2} = \frac{2k-3}{6}$

10. $\frac{s}{s-5} = \frac{s+4}{s-6}$

11. $\frac{2h}{h-1} = \frac{2h+1}{h+2}$

12. $\frac{2a-1}{6} - \frac{a}{3} = \frac{a+4}{18}$

Use with SOURCEBOOK Lesson 12-8, pages 320–321.

Solve. Check your solutions on a separate sheet of paper.

13. $\frac{x}{x^2 + x} + \frac{4}{x + 1} = \frac{2}{x}$

$\frac{x}{x(x + 1)} + \frac{4}{x + 1} = \frac{2}{x}$

$x(x + 1)\left(\frac{x}{x(x + 1)} + \frac{4}{x + 1}\right) = x(x + 1)\left(\frac{2}{x}\right)$

$x(x + 1)\left(\frac{x}{x(x + 1)}\right) + x(x + 1)\left(\frac{4}{x + 1}\right) = x(x + 1)\left(\frac{2}{x}\right)$

$\left(\frac{x(x + 1)x}{x(x + 1)}\right) + \left(\frac{x(x + 1)4}{(x + 1)}\right) = x(x + 1)\left(\frac{2}{x}\right)$

$x + 4x = 2x + 2$

$5x = 2x + 2$

$3x = 2$

$x = \frac{2}{3}$

14. $\frac{x}{x^2 + 3x} + \frac{5}{x + 3} = \frac{1}{x}$

15. $\frac{2}{r^2 - 4r + 3} = \frac{4}{r - 3} + \frac{2}{r - 1}$

16. $\frac{3}{h^2 - 7h + 10} = \frac{9}{h - 5} + \frac{3}{h - 2}$

Problem Solving

17. Alice can paint a room in 12 hours. Working together, Alice and Henry can paint the room in 7 hours. How long does Henry need to paint the room by himself?

18. Jimmy rows downstream 7 miles and then upstream 4 miles in the same amount of time. If he rows 3 mi/h faster than the speed of the current, how long does Jimmy row?

WRITE ABOUT IT

19. Explain why the equation $\frac{5}{x - 1} + \frac{2}{x + 1} = \frac{10}{x^2 - 1}$ has no solution.

12-9 Solve Rational Equations Resulting in Quadratic Equations

Name ______________________ Date __________

Solve: $\frac{1}{a-3} = \frac{4}{a^2-9}$

$a^2 - 9 = 4(a - 3)$ ← Apply the Cross-Products rule.

$a^2 - 9 = 4a - 12$ ← Apply the Distributive Property.

$a^2 - 4a + 3 = 0$ ← Write the equation in standard form.

$(a - 3)(a - 1) = 0$ ← Factor.

$a - 3 = 0$ or $a - 1 = 0$ ← Apply the Zero Product Property.

$a = 3$ or $a = 1$ ← Use the Addition Property of Equality.

Check each solution in the original equation.

So the solution set is {1}.

Check:

Let $a = 3$:

$\frac{1}{3-3} \stackrel{?}{=} \frac{4}{(3)^2-9}$

$\frac{1}{0} \stackrel{?}{=} \frac{4}{0}$ Undefined; exclude 3.

Let $a = 1$:

$\frac{1}{1-3} \stackrel{?}{=} \frac{4}{(1)^2-9}$

$\frac{1}{-2} \stackrel{?}{=} \frac{4}{-8}$ True

Solve. Check your solutions on a separate sheet of paper.

1. $\frac{v}{v+8} = \frac{v}{7}$

$7v = v(v + 8)$
$7v = v^2 + 8v$
$0 = v^2 + v$
$0 = v(v + 1)$
$0 = v$ or $0 = v + 1$
$0 = v$ or $-1 = v$
$\{-1, 0\}$

2. $\frac{m}{m+5} = \frac{m}{11}$

3. $\frac{c-3}{3c-7} = \frac{4}{2c}$

4. $\frac{n-5}{5n-21} = \frac{2}{2n}$

5. $\frac{p-2}{3p-10} = \frac{6}{2p}$

6. $\frac{b+7}{2b-4} = \frac{3}{8b}$

7. $\frac{e+4}{2e-3} = \frac{2}{6e}$

8. $\frac{d}{d+3} - \frac{2}{d-2} = \frac{26}{d^2+d-6}$

9. $\frac{k}{k+4} - \frac{3}{k-3} = \frac{15}{k^2+k-12}$

Solve. Check your solutions on a separate sheet of paper.

10. $\frac{2x + 1}{3} - \frac{3}{2x - 1} = -2$

$3(2x - 1)\left(\frac{2x + 1}{3} - \frac{3}{2x - 1}\right) = 3(2x - 1)(-2)$

$3(2x - 1)\left(\frac{2x + 1}{3}\right) - 3(2x - 1)\left(\frac{3}{2x - 1}\right) = -12x + 6$

$(2x - 1)(2x + 1) - 9 = -12x + 6$

$4x^2 - 1 - 9 = -12x + 6$

$4x^2 + 12x - 16 = 0$

$x^2 + 3x - 4 = 0$

$(x + 4)(x - 1) = 0$

$x + 4 = 0$ or $x - 1 = 0$

$\{-4, 1\}$

11. $\frac{4x + 1}{3} - \frac{3}{4x - 1} = -2$

12. $\frac{1}{x + 2} + \frac{3}{x^2 - 4} = \frac{4}{x^2 - x - 6}$

13. $\frac{1}{y + 3} + \frac{3}{y^2 - 9} = \frac{4}{y^2 - y - 12}$

Problem Solving

14. Hitomi, Paia, and Abigail can do the chores together in $1\frac{2}{7}$ hours. Working alone, Paia and Abigail take the same amount of time, and Hitomi takes 3 times as long. How much time do Paia and Abigail need to do the chores together?

TEST PREPARATION

15. Which is the common denominator for $\frac{n}{n - 1} + \frac{12 + n}{-n + 1} = \frac{1}{3n}$?

A. $3n(n - 1)$

B. $-3n(n - 1)$

C. $-3n(n - 1)(n + 1)$

D. $3n(n - 1)(n + 1)$

16. Which is a solution of $\frac{1}{x} + \frac{1}{x + 1} = \frac{1}{x + 2}$?

F. -1

G. -2

H. $2 + \sqrt{2}$

J. $-2 + \sqrt{2}$

12-10 Problem-Solving Strategy: Review of Strategies

Read › Plan › Solve › Check

Name ______________________________ Date ______________

Solve using a strategy that you have used before.

1. The shaded rectangular region is half as high as the trapezoid. What percent of the area of the trapezoid is occupied by the rectangle?

____

2. Can you time a 7-minute event using only one 4-minute timer and one 6-minute timer? Explain.

____

3. A string is exactly 800 cm. In how many ways can it be cut in two so that one of the pieces can be made into a circle in which both the diameter and the circumference are a whole number of centimeters?

____

4. You have a 200-cm wire. In how many ways can you cut it so that one of the pieces can be made into a square with an area that is divisible by 15? (Consider only squares with sides that are whole numbers.)

____

Use with SOURCEBOOK Lesson 12-10, pages 324–325.

5. Susan is one-fourth her grandmother's age. Half of Susan's age is the square root of her grandmother's age. How old is Susan?

---

6. A circle is placed into a corner so that one wall is tangent to point P and the other is tangent to point Q. Each of these points is 1 m from the corner. What is the area of the shaded region?

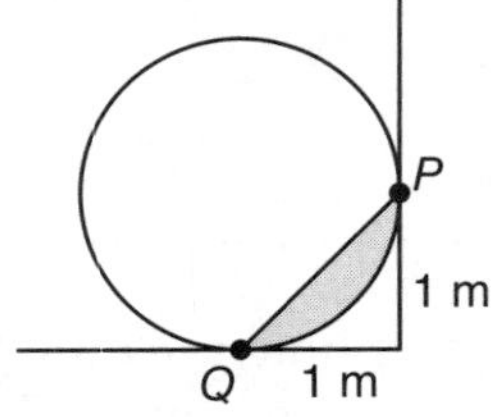

---

7. What is the least pair of perfect squares whose average is a whole number and whose sum is another perfect square?

---

8. The function $h(x)$ depends upon any value x. The first five values for $h(x)$, where $x = 1$ through 5 are listed in the table. What is the value of $h(x)$ if $x = 10$?

x	$h(x)$
1	1
2	15
3	79
4	256
5	621

Enrichment:
Continued Fractions

Name ______________________ Date ____________

Simplify the continued fraction: $3 + \cfrac{1}{2 + \cfrac{1}{4 + \cfrac{1}{2 + \frac{1}{5}}}}$.

$$3 + \cfrac{1}{2 + \cfrac{1}{4 + \cfrac{1}{2 + \frac{1}{5}}}} = 3 + \cfrac{1}{2 + \cfrac{1}{4 + \cfrac{1}{\frac{11}{5}}}}$$ ← Add $2 + \frac{1}{5}$ to get $\frac{11}{5}$; Then find the reciprocal of $\frac{11}{5}$.

$$= 3 + \cfrac{1}{2 + \cfrac{1}{4 + \frac{5}{11}}}$$ ← Add $4 + \frac{5}{11}$ to get $\frac{49}{11}$; Then find the reciprocal of $\frac{49}{11}$.

$$= 3 + \cfrac{1}{2 + \frac{11}{49}}$$ ← Add $2 + \frac{11}{49}$ to get $\frac{109}{49}$; Then find the reciprocal of $\frac{109}{49}$.

$$= 3 + \frac{49}{109} = 3\frac{49}{109}$$ ← Simplify.

Simplify the continued fraction.

1. $\cfrac{1}{2 + \cfrac{1}{1 + \frac{1}{3}}}$

$\cfrac{1}{2 + \cfrac{1}{\frac{4}{3}}} = \cfrac{1}{2 + \frac{3}{4}} = \cfrac{1}{\frac{11}{4}} = \frac{4}{11}$

____

2. $\cfrac{1}{4 + \cfrac{1}{1 + \frac{1}{2}}}$

____

3. $5 + \cfrac{1}{2 + \cfrac{1}{1 + \frac{1}{4}}}$

____

4. $2 + \cfrac{1}{3 + \cfrac{1}{4 + \frac{1}{5}}}$

____

5. $1 + \cfrac{1}{2 + \cfrac{1}{3 + \cfrac{1}{3 + \frac{1}{3}}}}$

____

6. $2 + \cfrac{1}{1 + \cfrac{1}{3 + \cfrac{1}{1 + \frac{1}{2}}}}$

____

Write the number as a continued fraction.

7. $\frac{8}{55}$

$$\frac{1}{\frac{55}{8}} = \frac{1}{6+\frac{7}{8}} = \frac{1}{6+\frac{1}{\frac{8}{7}}} = \frac{1}{6+\frac{1}{1+\frac{1}{7}}}$$

8. $\frac{13}{28}$

9. $\frac{35}{121}$

10. $\frac{30}{73}$

11. $\frac{12}{7}$

12. $\frac{41}{17}$

13. $\frac{53}{31}$

14. $\frac{245}{57}$

15. $\frac{8}{13}$

16. $\frac{75}{247}$

WRITE ABOUT IT

17. Continued fractions seem more of a mathematical puzzle than a useful tool. In fact, there are applications of a continued fraction. Research and explain an application of continued fractions and who first demonstrated its use.

Test Prep: Multiple-Choice Questions

Strategy: Understand Distractors

Name ______________________________ Date ______________

When solving problems, **make notes** to help organize your thoughts and information.

To select the correct answer in a multiple-choice item, try using the following strategies.
- Underline important words.
- Restate the question.
- Use the Test-Prep strategy.
- Apply appropriate rules, definitions, properties, or strategies.
- Analyze and eliminate answer choices.

Choose the correct answer. *TIP: Think before you answer. Be sure you understand the question.*

1. Nate and Sonyi volunteer to make calls about a school fundraiser. Alone, Nate can make all of the calls in 6 hours, and Sonyi can make all of the calls in 4 hours. How long will it take if they work together to make the calls?

A. 2 h

B. $2\frac{2}{5}$ h

C. 5 h

D. 10 h

2. Melanie and 2 friends go out to dinner. The total cost of the food is $36 and they leave a 20% tip. How much does each person pay if the total cost of the bill and the tip is divided evenly among the three?

F. $2.40

G. $12

H. $14.40

J. $43.20

3. Rafiq is buying a rug for his bedroom. He measures the dimensions as 10 ft by 12 ft. The actual measurements are 9.6 ft by 11.75 ft. What is the relative error in the measurement of the area to the nearest thousandth?

A. 0.001

B. 0.06

C. 0.064

D. 0.072

4. A store sells new and used video games. The store makes $20 profit on each new video game sold, and $5 on each used video game sold. The store makes at least $550 in profit. Which inequality describes the situation?

F. $20n + 5u \geq 550$

G. $20n - 5u \geq 550$

H. $20n + 5u \leq 550$

J. $20n - 5u \leq 550$

5. A cylinder has a volume of 108π cm^2. It has a height of 12 cm. What is its diameter?

A. 3 cm

B. 4.5 cm

C. 6 cm

D. 9 cm

6. There are 4 consecutive integers whose sum is 174. Which of the following is one of the numbers?

F. 14

G. 24

H. 34

J. 44

Use with SOURCEBOOK Test Prep Lesson, page 328.

Vocabulary Development

Name ______________________ Date ____________

Chapter 12 Vocabulary

excluded values	rational equation
mixed expression	rational expression

From the vocabulary list above, choose the term(s) that best complete each sentence. Write the term(s) in the space(s) provided.

1. The sum or difference of a polynomial and a rational expression is a(n) ____________.

2. An equation that contains at least one rational expression is a(n) ____________.

3. Any values of a variable that result in a denominator of zero are considered ____________.

4. An algebraic fraction whose numerator and denominator are polynomials is called a(n) ____________.

Tell whether each statement is *true* or *false*. If it is false, change it to make it true.

5. The only common factor of a rational expression in lowest terms is a prime number.

____

6. A quadratic equation with integral coefficients is a rational equation.

____

7. Solutions of a rational quadratic equation are always solutions of the original equation.

____

8. The expression $2\frac{1}{x}$ is a rational expression.

____

9. To write a rational expression in lowest terms, you may have to factor the numerator and denominator.

____

10. To solve a rational equation, find the GCF of the denominators.

____

11. A rational quadratic equation has one solution.

____

Use after SOURCEBOOK Lessons 12-1–12-9, pages 306–323.

Practice Chapter 12 Test

Name ______________________ Date __________

Simplify. Identify any excluded values.

1. $\frac{g + 9}{g - 11}$

2. $\frac{7v}{7v - 35}$

3. $\frac{14y^3}{7y^4 + 7y^3}$

4. $\frac{-t + 7}{t^2 - 49}$

5. $\frac{h^2 - h - 30}{h^2 + 10h + 25}$

6. $\frac{u^2 - 5u - 6}{u^2 - 9u + 8}$

Multiply or Divide. Write the product or quotient in simplest form.

7. $\frac{a^2 + 7a + 12}{-a - 5} \bullet \frac{a^2 + 10a + 25}{a^2 + 8a + 15}$

8. $\frac{x^2 + 2x - 35}{x^2 + 10x + 21} \div \frac{x^2 - 7x + 10}{x^2 - x - 12}$

Add or subtract. Write each sum or difference in simplest form. Identify any excluded values.

9. $\frac{11j + 3}{3j + 9} - \frac{4j - 18}{3j + 9}$

10. $\frac{3}{k + 5} + \frac{5}{k - 2}$

11. $\frac{2}{y - 4} - \frac{7}{y - 2}$

Simplify.

12. $d + 1 - \frac{3}{d + 4}$

13. $\frac{4 + \frac{3}{g}}{2 + \frac{5}{g}}$

14. $\frac{y - \frac{2y + 4}{y + 2}}{y - 2}$

Solve. Check your solutions on a separate sheet of paper.

15. $\frac{1}{8} + \frac{1}{w} = \frac{1}{8w}$

16. $\frac{d - 12}{7d - 84} = \frac{5}{9}$

17. $\frac{b - 1}{b + 48} = \frac{2}{2b}$

Problem Solving

18. Bruce can paint a boat in 5 hours. Working together, Janice and Bruce can paint the same type of boat in 4 hours. Working alone, how long would Janice need to paint the boat?

19. An off-road jeep went 60 miles in the same amount of time a dune buggy went 90 miles. The dune buggy's average speed was 10 miles per hour faster than the jeep's. What was the average speed of the jeep? (*Hint:* distance = rate • time)

Tell About It

Explain how you solve the problem. Show all your work.

20. Denny can build a doghouse in 8 hours. Soula can build the same doghouse in 10 hours. Working together, how long do they need to build the doghouse?

Cumulative Review: Chapters 1–12

Name ______________________ Date ____________

Circle the best answer.

1. Which set is not closed under addition?

A. {whole numbers} **B.** {integers}

C. {real numbers} **D.** {0, 1, 2, 3, 4}

2. What is the value of 8^{-2}?

F. -64

G. -16

H. $\frac{1}{64}$

J. $\frac{1}{16}$

3. Solve.

$r + 11.3 = 2.9$

A. $r = -8.6$ **B.** $r = -8.4$

C. $r = 8.4$ **D.** $r = 14.2$

4. Solve.

$y - 11 < 23$

F. $y < 12$ **G.** $y > 12$

H. $y < 34$ **J.** $y > 34$

5. Solve.

$-5g > 45$

A. $g > -9$ **B.** $g < -9$

C. $g > 40$ **D.** $g < 10$

6. Which function rule models this situation? the total cost, c, for h hours at an hourly rate of $45.85 per hour

F. $c(h) = 45.85h$

G. $c(h) = 45.85 + h$

H. $c(h) = 45.85 - h$

J. $c(h) = \frac{45.85}{h}$

7. The graph of which equation is perpendicular to the graph of $5x + 7y = 2$?

A. $5x + 7y = 11$ **B.** $5x - 7y = 2$

C. $7x + 5y = 9$ **D.** $7x - 5y = 1$

8. What is the vertex of $y = |x + 6|$?

F. $(-6, 0)$

G. $(6, 0)$

H. $(0, -6)$

J. $(0, 6)$

9. What is the solution of $\begin{cases} 5x - 2y = 7 \\ 2x + 5y = -3 \end{cases}$?

A. $(1, 1)$ **B.** $(1, -1)$

C. $(-1, 1)$ **D.** $(-1, -1)$

10. Simplify: $\frac{27t^5 + 18t^3 - 6t}{-3t}$.

F. $-9t^4 + 6t^2 + 2$ **G.** $-9t^4 - 6t^2 - 2$

H. $-9t^4 - 6t^2 + 2$ **J.** $-13t^6$

11. Divide: $(x^2 + 3x + 1) \div (x + 1)$.

A. $x + 2$

B. $x + 2 + \frac{1}{x + 1}$

C. $x + 2 - \frac{1}{x + 1}$

D. $x + 2 - \frac{1}{x^2 + 3x + 1}$

12. Which is a factor of $x^3 + 5x^2 + 3x + 15$?

F. $x + 3$ **G.** $x^2 + 5$

H. $x^2 + 3$ **J.** $x^2 + 15$

13. What is the distance between points $(-2, 9)$ and $(3, 7)$?

A. $\sqrt{29}$ **B.** $\sqrt{21}$

C. $\sqrt{17}$ **D.** $\sqrt{5}$

14. Which equation has solutions -3 and 7?

F. $b^2 + 4b - 21 = 0$ **G.** $b^2 - 4b + 21 = 0$

H. $b^2 - 4b - 21 = 0$ **J.** $b^2 + 3 = 7$

15. Multiply: $5\sqrt{6} \bullet -2\sqrt{3}$

A. $3\sqrt{9}$ **B.** -30

C. $-30\sqrt{2}$ **D.** $-30\sqrt{3}$

16. Which is a solution of $\begin{cases} y = 3 \\ y = 2x^2 - 3x + 3 \end{cases}$?

F. $\left(\frac{3}{2}, 3\right)$ **G.** $\left(3, \frac{3}{2}\right)$

H. $\left(\frac{3}{2}, 0\right)$ **J.** $\left(0, \frac{3}{2}\right)$

17. A blueprint has a scale of 5 centimeters = 3 meters. What is the actual length of a house that is 20.5 cm long on the blueprint?

A. 61.5 m **B.** 34.2 m

C. 12.3 m **D.** 4.7 m

18. Two angles of a triangle are 83° and 22°. What is the sine of the third angle?

F. 3.7321 **G.** 0.9659

H. 0.9218 **J.** -0.3878

19. If $\cos A \approx 0.9135$, what is the measure of angle A?

A. 67° **B.** 66°

C. 26° **D.** 24°

20. What are excluded values in the expression $\frac{w(w + 2)}{(w - 1)(w + 3)}$?

F. $w \neq -3, w \neq 1$

G. $w \neq -2, w \neq 0$

H. $w \neq -3, w \neq -2, w \neq 1$

J. $w \neq -3, w \neq -2, w \neq 0, w \neq 1$

21. Which is the product written in simplest form?

$$\frac{3n^3 + 12n^2 + 9n}{6n^2} \bullet \frac{n^4}{n^2 - 2n - 15}$$

A. $\frac{9n^3}{2}$ **B.** $\frac{18n^3(n + 1)}{n + 5}$

C. $\frac{n^3(n + 1)}{2n(n - 5)}$ **D.** $\frac{n^3(n + 1)}{2(n - 5)}$

22. Simplify: $3 + \frac{5}{z - 2}$.

F. $\frac{3z - 6}{z - 2}$ **G.** $\frac{3z - 1}{z - 2}$

H. $3z + 3$ **J.** $3z - 1$

Tell About It

Explain how you solve the problem. Show all your work.

23. A farmer takes 8 days to plow a field. His son takes 12 days to plow the same field. Working together, how long will it take them to plow the field?

24. The current of a river is 3 mi/h. Oliver sailed 81 miles downstream in the same amount of time it took him to sail 27 of the 81 upstream miles. If he sailed for 9 hours each day, how many days was his roundtrip sail? (*Hint:* distance = rate • time)

13-1 Inverse Variation

Name ______________________ Date ____________

Graph the inverse variation $xy = 20$. Describe the asymptotes.

Remember: An inverse variation can be written as an equation in the form $xy = k$, where $k \neq 0$.

Make a function table using both positive and negative values of x.

x	1	2	4	5	10	20	−1	−2	−4	−5	−10	−20
y	20	10	5	4	2	1	−20	−10	−5	−4	−2	−1

Graph the ordered pairs in the table on a coordinate plane. Draw smooth curves through them.

The graph of $xy = 20$ is shown at the right. Notice that the hyperbola gets very close to the lines $x = 0$ and $y = 0$ but do not touch them. Therefore, the asymptotes of the graph are the x- and y-axes.

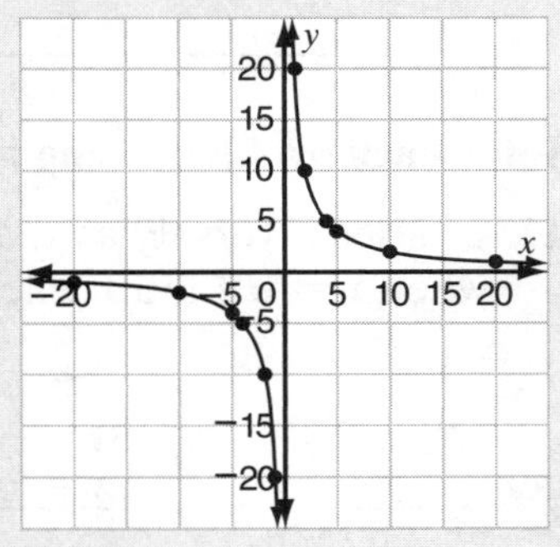

Remember: Asymptotes are lines that a graph approaches but never intersects.

Each table or graph represents a variation. Is it a direct or an inverse variation? Explain.

1.

x	y
2	6
4	3
6	2
−2	−6
−4	−3
−6	−2

____

2.

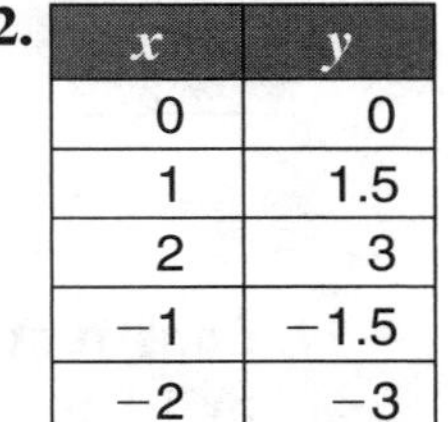

x	y
0	0
1	1.5
2	3
−1	−1.5
−2	−3

____

3.

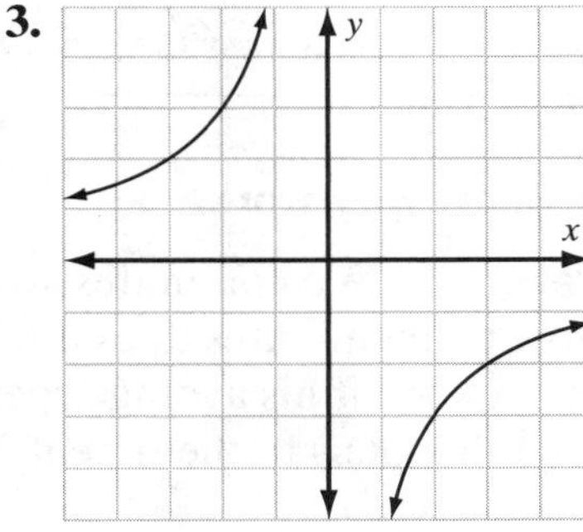

____

Make a function table for each equation. Tell whether the equation represents a direct or an inverse variation. Graph the relation on a separate sheet of paper.

4. $xy = 8$

x	y
1	**8**
2	**4**
4	**2**
−1	**−8**
−2	**−4**
−4	**−2**

inverse variation

5. $xy = -9$

____

6. $xy = \frac{1}{2}$

____

7. $y = -1.6x$

____

Solve each problem using the equation $xy = k$.

8. y varies inversely as x, and $y = 12$ when $x = 5$. Find x when $y = 6$.

$xy = k$	$xy = 60$
$5(12) = k$	$6x = 60$
$60 = k$	$x = 10$

9. y varies inversely as x, and $y = 7$ when $x = 6$. Find x when $y = 21$.

10. y varies inversely as x, and $y = 12.3$ when $x = 2$. Find y when $x = 3$.

11. y varies inversely as x, and $y = 15.25$ when $x = 8$. Find y when $x = 5$.

Solve each problem using a proportion.

12. y varies inversely as x, and $y = -9$ when $x = 2$. Find x when $y = 3$.

$$\frac{2}{x} = \frac{3}{-9}$$
$$3x = -18$$
$$x = -6$$

13. y varies inversely as x, and $y = -15$ when $x = 4$. Find x when $y = 5$.

14. y varies inversely as x, and $y = 9.2$ when $x = -4$. Find y when $x = 0.2$.

15. y varies inversely as x, and $y = 16.4$ when $x = -7$. Find y when $x = 0.4$.

Solve. Show your work.

16. **Travel** Mr. Wu commutes 40 mi to work. How many minutes does it take Mr. Wu to get to work if his average speed is 50 mph? What happens to the time if Mr. Wu's speed decreases?

17. **Construction** A factory building is 80 m by 10 m. How wide is another building with an equal floor area and length that is twice its width?

CHALLENGE

18. If y varies inversely with the *square* of x, the inverse variation can be written as $x^2y = k$. Make a function table and graph the equation $x^2y = 4$ on grid paper. What happens to y as x increases? decreases?

13-2 Graph Rational Functions

Name ______________________ Date __________

Identify and graph the asymptotes. Then graph the function.

$y = \frac{3}{x - 5} + 2$

Think

Use the general form of a rational function, $y = \frac{a}{x - b} + c$.
The vertical asymptote is $x = 5$ because $b = 5$.
The horizontal asymptote is $y = 2$ because $c = 2$.

Make a function table using both positive and negative values of x.

x	−4	−2	0	2	4	6	8	10	12
y	$\frac{5}{3}$	$\frac{11}{7}$	$\frac{7}{5}$	1	−1	5	3	$\frac{13}{5}$	$\frac{17}{7}$

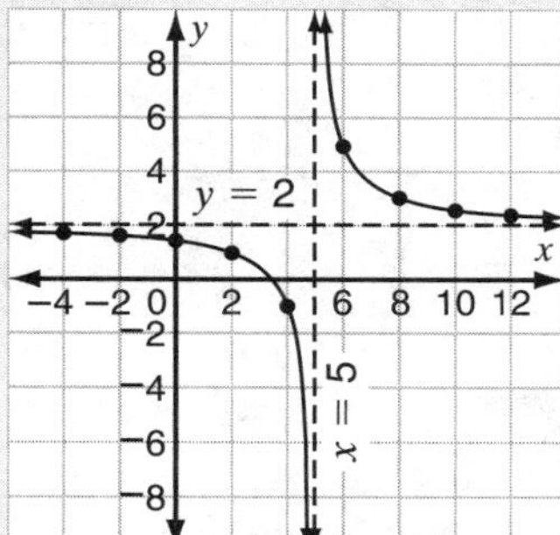

Graph the ordered pairs and draw smooth curves to connect the points.

The graph of $y = \frac{3}{x - 5} + 2$ is a translation of $y = \frac{3}{x}$, 5 units to the right and 2 units up.

For each rational function, identify the asymptotes. On grid paper, graph the asymptotes, make a function table, and graph the function.

1. $y = \frac{10}{x}$

$b = 0$; the vertical asymptote is $x = 0$.
$c = 0$; the horizontal asymptote is $y = 0$.
Asymptotes: $x = 0$ and $y = 0$

2. $y = \frac{15}{x}$

____

3. $y = \frac{2}{x} + 3$

____

4. $y = \frac{2}{x} + 5$

____

5. $y = \frac{2}{x - 3}$

____

6. $y = \frac{2}{x - 4}$

____

7. $y = \frac{2}{x + 7}$

____

8. $y = \frac{2}{x + 10}$

____

For each rational function, identify the asymptotes. On a separate sheet of paper, graph the asymptotes, make a function table, and graph the function.

9. $y = \frac{8}{x - 1} + 2$

10. $y = \frac{8}{x - 2} + 3$

11. $y = \frac{8}{x + 4} + 1$

12. $y = \frac{8}{x + 1} + 2$

13. $y = \frac{8}{x - 1} - 1$

14. $y = \frac{8}{x - 2} - 3$

15. $y = \frac{8}{x + 1} - 1$

16. $y = \frac{8}{x + 2} - 3$

Solve. Show your work.

17. The graphs of the equations $y = 2$ and $y = \frac{3}{x}$ intersect at how many points? Give the coordinates of the points of intersection.

18. How are the graphs of the following equations related?
$y = \frac{2}{x - 9} + 4$ and $y = \frac{2}{x + 3} - 5$

TEST PREPARATION

19. The graph of which equation translates the parent function $y = \frac{14}{x}$ 6 units to the right and 11 units down?

A. $y = \frac{14}{x + 6} - 11$

B. $y = \frac{14}{x - 6} - 11$

C. $y = \frac{14}{x + 6} + 11$

D. $y = \frac{14}{x - 6} + 11$

13-3 Graph Radical Functions

Name ______________________________ Date ______________

Graph $y = \sqrt{x+3} - 1$. Find the domain and range of the function.

The domain has values of x such that $x + 3 \geq 0$
$x \geq -3$

Think
Choose values for x that make the radicand a perfect square.

Make a function table.

$y = \sqrt{x+3} - 1$

x	−3	−2	1	6	13
y	−1	0	1	2	3

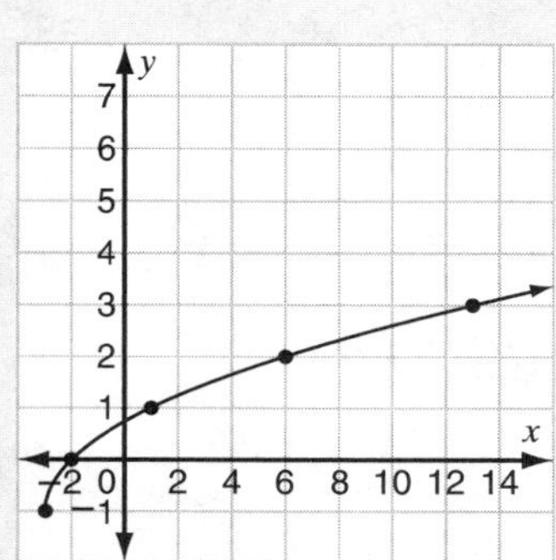

Graph the ordered pairs and draw smooth curves to connect the points. The range is $y \geq -1$.

The graph is translated 1 unit down and 3 units to the left of the parent function $y = \sqrt{x}$.

On a separate sheet of paper, graph each radical function using a table. State the domain and range. Describe how each graph relates to the graph of $y = \sqrt{x}$.

1. $y = \sqrt{x+5}$

$x + 5 \geq 0$; $x \geq -5$
$\sqrt{x+5} \geq 0$; so $y \geq 0$
domain: $x \geq -5$; range: $y \geq 0$
The graph is translated 5 units to the left.

2. $y = \sqrt{x+4}$

____

3. $y = \sqrt{x-6}$

____

4. $y = \sqrt{x-4}$

____

5. $y = \sqrt{x} - 7$

____

6. $y = \sqrt{x} - 3$

____

7. $y = \sqrt{x} + 1\frac{1}{2}$

____

8. $y = \sqrt{x} + 3\frac{1}{2}$

____

On a separate sheet of paper, graph each radical function using a table. State the domain and range. Describe how each graph relates to the graph of $y = \sqrt{x}$.

9. $y = \sqrt{x + 9} - 2$

10. $y = \sqrt{x + 3} - 4$

11. $y = \sqrt{x - 6} + 7$

12. $y = \sqrt{x - 3} + 6$

13. $y = \sqrt{x - 5} - 1.5$

14. $y = \sqrt{x - 9} - 2.5$

15. $y = \sqrt{x + 4} + \frac{1}{2}$

16. $y = \sqrt{x + 6} + 2\frac{1}{2}$

Solve.

17. Find the solution of the system $y = x$ and $y = \sqrt{x + 6}$ and check. Then graph the equations on a separate sheet of paper.

18. Find the solution of the system $y = 2x$ and $y = \sqrt{x + 3}$. Check your answer by graphing the equations on grid paper.

CRITICAL THINKING

19. How do the graphs of $y = \sqrt{x}$ and $y = \sqrt{2x}$ differ? Test your observation by replacing the coefficient of x with other values.

13-4 Identify Exponential Functions and Their Graphs

Name ______________________ Date ____________

Compare the graphs of the exponential functions $y = 3^x$ and $y = \left(\frac{1}{3}\right)^x$.

Remember: An exponential function has the form $y = ab^x$, where $a \neq 0$, $b \neq 1$, $b > 0$, and x is a real number.

Make a function table for the parent function $y = 3^x$ and for $y = \left(\frac{1}{3}\right)^x$.

Then graph both functions on the same coordinate plane.

$y = 3^x$

x	−3	−2	−1	0	1
y	$\frac{1}{27}$	$\frac{1}{9}$	$\frac{1}{3}$	1	3

$y = \left(\frac{1}{3}\right)^x$

x	−1	0	1	2	3
y	3	1	$\frac{1}{3}$	$\frac{1}{9}$	$\frac{1}{27}$

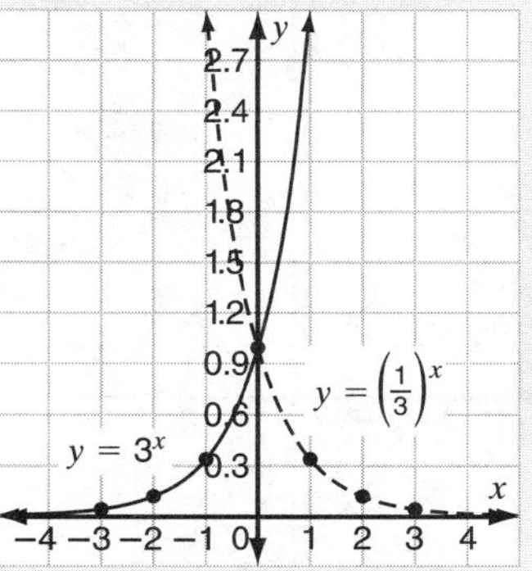

The graph of $y = \left(\frac{1}{3}\right)^x$ is a reflection of $y = 3^x$ across the y-axis.

The x-axis is an asymptote for both graphs.
The range for both functions is $y > 0$.

Evaluate $y = 7(4^x)$ for the given value of x.

1. $x = 1$

$y = 7(4^1) = 7(4)$
28

2. $x = 2$

3. $x = -2$

4. $x = -1$

5. $x = \frac{1}{2}$

6. $x = \frac{3}{2}$

Evaluate $y = -3\left(\frac{1}{9}\right)^x$ for the given value of x.

7. $x = -1$

$y = -3\left(\frac{1}{9}\right)^{-1} = -3(9)$
−27

8. $x = -2$

9. $x = 1$

10. $x = 2$

11. $x = -\frac{1}{2}$

12. $x = -\frac{5}{2}$

Select the graph that best matches each equation.

13. $y = 4^x$ __________

14. $y = -4^x$ __________

15. $y = \left(\frac{1}{4}\right)^x$ __________

16. $y = -\left(\frac{1}{4}\right)^x$ __________

A.

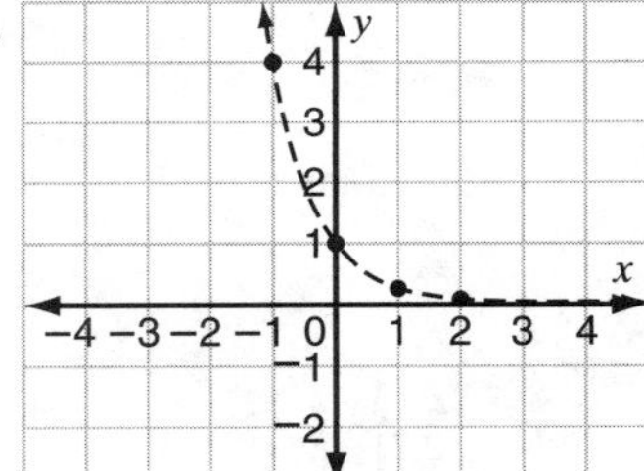

B.

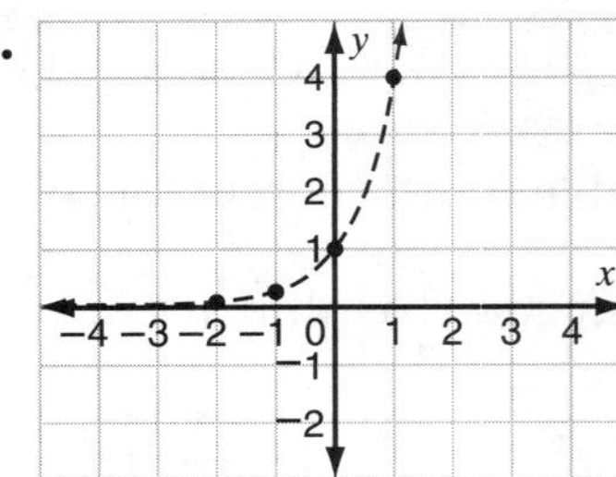

C.

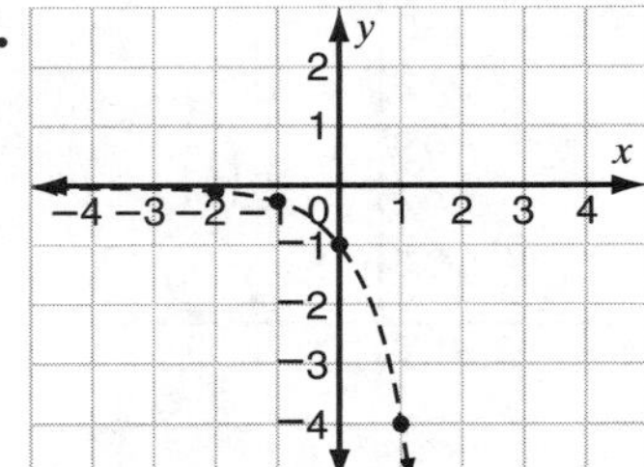

D.

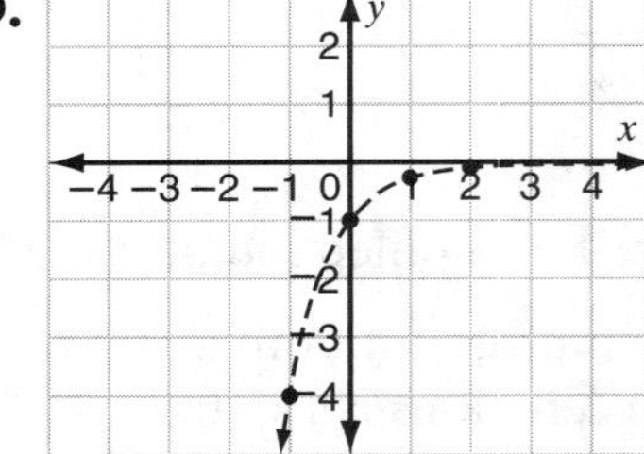

17. $y = 4(10)^x$ __________

18. $y = -3(10)^x$ __________

19. $y = \frac{1}{2}(10)^x$ __________

20. $y = -\frac{1}{5}(10)^x$ __________

A.

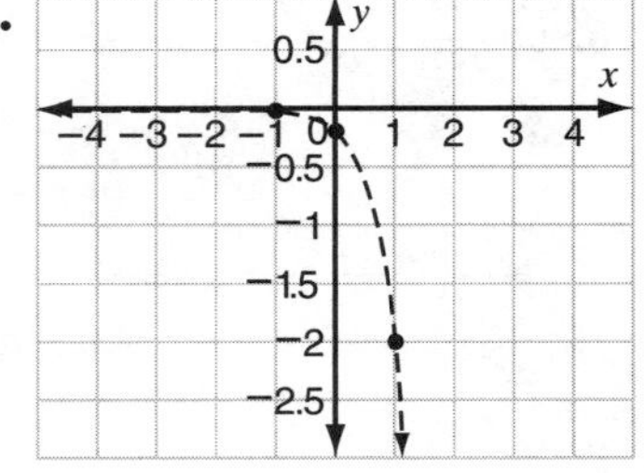

B.

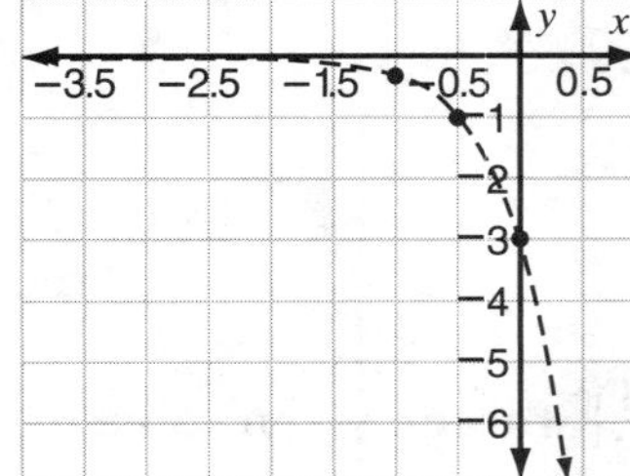

C.

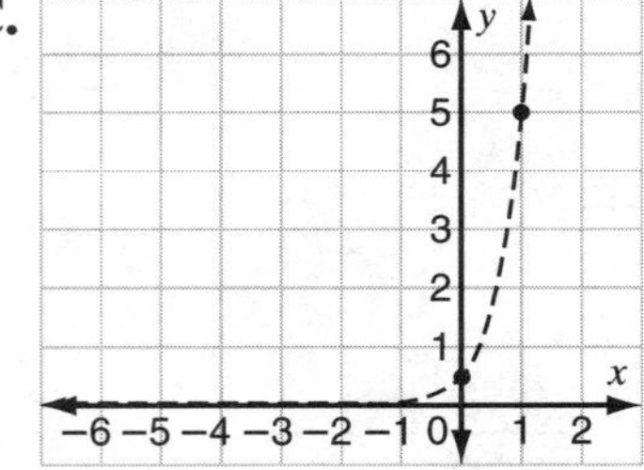

D.

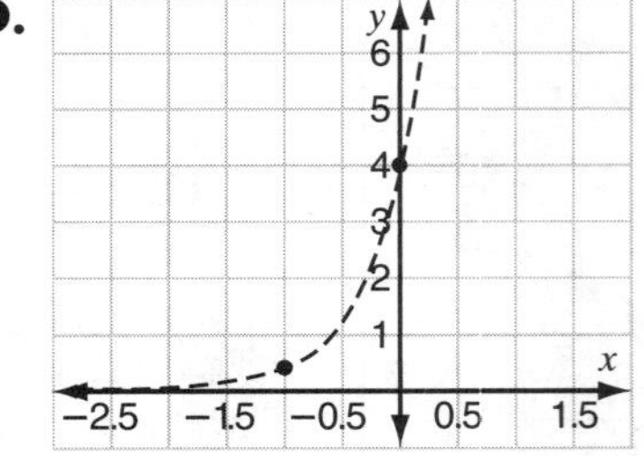

On a separate sheet of paper, make a function table to graph each pair of functions. Describe the similarities and differences in the graphs.

21. $y = 2(3^x)$ and $y = 2\left(\frac{1}{3}\right)^x$

The range for both functions is $y > 0$.
The x-axis is an asymptote for both graphs.
The graphs are reflections across the y-axis.

22. $y = 3(4^x)$ and $y = 3\left(\frac{1}{4}\right)^x$

23. $y = 2\left(\frac{1}{3}\right)^x$ and $y = -2\left(\frac{1}{3}\right)^x$

24. $y = 4\left(\frac{1}{5}\right)^x$ and $y = -4\left(\frac{1}{5}\right)^x$

25. $y = -1.5\left(\frac{1}{3}\right)^x$ and $y = 1.5\left(\frac{1}{3}\right)^x$

26. $y = -2.5\left(\frac{1}{3}\right)^x$ and $y = 2.5\left(\frac{1}{3}\right)^x$

27. $y = 2(-3^x)$ and $y = 2(3^x)$

28. $y = 4(-3^x)$ and $y = 4(3^x)$

29. $y = 0.5(-3^x)$ and $y = 2\left(\frac{1}{3}\right)^x$

30. $y = 0.25(-5^x)$ and $y = 4\left(\frac{1}{5}\right)^x$

For More Practice Go To:
ONLINE www.progressinmathematics.com
Practice/Test Generator

On a separate sheet of paper, make a function table to graph each pair of functions. Describe the similarities and differences in the graphs.

31. $y = \frac{1}{2}(2^x)$ and $y = 2(2^x)$

32. $y = \frac{1}{4}(3^x)$ and $y = 4(3^x)$

33. $y = 2(4^x)$ and $y = -2(4^x)$

34. $y = 4(2^x)$ and $y = -4(2^x)$

35. $y = -3(0.4^x)$ and $y = 3\left(\frac{2}{5}\right)^x$

36. $y = -\frac{3}{4}(0.1^x)$ and $y = \frac{3}{4}\left(\frac{1}{10}\right)^x$

Solve.

37. Use tables and a separate sheet of paper to find where the graphs of $y = 2^x + 1$ and $y = -2^x + 5$ intersect. Verify the point(s) of intersection algebraically.

38. The graphs of $y = 2^x - 3$ and $y = -2^x - 7$ will never intersect. Explain why, using algebra and what you know of asymptotes.

SPIRAL REVIEW

39. y varies inversely as x, and $y = 10$ when $x = 11$. Find x when $y = 50$.

40. Solve: $\frac{3}{2a} = \frac{5}{4a - 1}$

13-5 Exponential Growth and Decay

Name ______________________ Date ____________

Martha invested \$2000 at a rate of 4% compounded weekly. What will the value of her investment be after 10 years?

Use the Compound Interest Formula $A = P\left(1 + \frac{r}{n}\right)^{nt}$.

Think

There are about 52 weeks in a year.

$A = 2000\left(1 + \frac{0.04}{52}\right)^{52(10)}$ ← Substitute 2000 for P, 0.04 for r, 52 for n, and 10 for t.

$\approx 2000(1.0008)^{520}$ ← Simplify.

≈ 3031.2676 ← Round.

The investment will be worth about \$3031.27 after 10 years.

Solve using the equation for exponential growth or decay.

1. If \$5000 is invested at 6% compounded quarterly, what will the value of the investment be after 5 years?

   Substitute 5000 for P, 0.06 for r, 4 for n, and 5 for t.

   $A = 5000\left(1 + \frac{0.06}{4}\right)^{4(5)}$

   $= 5000(1.015)^{20}$

   ≈ 6734.2750

   The investment will be \$6734.28 after 5 years.

2. If \$8000 is invested at 5% compounded quarterly, what will the value of the investment be after 6 years?

   ____

3. Horace invested \$2358 at 4% compounded monthly. What will the value of his investment be after 9 years? How much is interest?

   ____

4. Paulina invested \$3052 at 7% compounded monthly. What will the value of her investment be after 8 years? How much is interest?

   ____

5. Lenil invested \$50.25 at 1.25% compounded weekly. What will the value of his investment be after 25 years? How much is interest?

   ____

6. Mae invested \$90.75 at 2.5% compounded weekly. What will the value of his investment be after 50 years? How much is interest?

   ____

Solve using the equation for exponential growth or decay.

7. A car that costs \$28,650 depreciates 18% per year. What will the car be worth after 3 years?

1 − 0.18 = 0.82; $y = ab^x$
28,650(0.82)^3 = 28,650(0.551368)
= 15,796.6932
The car will be worth \$15,796.69.

8. A car that costs \$34,219 depreciates 20% per year. What will the car be worth after 4 years?

9. Two cites have an annual growth rate of 12%. One city's population is 85,000 and the other's is 54,000. Predict the difference in their populations after 20 years.

10. Two cites have an annual growth rate of 16%. One city's population is 120,000 and the other's is 200,000. Predict the difference in their populations after 10 years.

Problem Solving

11. Investments Raul invested \$4000 at 5% compounded quarterly. About how long will it take to double his investment?

12. Population A park's deer population is 50,000 and growing at 12% per year. Another park's deer population is 80,000 but declining at 8% per year. When will the two parks have about the same deer population?

MENTAL MATH

13. 48(96)

14. 71(103)

15. 102(98)

16. 74(86)

13-6 Technology: Graph Rational Functions

Name ______________________ Date __________

You can use a handheld to graph the rational function $y = \frac{5}{x+1} - 2$.

Step 1 Press (⌂). Then choose (2) for **Graphs & Geometry**.

Step 2 Enter $\frac{5}{x+1} - 2$ as $5 \div (x + 1) - 2$.

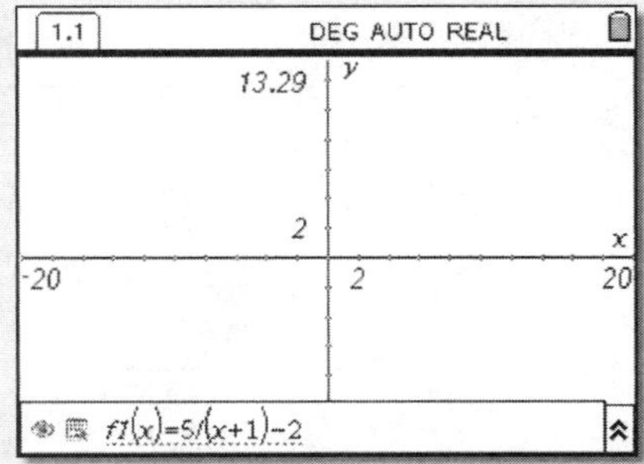

Then press (enter).

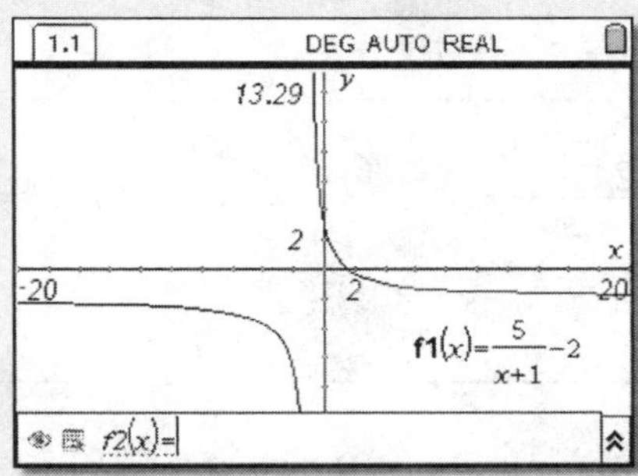

The vertical asymptote is $x = -1$ and the horizontal asymptote is $y = -2$.

Remember: The graph of $y = \frac{a}{x-b} + c$ has vertical asymptote $y = c$ and horizontal asymptote $x = b$.

Use a handheld to graph the function. Identify any vertical or horizontal asymptotes.

1. $y = \frac{9}{x+5}$
   vert: $x = -5$; horiz: $y = 0$

2. $y = \frac{3}{x+6}$ ______________

3. $y = \frac{4}{x-7}$ ______________

4. $y = \frac{2}{x-8}$ ______________

5. $y = \frac{1}{x} - 6$ ______________

6. $y = \frac{1}{x} - 3$ ______________

7. $y = \frac{1}{x} + 4$ ______________

8. $y = \frac{1}{x} + 9$ ______________

9. $y = \frac{6}{x-7} + 4$ ______________

10. $y = \frac{2}{x-3} + 10$ ______________

11. $y = \frac{13}{x-4.6} - 7$ ______________

12. $y = \frac{15}{x-6.6} - 11$ ______________

13. $y = \frac{2}{x-\frac{1}{2}} - 8.5$ ______________

14. $y = \frac{1}{x-\frac{3}{4}} - 11.2$ ______________

15. $y = \frac{2.6}{x+2.71} + \frac{11}{3}$ ______________

16. $y = \frac{5.26}{x+7.4} + \frac{9}{5}$ ______________

17. $y = \frac{\frac{7}{8}}{x+\frac{5}{6}} + \sqrt{5}$ ______________

18. $y = \frac{\frac{11}{5}}{x+\frac{7}{9}} + \sqrt{3}$ ______________

Use with **SOURCEBOOK Lesson 13-6, pages 346–347.**

Use a handheld to graph the function. Identify any vertical or horizontal asymptotes.

19. $y = \frac{-2}{x}$

vert. $x = 0$; horiz: $y = 0$

20. $y = \frac{-3}{x}$

21. $y = \frac{-5}{x + 3}$

22. $y = \frac{-9}{x + 11}$

23. $\frac{-6}{x - 4} + 13 = y$

24. $\frac{-15}{x - 5} + 14 = y$

25. $y = \frac{2}{2x - 3} + 1$

26. $y = \frac{7}{3x - 4} + 2$

27. $y = \frac{x^2}{x + 8}$

28. $y = \frac{x^2}{x + 11}$

29. $y - 9 = \frac{-x^2}{x - 17}$

30. $y - 15 = \frac{-x^2}{x - 14}$

Problem Solving

31. Al cannot read the equation on the display of his handheld. He can see that the asymptotes of the graph are $x = -4$ and $y = 16$. What equation is graphed?

32. Maria says the graphs of the equations below intersect once. Carol says they intersect twice. Graph them on a handheld to find who is correct. Then find the point(s) of intersection to the nearest tenth.

$y = \frac{1}{2}x - 4$ and $y = \frac{4}{x - 2}$

CHALLENGE

33. Use a handheld to graph the equation $y = \frac{x^2 + 2x + 1}{x + 2}$. Find the vertical asymptote. Predict the equation of the slant asymptote. Then divide the polynomial and graph the simplified equation, ignoring the remainder. What is the equation of the slant asymptote? Was your prediction correct?

13-7 Technology: Graph Radical Functions

Name ______________________ Date __________

You can use a handheld to graph $y = \sqrt{x - 8}$.

Step 1 Press (home). Then choose (2) for **Graphs & Geometry**.

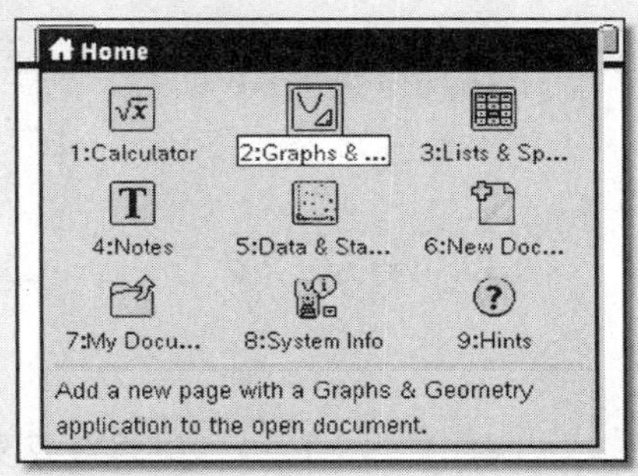

Step 2 Enter $\sqrt{x - 8}$. Use (ctrl) (x^2) for the radical sign.

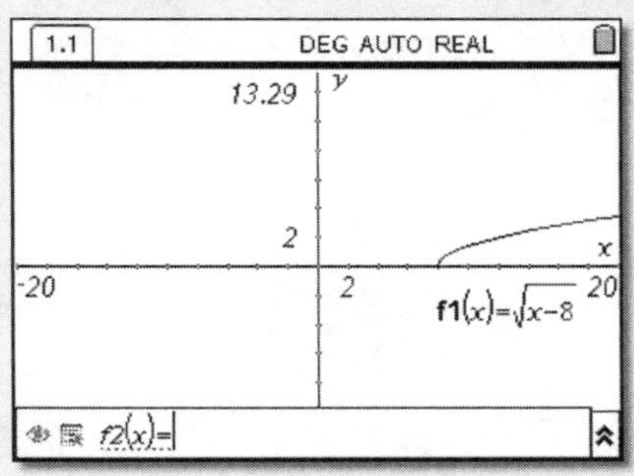

Use a handheld to graph each radical function.

1. $y = \sqrt{x + 2}$

2. $y = \sqrt{x + 3}$

3. $y = \sqrt{x - 5}$

4. $y = \sqrt{x - 2}$

5. $y = \sqrt{x - 4.9}$

6. $y = \sqrt{x - 7.8}$

7. $y = \sqrt{x + 11.1}$

8. $y = \sqrt{x + 5.6}$

9. $y = \sqrt{x} + 8$

10. $y = \sqrt{x} + 2$

11. $y = \sqrt{-x} - 4.1$

12. $y = \sqrt{-x} - 9.7$

13. $y = \sqrt{x + 5} - 3$

14. $y = \sqrt{x + 6} - 7$

15. $y = \sqrt{x - 3.3} - 10$

16. $y = \sqrt{x - 2.6} - 8$

17. $y = \sqrt{x - 7} + 4$

18. $y = \sqrt{x - 1} + 12$

19. $y = \sqrt{6x}$

20. $y = \sqrt{6x + 7}$

21. $y = \sqrt{6x - 7}$

22. $y = \sqrt{-6x}$

23. $y = \sqrt{-6x + 7}$

24. $y = \sqrt{-6x - 7}$

25. $y = \sqrt{6x} + 7$

26. $y = \sqrt{6x} - 7$

27. $y = \sqrt{-6x} + 7$

Use a handheld to graph each radical function.

28. $y = \sqrt{-6x} - 7$

29. $y = 2\sqrt{6x}$

30. $y = 2\sqrt{6x} + 7$

31. $y = 2\sqrt{6x} - 7$

32. $y = -2\sqrt{6x}$

33. $y = -2\sqrt{-6x}$

34. $y = \sqrt{3x}$

35. $y = \sqrt{4x}$

36. $y = \sqrt{1.8x}$

37. $y = \sqrt{3.4x}$

38. $y = \sqrt{-4x}$

39. $y = \sqrt{-2x}$

40. $y = \sqrt{5x - 11}$

41. $y = \sqrt{4x - 2}$

42. $y = \sqrt{1.1x + 3.5} + 7.9$

43. $y = \sqrt{5.5x + 6.1} + 9.1$

44. $y = 4\sqrt{-x + 8}$

45. $y = 2\sqrt{-x + 5}$

46. $y = -3\sqrt{x + 14}$

47. $y = -5\sqrt{x + 2}$

48. $y = -2\sqrt{x} + 8$

49. $y = -3\sqrt{x} + 9$

50. $y = 2\sqrt{x - 7} - 4$

51. $y = 3\sqrt{x - 1} - 5$

Problem Solving

52. Landscape Architecture Mitchell designed five square gardens, all with areas represented by the expression $3x^2 + 15$. Use a handheld to estimate to the nearest tenth the values of x for the areas 50 ft^2, 100 ft^2, 250 ft^2, 300 ft^2, and 400 ft^2.

____

53. Geometry The cover of Tehseen's circular swimming pool is 298 ft^2. The cover of Ole's circular swimming pool is 357 ft^2. Use a handheld to find the difference, rounded to the nearest whole number, in the diameters of their swimming pools. Use 3.14 for π. (*Hint:* The formula for the area of a circle is $A = \pi r^2$.)

____

CHALLENGE

54. At about what point(s) do the graphs of $y = \sqrt{x - 5}$ and $y = \frac{2}{x}$ intersect? Round the coordinates to the nearest tenth.

____

13-8 Technology: Compare Exponential Growth and Decay

Name ______________________________ Date ______________

Kitty deposited \$100 into an account that pays 7% interest compounded annually. To the nearest tenth of a year, how long will it take for the money she deposited to double?

Let $f(x)$ represent the amount in Kitty's account. Let x represent the number of years.

$f(x) = 100(1.07)^x$

You can use a handheld to graph the equation $y = 100(1.07)^x$.

Step 1 Press (home). Then choose (2) for **Graphs & Geometry**.

Step 2 Press (menu). Select **Window**, then **Window Settings**. Enter 0 for XMin, 30 for XMax, 100 for YMin, and 250 for YMax.

Step 3 Enter $100(1.07)^x$. Press (enter).

Remember: Growth slopes up. Decay slopes down.

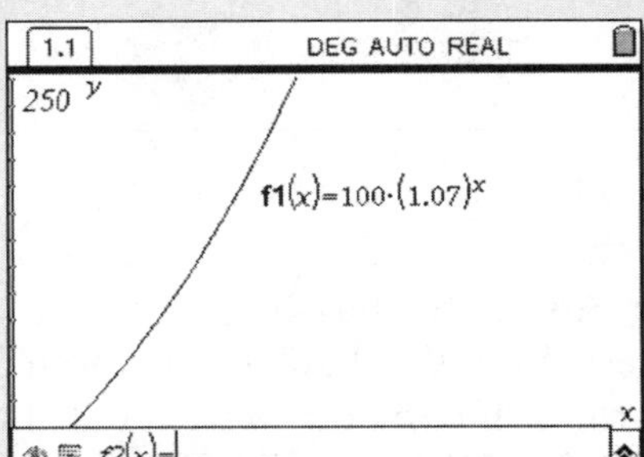

Step 4 Press (menu). Select **Trace**, then **Graph Trace**.

Step 5 Press (menu). Select **Trace**, then **Trace Settings**. Change **Trace Step** to 0.1.

Step 6 Press (▶) to move the trace along the curve until the first value of $y \geq 200$. The point is (10.3, 200.749).

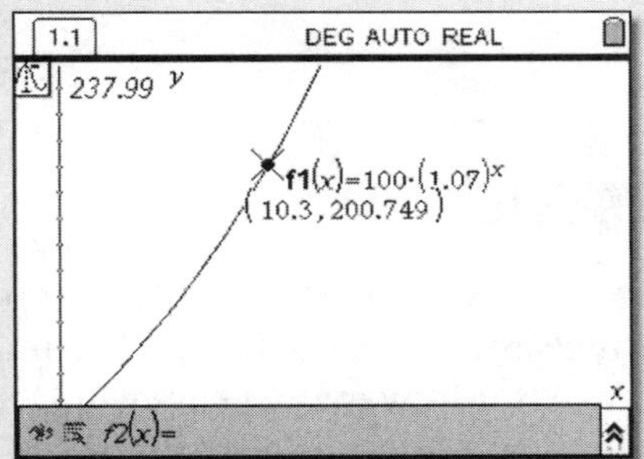

So Kitty will have \$200 in her account after 10.3 years.

Use a handheld to graph the function. Determine if it represents exponential growth or decay.

1. $y = 2.5^x$ growth

2. $y = 9.8^x$ ____________

3. $y = 0.5^{5x}$ ____________

4. $y = 0.9^{3x}$ ____________

5. $y = 15(1.2)^{0.3x}$ ____________

6. $y = 0.9(2.3)^{0.7x}$ ____________

7. $y = 13 + 8\left(\frac{2}{3}\right)^{0.7x}$ ____________

8. $y = 24 + 20\left(\frac{1}{4}\right)^{0.6x}$ ____________

9. $y = 3^{-x}$ ____________

10. $y = 6^{-2x}$ ____________

11. $y = 0.2^{-4x}$ ____________

12. $y = 0.8^{-6x}$ ____________

Solve.

13. Oscar deposits $500 into an account that pays 4% interest compounded annually. To the nearest tenth of a year, how many years will it take for his money to double?

Graph $y = 500(1.04)^x$ and find the value of x when $y = 2 \cdot 500 = 1000$.
It will take about 17.7 years for Oscar's money to double.

14. Lucy deposits $900 into an account that pays 5.5% interest compounded annually. To the nearest tenth of a year, how many years will it take for her money to triple?

15. The half-life of cesium-137 is about 30 years. To the nearest thousandth, about how many grams of a 10-g sample will be left after 120 years?

16. The half-life of sodium-22 is about 2.6 years. To the nearest thousandth, about how many grams of a 20-g sample will be left after 26 years?

17. The half-life of iron-59 is about 45 days. In about how many weeks and days will a 40-g sample have 5 grams remaining?

18. The half-life of oxygen-15 is about 120 seconds. In about how many minutes and seconds will a 100-g sample have 30 grams remaining?

Problem Solving

19. Finance Tony invests $900 at 6% compounded quarterly. Betta invests $500 at 8% compounded annually. After how many years will Betta's investment be worth more than Tony's?

20. Science A scientist has 40 grams of manganese-54 with a half-life of about 314 days and 50 grams of cobalt-57 with a half-life of about 270 days. Which will have a mass of 15 grams first? How many days before the other radioisotope?

CHALLENGE

21. Pia invested $1000 at 3% compounded monthly. Two years later, Yuri invested $600 at 7% compounded quarterly. How many years will it take for Yuri's investment to be worth more than Pia's?

13-9 Problem-Solving Strategy:
Organize Data

Read Plan Solve Check

Name ______________________________ Date __________

Solve by organizing data.

1. Simplify: $16^2 - 15^2 + 14^2 - 13^2 + 12^2 - 11^2 + \ldots + 4^2 - 3^2 + 2^2 - 1^2$

____

2. In how many different ways can a baseball team win a best of five playoff series?

____

3. In how many ways can the three slots _ _ _ be filled if the first must be filled from only among the numbers 1, 2, and 3; the second from among the letters A and B; and the third from among the symbols # and &?

____

4. How many rectangles are in the figure seen here?

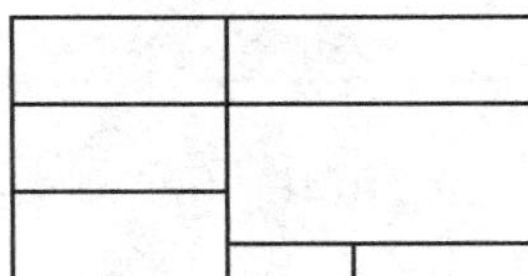

____

Use with SOURCEBOOK Lesson 13-9, pages 352–353.

5. Of 40 high school students, 14 are in theater, 21 are in band, 20 are in sports, and 6 are not involved in these three activities. Of the students involved with one or more of these activities, 2 are in both theater and band, 11 are in both band and sports, and 6 are in both theater and sports. If there are twice as many students who only play sports as students who are in all three activities, how many students are only in theater?

---

6. A certain code consists of four positive integers, each one less than a hundred. It is easy to remember because the integers are in numerical order from least to greatest and the first two numbers are the only such consecutive numbers that are both powers of whole numbers, and the last two numbers are the only such *consecutive odd* numbers that are both powers of whole numbers. What are the four numbers?

---

7. How many positive integers that are greater than or equal to 1,000,000 and less than or equal to 64,000,000 are perfect squares or perfect cubes or both perfect squares and perfect cubes?

---

8. How many triangles are in the figure seen here?

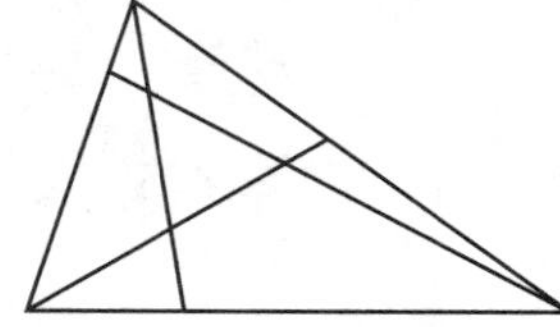

Enrichment:
Geometric Series

Name ______________________ Date __________

Suppose you deposit \$40 into a high-interest account at the start of each month. The account earns 6% interest a year, compounded monthly. Find the amount of money in the account after 15 months and after 30 months. Round to the nearest cent.

Calculate r. 6% compounded monthly: $\frac{0.06}{12} = 0.005$; so $r = 1.005$.

After 15 months: $S_n = a\frac{1 - r^n}{1 - r}$ ← Use the formula for calculating partial sums of a geometric series.

$S_{15} = (40)\frac{1 - (1.005)^{15}}{1 - 1.005}$ ← Substitute 40 for a, 1.005 for r, and 15 for n; Simplify.

≈ 621.46

After 30 months: $S_{30} = (40)\frac{1 - (1.005)^{30}}{1 - 1.005}$ ← Substitute 40 for a, 1.005 for r, and 30 for n; Simplify.

≈ 1291.20

After 15 months, the account has \$621.46; after 30 months it has \$1291.20.

Find S_6 and S_{16}. Round to the nearest hundredth.

1. $5 + 5(0.1) + 5(0.1)^2 + 5(0.1)^3 + \ldots$

$a = 5$; $r = 0.1$

$S_6 = 5 \cdot \frac{1 - 0.1^6}{1 - 0.1} \approx 5.56$

$S_{16} = 5 \cdot \frac{1 - 0.1^{16}}{1 - 0.1} \approx 5.56$

2. $7 + 7(1.5) + 7(1.5)^2 + 7(1.5)^3 + \ldots$

3. $12 + 12(2.75) + 12(2.75)^2 + 12(2.75)^3 + \ldots$

4. $19 + 19(3.025) + 19(3.025)^2 + 19(3.025)^3 + \ldots$

5. $31 + 31(0.57) + 31(0.57)^2 + 31(0.57)^3 + \ldots$

6. $84.1 + 84.1(1.1) + 84.1(1.1)^2 + 84.1(1.1)^3 + \ldots$

7. $75.3 + 75.3(2.2) + 75.3(2.2)^2 + 75.3(2.2)^3 + \ldots$

8. $99 + 99(2.5) + 99(2.5)^2 + 99(2.5)^3 + \ldots$

Find S_6 and S_{16}. Round to the nearest hundredth.

9. $250 + 250\left(\frac{3}{8}\right) + 250\left(\frac{3}{8}\right)^2 + 250\left(\frac{3}{8}\right)^3 + \ldots$

10. $400 + 400\left(\frac{16}{15}\right) + 400\left(\frac{16}{15}\right)^2 + 400\left(\frac{16}{15}\right)^3 + \ldots$

11. $1068 + 1068\left(\frac{7}{5}\right) + 1068\left(\frac{7}{5}\right)^2 + 1068\left(\frac{7}{5}\right)^3 + \ldots$

12. $1500 + 1500\left(\frac{9}{4}\right) + 1500\left(\frac{9}{4}\right)^2 + 1500\left(\frac{9}{4}\right)^3 + \ldots$

Solve.

13. Mrs. Topeka deposits \$35.25 in an account at the end of each week. The account earns 5.25% interest a year, compounded weekly. How much money is in the account at the end of 1 year? 3 years? Round to the nearest cent. (*Hint:* 1 yr = 52 weeks.)

14. Mr. Alvarez deposits \$11.11 in an account at the end of each day. The account earns 7.83% interest a year, compounded daily. How much money is in the account at the end of 360 days? 3 years? Round to the nearest cent. (*Hint:* 1 yr = 365 days.)

TEST PREPARATION

15. Which is the solution set for the inequality using interval notation?
$18 - 4x < 2(4 - x)$

A. $(5, \infty)$

B. $(-\infty, 5)$

C. $\left(\frac{10}{3}, \infty\right)$

D. $\left(-\infty, \frac{10}{3}\right)$

16. Which is the common denominator for $\frac{2x}{x-1} + \frac{5+x}{-1+x} = \frac{1}{2x}$?

F. $2x(x + 1)(x - 1)$

G. $-2x(x + 1)(x - 1)$

H. $2x(x - 1)$

J. $-2x(x - 1)$

Test Prep: Multiple-Choice Questions

Strategy: Apply Mathematical Reasoning

Name ______________________ Date ____________

When answering multiple-choice questions, try to think of a **related problem**. Sometimes it is helpful to break the problem into smaller parts.

To select the correct answer in a multiple-choice item, try using the following strategies.

- Underline important words.
- Restate the question.
- Use the Test-Prep strategy.
- Apply appropriate rules, definitions, properties, or strategies.
- Analyze and eliminate answer choices.

Choose the correct answer. *TIP: If you have time, go back to any problems you skipped.*

1. An antique vase increases in value at a rate of 10% per year. Its current value is $250. How much will it be worth in 6 years?

A. $132.86 **C.** $402.63
B. $400 **D.** $442.89

2. One leg of a right triangle measures x meters. The other leg is 0.75 the length of the first. What is the length of the hypotenuse?

F. $0.4375x$ m **H.** $1.5625x$ m
G. $1.25x$ m **J.** $1.75x$ m

3. Paul has a collection of 34 fiction and nonfiction books. He has 1 more than twice as many fiction books as nonfiction books. How many nonfiction books does he have?

A. 11 **C.** 18
B. 16 **D.** 23

4. A store sets the retail price of a DVD player at 220% of the wholesale price of $35. The DVD player later goes on sale for 15% off. What is the sale price of the DVD player?

F. $40.25 **H.** $77
G. $65.45 **J.** $88.55

5. A square has a side length of $x + 3$ in. A smaller square has a side length of $x - 4$ in. What is the difference in the areas of the squares?

A. $-2x + 25$ in.^{2}
B. $14x - 7$ in.^{2}
C. $x^2 - x - 12$ in.^{2}
D. $2x^2 - 2x + 25$ in.^{2}

6. A line has a slope of $-\frac{1}{2}$ and a y-intercept of 7. Which point is *not* on the line?

F. $(-10, 12.5)$
G. $(-3, 8.5)$
H. $(6, 4)$
J. $(12, 1)$

7. Solve: $|5 - 2x| \leq 9$

A. $-2 \leq x \leq 7$ **C.** $x \leq -2$ or $x \geq 7$
B. $-7 \leq x \leq 2$ **D.** $x \leq -7$ or $x \geq 2$

8. A map uses a scale of 0.5 in. : 4 mi. Kevin travels 3 mi south then 4 mi east to get to school. What is the map distance of Kevin's route to school?

F. 5 in. **H.** 1.75 in.
G. 2.5 in. **J.** 0.875 in.

Use with SOURCEBOOK Test Prep Lesson, page 356.

For More Practice Go To:
ONLINE www.progressinmathematics.com

Vocabulary Development

Name ______________________ Date __________

Chapter 13 Vocabulary

asymptotes
constant of variation
decay factor
exponential decay
exponential function
exponential growth
growth factor
hyperbola
inverse variation
radical function
square-root function

From the vocabulary list above, choose the term(s) that best complete each sentence. Write the term(s) in the space(s) provided.

1. In the equation $xy = 24$, 24 is called the ______________________.
2. A line that a graph approaches more and more closely without touching it is called a(n) ______________________.
3. One type of radical function is a(n) ______________________.
4. The graph of an inverse variation is a(n) ______________________.
5. A function in the form $y = ab^x$, where $a \neq 0$, $b \neq 1$, $b > 0$, and x is a real number, is called a(n) ______________________.
6. In the equation $y = 12(1.05)^x$, 1.05 is called the ______________________.
7. A quantity that increases by the same rate each time period shows ______________________.
8. A quantity that decreases by the same rate each time period shows ______________________.

Choose three terms from the list that you did not use in Questions 1–8. For each term, write a definition in your own words and give an example.

9. ____

Use after SOURCEBOOK Lessons 13-1–13-5, pages 330–345.

Practice Chapter 13 Test

Name ______________________________ Date ____________

Make a function table. Then graph the inverse variation on grid paper.

1. $xy = 40$

2. $xy = -24$

Solve each problem using $xy = k$.

3. y varies inversely as x, and $y = 2$ when $x = 9$. Find x when $y = 6$.

____

4. y varies inversely as x, and $y = 12.5$ when $x = 6$. Find y when $x = 4$.

____

Solve each problem using a proportion.

5. y varies inversely as x, and $y = -12$ when $x = 8$. Find x when $y = 4$.

____

6. y varies inversely as x, and $y = 1.4$ when $x = -2$. Find y when $x = 0.7$.

____

For each rational function, identify the asymptotes. On a separate sheet of paper, graph the asymptotes, make a function table, and graph the function.

7. $y = \frac{8}{x} + 2$

____

8. $y = \frac{4}{x} - 3$

____

9. $y = \frac{5}{x - 2}$

____

10. $y = \frac{1}{x + 3}$

____

11. $y = \frac{3}{x + 2} - 3$

____

12. $y = \frac{4}{x - 1} + 2$

____

For each function, make a function table. Graph each function on a separate sheet of paper. State the domain and range. Describe its relationship to the parent function $y = \sqrt{x}$.

13. $y = \sqrt{x + 11}$

14. $y = \sqrt{x - 25}$

15. $y = \sqrt{x} - 12$

16. $y = \sqrt{x} + 20$

17. $y = \sqrt{x + 3} - 8$

18. $y = \sqrt{x - 2} + 4$

Make a function table. On a separate sheet of paper, graph each pair of functions on the same coordinate plane. Describe their similarities and differences.

19. $y = \frac{1}{5}(2^x)$ and $y = 5(2^x)$

20. $y = 3(2^x)$ and $y = -3(2^x)$

Problem Solving

21. Science A colony of hares increases by 24% each year. How many years must pass for a colony of 48 hares to increase beyond 115 hares?

22. Population A town's population is 286,000. If it declines by 8% annually, in about how many years will the population be less than 180,000?

Tell About It

Explain how you solve the problem. Show all your work.

23. Logan invested \$4000 at 4% compounded quarterly. He wants to buy a car that costs \$28,000 now but depreciates 12% each year. If he leaves his money in the bank for 4 years and buys the car then, how much more money will he need?

Cumulative Review: Chapters 1–13

Name ______________________________ Date ______________

Circle the best answer.

1. Matrix A has dimensions 3×5. Matrix B has dimensions 5×4. What are the dimensions of matrix AB?

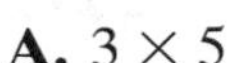

A. 3×5

B. 5×4

C. 3×4

D. 5×5

7. What is the domain of this function?

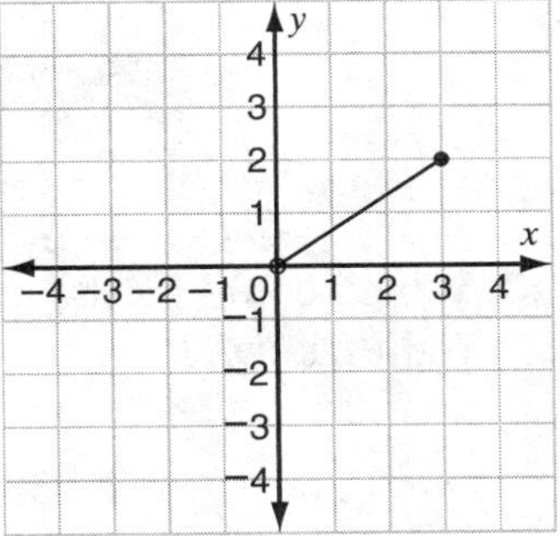

A. $\{x \mid 0 < x \leq 3\}$

B. $\{x \mid 0 \leq x < 3\}$

C. $\{y \mid 0 < y < 2\}$

D. $\{y \mid 0 < y \leq 2\}$

2. Solve: $\frac{d}{5} = -10$

F. $d = -2$ **G.** $d = -15$

H. $d = -50$ **J.** $d = -500$

8. Which line is parallel to $3x + 2y = 16$?

F. $2x + 3y = 16$ **G.** $3x - 2y = 16$

H. $3x + 2y = 20$ **J.** $2x - 3y = 20$

3. Solve: $-8 < g + 19$

A. $g > -27$ **B.** $g < -27$

C. $g > 11$ **D.** $g < 11$

9. Simplify: $(7a^2 + 5ab) - (4a^2 - 3ab - 11b^2)$

A. $3a^2 + 8ab + 11b^2$ **B.** $3a^2 + 2ab - 11b^2$

C. $3a^2 + 2ab + 11b^2$ **D.** $16a^2b^2$

4. Which equation is the slope-intercept form of $4x + 7y = 14$?

F. $7y = -4x + 14$ **G.** $x = -\frac{7}{4}x + \frac{7}{2}$

H. $y = -\frac{4}{7}x + 14$ **J.** $y = -\frac{4}{7}x + 2$

10. Multiply: $(2x^2 + 4x - 1)(2x^2 - 3x + 3)$

F. $4x^4 - 12x^2 - 3$
G. $4x^4 + 2x^3 - 8x^2 + 15x - 3$
H. $4x^4 + 14x^3 - 20x^2 + 15x - 3$
J. $4x^4 + 2x^6 - 8x^6 + 15x^2 - 3$

5. Solve: $\frac{y}{2} \geq -12$

A. $y \geq -24$ **B.** $y \leq -24$

C. $y \geq -6$ **D.** $y \leq -6$

11. Factor completely: $64m^2 - 81$

A. $(8m + 9)(8m + 9)$
B. $(8m - 9)(8m - 9)$
C. $(8m - 9)(8m + 9)$
D. $(32m - 27)(2m + 3)$

6. What is the solution of this system? $\begin{cases} x = 3y + 7 \\ x + 2y = -8 \end{cases}$

F. $(-2, 3)$ **G.** $(-3, -2)$

H. $(-2, -3)$ **J.** $(3, 2)$

12. Which is a factor of $2a^3 + 3a^2 + 10a + 15$?

F. $2a + 5$ **G.** $a^2 + 3$

H. $a^2 + 5$ **J.** $2a^2 + 15$

13. Simplify: $3\sqrt{18} - 2\sqrt{50} + 3\sqrt{8} + 4\sqrt{3}$

A. $9\sqrt{6}$ **B.** $5\sqrt{2} + 4\sqrt{3}$

C. $8\sqrt{79}$ **D.** $3\sqrt{2} + 6\sqrt{3}$

17. Divide: $\frac{2}{x^2 + x - 6} \div \frac{3}{x^2 - x - 2}$

A. $\frac{6(x + 1)}{x + 3}$ **B.** $\frac{x + 1}{x + 3}$

C. $\frac{2(x + 1)}{3(x + 3)}$ **D.** $\frac{4}{12}$

14. Which could be the lengths of the sides of a right triangle?

F. 3, 4, 6 **G.** 1, 3, 6

H. 2, $\sqrt{2}$, 6 **J.** 2, $\sqrt{2}$, $\sqrt{6}$

18. y varies inversely as x, and $y = 12$ when $x = 4$. Find x when $y = -8$.

F. -6 **G.** 16

H. 24 **J.** 32

15. Jolene measures a rectangular room as 20 m by 25 m. The actual measurements are 20.5 m by 25.4 m. What is the percent of error for the area to the nearest tenth percent?

A. 96.0% **B.** 4.1%

C. 4.0% **D.** 3.9%

19. The graph of which equation is a translation of $y = \frac{7}{x}$, 3 units to the left and 4 units down?

A. $y = \frac{7}{x - 4} + 3$ **B.** $y = \frac{7}{x + 3} + 4$

C. $y = \frac{7}{x + 3} - 4$ **D.** $y = \frac{7}{x - 4} - 3$

16. What is the vertex of parabola $y = 2x^2 + 8x - 7$?

F. (1, 3) **G.** $(-2, -7)$

H. (2, 17) **J.** $(-2, -15)$

20. Which function has a domain of $x \geq 7$?

F. $y = \sqrt{x} - 7$ **G.** $y = \sqrt{x} + 7$

H. $y = \sqrt{x + 7}$ **J.** $y = \sqrt{x - 7}$

Tell About It

Explain how you solve each problem. Show all your work.

21. Explain how the graphs of $y = -(5^x)$ and $y = \left(\frac{1}{5}\right)^x$ are related to the parent graph $y = 5^x$.

22. Victor invested $10,000 at 6% compounded monthly. Will his investment be worth enough in 10 years to pay at least half the cost of a $36,450 bill?

14-1 Sampling Techniques

Name ______________________ Date __________

Identify the population, sample, and variable. Tell whether the variable is qualitative or quantitative. Identify the sample method used. Determine whether or not the sample may be biased.

A ranger divides a forest into grids, and then counts the number of trees in several grids to estimate the total number of trees in the forest.

Population: the entire forest

Sample: the trees in several grids

Variable: the number of trees; quantitative

Think
Number is always quantitative.

The population is divided into groups and all trees in several groups are counted. This is cluster sampling.
This is a random sample if grids are randomly selected so all types of trees in the forest have an equal chance of being chosen. In this case the sample is unlikely to be biased.

Identify the population, sample, and variable. Tell whether the variable is qualitative or quantitative.

1. One week, a supermarket surveys every customer who enters to find out how customers rate the freshness of the produce.

Population: all customers of the store

Sample: customers who shopped that week

Variable: freshness of the produce; qualitative

2. Lisa asks her neighbors how they like the proposed city motto to determine how everyone in the city likes it.

3. For a month, fishermen record each type of fish caught in the lake to find which type of fish is most numerous.

4. City Hall counts the daily calls about local recreation events to find how many people are interested in each event.

5. A pollster speaks with every 10 visitors to the museum to see which exhibit is the most popular.

6. Paolo asks his friends about their favorite novelist to gauge which novelists are most popular amongst his grade.

Identify the sampling method used.

7. After shopping online, customers are asked to complete a survey.
Shoppers have the choice of completing the survey; voluntary response

8. A hardware store mails a survey to all its customers.

9. Oscar asks students in 7 out of 160 third-period classes if they know the school motto.

10. A movie theater polls every third person in line about his or her favorite type of movie.

Tell whether or not the sample may be biased. Explain.

11. Marissa puts all her classmates' names in a hat and draws 10 names. She asks them to name their favorite color.
Everyone has an equal chance of being chosen. The sample should not be biased.

12. The phone company calls all of its customers to ask them to rate its quality of service.

13. Students in a school music club were surveyed to determine the favorite pastime of high school students.

14. A phone survey asks every person in 4 out of 10 city districts about a new city ordinance.

Tell whether the survey question is biased or not. Explain.

15. What is your favorite color? Mine is red.
Biased; it suggests red.

16. Do you like the repressive new tardy policy?

17. What is your favorite brand of car?

18. What is your favorite type of pet?

Solve. Show all your work.

19. Wendy and Larry use a list of 100 people to conduct a survey. Wendy calls every third person on the list. Larry calls every fourth person on the list. What sampling method do they use? How many people received a call from both of them?

20. A park employee counts the number of squirrels in a 200-square-foot region to estimate the number of squirrels in the 5,000-square-foot park. What sampling method is used? If 17 squirrels are counted, about how many are in the park?

TEST PREPARATION

21. Tanya surveys everyone in her neighborhood to find the favored candidate in an election. Identify her sampling method.

A. systematic **B.** convenience **C.** cluster **D.** stratified

14-2 Measures of Central Tendency and Range

Name ____________________ Date __________

Find the mean, median, mode(s), and range of 95, 72, 64, 83, 72, 90.
Which measure of central tendency best describes the data?

Remember: Measures of central tendency are mean, median, and mode.

- mean: $\frac{476}{6} = 79\frac{1}{3}$ ← 476 is the sum of 6 data items.
- median: 64, 72, 72, 83, 90, 95; mean of 72 and 83: $\frac{72 + 83}{2} = 77.5$
- mode: 72 ← the number that occurs most often.
- range: $95 - 64 = 31$ ← the difference between the greatest and least values.

Both mean and median are close in value to most of the data, so the mean or the median best describes the data.

Find the mean, median, mode(s), and range of each data set. Determine which measure of central tendency best represents the data.

1. 33, 38, 30, 30, 39

mean: $\frac{170}{5} = 34$
median: 30, 30, <u>33</u>, 38, 39
mode: 30 occurs twice.
range: $39 - 30 = 9$
34; 33; 30; 9; mean or median

2. 52, 60, 52, 57, 64

____

3. 17, 90, 15, 16, 21

____

4. 34, 33, 2, 36, 37

____

5. 112, 145, 145, 120, 145

____

6. 81, 80, 80, 80, 98

____

7. 18, 33, 18, 18, 33, 18

____

8. 5, 10, 5, 5, 12, 5

____

9. 24.5, 26.5, 28.2, 32.4, 42.5, 49.9

____

10. 39.9, 40.5, 40.6, 41.5, 43.0, 43.5

____

11. $8\frac{5}{8}, 8\frac{1}{2}, 8\frac{5}{8}, 8\frac{3}{8}, 8\frac{7}{8}, 8\frac{3}{4}$

____

12. $5\frac{2}{3}, 4\frac{5}{6}, 4\frac{5}{6}, 3\frac{1}{3}, 5\frac{1}{6}, 6\frac{2}{3}$

____

Use the data set in Exercise 8. Find the mean, median, mode, and range of the new data set. Determine the effect of the linear transformation on the mean, median, mode, and range.

13. Add 10 to each number.

15, 20, 15, 15, 22, 15
mean: $\frac{102}{6} = 17$
median: 15, 15, <u>15</u>, <u>15</u>, 20, 22
mode: 15; range: 22 − 15 = 7
17; 15, 15; 7; mean, median, and mode are increased by 10 and range stays the same.

14. Subtract 30 from each number.

15. Multiply each number by 4.

16. Divide each number by 10.

Problem Solving

17. Nuria's neighbors collect cans to recycle. In 7 days, they collected 235, 287, 297, 242, 268, 41, and 275 cans. Identify any outlier(s). Find the mean, median, and mode(s) of the data set with and without the outlier. Does the mean, median, or mode change more without the outlier?

18. Irene's mean score on 5 tests is 88%. What is the lowest score she can get on her next test to raise her mean test score to 91%?

CHALLENGE

19. The range of five numbers is 10, the mean is 13.6, the median is 14, and there is no mode. Find a possible data set.

14-3 Stem-and-Leaf Plots

Name ______________________________ Date ______________

Make a stem-and-leaf plot of the data in the table.

Heights of High School Freshmen Males (in centimeters)
182, 178, 164, 175, 186, 181, 163, 152, 171, 160

For each number, list the tens and hundreds digits as Stem and the ones digit as Leaf. The stems range from 15 to 18.

- Write each stem on the left side.
- Write each corresponding leaf on the right side, in increasing order.
- Write a title and a key to show the meaning of each data in the plot.

Heights of High School Freshmen Males (in cm)

Stem	Leaf
15	2
16	0 3 4
17	1 5 8
18	1 2 6

Key: 15|2 represents 152.

Make a stem-and-leaf plot for each data set on a separate sheet of paper. Then find the measures of central tendency for the data set.

1.

Bowling Scores
112, 123, 109, 132, 156, 152, 167, 91, 128, 132, 149, 128, 132, 145, 97, 136, 138

Order data: 91, 97, 109, 112, 123, 128, 128, 132, 132, 132, 136, 138, 145, 149, 152, 156, 167

mean: $\frac{2227}{17}$ = 131; median: 132; mode: 132

Bowling Scores

Stem	Leaf
9	1 7
10	9
11	2
12	3 8 8
13	2 2 2 6 8
14	5 9
15	2 6
16	7

Key: 9|1 represents 91.

2.

Cricket Batting Averages
45, 21, 25, 31, 11, 8, 12, 29, 35, 24, 15, 6, 19, 21, 24, 17, 20, 7,11, 15, 36, 52

____

3.

High School Basketball Scores
68, 82, 53, 49, 52, 67, 79, 81, 49, 51, 58, 62, 64, 72, 71, 78, 60, 50, 48, 46

____

4.

Test Scores
71, 75, 88, 61, 98, 100, 99, 86, 87, 87, 84, 96, 73, 71, 94, 100, 81, 90, 87, 72

____

The double stem-and-leaf plot shows the number of bolts produced per minute by two machines. Use the plot for Exercises 5–9.

5. List the data values shown in the double stem-and-leaf plot.

Bolts Produced by Machines X and Y

Machine X Leaf	Stem	Machine Y Leaf
2 2	12	1 7 7 8
6 5 5 4	13	0 6 7 8 8 8 9
8 8 8 6 5 2	14	2 3 6
8 5	15	

Key: 2|12|1 represents 122 and 121.

6. Which machine's mean is greater? How much greater? What does this tell you about the machines?

7. Which machine's mean is closer to its median?

8. Which machine's range is greater? What does it mean?

9. Which machine's mode is greater?

SPIRAL REVIEW

10. Identify the asymptotes. On grid paper, graph the asymptotes, make a function table, and graph the function.

$y = \frac{1}{x - 5}$

11. Identify the asymptotes. On grid paper, graph the asymptotes, make a function table, and graph the function.

$y = \frac{3}{x} + 1$

12. Milton invested $12,000 at 4% compounded monthly. What will be the value of his investment after 10 years?

13. Simplify: $3 + \frac{2}{x - 1}$

14-4 Histograms

Name ______________________________ Date ______________

The frequency table shows the distances that workers commute one-way to work. It shows the frequency of each data value. It also shows the data divided into equal intervals.

Commuting to Work (in miles)	
Interval	**Frequency**
0–9	18
10–19	19
20–29	17
30–39	24
40–49	3
50–59	10

To organize and display the data, construct a histogram.

- Draw and label the horizontal and vertical axes.
- Determine a scale for the vertical axis, such as 0–30 by 2s.
- Draw bars that touch but do not overlap. The height of each bar is the frequency of each interval.
- Write a title for the histogram.

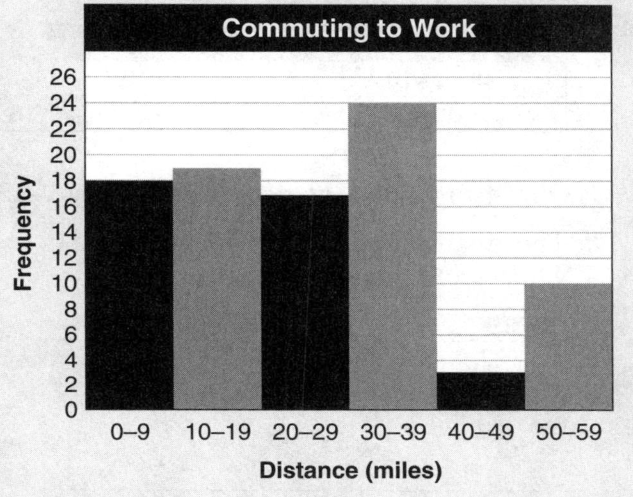

On a separate sheet of paper, make a histogram for each set of data.

1.

Length of Newborns (in mm)	
Interval	**Frequency**
400–449	6
450–499	38
500–549	32
550–599	11

2.

Number of Phone Calls by Teens in 24-Hour Period	
Interval	**Frequency**
0–4	2
5–9	21
10–14	26
15–19	15

3.

Number of Raisins in a Cookie	
Interval	**Frequency**
10–11	8
12–13	22
14–15	14
16–17	10

4.

Shoe Sizes	
Interval	**Frequency**
5–5.5	6
6–6.5	12
7–7.5	16
8–8.5	8
9–9.5	4

Use with SOURCEBOOK Lesson 14-4, pages 366–369.

5. On a separate sheet of paper, make a frequency table and a histogram of the data.

New Cars Sold			
Price	Number of Cars	Price	Number of Cars
\$10,000–\$14,999	𝍸	\$30,000–\$34,999	𝍸 /
\$15,000–\$19,999	𝍸 𝍸	\$35,000–\$39,999	𝍸 𝍸
\$20,000–\$24,999	///	\$40,000–\$44,999	////
\$25,000–\$29,999	𝍸 ////	\$45,000–\$49,999	//

6. On a separate sheet of paper, make a cumulative frequency table and a cumulative frequency histogram of the data.

Weight of Largemouth Bass Caught During a Tournament							
Weight (lb)	7–8	9–10	11–12	13–14	15–16	17–18	19–20
Frequency	3	12	16	12	9	4	2

Use the histogram at the right for Exercises 7–13.

7. The greatest number of students tested in which score range?

90–99

8. The fewest students tested in which score range?

9. How many students took the test?

10. How many students scored from 70 through 99 on the test?

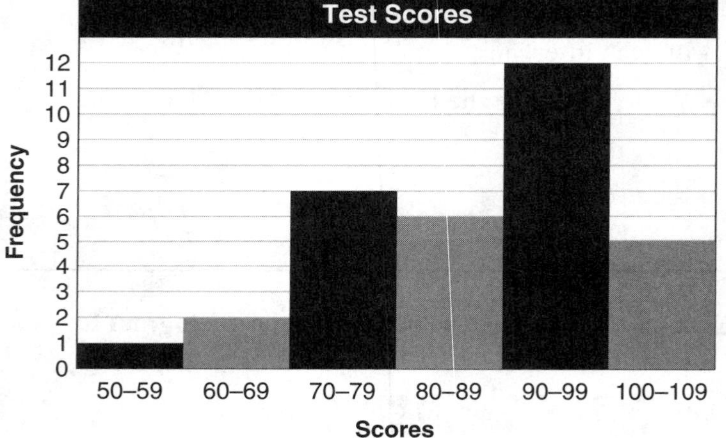

Problem Solving

11. What is the range of test scores? Explain.

12. What is the median score? Explain.

CRITICAL THINKING

13. What are the greatest and least possible mean test scores?

14-5 Quartiles and Box-and-Whisker Plots

Name ______________________ Date __________

The quiz scores for 10 students are shown in the table below.
Make a box-and-whisker plot to show the distribution of the data.

Quiz Scores										
Student	May	Hideki	Sal	Xin	Tonya	Maria	Wu	Olivia	Carlos	Yolanda
Score	16	12	18	19	20	16	17	14	10	12

- Order the data from least to greatest to find the quartiles and the median of the entire data set.

first quartile — 16 — third quartile

10 12 12 14 16 16 17 18 19 20

median of the lower half of the values — median — median of the upper half of the values

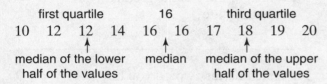

The minimum value is 10. The maximum value is 20.

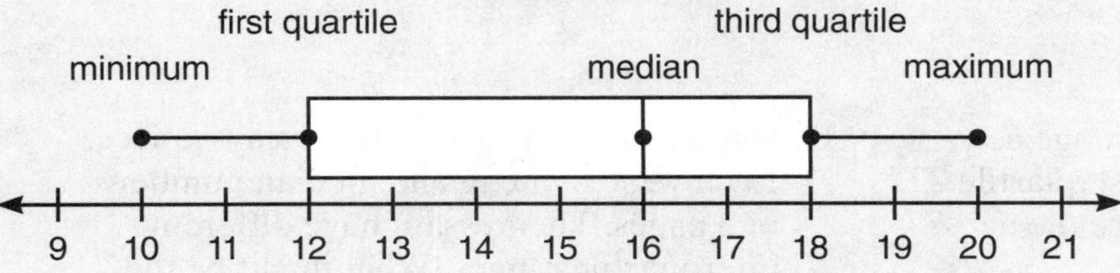

Find the first, second, and third quartiles and the interquartile range of each data set. Then make a box-and-whisker plot of the data on a separate sheet of paper.

1. 27, 38, 42, 29, 58

27, 29, 38, 42, 58
Q_2 (median) = 38
Q_1 = 27 + 29 = 56, 56 ÷ 2 = 28
Q_3 = 42 + 58 = 100, 100 ÷ 2 = 50
interquartile range: 50 − 28 = 22

2. 74, 82, 71, 86, 53

____

3. 91, 52, 48, 73, 86, 102

____

4. 19, 26, 34, 7, 16, 52

____

5. 22, 34, 41, 46, 52, 59, 62, 74, 38

____

6. 72, 48, 37, 62, 78, 49, 53, 33, 84

____

Use with SOURCEBOOK Lesson 14-5, pages 370–371.

Use the double box-and-whisker plot for Exercises 7–11.

7. What is the median battery life for Brand X?

____

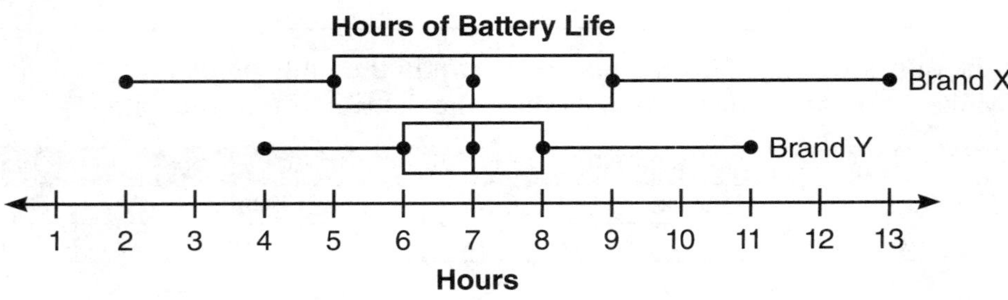

8. What is the third quartile battery life for Brand Y?

____

9. Which brand has the greatest range of battery life?

____

10. Which battery has the greatest interquartile range?

____

11. Which battery would you buy and why?

____

Problem Solving

12. The set of ages of five sisters has range 6, mean 23, median 23, no mode, first quartile 22, and interquartile range 2. What are the ages?

____

13. Carlos and Anya wrote five essays apiece. Each wrote a mean and median number of 3 pages. Their essays have different interquartile ranges. What might be the number of pages each wrote?

____

MENTAL MATH

14. 71(42) _______________

15. 135(98) _______________

16. 27(55) _______________

17. $29\frac{3}{4} + 13\frac{5}{6} + 37\frac{1}{4}$ _______________

18. $59 - 28\frac{2}{3}$ _______________

19. 234.9 + 11.2 + 50.1 _______________

14-6 Percentiles

Name ______________________ Date ____________

Find the percentile rank of 42 in the following 20 heights:
32, 34, 36, 37, 39, 39, 42, 42, 43, 43, 43, 44, 46, 48, 49, 50, 52, 52, 52, 55

- Add the number of heights less than 42 and one-half the number of 42s.

Number of heights less than 42 = 6
Half the number of 42 heights = + 1
7

- Divide the sum, 7, by the total number of heights, 20.

Write the quotient as a percent. $\frac{7}{20} = 0.35 = 35\%$

A height of 42 is at the 35th percentile.

Use the following data for Exercises 1–10.
72, 72, 75, 78, 79, 80, 80, 82, 84, 86, 88, 89, 90, 95, 98, 99, 100, 110, 110, 124

1. What is the percentile rank of 75?

number of data less than 75: 2
half the number of 75s: 0.5
sum: 2 + 0.5 = 2.5
$\frac{2.5}{20} = 0.125 = 12.5\%$ **or ≈ 13th percentile**

2. What is the percentile rank of 82?

3. What is the percentile rank of 80?

4. What is the percentile rank of 110?

5. What number is at the 25th percentile?

6. What number is at the 75th percentile?

7. What number is at the 20th percentile?

8. What number is at the 60th percentile?

9. What number is at the 15th percentile?

10. What number is at the 35th percentile?

Construct a cumulative frequency table based on the given frequency table. Then use the cumulative frequency to answer Exercises 11–12.

Interval	Frequency
0–10	22
11–20	15
21–30	11
31–40	29
41–50	23

11. Which interval contains the 25th percentile?

____

12. Which interval contains the 75th percentile?

____

Construct a cumulative frequency table based on the given frequency table. Then use the cumulative frequency to answer Exercises 13–14.

Interval	Frequency
0–100	11
101–200	5
201–300	19
301–400	10
401–500	6

13. Which interval contains the 25th percentile?

____

14. Which interval contains the 75th percentile?

____

Problem Solving

The table at the right shows the scores on 80 math tests. Use the table to answer Exercises 15–16.

Interval	Cumulative Frequency
0–20	6
21–40	25
41–60	57
61–80	75
81–100	80

15. How many students scored 61–80?

____

16. On a separate sheet of paper, construct a cumulative frequency histogram.

WRITE ABOUT IT

17. Explain how to use the histogram you constructed in Exercise 16 to find the approximate score of a student scoring in the 80th percentile.

____

____

____

14-7 Scatter Plots

Name ______________________________ Date ______________

Make a scatter plot of the data at the right to show the relationship between the height and age of trees. Determine the type of correlation, if any. If there is a correlation, determine whether the relationship is likely to be causal.

Age (years)	Height (ft)
1	2
2	5
3	6
4	12
5	13
6	18
7	19
8	23

- Draw and label an axis for each set of data. Label the horizontal axis *Age* and the vertical axis *Height*.
- Create a scale for the graph.
- Graph a point for each ordered pair in the table.

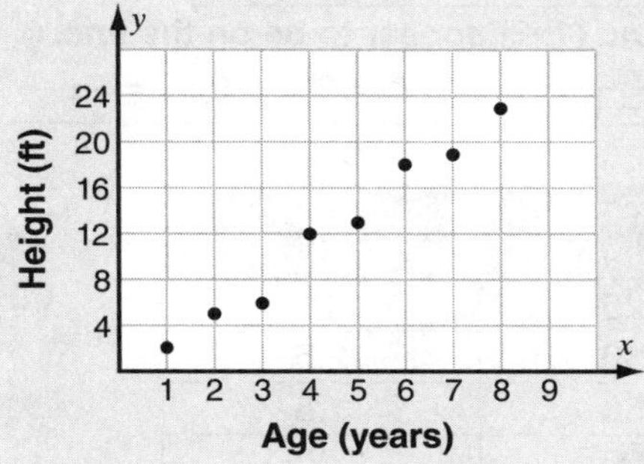

The points rise, so the scatter plot shows a positive correlation. Trees get taller as they age, so the relationship is likely to be causal.

Remember: Not every positive or negative correlation is a causal relationship.

Select the graph that most likely represents the relationship.

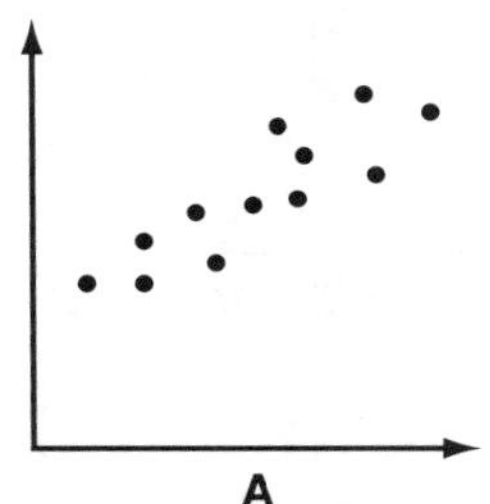

A

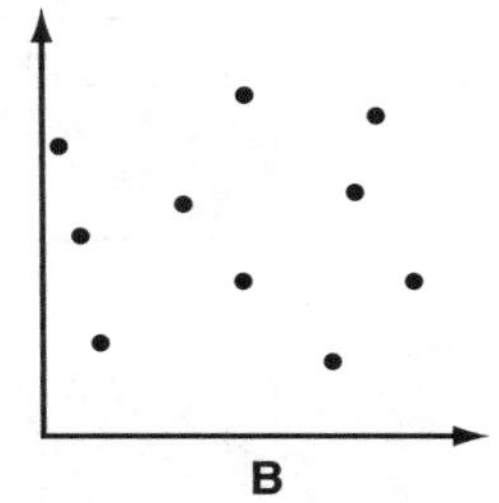

B

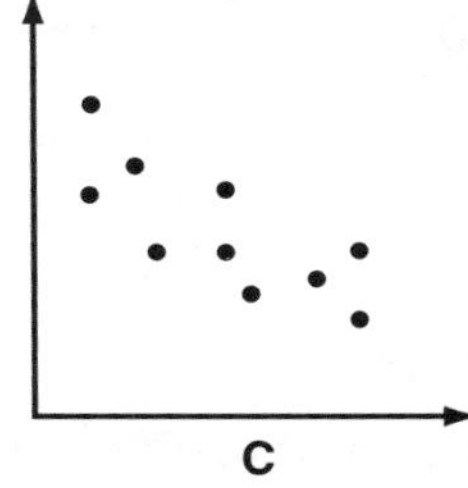

C

1. tree's age and diameter
A
Trunks thicken as trees age.

2. used car's age and its value ______________

3. time reading and height ______________

Determine the type of correlation (if any) between the two data sets. If there is a correlation, determine whether the relationship is causal.

4. driving distance and gas used
As distance increases, more gas is used.
Positive, causal.

5. degrees outside and air conditioning cost ______________

6. nose length and time spent reading ______________

7. day of week and amount of rain ______________

8. miles driven and tire tread depth ______________

9. exercise time and heart rate ______________

On a separate sheet of paper make a scatter plot of each data. Draw a line of best fit and then write an equation of the line.

10.

Years	$ Savings (thousands)
1	2
2	5
3	7
4	8
5	9
6	15
7	16
8	17

(0, 0) and (1, 2) appear to be on the line.
$m = \frac{2 - 0}{1 - 0} = 2$; $y - 0 = 2(x - 0)$; $y = 2x$

11.

Number of Employees	Accidents per Month
2	0
4	1
5	2
8	10
12	11
20	13
30	15
40	20

12.

Car Speed (mph)	Time to Destination (hr)
25	3
30	2.5
50	1.5
60	1.25
75	1
100	0.75
125	0.6
150	0.5

13.

Time Reading (hr)	Time Watching TV (hr)
0	3
1	2.5
1.5	2
2	1.5
2.5	1.25
3	1
3.5	0.75
4	0.5

Problem Solving

Use the scatter plot for Exercises 14–16.

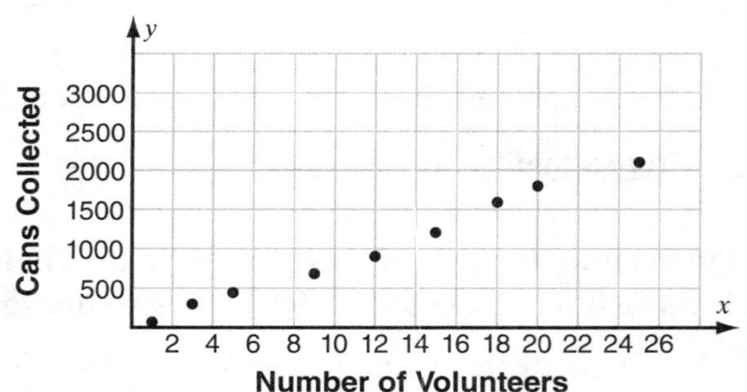

14. About how many cans could 7 people collect?

15. About how many volunteers would be needed to collect 3000 cans?

TEST PREPARATION

16. Which best describes the correlation?

A. positive, causal **B.** negative, causal **C.** positive, not causal **D.** no correlation

14-8 Empirical Probability

Name ______________________________ Date ______________

A bag contains five different colors of blocks. Ben drew a block, recorded the color, and put the block back into the bag. The table shows the number of times Ben drew each color. About how many purple blocks would you predict in 230 draws?

Outcome	Frequency
blue	7
green	11
yellow	19
purple	10
orange	3

- Find the experimental probability of drawing purple.

$$\text{Exp } P(\text{purple}) = \frac{\text{number of purples drawn}}{\text{total number of trials}} = \frac{10}{50} = 0.2 = 20\%$$

- Find 20% of 230. (0.2)230 = 46 ⟵ Write 20% as a decimal.

So you would predict about 46 purple blocks in 230 draws.

Devon draws cards with shapes and records the outcomes. Use the table at the right for Exercises 1–8.

Outcome	Frequency
star	7
diamond	3
half-moon	8
hexagon	1
lightning bolt	2
trapezoid	4

1. What is the experimental probability of drawing a diamond?

Exp P(diamond) = $\frac{3}{25}$ = 0.12 = 12%

$\frac{3}{25}$, or 0.12, or 12%

2. What is the experimental probability of drawing a half-moon?

____

3. What is the experimental probability of drawing a star or hexagon?

____

4. What is the experimental probability of drawing a trapezoid or lightning bolt?

____

5. Predict about how many stars would be drawn in 300 draws.

____

6. Predict about how many trapezoids would be drawn in 400 draws.

____

7. About how many of 560 draws would be hexagons or half-moons?

____

8. About how many of 730 draws would be stars or trapezoids?

____

Use with SOURCEBOOK Lesson 14-8, pages 378–379.

Lydia spins a spinner and records the outcomes. Use the table for Exercises 9–14.

Outcome	Frequency
A	17
B	19
C	22
D	42
E	16
F	21
G	34
H	29

9. What is the experimental probability of landing on B?

Exp P(B) = $\frac{19}{200}$ = 0.095 = 9.5%

$\frac{19}{200}$, or 0.095, or 9.5%

10. What is the experimental probability of landing on F?

11. What is the experimental probability of landing on C or F?

12. What is the experimental probability of landing on A or G?

13. Predict about how many times the spinner would land on E in 300 spins.

14. Predict about how many times the spinner would land on B or G in 572 spins.

Problem Solving

15. Mary caught, tagged, and released 50 fish at Blue Lake. The next day, she caught and released 30 fish. Only 2 had tags. About how many fish are in Blue Lake?

16. Hugh has 2 pounds of seeds. He planted 200 seeds weighing 8 ounces and got 129 yellow plants and 71 orange plants. About how many orange plants he will get if he plants all the seeds?

WRITE ABOUT IT

17. Peter drew marbles from a bag, recorded the colors, and returned them to the bag. He drew 33 red, 12 green, and 5 yellow marbles in 50 draws. He claims that the bag contains only red, green, and yellow marbles, and most are red. Is Peter correct? Explain.

14-9 Theoretical Probability

Name ______________________ Date __________

Morgan's class has 25 students, all with different first names. The name of each student is written on a card and the cards are shuffled. One card is drawn at random. What is the probability that the card with Morgan's name is chosen?

$P(\text{Morgan}) = \frac{1}{25}$ ← number of students named Morgan / ← total number of students

Remember: For experiments with equally likely outcomes,

$P(E) = \frac{\text{number of favorable outcomes}}{\text{total number of possible outcomes}}$

A 1–12 dodecahedron is rolled. Find the probability of each event.

1. $P(6)$

equally likely outcomes
1 favorable, 12 possible; $\frac{1}{12}$

2. $P(10)$ ______

3. $P(1 \text{ or } 7)$ ______

4. $P(2 \text{ or } 9)$ ______

5. $P(1, 2, \text{ or } 5)$ ______

6. $P(5, 7, \text{ or } 11)$ ______

7. $P(\text{not } 4)$ ______

8. $P(\text{not } 10)$ ______

9. $P(\text{less than } 7)$ ______

10. $P(\text{less than } 9)$ ______

11. $P(\text{greater than } 2)$ ______

12. $P(\text{greater than } 8)$ ______

13. $P(\text{greater than } 12)$ ______

14. $P(\text{less than } 1)$ ______

15. $P(\text{greater than } 0)$ ______

16. $P(\text{less than } 13)$ ______

17. $P(\text{multiple of } 3)$ ______

18. $P(\text{multiple of } 4)$ ______

A letter is chosen at random from the word MATHEMATIC. Find the probability of the complement of the event.

19. choose H

$P(\text{not H}) = 1 - P(\text{H})$

$= 1 - \frac{1}{10} = \frac{9}{10} = 0.9 = 90\%$

$\frac{9}{10}$, or 0.9, or 90%

20. choose C

21. choose M or C

22. choose T or A

23. choose a vowel

24. choose a consonant

25. choose A, E, or M

26. choose T, I, or C

27. choose B

Problem Solving

28. A spinner is divided in equal parts colored red, green, or yellow. The probability of landing on red is twice the probability of landing on green. The probability of landing on green is three times the probability of landing on yellow. What is the probability of landing on red?

29. Lee rolls a 1–20 icosahedron and May rolls a 1–24 deltoidal icositetrahedron. Lee wins if he lands on a multiple of 4. May wins if she lands on a number less than 8. Who has a greater probability of winning? how much greater?

SPIRAL REVIEW

30. Simplify: $3\sqrt{3} \bullet 2\sqrt{14} \bullet 3\sqrt{6}$

31. $(r - 7)^2$

32. Are the lines parallel, perpendicular, or neither?

$3x + 2y = 9$ and $y = 5x + 9$

33. Is the sequence algebraic, geometric, or neither?

$160, 40, 10, \frac{5}{2}, \ldots$

14-10 Independent and Dependent Events

Name ______________________________ Date ______________

Raini spins the spinner at the right twice. What is the probability of spinning A first and E second?

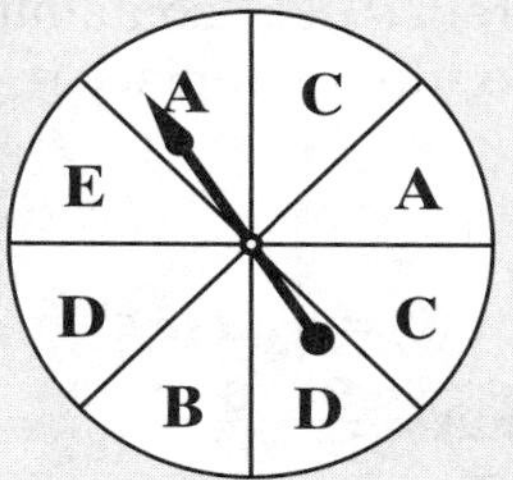

Landing on A first does not affect the probability of landing on E second. The events are independent.

$P(\text{A, E}) = P(\text{A}) \bullet P(\text{E})$

$= \frac{2}{8} \bullet \frac{1}{8}$ ← There are 8 sectors, 2 with A and 1 with E.

$= \frac{2}{64} = \frac{1}{32}$

So the probability of spinning A first and E second is $\frac{1}{32}$.

Remember:
If A and B are independent events, then $P(\text{A, B}) = P(\text{A}) \bullet P(\text{B})$.
If A and B are dependent events, then $P(\text{A, B}) = P(\text{A}) \bullet P(\text{B after A})$.

On a separate sheet of paper, draw a tree diagram and use the Fundamental Counting Principle to find the number of possible outcomes.

1. Spin a spinner with equal sectors labeled 1, 2, and 4 three times.

   3 • 3 • 3 = 27; 27

2. Roll a 1–6 number cube twice.

   ____

3. Toss a coin twice and roll a 1–6 number cube.

   ____

4. Choose an entree, salad, and drink from 6 entrees, 4 salads, and 3 drinks.

   ____

5. Spin a spinner with equal sectors labeled 1 and 2 and toss a coin three times.

   ____

6. Choose an omelet, potato, and toast from 4 omelets, 3 types of potatoes, and 4 types of toast.

   ____

Use the Fundamental Counting Principle to find the number of possible outcomes.

7. Choose a shirt, pants, shoes, and jacket from 8 shirts, 9 pairs of pants, 4 pairs of shoes, and 3 jackets.

   8 • 9 • 4 • 3 = 864; 864

8. Choose a blouse, skirt, scarf, and shoes from 10 blouses, 6 skirts, 5 scarves, and 10 pairs of shoes.

   ____

9. Pick one name from a list of 32 names and another name from a list of 17 names.

   ____

10. Pick a student from a class of 30 students and another student from a class of 32 students.

   ____

11. Spin a spinner with equal sectors labeled A through Z twice and toss a coin 5 times.

   ____

12. Roll a 1–6 number cube twice and choose a name from a hat with 12 names in it.

   ____

Determine whether the events are independent or dependent. Then find the probability.

13. Draw a 2 from a deck containing five 2s, six 3s, and three 4s, do not replace it, then draw a 3.

dependent; $P(2) = \frac{5}{14}$, $P(3 \text{ after } 2) = \frac{6}{13}$
$P(2, 3 \text{ after } 2) = \frac{5}{14} \cdot \frac{6}{13} = \frac{30}{182} = \frac{15}{91}; \frac{15}{91}$

14. Draw a green disc from a bag containing 3 yellow, 5 green, and 4 blue discs, do not replace it, then draw a yellow disc.

15. Pick an X from a bag containing 12 Xs, 9 Ys, and 3 Zs, replace it, then pick a Y.

16. Pick a vowel (A, E, I, O, U, or Y) from a bag containing all 26 letters of the alphabet, replace it, then pick a consonant.

17. Choose 2 apples to eat from a bowl containing 6 apples, 8 oranges, and 4 bananas.

18. Choose 2 girls from a class of 12 boys and 8 girls.

Problem Solving

19. Joanna has a bag of 6 green, 1 yellow, and 3 purple blocks. She draws a block, replaces it, and then draws another block. What is the probability that the two blocks are the same color?

20. Bo has a pail of 8 bolts that are 2 inches long, 10 that are $2\frac{1}{16}$ inches long, and 2 that are $2\frac{1}{8}$ inches long. He picks and keeps 2 bolts. What is the probability that they are not the same length?

CHALLENGE

21. Ted rolls a 1–6 number cube twice. What is the probability that the sum is greater than 8?

14-11 Mutually Exclusive Events

Name ______________________________ Date ____________

Mary picks a seedling at random from 20 pine, 12 fir, and 7 spruce seedlings. What is the probability that it is a pine or spruce seedling?

The events are mutually exclusive, or disjoint.

Remember: Mutually exclusive, or disjoint, events have no outcome in common.

Total number of possible outcomes: $20 + 12 + 7 = 39$

Number of favorable outcomes: $20 + 7$ ← A *or* B contains 27 of the 39 possible outcomes.

$$P(\text{A } or \text{ B}) = \frac{20}{39} + \frac{7}{39}$$ ← $P(\text{A or B}) = P(\text{A}) + P(\text{B})$

$$= \frac{27}{39}$$

So the probability of picking a pine or spruce seedling is $\frac{27}{39}$.

Determine if the events are *mutually exclusive* or *overlapping*.

1. Spinning an even number or a multiple of 4 on a spinner with 10 equal sectors numbered 1–10

4 and 8 are both even and multiples of 4; overlapping

2. Rolling a prime number or a multiple of 3 on a 1–30 rhombic triacontahedron

____

3. Rolling an odd number or an even number on a 1–6 number cube

____

4. Rolling 5 or a multiple of 3 on a 1–6 number cube

____

5. Rolling a sum of 5 or doubles on two 1–6 number cubes

____

6. Rolling 6 and 3 or a sum of 8 on two 1–6 number cubes

____

7. Choosing red or 5 from a deck of ten 1–10 red and ten 1–10 blue cards

____

8. Choosing blue or an even number from a deck of ten 1–10 red and ten 1–10 blue cards

____

9. Drawing a letter in ACE or in SIX from all the letters of the alphabet

____

10. Drawing a consonant or a vowel from all the letters of the alphabet

____

11. Drawing an even number or a multiple of 4

____

12. Drawing a factor of 98 or a power of 7

____

Use with SOURCEBOOK Lesson 14-11, pages 386–387.

A bag contains 10 red blocks numbered 1–10, 10 green blocks numbered 6–15, and 10 orange blocks numbered 16–25. A block is selected at random from the bag. Determine if the events are mutually exclusive or overlapping. Then find the probability.

13. *P*(red or green)

mutually exclusive
$\frac{10}{30} + \frac{10}{30} = \frac{20}{30} = \frac{2}{3}; \frac{2}{3}$

14. *P*(red or orange)

15. P(red or even)

16. *P*(orange or odd)

17. *P*(less than 10 or greater than 20)

18. *P*(less than 19 or greater than 22)

19. *P*(orange or a multiple of 5)

20. *P*(green or a multiple of 7)

Problem Solving

21. In Jose's class, 25 students like pizza, 22 like hamburgers, and 17 like both. His teacher selects a student at random. What is the probability that the student likes only pizza or only hamburgers?

22. A spinner is divided into 6 equal sectors labeled 1–6. Grace spun the spinner three times. What is the probability that the sum of her spins is less than 13 or greater than 15?

WRITE ABOUT IT

23. How can a Venn diagram of two mutually exclusive events model the formulas for mutually exclusive and overlapping events?

14-12 Conditional Probability

Name ______________________________ Date ____________

The probability that a person owns a dog is $\frac{5}{8}$. The probability that a person owns a dog and drives a truck is $\frac{2}{5}$. What is the probability that a person drives a truck given that he or she owns a dog?

$$P(\text{drives a truck} \mid \text{owns a dog}) = \frac{P(\text{owns a dog and drives a truck})}{P(\text{owns a dog})} \leftarrow P(B \mid A) = \frac{P(A \text{ and } B)}{P(A)}$$

$$= \frac{\frac{2}{5}}{\frac{5}{8}} \leftarrow \text{Substitute given values into the formula for conditional probability.}$$

$$= \frac{2}{5} \bullet \frac{8}{5} = \frac{16}{25}$$

So the probability that a person drives a truck given that he or she owns a dog is $\frac{16}{25}$.

Find $P(B \mid A)$.

1. $P(A \text{ and } B) = \frac{3}{7}$; $P(A) = \frac{1}{2}$

$\frac{\frac{3}{7}}{\frac{1}{2}} = \frac{3}{7} \bullet \frac{2}{1} = \frac{6}{7}; \frac{6}{7}$

2. $P(A \text{ and } B) = \frac{5}{9}$; $P(A) = \frac{3}{4}$

3. $P(A \text{ and } B) = 15\%$; $P(A) = 40\%$

4. $P(A \text{ and } B) = 25\%$; $P(A) = 40\%$

5. $P(A \text{ and } B) = 12\%$; $P(A) = 44\%$

6. $P(A \text{ and } B) = 8\%$; $P(A) = 30\%$

7. $P(A \text{ and } B) = 0.\overline{3}$; $P(A) = 0.\overline{6}$

8. $P(A \text{ and } B) = 0.2\overline{7}$; $P(A) = 0.\overline{11}$

Find the conditional probability.

9. In a school, 50% of students have dark hair and 30% of students are boys with dark hair. What is the probability that a student is a boy given that the student has dark hair?

$\frac{0.3}{0.5} = \frac{3}{5} = 0.6$ or 60%

The probability is 60%.

10. A survey shows that 80% of people own two cars and 40% of people own two cars and a boat. What is the probability that a person owns a boat given that the person owns two cars?

Find the conditional probability.

11. The probability of buying kiwi is 8% and the probability of buying melon and kiwi is 5%. What is the probability that a shopper buys melon given that he or she buys kiwi?

12. The probability that a nurse wears white is 80% and the probability that a nurse wears white and carries a stethoscope is 70%. What is the probability that a nurse carries a stethoscope given that he or she wears white?

13. At a food stand, 55% of customers bought hamburgers and 20% of customers bought hamburgers and hot dogs. What is the probability that a person bought hot dogs given that he or she bought hamburgers?

14. A florist found that 45% of customers bought roses and 40% of customers bought roses for a spouse. What is the probability that a customer bought for a spouse given that he or she bought roses?

Problem Solving

Use the situation for Exercises 15–17.

Jar 1 has 4 green tickets and 3 red tickets. Jar 2 has 2 green tickets and 4 red tickets. A spinner has 3 equal sectors labeled 1, 1, and 2. The spinner is spun to decide which container to draw the ticket from.

15. What is the probability that a drawn ticket came from jar 1 given that the ticket is green?

16. What is the probability that a drawn ticket came from jar 2 given that the ticket is red?

CRITICAL THINKING

17. What is the probability that a drawn ticket did not come from jar 1 given that the ticket is not red?

14-13 Permutations

Name ______________________________ Date ____________

Susan has 42 DVDs. She randomly chooses 5 DVDs to watch with her friends. How many ways can they watch 5 DVDs?

To find how many ways, find ${}_{42}P_5$.

Remember: A permutation is an arrangement of objects where the order matters.

$${}_{42}P_5 = \frac{42!}{(42-5)!}$$ ← Use the formula: ${}_nP_r = \frac{n!}{(n-r)!}$

$$= \frac{42!}{37!} = \frac{42 \bullet 41 \bullet 40 \bullet 39 \bullet 38 \bullet 37 \bullet 36 \bullet 35 \bullet\bullet\bullet 4 \bullet 3 \bullet 2 \bullet 1}{37 \bullet 36 \bullet 35 \bullet\bullet\bullet 4 \bullet 3 \bullet 2 \bullet 1}$$ ← Apply the definition of factorial.

$$= \frac{42 \bullet 41 \bullet 40 \bullet 39 \bullet 38 \bullet \cancel{37} \bullet \cancel{36} \bullet \cancel{35} \bullet\bullet\bullet \cancel{4} \bullet \cancel{3} \bullet \cancel{2} \bullet \cancel{1}}{\cancel{37} \bullet \cancel{36} \bullet \cancel{35} \bullet\bullet\bullet \cancel{4} \bullet \cancel{3} \bullet \cancel{2} \bullet \cancel{1}} = 102{,}080{,}160$$ ← Simplify.

So there are 102,080,160 ways they can watch 5 out of 42 DVDs.

Evaluate each expression.

1. ${}_7P_4$

$$\frac{7!}{(7-4)!} = \frac{7!}{3!}$$

$$\frac{7 \bullet 6 \bullet 5 \bullet 4 \bullet \cancel{3} \bullet \cancel{2} \bullet \cancel{1}}{\cancel{3} \bullet \cancel{2} \bullet \cancel{1}} = 840;\ 840$$

2. ${}_7P_2$ ____________

3. ${}_7P_1$ ____________

4. ${}_8P_1$ ____________

5. ${}_{20}P_2$ ____________

6. ${}_{14}P_2$ ____________

7. ${}_8P_5$ ____________

8. ${}_8P_4$ ____________

9. ${}_{12}P_3$ ____________

10. ${}_{15}P_3$ ____________

11. ${}_{16}P_1$ ____________

12. ${}_{40}P_1$ ____________

13. ${}_{18}P_3$ ____________

14. ${}_{19}P_3$ ____________

15. ${}_4P_4$ ____________

Find the number of possible arrangements of the letters.

16. L, M, N, N

2 N's: $\frac{4!}{2!} = \frac{4 \cdot 3 \cdot \cancel{2} \cdot \cancel{1}}{\cancel{2} \cdot \cancel{1}} = 12$; 12

17. L, L, L, M

18. L, L, M, M, N

19. L, L, L, M, M

20. BOOKS

21. GREET

22. HAWAII

23. POTATO

24. AARDVARK

25. GUESSES

26. SCHOLASTICISM

27. MISSISSIPPI

Problem Solving

28. Mr. Landis randomly chooses a boy and a girl from his class of 18 boys and 13 girls to be peer tutors. How many ways can he choose a boy and a girl? How many ways can he randomly choose any two students? What is the difference in methods?

29. Don made a CD of 6 songs. Lena will make a label listing the songs. If Don forgets to tell Lena the order of the songs, what is the probability that Lena lists the song titles in the correct order?

MENTAL MATH

30. 129(30)

31. $9 \cdot 8 \cdot 6 \cdot 5$

32. $15\frac{2}{5} + 5\frac{3}{10} + 19\frac{7}{10}$

33. $74 - 33\frac{1}{5}$

14-14 Combinations

Name ______________________ Date ____________

Ana tosses a penny 7 times. How many different ways can she toss 3 heads?

Find the number of combinations of 7 objects taken 3 at a time, ${}_7C_3$.

> **Remember:** A combination is an arrangement of objects where the order is *not* important.

$${}_7C_3 = \frac{7!}{3!(7-3)!} \quad \longleftarrow \text{Use the formula } {}_nC_r = \frac{n!}{r!(n-r)!}.$$

$$= \frac{7!}{3!4!} = \frac{7 \cdot 6 \cdot 5 \cdot 4 \cdot 3 \cdot 2 \cdot 1}{3 \cdot 2 \cdot 1 \cdot 4 \cdot 3 \cdot 2 \cdot 1} \quad \longleftarrow \text{Apply the definition of factorial.}$$

$$= \frac{7 \cdot \not{6} \cdot 5 \cdot \not{4} \cdot \not{3} \cdot \not{2} \cdot \not{1}}{\not{3} \cdot \not{2} \cdot \not{1} \cdot \not{4} \cdot \not{3} \cdot \not{2} \cdot \not{1}} = 35 \quad \longleftarrow \text{Simplify.}$$

So Ana can toss 3 heads out of 7 tosses in 35 ways.

Evaluate each expression.

1. ${}_7C_5$

$$\frac{7!}{5!(7-5)!} = \frac{7!}{5!2!}$$

$$\frac{7 \cdot \overset{3}{\not{6}} \cdot \not{5} \cdot \not{4} \cdot \not{3} \cdot \not{2} \cdot \not{1}}{\not{5} \cdot \not{4} \cdot \not{3} \cdot \not{2} \cdot \not{1} \cdot \not{2} \cdot \not{1}} = 21; \ 21$$

2. ${}_7C_2$ ____________

3. ${}_{12}C_1$ ____________

4. ${}_{17}C_1$ ____________

5. ${}_{20}C_2$ ____________

6. ${}_{14}C_2$ ____________

7. ${}_9C_5$ ____________

8. ${}_{10}C_5$ ____________

9. ${}_{12}C_{11}$ ____________

10. ${}_{15}C_{14}$ ____________

11. ${}_{16}C_{13}$ ____________

12. ${}_{40}C_{38}$ ____________

13. ${}_{18}C_{15}$ ____________

14. ${}_{19}C_{17}$ ____________

15. ${}_{20}C_{17}$ ____________

Solve. Show your work.

16. How many ways can Moe choose 4 players from 8 friends?

17. How many ways can Xi choose 2 flavors from 12 flavors?

18. A bag contains 4 blue and 6 yellow marbles. How many groups of 6 marbles will have 2 blue and 4 yellow marbles?

19. A bag contains 9 striped and 5 plain rocks. How many groups of 6 rocks will have 3 striped and 3 plain rocks?

Problem Solving

20. Al orders 4 different scoops of ice cream and 2 different toppings in any order. Kileen orders 2 different scoops of ice cream, and 3 different toppings where order matters. If the store has 10 flavors and 12 toppings, who has more ways of ordering? How many more?

21. Ms. Abu randomly chooses 2 people from your class of 30, and then chooses one to be president and the other vice-president. Would you have a better chance of being president if she randomly chose a president and then a vice-president from the 30 students?

CRITICAL THINKING

22. Your class is voting for 2 representatives to student council. There are 12 people running for the 2 positions. You can vote for at most 2 people. How many ways can you vote?

14-15 Technology: Simulate Events

Name ______________________________ Date ____________

A spinner is divided into 5 equal sectors labeled A, B, C, D, and E. Find the experimental probability of landing on B in 20 spins.

Assign 1 for A, 2 for B, 3 for C, 4 for D, and 5 for E.

You can use a handheld to find the experimental probability of landing on B when spinning the spinner.

1: Actions | 1: Define
2: Number | 2: Recall Definition...
3: Calculations | 3: Delete Variable
4: Probability | 4: Clear a–z...
5: Statistics | 5: Clear History
6: Matrix & Vector | 6: Insert Comment
7: Functions & Prog | 7: Library
0/99

Step 1 Press (home). Then choose (1) to select **Calculator**.

Step 2 Press (menu). Then choose **Actions** and **Define**.

Step 3 Input x =. Then press (menu). Select **Probability**, then select **Random** and **Integer**.

Step 4 Input (1, 5, 20) and press (enter). This defines x as a list of 20 randomly generated integers between 1 and 5 inclusive.

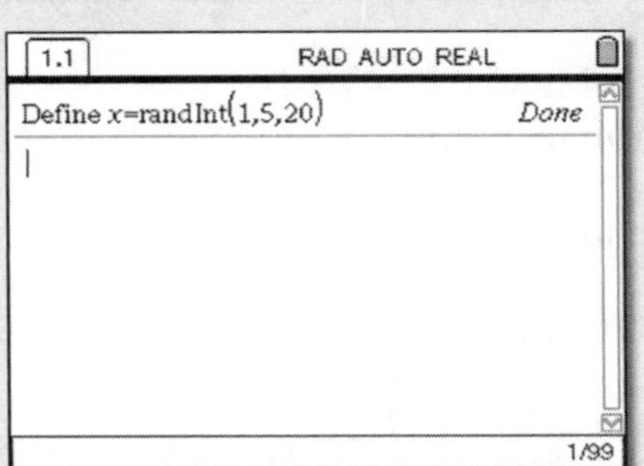

Step 5 Enter x and press (enter) to see the list.

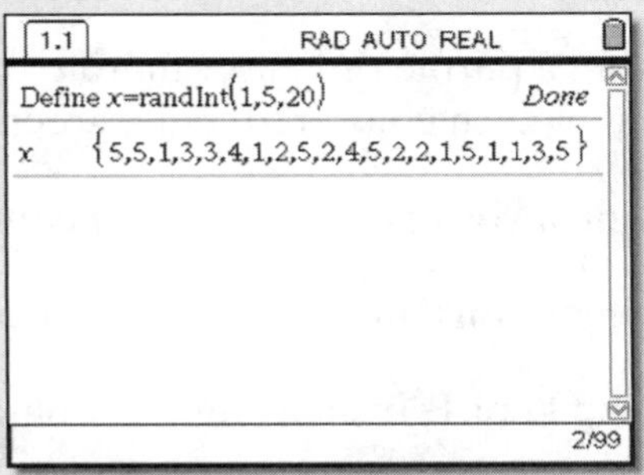

Step 6 Press (menu). Then choose **Statistics**, **List Operations**, and **Sort Ascending**.

Then enter x and press (enter).

Step 7 Enter x and press (enter) again to see the sorted list.

Since 2 was assigned for B and there are four 2s, the experimental probability of landing on B is $\frac{4}{20} = \frac{1}{5} = 20\%$.

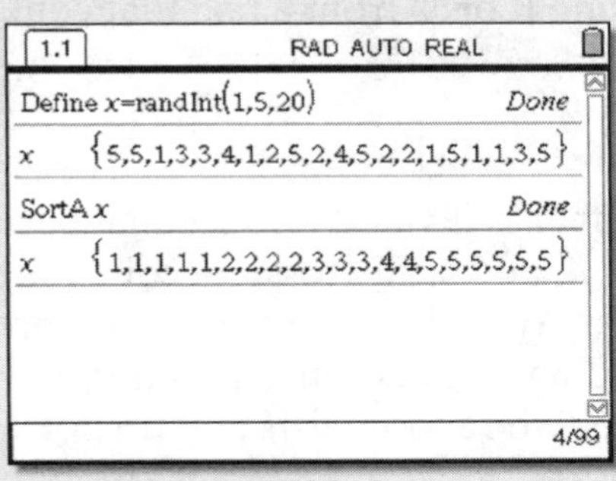

Use a handheld to simulate the experiment and find the experimental probability.

1. Rolling a 4 or 5 when rolling a number cube ____________
2. Rolling a 1 or 2 when rolling a number cube ____________
3. Rolling a number less than 6 when rolling a number cube ____________
4. Rolling a number greater than 2 when rolling a number cube ____________
5. Rolling an even number when rolling a number cube ____________
6. Rolling an odd number when rolling a number cube ____________

Use a handheld to simulate the experiment and find the experimental probability. Conduct the experiment 50 times.

7. Landing on A on a spinner divided into 10 equal parts labeled A– J ______

8. Landing on F on a spinner divided into 10 equal parts labeled A– J ______

9. Landing on A, B, or C on a spinner divided into 10 equal parts labeled A– J ______

10. Landing on F, G, H, or I on a spinner divided into 10 equal parts labeled A– J ______

11. Drawing a green marble from a bag of 8 marbles having a marble of each color: red, blue, green, yellow, pink, purple, orange, white ______

12. Drawing an orange marble from a bag of 8 marbles having a marble of each color: red, blue, green, yellow, pink, purple, orange, white ______

13. Drawing a red, blue, or green marble from a bag of 8 marbles having a marble of each color: red, blue, green, yellow, pink, purple, orange, white ______

14. Drawing a purple or yellow marble from a bag of 8 marbles having a marble of each color: red, blue, green, yellow, pink, purple, orange, white ______

15. Drawing a vowel from a bag that contains all the letters of the alphabet ______

16. Drawing a constant from a bag that contains all the letters of the alphabet ______

17. Drawing G or B from a bag that contains the letters in the word GLOB ______

18. Drawing L or V from a bag that contains the letters in the word LOVE ______

Problem Solving

19. A spinner is divided into 5 equal parts labeled 1, 2, 3, 4, and 5. Jay tosses a coin and spins the spinner. What is the experimental probability of landing on heads and spinning 5? (*Hint:* Create two random lists and do not sort.)

______

20. A bag contains 3 red and 2 blue disks. What is the experimental probability of drawing a red disk? (*Hint:* Assign the numbers 1, 2, and 3 to red and the numbers 4 and 5 to blue.)

______

CHALLENGE

21. A True-False test has 20 questions. What is the experimental probability of *True* being the correct answer to the fifth question? (*Hint:* One list of 20 random numbers represents 1 test.) Explain your answer.

______

14-16 Technology: Calculator Statistics

Name ____________________ Date __________

You can use a handheld to find the mean, median, and range of these scores: 298, 256, 345, 198, 344, 320, 315, and 164.

Step 1 Press (home). Then choose (3) to select **Lists & Spreadsheets**.

Step 2 Enter the scores in column A.

1.1 DEG AUTO REAL

	A	B	C	D
◆				
1	298			
2	256			
3	345			
4	198			
5	344			

A1 298

Step 3 Press (menu). Select **Statistics**, then **Stat Calculations**. Choose **One-Variable Statistics**.

Step 4 Enter 1 for number of lists. Accept the defaults in the next screen to use the data in column A (a[]) and store the results in column B (b[]).

Step 5 Tab to OK and press (enter).

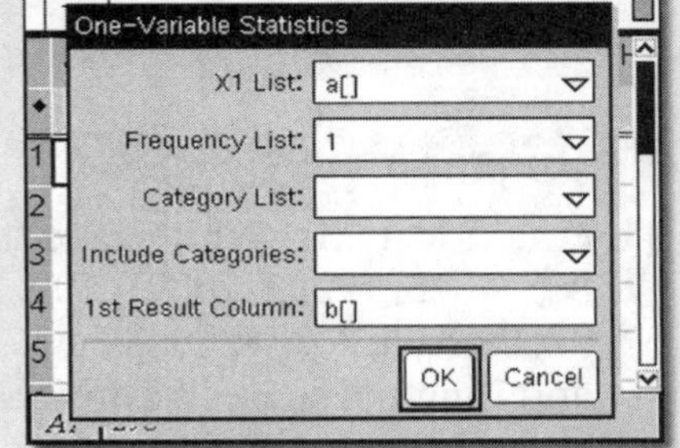

The statistics you need, as they are listed in column B, are the mean $\bar{x}$, the minimum Min, the median Med, and the maximum Max.

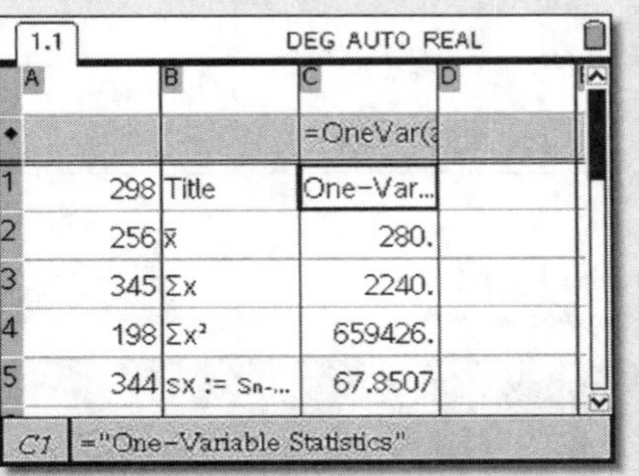

1.1 DEG AUTO REAL

	A	B	C	D
◆			=OneVar(	
1	298	Title	One-Var...	
2	256	$\bar{x}$	280.	
3	345	Σx	2240.	
4	198	Σx²	659426.	
5	344	sx := Sn-...	67.8507	

C1 ="One-Variable Statistics"

1.1 DEG AUTO REAL

	A	B	C	D
◆			=OneVar(	
8	164	MinX	164.	
9		Q₁X	227.	
10		MedianX	306.5	
11		Q₃X	332.	
12		MaxX	345.	

C12 =345.

The mean is 280. The median is 306.5. The range of the values is Max − Min = 345 − 164 = 181.

Use a handheld to find the mean, median, and range of the data.

1. 28, 32, 45, 61, 59, 64, 74, 49

51.5; 54; 46

2. 96, 86, 79, 84, 93, 96, 84, 92

____

3. 2, 7, 11, 13, 19, 8, 4, 5, 7, 10

____

4. 5, 8, 12, 14, 1, 15, 3, 6, 9, 7

____

5. 17.2, 29.3, 34.6, 42.8, 79.8

____

6. 26.8, 36.8, 19.5, 51.7, 6.3

____

Use a handheld to find the mean, median, and range of the data.

7. 2.95, 3.84, 4.82, 4.25, 3.96, 3.45, 2.70, 3.85, 4.03, 4.25

____

8. 1.06, 2.33, 2.15, 1.84, 0.64, 2.24, 1.99, 1.76, 0.98, 2.47

____

Use a handheld to make a scatter plot of the data.

9.

Year	Rainfall (in.)
2002	26.2
2003	25.5
2004	24.9
2005	23.8
2006	26.2
2007	21.2
2008	16.8

10.

Year	Snowfall (ft)
2002	15.2
2003	13.4
2004	12.8
2005	11.9
2006	16.8
2007	13.5
2008	11.7

Problem Solving

11. Education Mr. White gave the following scores on a math test: 72, 78, 98, 86, 84, 75, 79, 83, 70, 95, 100, 100, 83, 100, 102, 96, 80, 72, 79, 86, 83, 84, 93, 97, 99, 106, 83, 78, 86, 84, 83, 79, 81, and 104. What are the mean, median, and range of scores? Tony's 70 should have been marked 85. What are the correct mean, median, and range of test scores? What is the probability that a student chosen at random scored an A (≥ 90) on the test?

____

CHALLENGE

12. The table shows U.S. K–12 enrollment by grade levels for selected years. Which year had the greatest mean enrollment? What was that enrollment? Which year had the least mean enrollment? What was that enrollment? Round to the nearest whole number.

Grade	1980	1985	1995	2000	2004
PK/K	2,689	3,192	4,173	4,158	4,534
1	2,894	3,239	3,671	3,636	3,663
2	2,800	2,941	3,507	3,634	3,560
3	2,893	2,895	3,445	3,676	3,580
4	3,107	2,771	3,431	3,711	3,612
5	3,130	2,776	3,438	3,707	3,635
6	3,038	2,789	3,395	3,663	3,735
7	3,085	2,938	3,422	3,629	3,818
8	3,086	2,982	3,356	3,538	3,825
9	3,377	3,439	3,704	3,963	4,281
10	3,368	3,230	3,237	3,491	3,750
11	3,195	2,866	2,826	3,083	3,369
12	2,925	2,550	2,487	2,803	3,094

____

14-17 Problem-Solving Strategy:
Review of Strategies

Read Plan Solve Check

Name ______________________ Date __________

Solve using a strategy that you have used before.

1. If $3x = 3 + 3^2 + 3^3 + 3^4 + \ldots + 3^{10} + 3^{11}$, what is the value of x?

____

2. While surveying a certain field Fred moved 10 m east, 4 m north, 6 m west, 8 m north, and 1 m east. Exactly how far is Fred now from where he began?

____

3. If you ascend these 8 steps by taking only 1 or 3 steps at a time, in how many different ways can you get to the top?

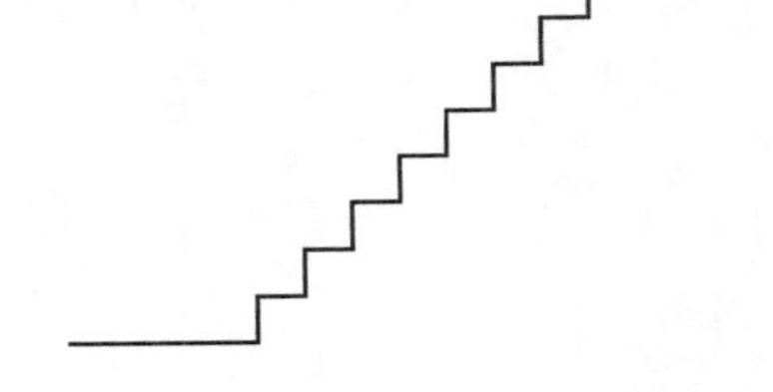

____

4. Right now, a container holds 24 marbles—5 red and 19 blue. You may add 4 marbles at a time, any of which are red or blue. Is it possible in this manner, to get fewer than 100 marbles in the container with exactly a third of them being red? Explain.

____

5. Given the sequence of integers 1, 2, 2, 3, 3, 3, 4, 4, 4, 4, 5, 5, 5, 5, 5, . . . , where each positive integer, n, occurs in a group of n consecutive terms, how many terms are needed so that the sum of the *reciprocals* is 100?

6. What is the sum of the numbers in the 32nd row of the array shown here?

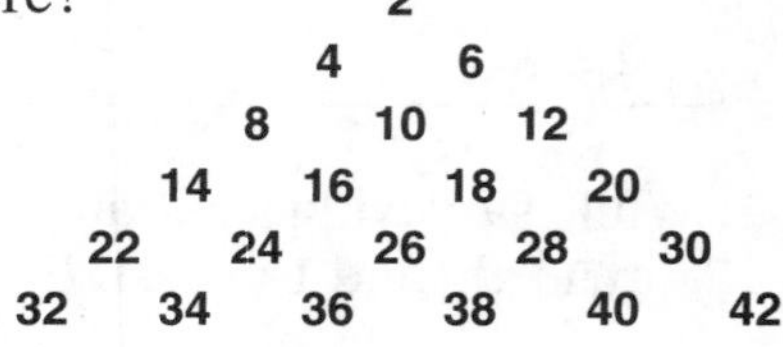

7. Find the real number values that satisfy the following three equations simultaneously:

$abc^3 = 320$ $\qquad$ $ab^3c = 500$ $\qquad$ $a^3bc = 20$

8. Find all the integral values of x that satisfy: $(4x - 7)^{(x^2 - 16)} = 1$

Enrichment: Geometric Probability

Name ______________________________ Date ______________

Find the probability that a point chosen at random from inside the circle lies outside the square. Round to the nearest hundredth of a percent.

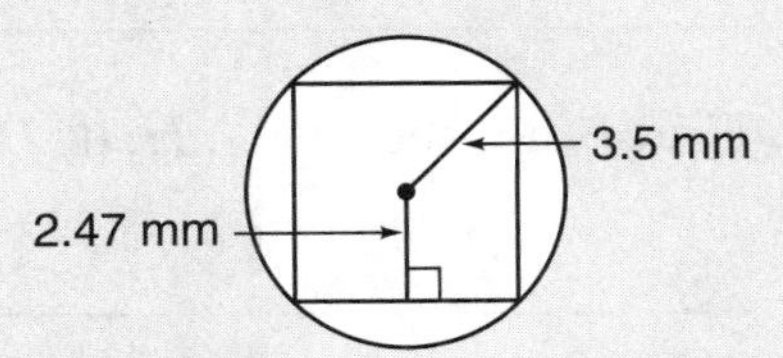

Find the area of the circle that lies outside the square.

$$A_{\text{outside square}} = A_{\text{circle}} - A_{\text{square}}$$
$$= (\pi \cdot 3.5^2) - (4.94^2)$$
$$\approx 14.08 \text{ mm}^2$$

$$P(\text{point outside square}) = \frac{\text{area outside of square}}{\text{area of circle}} = \frac{14.08}{38.48} \approx 0.3659 \text{ or about } 37\%$$

Suppose a point is chosen at random from $\overline{WZ}$. Round to the nearest hundredth of a percent.

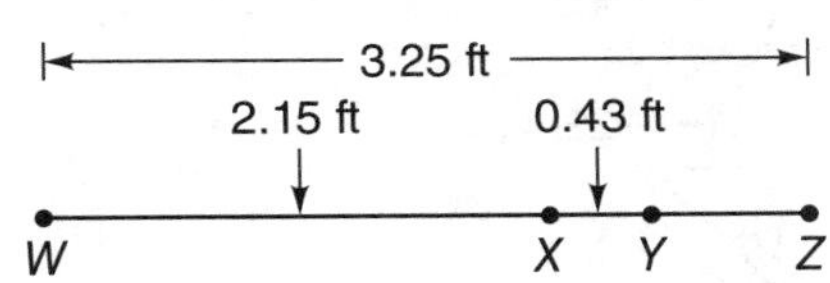

1. Find $P(\overline{YZ})$.

$3.25 - (2.15 + 0.43) = 0.67$

$\frac{0.67}{3.25} \approx 0.2062 = 20.62\%$

2. Find $P(\overline{XZ})$. ______________

3. Find $P(\text{not } \overline{XY})$. ______________

Suppose a point is chosen at random from $\overline{AE}$. Round to the nearest hundredth of a percent.

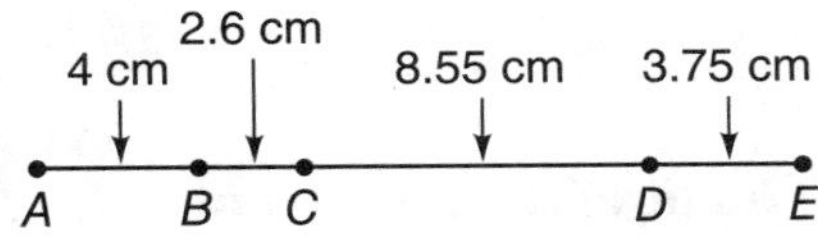

4. Find $P(\text{not } \overline{BC})$. ______________

5. Find $P(\overline{AD})$. ______________

6. Find $P(\text{not } \overline{BD})$. ______________

Suppose a point is chosen at random from $\overline{FK}$. Round to the nearest hundredth of a percent.

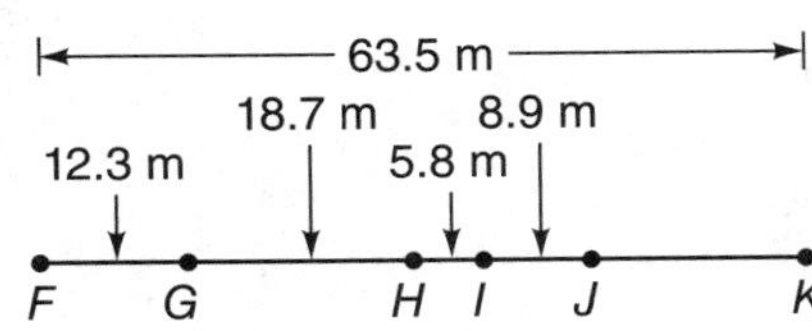

7. Find $P(\text{not } \overline{IK})$. ______________

8. Find $P(\text{not } \overline{GJ})$. ______________

9. Find $P(\text{not } \overline{FG} \text{ nor } \overline{IJ})$. ______________

Suppose a point is chosen at random from inside the circle.
Round to the nearest hundredth of a percent.

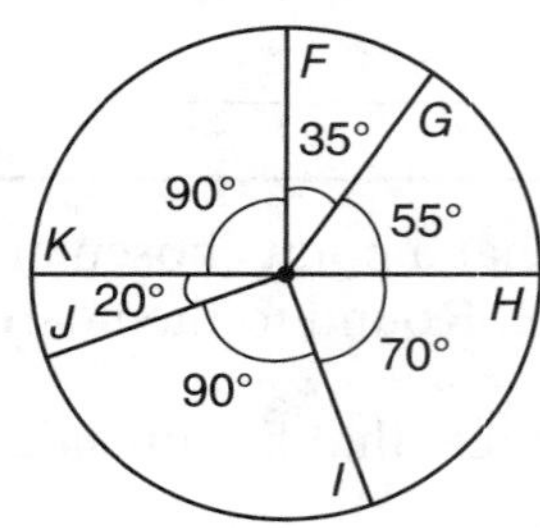

10. Find P(sector I, J, or K).

____

11. Find P(not sectors G, H, or I).

____

Solve. Show your work.
Round each answer to the nearest hundredth of a percent.

12. Find the probability that a point chosen at random from inside the circle below lies outside of the shaded region.

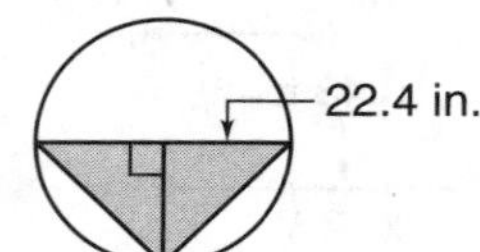

____

13. What is the probability that a point chosen at random from inside the large rectangle is not in the square or the circles?

16.7 in.
1.5 in.
7.2 in.
9.3 in.
7.2 in.

____

Problem Solving

Round to the nearest hundredth of a percent

14. A rectangular board with dimensions 16 m by 20 m is covered with red circular regions that each have a diameter of 20 cm. The circular regions are placed in 80 rows of 100. If a dart is thrown randomly at the board, what is the probability it will *not* hit a circular region? Assume the dart does not miss the board.

____

MENTAL MATH

Approximate.

15. What is 15% of \$35.78?

____

16. What is 12.5% of \$52.96?

____

17. x qt = 7.925 gal?

____

Test Prep: Extended-Response Questions

Strategy: Organize Information

Name ______________________ Date __________

Make an organized list to help systematically arrange data and account for all possibilities.

To solve the problem, try using these strategies:

- Reread the test item.
- Use the Test-Prep strategy.
- Apply appropriate rules, definitions, properties, or strategies.
- Analyze your answers.

Solve. *TIP: Focus on the important information.*

1. At camp, Joanna must pick three different activities from the choices of canoeing, archery, arts and crafts, and swimming.

Part A
What are the possible combinations of three activities Joanna can choose?

Answer: ______________________

Part B
Joanna can also decide the order of the activities she participates in. How many choices does she have?

Show all your work.

Answer: ______________________

2. A baseball team is choosing colors for new uniforms, consisting of shirts, pants, and hats. The color choices for shirts are green, gold, and black. The color choices for pants are white, black, and grey. The color choices for hats are green and gold.

Part A
Using a tree diagram on a separate sheet of paper, find the number of possible uniforms.

Answer: ______________________

Part B
If the team decides to get grey pants, how many uniforms will they have to choose from?

Answer: ______________________

3. Use the letters in the word MATH

Part A
How many 3-letter arrangements can be made with the letters if no letter can be used more than once?

Show all your work.

Answer: ______________________

Part B
How many 3-letter arrangements can be made with the letters if a letter can be used more than once?

Show all your work.

Answer: ______________________

Use with SOURCEBOOK Test Prep Lesson, page 402.

For More Practice Go To:
ONLINE www.progressinmathematics.com

Vocabulary Development

Name ______________________________ Date ______________

Chapter 14 Vocabulary

back-to-back stem-and-leaf plot
bias
biased question
biased sample
box-and-whisker plot
combination
complement
complementary events
compound event
conditional probability
correlation
cumulative frequency histogram
cumulative frequency table
disjoint events
experiments
experimental probability
extremes
factorial
first quartile
frequency table
Fundamental Counting Principle
histogram
interquartile range
linear transformation
line of best fit
mean
measures of central tendency
median
misleading graphs
mode
mutually exclusive
overlapping events
percentile
percentile rank
permutation
population
prediction
probability
qualitative variables
quantitative variables
quartiles
range
representative sample
sample
sample space
second quartile
scatter plot
stem-and-leaf plot
survey
theoretical probability
third quartile
tree diagram
variable

From the vocabulary list above, choose the term(s) that best complete each sentence. Write the term(s) in the space(s) provided.

1. The entire group of individuals or objects considered for a(n) ______________________ is called a(n) ______________________.

2. The whiskers of a box-and-whisker plot represent the ______________________ of the data.

3. The measure that tells what percent of the total items in a data set is at or below a given measure is the ______________________.

4. To find the total number of possible outcomes of a compound event, use the ______________________.

Tell whether the statement is true or false. If it is false, change it to make it true.

5. A permutation is an arrangement or listing of objects in a specific order.

____

Use after SOURCEBOOK Lesson 14-1–14-14, pages 358–393.

Practice Chapter 14 Test

Name ______________________ Date ________

Identify the sampling method used.

1. A city asks residents of 4 out of 6 districts if they approve the new park regulations.

____

2. A clothing store mails a survey to all its credit card customers.

____

Use a separate sheet of paper and the table of test scores to make a stem-and-leaf plot. Then find the measures of central tendency and the range.

3.

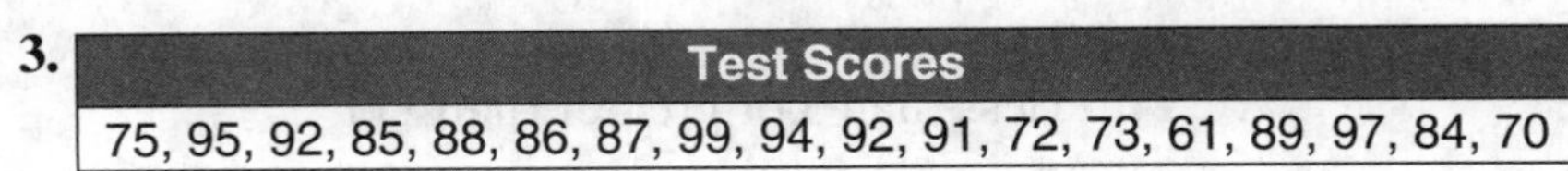

Test Scores
75, 95, 92, 85, 88, 86, 87, 99, 94, 92, 91, 72, 73, 61, 89, 97, 84, 70

____

Find the first, second, and third quartiles and the interquartile range of each data set. Then make a box-and-whisker plot of the data on a separate sheet of paper.

4. 36, 32, 48, 42, 40

____

5. 141, 124, 120, 100, 90, 130

____

Use the following data for Exercises 6–7.
74, 76, 79, 80, 81, 83, 83, 83, 83, 84, 87, 89, 90, 92, 93, 94, 96, 96, 97, 98

6. What is the percentile rank of 83?

____

7. What number is at the 75th percentile?

____

Select the graph that most likely represents the relationship. Determine the type of correlation between the data sets. If there is a correlation, write *causal* or *not causal*.

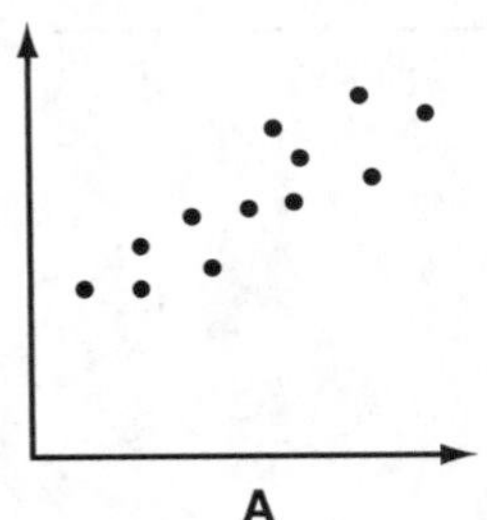

A

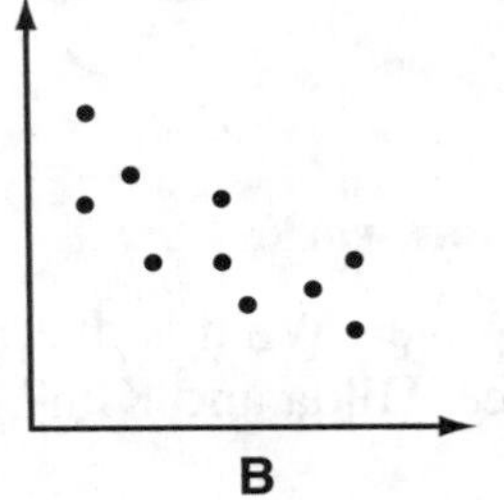

B

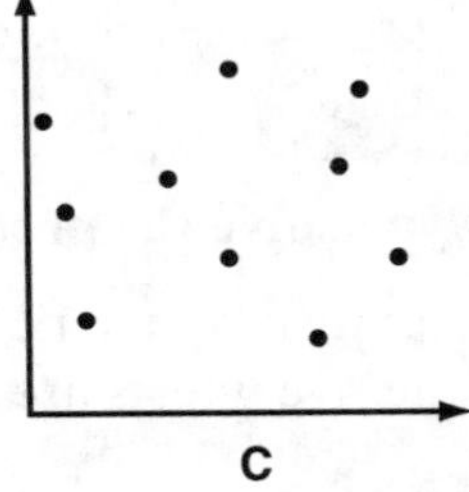

C

8. antique car age and value

____

9. rain and draught

____

10. food bills and test scores

____

On a separate sheet of paper, draw a tree diagram and use the Fundamental Counting Principle to find the number of possible outcomes. Determine whether the events are independent or dependent.

11. Roll a 1–6 number cube twice and spin a spinner with equal sectors labeled A, B, and C.

12. Toss a coin four times.

A spinner is divided into 12 equal sectors labeled 1–12. Determine whether the events are mutually exclusive or overlapping. Then find the probability.

13. P(multiple of 2 or multiple of 3)

14. P(less than 3 or greater than 11)

Find $P(B|A)$.

15. $P(\text{A and B}) = \frac{1}{3}$; $P(\text{A}) = \frac{5}{8}$

16. $P(\text{A and B}) = 20\%$; $P(\text{A}) = 64\%$

Solve. Check your work.

17. Students randomly choose a president and secretary to represent their class of 28 students. How many ways can they choose the two positions?

18. Ms. Liu randomly chooses groups of 8 from her class of 24 students and groups of 6 from her class of 8 students. How many different groups can she make?

Tell About It

Explain how you solve the problem. Show all your work.

19. Nan may invite 5 of her 12 friends to a sleepover. What is the probability that 3 of the five guests are her friends Grace, Hilda and Kim?

Cumulative Review: Chapters 1–14

Name ______________________________ Date __________

Circle the best answer.

1. Which is equivalent to the expression below?

$(1.8 \times 10^{12})(1.5 \times 10^{4})$

A. 3.3×10^{48}
B. 3.3×10^{16}
C. 2.7×10^{48}
D. 2.7×10^{16}

2. Solve.

$d - 15 = -23$

F. $d = -38$ **G.** $d = -8$
H. $d = 8$ **J.** $d = 38$

3. Solve.

$|w| - 4 > 7$

A. $w > 11$
B. $w < 11$
C. $-11 < w < 11$
D. $w < -11$ or $w > 11$

4. Which function best represents the situation: the total cost, c, for h hours at an hourly rate of $32.45 per hour?

F. $c(h) = 32.45^h$
G. $c(h) = 32.45 + h$
H. $c(h) = 32.45h$
J. $c(h) = 32.45 - h$

5. Which best describes the graph of $x + 12y < 0$?

A. dashed line shaded below
B. dashed line shaded above
C. solid line shaded below
D. solid line shaded above

6. Solve: $\begin{cases} 3x - 2y = -29 \\ x + 5y = 30 \end{cases}$

F. $(5, 7)$ **G.** $(5, -7)$
H. $(-7, 5)$ **J.** $(-5, 7)$

7. Simplify: $\dfrac{16b^3 + 12b^2 - 8b}{-4b}$

A. $5b^3$
B. $20b^3 + 16b^2 - 12$
C. $-4b^2 + 12b^2 - 8b$
D. $-4b^2 - 3b + 2$

8. Multiply: $(12x + 5)(12x - 5)$

F. $144x^2 - 25$
G. $144x^2 + 25$
H. $144x^2 + 120x - 25$
J. $25x^2 + 34x - 10$

9. Factor: $6x^2 + 13x + 5$

A. $(3x + 1)(2x + 5)$
B. $(3x + 5)(2x + 1)$
C. $(5x + 1)(2x + 3)$
D. $(3x + 2)(x + 5)$

10. Which is the unknown length of the triangle in simplest radical form?

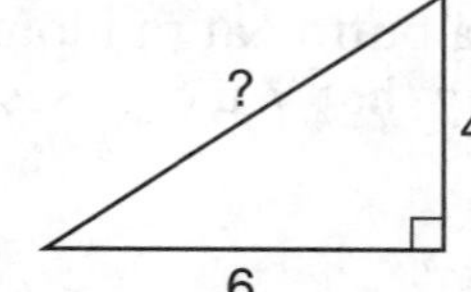

F. 20
G. $13\sqrt{2}$
H. $2\sqrt{13}$
J. $\sqrt{52}$

11. Solve: $5 + \sqrt{w - 4} = 2$

A. $w = 53$
B. $w = 13$
C. $w = 5$
D. no real solution

12. Solve: $\begin{cases} x = -1 \\ y = 3x^2 - 4x + 1 \end{cases}$

F. $(-1, -8)$ **G.** $(-1, 8)$
H. $(-1, -6)$ **J.** $(-1, 2)$

13. What is the cost of a \$32.95 pair of jeans with a 7% sales tax?

A. \$30.64 **B.** \$33.65
C. \$34.01 **D.** \$35.26

14. Simplify: $\frac{7m + 3}{2m + 3} - \frac{5m - 3}{2m + 3}$

F. $\frac{m}{2m + 3}$ **G.** 3
H. $\frac{2m + 6}{2m + 3}$ **J.** $\frac{2m}{2m + 3}$

15. Which is a reflection of the graph of $y = 2^x$ across the y-axis?

A. $y = -2^x$
B. $y = 0.5(2^x)$
C. $y = \left(\frac{1}{2}\right)^x$
D. $y = 5(2^x)$

16. What is the vertex of the graph of $f(x) = 2x^2 + 8x - 7$?

F. (1, 3) **G.** (−2, −7)
H. (2, 17) **J.** (−2, −15)

17. An urn contains 23 red, 16 green, and 3 white buttons. Wu chooses a button at random. What is the probability that Wu chooses a red or white button?

A. $\frac{23}{42}$ **B.** $\frac{1}{3}$
C. $\frac{13}{21}$ **D.** $\frac{1}{26}$

18. Cynthia invested \$3,000 at 4% compounded quarterly. How much did she have after 4 years?

F. \$3030.14 **G.** \$3314.69
H. \$3480.00 **J.** \$3517.74

19. Which is a translation of $y = \frac{2}{x}$, 4 units to the left and 5 units up?

A. $y = \frac{2}{x + 4} + 5$ **B.** $y = \frac{2}{x - 4} + 5$
C. $y = \frac{2}{x - 5} + 4$ **D.** $y = \frac{2}{x + 5} + 4$

20. What are the mean, median, mode, and range of the data?

22, 23, 24, 26, 23

F. 23.6, 24, 23, 4
G. 23.6, 24, no mode, 4
H. 23.6, 23, 23, 4
J. 23.6, 23, 23, 1

21. Evaluate: ${}_{21}P_2$

A. 21 **B.** 42
C. 210 **D.** 420

22. In which interval is the median?

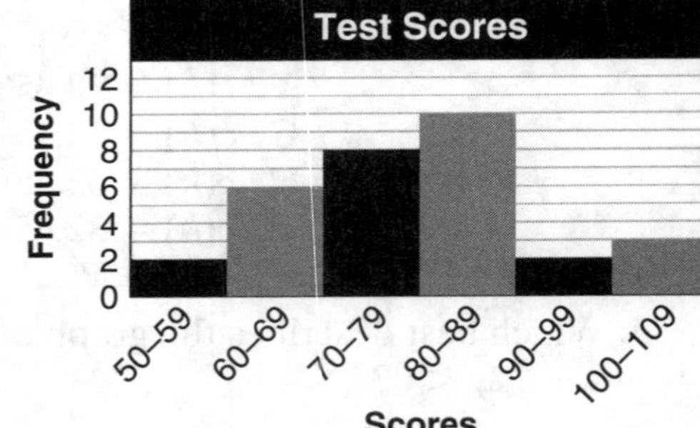

F. 60–69
G. 70–79
H. 80–89
J. 90–99

Tell About It

Explain how you solve the problem. Show all your work.

23. Explain how to find the quartiles for the data set below. Then find the interquartile range.

12, 40, 24, 32, 22

Symbols

Numbers and Operations

$a \bullet b$, ab	a times b
$a \div b$, $\frac{a}{b}$	a divided by b
$\pm$	plus or minus; positive or negative
$=$	is equal to
$\stackrel{?}{=}$	is it equal to?
$\neq$	is not equal to
$\approx$	is approximately equal to
$>$	is greater than
$<$	is less than
$\geq$	is greater than or equal to
$\leq$	is less than or equal to
...	continues without end
∞	infinity
a^2	a squared, or a to the second power
$0.\overline{3}$	0.333 … (repeating decimal)
%	percent
$-a$	the additive inverse or opposite of a
$\frac{1}{a}$, $a \neq 0$	the reciprocal of a
$a : b$	the ratio of a and b, or $\frac{a}{b}$

Sets, Probability, and Logic

$\cup$	union
$\cap$	intersection
$\{\}$, $\varnothing$	the empty set
$\subset$, $\subseteq$	is a subset of
A'	the complement of A
$P(E)$	probability of an event
$n!$	n factorial $[n \bullet (n-1) \bullet (n-2) \bullet \ldots \bullet 1]$
$P(n, r)$	permutation of n things taken r at a time
$C(n, r)$	combination of n things taken r at a time
$\wedge$	and, conjunction
$\vee$	or, disjunction
$\rightarrow$	if-then, implication
$\leftrightarrow$	if and only if, biconditional

Geometry and Measurement

$\cong$	is congruent to
$\sim$	is similar to
$^\circ$	degree(s)
$\overleftrightarrow{AB}$	line AB
$\overline{AB}$	segment AB
$\overrightarrow{AB}$	ray AB
$\overset{\frown}{AB}$	arc AB
$\angle ABC$	angle ABC
AB	length of $\overline{AB}$, distance between A and B
ABC	plane ABC
$\triangle ABC$	triangle ABC
$m\angle ABC$	measure of angle ABC
$\parallel$	is parallel to
$\perp$	is perpendicular to
π	pi (approximately 3.14 or $\frac{22}{7}$)
$\sin A$	sine of angle A
$\cos A$	cosine of angle A
$\tan A$	tangent of angle A

Algebra and Functions

a'	a prime
a^n	a to the nth power
a^{-n}	$\frac{1}{a^n}$ (one over a to the nth power)
a_n	the nth term of a sequence
$a^{\frac{1}{2}}$	$\sqrt{a}$
$\begin{bmatrix} a & b \\ c & d \end{bmatrix}$	matrix
$\lvert x \rvert$	absolute value of x
$[x]$	greatest integer
$\sqrt{x}$	principal (positive) square root of x
$f(x)$	f of x, the value of the function at x
(x, y)	ordered pair

Probability

Theoretical Probability

$$P(\text{E}) = \frac{\text{number of favorable outcomes}}{\text{total number of outcomes}}$$

Probability of Two Independent Events

$P(\text{A } \textit{and} \text{ B}) = P(\text{A}) \bullet P(\text{B})$

Probability of Mutually Exclusive Events

$P(\text{A } \textit{or} \text{ B}) = P(\text{A}) + P(\text{B})$

Experimental Probability

$$\text{Exp } P(\text{E}) = \frac{\text{number of times the event occurs}}{\text{total number of trials}}$$

Probability of Two Dependent Events

$P(\text{A } \textit{and} \text{ B}) = P(\text{A}) \bullet P(\text{B } \textit{after} \text{ A})$

Probability of Overlapping Events

$P(\text{A } \textit{or} \text{ B}) = P(\text{A}) + P(\text{B}) - P(\text{A } \textit{and} \text{ B})$

Measurement Conversions

Length

Metric

1 millimeter (mm)	= 0.001 meter (m)		1 dekameter (dam)	= 10 meters	
1 centimeter (cm)	= 0.01 meter		1 hectometer (hm)	= 100 meters	
1 decimeter (dm)	= 0.1 meter		1 kilometer (km)	= 1000 meters	

Customary

1 foot (ft)	= 12 inches (in.)	1 mile (mi)	= 5280 feet
1 yard (yd)	= 3 feet	1 mile	= 1760 yards
1 yard	= 36 inches		

Customary to Metric

1 inch	= 2.54 centimeters	1 yard	≈ 0.914 meter
1 foot	≈ 0.305 meter	1 mile	≈ 1.61 kilometers

Capacity and Volume

Metric

1 milliliter (mL)	= 0.001 liter (L)	1 kiloliter (kL)	= 1000 liters

Customary

3 teaspoons (tsp)	= 1 tablespoon (tbsp)	1 quart (qt)	= 2 pints
1 cup (c)	= 8 fluid ounces (fl oz)	1 quart	= 4 cups
1 pint (pt)	= 2 cups	1 gallon (gal)	= 4 quarts

Customary to Metric

1 fluid ounce	≈ 29.6 milliliters	1 quart	≈ 0.946 liter
1 pint	≈ 0.473 liter	1 gallon	≈ 3.78 liters

Mass and Weight

Metric

1 milligram (mg)	= 0.001 gram (g)	1 metric ton (t)	= 1000 kilograms
1 kilogram (kg)	= 1000 grams		

Customary

1 pound (lb)	= 16 ounces (oz)	1 ton (T)	= 2000 pounds

Customary to Metric

1 ounce ≈ 28.4 grams

1 pound ≈ 454 grams

Temperature

Metric

0° Celsius (C) …… Water freezes

100° Celsius (C) ……………… Water boils

Customary

32° Fahrenheit (F) …… Water freezes

212° Fahrenheit (F) ………….. Water boils

Time

1 century (cent.)	= 100 years (y)	1 leap year	= 366 days	1 day	= 24 hours (h)
1 year	= 12 months (mo)	1 year	= 52 weeks (wk)	1 hour	= 60 minutes (min)
1 year	= 365 days (d)	1 week	= 7 days	1 minute	= 60 seconds (s)

Formula Chart

Perimeter & Circumference	square	$P = 4s$	regular polygon	$P = ns$
	rectangle	$P = 2(\ell + w)$ or $P = 2\ell + 2w$	circle	$C = 2\pi r$ or $C = \pi d$
Area	square	$A = s^2$	trapezoid	$A = \frac{1}{2}(b_1 + b_2)h$
	rectangle	$A = \ell w$ or $A = bh$	regular polygon	$A = \frac{1}{2}aP$
	parallelogram	$A = bh$	circle	$A = \pi'' r^2$
	triangle	$A = \frac{1}{2}bh$		
Surface Area	cube	$S = 6e^2$	cone	$S = \pi r\ell + \pi r^2$
	prism	$S = Ph + 2B$	sphere	$S = 4\pi r^2$
	rectangular prism	$S = 2(\ell w + \ell h + wh)$	regular pyramid	$S = \frac{1}{2}P\ell + B$
	cylinder	$S = 2\pi rh + 2\pi r^2$		
Volume	cube	$V = e^3$	cylinder	$V = \pi r^2 h$
	rectangular prism	$V = \ell wh$	cone	$V = \frac{1}{3}\pi r^2 h$
	prism	$V = Bh$	sphere	$V = \frac{4}{3}\pi r^3$
	pyramid	$V = \frac{1}{3}Bh$		
***n*th term of a Sequence**	Arithmetic	$a_n = a_{n-1} + d$	Geometric	$a_n = a_{n-1} \bullet r$
Linear Functions	Standard form	$Ax + By = C$	Point-slope form	$y - y_1 = m(x - x_1)$
	Slope-intercept form	$y = mx + b$	Slope Formula	$m = \frac{y_2 - y_1}{x_2 - x_1}$
Variation	Direct	$y = kx$ or $k = \frac{y}{x}, k \neq 0$	Inverse	$y = \frac{k}{x}$ or $k = xy, k \neq 0$
Quadratic Equations	Standard form	$ax^2 + bx + c = 0$	Discriminant	$\sqrt{b^2 - 4ac}$
	Quadratic Formula	$x = \frac{-b \pm \sqrt{b^2 - 4ac}}{2a}$	Axis of symmetry	$x = \frac{-b}{2a}$
Nonlinear Functions	Absolute-Value Function	$y = \|x\|$	Rational Function	$y = \frac{a}{x}$
	Exponential Function	$y = ab^x$	Radical Function	$y = \sqrt{x}$
	Quadratic Function	$y = ax^2 + bx + c$		
Pythagorean Theorem	right triangle with legs *a* and *b* and hypotenuse *c*		$a^2 + b^2 = c^2$	
Trigonometric Ratios	sine (sin) $= \frac{\text{opposite leg}}{\text{hypotenuse}}$		**Exponential Growth**	$y = ab^x$, $a > 0$ and $b > 1$
	cosine (cos) $= \frac{\text{adjacent leg}}{\text{hypotenuse}}$		**Exponential Decay**	$y = ab^x$, $a > 0$ and $0 < b < 1$
	tangent (tan) $= \frac{\text{opposite leg}}{\text{adjacent leg}}$			
Distance Formula	$d = \sqrt{(x_2 - x_1)^2 + (y_2 - y_1)^2}$		**Midpoint Formula**	$M = \left(\frac{x_1 + x_2}{2}, \frac{y_1 + y_2}{2}\right)$
Other Formulas	Simple Interest	$I = prt$	distance traveled	$d = rt$
	Compound Interest Balance	$A = P(1 + \frac{r}{n})^{nt}$	percentage proportion	$\frac{\text{part}}{\text{whole}} = \frac{\text{percent}}{100}$
	Half-life	$A = P(0.5)^t$	percentage = rate • base	$p = rb$

Table of Trigonometric Ratios

Angle	Sin	Cos	Tan	Angle	Sin	Cos	Tan
0°	0.000	1.000	0.000	45°	0.707	0.707	1.000
1°	0.017	1.000	0.017	46°	0.719	0.695	1.036
2°	0.035	0.999	0.035	47°	0.731	0.682	1.072
3°	0.052	0.999	0.052	48°	0.743	0.669	1.111
4°	0.070	0.998	0.070	49°	0.755	0.656	1.150
5°	0.087	0.996	0.087	50°	0.766	0.643	1.192
6°	0.105	0.995	0.105	51°	0.777	0.629	1.235
7°	0.122	0.993	0.123	52°	0.788	0.616	1.280
8°	0.139	0.990	0.141	53°	0.799	0.602	1.327
9°	0.156	0.988	0.158	54°	0.809	0.588	1.376
10°	0.174	0.985	0.176	55°	0.819	0.574	1.428
11°	0.191	0.982	0.194	56°	0.829	0.559	1.483
12°	0.208	0.978	0.213	57°	0.839	0.545	1.540
13°	0.225	0.974	0.231	58°	0.848	0.530	1.600
14°	0.242	0.970	0.249	59°	0.857	0.515	1.664
15°	0.259	0.966	0.268	60°	0.866	0.500	1.732
16°	0.276	0.961	0.287	61°	0.875	0.485	1.804
17°	0.292	0.956	0.306	62°	0.883	0.469	1.881
18°	0.309	0.951	0.325	63°	0.891	0.454	1.963
19°	0.326	0.946	0.344	64°	0.899	0.438	2.050
20°	0.342	0.940	0.364	65°	0.906	0.423	2.145
21°	0.358	0.934	0.384	66°	0.914	0.407	2.246
22°	0.375	0.927	0.404	67°	0.921	0.391	2.356
23°	0.391	0.921	0.424	68°	0.927	0.375	2.475
24°	0.407	0.914	0.445	69°	0.934	0.358	2.605
25°	0.423	0.906	0.466	70°	0.940	0.342	2.747
26°	0.438	0.899	0.488	71°	0.946	0.326	2.904
27°	0.454	0.891	0.510	72°	0.951	0.309	3.078
28°	0.469	0.883	0.532	73°	0.956	0.292	3.271
29°	0.485	0.875	0.554	74°	0.961	0.276	3.732
30°	0.500	0.866	0.577	75°	0.966	0.259	
31°	0.515	0.857	0.601	76°	0.970	0.242	4.011
32°	0.530	0.848	0.625	77°	0.974	0.225	4.331
33°	0.545	0.839	0.649	78°	0.978	0.208	4.705
34°	0.559	0.829	0.675	79°	0.982	0.191	5.145
35°	0.574	0.819	0.700	80°	0.985	0.174	5.671
36°	0.588	0.809	0.727	81°	0.988	0.156	6.314
37°	0.602	0.799	0.754	82°	0.990	0.139	7.115
38°	0.616	0.788	0.781	83°	0.993	0.122	8.144
39°	0.629	0.777	0.810	84°	0.995	0.105	9.514
40°	0.643	0.766	0.839	85°	0.996	0.087	11.430
41°	0.656	0.755	0.869	86°	0.998	0.070	14.301
42°	0.669	0.743	0.900	87°	0.999	0.052	19.081
43°	0.682	0.731	0.933	88°	0.999	0.035	28.636
44°	0.695	0.719	0.966	89°	1.000	0.017	57.290
45°	0.707	0.707	1.000	90°	1.000	0.000	—

Table of Squares and Square Roots

No.	Square	Sq. Root	No.	Square	Sq. Root	No.	Square	Sq. Root
1	1	1.000	51	2601	7.141	101	10,201	10.050
2	4	1.414	52	2704	7.211	102	10,404	10.100
3	9	1.732	53	2809	7.280	103	10,609	10.149
4	16	2.000	54	2916	7.348	104	10,816	10.198
5	25	2.236	55	3025	7.416	105	11,025	10.247
6	36	2.449	56	3136	7.483	106	11,236	10.296
7	49	2.646	57	3249	7.550	107	11,449	10.344
8	64	2.828	58	3364	7.616	108	11,664	10.392
9	81	3.000	59	3481	7.681	109	11,881	10.440
10	100	3.162	60	3600	7.746	110	12,100	10.488
11	121	3.317	61	3721	7.810	111	12,321	10.536
12	144	3.464	62	3844	7.874	112	12,544	10.583
13	169	3.606	63	3969	7.937	113	12,769	10.630
14	196	3.742	64	4096	8.000	114	12,996	10.677
15	225	3.873	65	4225	8.062	115	13,225	10.724
16	256	4.000	66	4356	8.124	116	13,456	10.770
17	289	4.123	67	4489	8.185	117	13,689	10.817
18	324	4.243	68	4624	8.246	118	13,924	10.863
19	361	4.359	69	4761	8.307	119	14,161	10.909
20	400	4.472	70	4900	8.367	120	14,400	10.954
21	441	4.583	71	5041	8.426	121	14,641	11.000
22	484	4.690	72	5184	8.485	122	14,884	11.045
23	529	4.796	73	5329	8.544	123	15,129	11.091
24	576	4.899	74	5476	8.602	124	15,376	11.136
25	625	5.000	75	5625	8.660	125	15,625	11.18
26	676	5.099	76	5776	8.718	126	15,876	11.225
27	729	5.196	77	5929	8.775	127	16,129	11.269
28	784	5.292	78	6084	8.832	128	16,384	11.314
29	841	5.385	79	6241	8.888	129	16,641	11.358
30	900	5.477	80	6400	8.944	130	16,900	11.402
31	961	5.568	81	6561	9.000	131	17,161	11.446
32	1024	5.657	82	6724	9.055	132	17,424	11.489
33	1089	5.745	83	6889	9.110	133	17,689	11.533
34	1156	5.831	84	7056	9.165	134	17,956	11.576
35	1225	5.916	85	7225	9.220	135	18,225	11.619
36	1296	6.000	86	7396	9.274	136	18,496	11.662
37	1369	6.083	87	7569	9.327	137	18,769	11.705
38	1444	6.164	88	7744	9.381	138	19,044	11.747
39	1521	6.245	89	7921	9.434	139	19,321	11.790
40	1600	6.325	90	8100	9.487	140	19,600	11.832
41	1681	6.403	91	8281	9.539	141	19,881	11.874
42	1764	6.481	92	8464	9.592	142	20,164	11.916
43	1849	6.557	93	8649	9.644	143	20,449	11.958
44	1936	6.633	94	8836	9.695	144	20,736	12.000
45	2025	6.708	95	9025	9.747			
46	2116	6.782	96	9216	9.798			
47	2209	6.856	97	9409	9.849			
48	2304	6.928	98	9604	9.899			
49	2401	7.000	99	9801	9.950			
50	2500	7.071	100	10,000	10.000